Dibble Army Hospital, SRI's Future site ~1946

SRI International ~1989

A
Heritage
of
Innovation

SRI's First Half Century

Donald L. Nielson

1947

1952

1955

1962

1965

1977

Copyright 2004, 2006 Donald L. Nielson
1st Edition (Revised)

ISBN-13: 978-0-9745208-1-0
ISBN-10: 0-9745208-1-0
Library of Congress Control No. 2006932482

SRI International
333 Ravenswood Avenue
Menlo Park, California 94025

From the SRI Charter

"...to promote and foster the application of science in the development of commerce, trade and industry, the discovery and development of methods for the beneficial utilization of natural resources, the industrialization of the Western United States of America, and the improvement of the general standard of living and...

...DEDICATED TO THE PEACE AND PROSPERITY OF MANKIND."

CONTENTS

Appendixes

Index

The Setting

Just whose vision gets to define the future?

What confluence brings a place or a season of innovation?

Does creativity respond to rules or just to will,

And a dream, nourished inside by

An atmosphere as illusive as it is magical,

Like a fragile zephyr that reflects

Its presence only in the trees it visits?

If so, one has passed this way for a time

Leaving a fragrance of inquisitive openness,

Amid the sunshine and oaks,

For us to delve...freely.

Here, a unique and fertile valley gave root

To fertile minds that helped change the world.

At the southern end of San Francisco Bay lies one of the world's most appealing climatic settings. Over a half-century ago, before its major crops were silicon and equity, before venture capital inflated the soil, and before the grazing land and orchards were sold by the square foot, there was born a place of uncommon inquiry. It was 1946 and with some aim at growth, the Fathers of Stanford University formed a subsidiary, Stanford Research Institute, that became one of the largest independent research organizations in the world. In just over a half century it has provided a wealth of innovation about which that same world is largely oblivious. Today, it struggles for recognition in what has become a cauldron of creativity known the world over as Silicon Valley. That SRI helped in significant ways to formulate this pattern for progress is mostly unappreciated, even here in this Valley where it was born. To those who come to add their part to the regional luster, including the recent wave of Internet entrepreneurs, its history and even its beautiful climate seem as irrelevant as the vale in its famous name. Such is the preoccupation and consuming power of innovation.

Preface

Most Americans, perhaps most people in the industrialized world, have a certain reverence for research. We see it as the necessary wellspring that launches those concepts that elevate our standard of living, ease our burdens, or enable us to live and work more productively. We subscribe to the overly simplistic model that science or research begets technology, which in turn begets substances, devices, and systems that enrich our lives. These processes that touch us every day are much more complex than such a linear notion implies, but clearly research and development, or R&D, are critical to a growing industrialized economy. Our economic practices and our reward system, together with a penchant to innovate, go a long way in explaining the economic vitality of the United States in the world setting.

This is a story about an active, ongoing research institute created at Stanford University in the latter half of the 1940s. It consists of a brief look at that institute's origins and a much longer review of some of its important accomplishments. The institute began life as the Stanford Research Institute (SRI) and, given a half-century of achievement in a turbulent world of research priorities, its history provides a framework for discussing the relevance of its particular form of research. SRI has always engaged in contract research, in effect seeking to do something not done before, but under the stipulations of a client contract. Though SRI calls itself a *contract research* organization, some of its contracts are, in fact, grants. Grants are usually the province of more fundamental research and they often permit more latitude in both approach and outcome. However, as in the case of grant-issuing foundations, the nature of the client organization can also define the type of working agreement. Another distinction is financial, with a grant implying some type of cost sharing, including no fee or profit. Research institutions like SRI, even though nonprofit, usually prefer fee-bearing contracts, for it is accrued fees or profit that enable discretionary investments. In spite of these distinctions, either type of research can be a recipe for researchers' exhilaration or frustration, or both. Even though it has more

rigorously defined expectations than grant research, contract research is anything but dull.

This book is also about innovation—the act of introducing something new. Many avenues other than research lead to innovation, but most of what SRI has done over the years could be classified as just that, innovation through research. Research differs from innovation in that it generally involves newly discovered facts that revise or add to fundamental knowledge. SRI is a research institute, and how such an institute wends its way for a half-century or so is an intriguing process in itself, as will be evident in the chapters that follow. Like any aspect of a market economy, research also has its ups and downs, and some time is spent here exploring how contract research is expected to fare in the dramatically changing world of research in both industry and government.

To set the stage for a discussion of research, it is necessary to mention two, but not always separable, kinds of research. The timeworn expressions are "basic" and "applied" research, and differentiating between the two types is about as confusing as distinguishing between the terms "science" and "technology." Basic research generally deals with discovering unknowns, the consequences of which, beyond obvious contribution to knowledge, are not easily foreseen. Applied research begins with envisioning a fairly specific end use for an investigation and is based, at least in part, on existing knowledge. Both are full of discovery, but the reward system for each is usually different.

Characteristically, the more basic the research, the greater the freedom about where the work can lead. Time horizons are long, and researcher distraction associated with attaining funding renewals or immediately satisfying clients is minimized. Applied research, on the other hand, is more focused, may have imposed deadlines, and is often accompanied by requirements for salesmanship and detailed accountability. Both kinds can be very engaging for researchers who are passionate about and dedicated to their work. Traditionally, basic research has often been thought of as a lonely, sometimes romantic adventure whose reward system consists mostly of recognition for an individual's discovery. Increasingly, however, the complexity of modern science demands more collaborative efforts, often from different laboratories. Applied work, on the other hand, is highly collegial and intensive and its researchers are more likely rewarded by seeing an ultimate use. Sometimes they may even receive royalties or equity for their efforts. Basic research is increasingly the province of universities because many corporate or government research laboratories have been forced to pursue more predictable near-term outcomes. Contract research, such as that done by SRI, is by nature almost totally applied, but it is a measure of the ingenuity of SRI staff that they also are able to perform some fundamental work as well.

This book thus describes an independent research organization that has successfully carried out contract research for more than 55 years—without endowment or top-down largess—by providing a framework within which innovation can happen. While its half-century has not all been growth and progress for SRI, it continues on its course, exploring new orientations of itself and helping define the character of research in our increasingly rapid, information-intensive world.

The book provides glimpses into the excitement of discovery, conveyed through the lives of many SRI people, their projects, and those projects' notable and positive effects on the world. Keep in mind that apart from perhaps one or two well-known scientific prizes, little public recognition is afforded those whose everyday job it is to break new ground, bringing innovative and useful changes for our world.

Deciding What to Tell About SRI

During its lifetime, the Institute, as I like to call it, has completed well over 50,000 projects. With such voluminous output, selecting examples that illustrate the creativity and resourcefulness of SRI staff from many disciplines has involved several choices. First, I have chosen to concentrate, but not exclusively so, on project outcomes rather than on the work of specific individuals or for specific clients. Second, I have looked for significant impacts from projects; that is, noteworthy

alterations in how science or technology is practiced, how our economy or social systems operate, or how ordinary people conduct their lives. Moreover, with but a few exceptions, I have sought to describe areas that a typical reader can understand.

I started out seeking 30-40 such impacts, but my investigations were not that easily contained. To try to be representative of the Institute's breadth the number has swollen to more like 60, and some of those are more comprehensive than I once anticipated. Regrettably, by providing insights about any small set of chosen outcomes, I risk having some readers conclude that the vast majority of SRI work is unimportant; that these major impacts are all that are worth knowing about. Such a notion would be emphatically wrong, for SRI's real strength is its collective and continuous contribution to its clients, and there are thousands of interesting and meaningful stories to tell. In any case, you will thus find the work described here wide-ranging—breadth that is typical of what goes on at SRI every day. The danger in that breadth, of course, is that unless you have a healthy curiosity, a research bent, or simply want to know more about SRI, only parts of the account will hold your interest.

Through research and other insights, SRI's world is clearly one of innovation. It is built into the life cycle of thousands of projects that are SRI's life blood. Indeed, for over a half century the people of SRI have provided, by almost any reckoning, a long and striking heritage of innovation. It is the embodiment of its culture.

But one topic of SRI's operations I have chosen to avoid is the detail of its overall financial history. Certainly, contract research has its financial constraints, aggravated at times by changes in the research marketplace and the absence of that always critical combination: a creative and compelling idea matched against a corresponding and expressed client need. SRI's first 2 decades saw solid growth, followed by 2 decades of relative stability, and then a decade of challenge stemming mainly from the restructuring and subsequent demise of its business consulting group. Over the past few years, SRI has again hit its stride and is growing. In a demonstration of broad-based innovation, each of its individual and varied research divisions is doing very well. That means that its varied disciplines, as well as its unique inter-discipline strengths, continue in evidence.

Discovery and Impact: The Core Motivations of Research

For those wishing to dedicate their lives to research, the principal motivation is usually not money because, with some exceptions, such careers are not lucrative. Instead, most of those who become researchers do so for other reasons. One is the thrill of discovery or the satisfaction of solving an unsolved puzzle. Often, success in achieving these goals is manifested by advancing the state of knowledge and documenting findings for the research community. Another motivation is to create something new that can have an important result for a research client and for the world beyond. The typical SRI researcher thus seeks the challenge of discovery, which if successful can result in a common but often unspoken exhilaration of doing something for the first time.

But research also carries with it the obligation of adhering to scientific ethics or professional standards. These overlays on the work require that the research context and background be studied sufficiently and cited to prove to *others* that new ground has been covered, and this process must occur even if the results appear obvious or if a client insists they remain confidential. Such integrity is not just desired in a research environment, it is its very essence.

While doing things for the first time is an inherent part of a good research environment, making an impact is not. Whether or not new outcomes will have an impact is often unclear when they are first realized, and sometimes the subsequent extent of such impacts depends purely on serendipity. In most cases, of course, outcomes do not result in momentous impacts, and when a research outcome does have an impact, it may not take place until a great while after the research has been completed. Many are surprised to learn that the first Internet transmission occurred at SRI more than 30 years ago (or 37, depending on which benchmark is used). Even startling change and exponential growth patterns may be rooted in modest and often obscure beginnings.

Though SRI has a rich history of firsts, client desires for confidentiality and government classification sometimes restrict the Institute's ability to publish, resulting in lack of credit for such discoveries. SRI always describes the results of its work to the clients for that work, but there is some truth in asserting that something happened only if it actually occurred and *was written about openly*. Over and above restrictions on disclosing work, SRI researchers, their managers, or their clients may judge publishing to be unnecessary or extravagant. As a consequence of these constraints, much of SRI's research legacy has been hidden, and ferreting it out is often difficult. (Appendix A provides a few examples of such lack of attribution.)

One of the regrettable aspects of compiling a historical account is that it tends to relegate all the excitement of discovery and innovation to the past, when we all know that these events are in fact continuing all about us, especially at SRI. In this light, in a few cases I have, and possibly been foolhardy in doing so, predicted an important impact that may never actually occur. But SRI continues its work and some will assuredly result in innovations and impacts that we currently cannot imagine. As long as research is the Institute's middle name (figuratively if no longer literally), that will happen.

Finally, although discussions of research tend to dwell on science and technology, innovations in social and economic fields have clearly been part of SRI's applied research horizons as well. Over the years, these SRI disciplines have also made significant contributions to their fields and they too will be touched on.

The Biggest Burden

My major regret as I finished this book was the necessity of leaving out so much important material and so many talented people because of space limitations. I could not mention many of the bright, dedicated, objective, and thoroughly honest people who were instrumental in keeping me, and many others like me, in just this one place for our entire working lives; I would be proud to be with them anywhere. Working on research of one's choosing, espousing the scientific ethic, and finding the resources to do so attracts, I believe, such people. As with all enterprises, most of SRI's dedicated, hardworking contributors will never achieve prominence, nor will their work be widely acclaimed. Though working to satisfy their clients, SRI researchers also set their own goals that serve to stretch their minds into new territory. Whatever other recognition they may receive in that process, meeting or exceeding their own expectations is always the most rewarding. Failing that, no other award is worthwhile.

Thus this book seeks to illuminate a somewhat invisible Institute, known well only in the limited contexts of research and consulting. It also seeks to provide those around the world already acquainted with SRI with broader information about SRI's accomplishments. I tell the stories of 60 or so projects or programs, selected from the 50,000 SRI has completed, that in some way changed the world. As you might expect, these stories can convey only a small part of SRI's history, adventures, and impacts. While SRI has supported much of the cost of editing and printing this work, there has been no influence or stipulations on what I have written. What you read, then, will be unfettered expressions about topics of my own choosing. That latitude, common in the SRI culture, is, of course, appreciated.

Finally, a personal note. I have spent almost my entire professional life at SRI, about 40 years. During that time, I filled a number of roles in the organization that, I believe, have given me a reasonably good perspective on its culture. But perspectives in a large and complex organization, particularly one as internally diverse as SRI, will obviously differ. Although I have endeavored to recount SRI's achievements objectively, I admit a certain bias in favor of the individualistic, self-determined inventiveness of the place and its people. In retrospect my stay here has been a very positive one and I hope that my perspective sits well with SRI's research staff and that my fondness for that culture will be apparent in what you read. Though I would have liked to be completely representative of the Institute's broad range of work, I have admittedly lent more coverage toward those areas with which I was already familiar.

Just one note of guidance: the references given are divided into footnotes, which appear on the same page and are generally explanations or expansions on the text, and endnotes, which are information sources and are located at the end of each chapter.

While this effort has been almost totally my own, I would like to acknowledge the help of those who took the time to make my accounts concerning them more accurate and interesting. You will find many of their names in the project accounts. I have a few others to thank as well: Lisa Beffa, who cheerfully tolerated my countless investigations in SRI's archives; the editors who made English of my efforts, most particularly Jeanie Graham[1]; Ray Vincent, who gave me entry into this amazing institution; the wonderfully interesting people of SRI who made 40 years go too quickly and whose individual pursuits were so often contagious; the wonderful colleagues and associates who over the years walked the SRI path close beside me, particularly those in the laboratory, division, and group offices and organizations in Engineering. Some of their images can be found just inside the covers of this book, but in any case, they know who they are without my saying.

But far above all, there is my devoted lifetime partner, Helen, who has tolerated this other love in my life and who, although she thought my retirement was at hand in 1998, graciously accepted what were supposed to be a few more years of sharing me with the Institute as I researched and wrote this account. To her and to the rest of my real family, David, Richard, Sandra, and Greg, this book is gratefully dedicated.

Don Nielson
Menlo Park, California
December 2004

---

[1] Other editors were Michael Smith, Kitta Reeds, Lynn Johannesen, and especially Klaus Krause. Sheila Igne did the layout and Shari Fisher helped with the incovers, printing, and required permissions.

Chapter 1
The Origin and Character of SRI

The Origin of SRI

Informal discussions about a research institute at Stanford University were held on campus as early as the 1920s. But it wasn't until 1942 that a serious proposition was made, and that initiative had to await the end of World War II before enough momentum could be gained to pursue it to completion. That momentum ultimately came from the confluence of the desires of the University leadership for more contact with Western U.S. industry and a set of those same Western industrialists wanting a place to bring problems of importance to them. It was a fortunate, if slightly chaotic, confluence of complementary needs.[1]

The first formal step in the creation of Stanford Research Institute came when the Trustees of Stanford University voted in February 1946 to establish in principle a research affiliate of the University. Over the subsequent summer, the University and business leaders in the San Francisco Bay Area, aided by suggestions from other research foundation leaders, developed a charter for the Institute. Their justification came from Stanford's Founding Grant, which states: "the public at large, and not alone the comparatively few students..., are the chief and ultimate beneficiaries of Stanford University." Acting on behalf of the Stanford Trustees, a small incorporating board filed the Institute's articles and bylaws with the State of California in November 1946, and the Trustees accepted the Charter and appointed SRI's new Board of Directors the following month. The Charter, defining SRI as a nonprofit subsidiary of the University under the laws of the State of California, set forth a set of purposes that benefited both the University and industry in the western United States. A few of the more important stipulations of the Charter follow:

- To promote the educational purposes of the...University...in the conducting of pure and applied research...in the promotion and extension of knowledge and learning.

- To provide...laboratories...and other facilities...for scientific and industrial research.

- To engage...a staff of qualified educators, scientists, and research experts...

- To establish a center for the accumulation of information...and foster...[its] exchange...with other research and educational institutions...and publish...findings...deemed in the general public interest.

- To promote and foster the application of science in the development of commerce, trade, and industry..., the industrialization of the Western United States..., and the improvement of the general standard of living and the peace and prosperity of mankind.

While a few in the University discussed such an institute as early as the 1920s, SRI owed its real genesis to perhaps four or five, somewhat loosely correlated efforts starting just after the conclusion of World War II: Western industrialists were looking for a Pacific Coast research enterprise that would operate under the aegis of a university. And within Stanford itself, the defining effort was that of its President Donald B. Tressider and his Vice President for Development, Alvin Eurich. Stanford's lawyers, with input from one of the industrial groups led by Atholl McBean and the insights of Henry Heald, then President of the Illinois Institute of Technology (IIT), drafted the Institute's Charter. The Charter gave the University two means of controlling its new offspring: allowing the Board of Trustees to select SRI's directors, and having Stanford's President serve as the Chairman of the SRI Board. SRI's initial directors consisted of 32 of the most prestigious western executives imaginable, giving SRI, it seemed, a good

---

[1] Appendix B provides a more complete account of SRI's genesis and the major aspects of its history. A much more detailed coverage of the SRI founding process and its players can be found in two books by Weldon B. Gibson: *SRI – The Founding Years* and *SRI – The Take-Off Years*, William Kaufman's Publishing Services Center, 1980 and 1986, respectively.

bloodline.[2] In addition, in a departure from similar research organizations, Stanford's president did not limit SRI's field of research to the natural sciences, indicating instead that it could pursue "all research problems."[A]

To get the Institute under way, Stanford was to advance $500,000 to SRI. But according to the *San Francisco Chronicle* of December 15, 1952, the University's advance amounted to $625,000 with another $600,000 lent by six San Francisco banks. While there were the normal jitters associated with a fledgling enterprise, and although there were times in the first year or two when it looked as though the fledgling might die, all of these loans were eventually repaid. The Institute started on Stanford's campus but soon moved its growing staff to a surplus Army hospital in nearby Menlo Park, portions of which Stanford had acquired from the government. That location still houses SRI's main campus.

Since the founding documents didn't stipulate *how* SRI was to be built, during the Institute's formative years, differences in opinion regarding SRI governance were held by Stanford President Tressider and SRI's first director, William Talbot. Treating SRI and Talbot much as he would an on-campus department and dean, Tressider reviewed in detail each SRI expenditure, which at the time were managed just the same as other accounts handled by the University. The early projects were approved by the SRI Board but were also subject to University policy, particularly when cooperation or competition between the two institutions might arise. Talbot saw the need for greater operational independence, especially when requests as mundane as those for administrative supplies would find their way to Tressider's desk. This conflict between Stanford's husbanding of funds and an SRI bent on greater self-determination led to Talbot's resignation by the end of SRI's first year.

But SRI continued its path toward greater autonomy with two important events in early 1948. President Tressider died unexpectedly in January, and his and Eurich's choice as the Institute's second director joined the Institute in late March. The new leader was the energetic, independent-minded director of the Armour Research Foundation, Dr. Jesse Hobson. He quickly developed a good working relationship with Alvin Eurich, who had become Stanford's

acting president, and thus chairman of SRI's Board, and he gained the confidence of the University Trustees. Hobson's acumen and enthusiasm garnered the investment money needed to launch the Institute into 20 years of remarkable growth.[3] Though Hobson would leave SRI at the end of 1955, SRI had grown from a staff of 50 to 1,161 with annual revenues exceeding $10 million. Under his successor, Finley Carter, the staff reached 3,000, and revenues grew to more than $54 million annually by 1966. This was all real, not inflationary growth.

Thus, without explicitly violating Stanford's governing stipulations, SRI had become an eclectic and self-sufficient research institute. The one area of SRI that the University continued to monitor, however, was business consulting. The University wanted SRI to objectively research a given situation and lay the results before clients for their own interpretation and not to interpret the research findings nor consult regarding their implications. SRI's commercial business groups would have difficulties with this distinction until SRI separated from the University in 1970.[4] Except for a relatively small number of shared staff (faculty) and projects, the rest of SRI operated quite autonomously from the University once it relocated in Menlo Park.

How SRI Conducts Business

The pattern that defined how SRI would do business derived from a combination of its discipline-oriented University heritage and the U.S. marketplace for research funding. The establishment of laboratories with the freedom to pursue self-defined research interests and goals existed almost from SRI's beginning. Subject only to the "consulting" restrictions mentioned above, the Institute expanded into applied research in engineering, science, and economics. Those research areas were eventually augmented with significant research in education, government policy, and international development.

---

[3] Perhaps as significant as any of Hobson's insights was his belief in the need for comfortable separation between the University and the Institute. According to William McGuigan, SRI Director of Planning in the 1960s, Hobson had learned that necessity well from his sojourns at Armour and IIT. (Interviewed by John Lomax, July 20, 1998)

[4] Appendix B discusses the separation, the reasons for it, and its consequences, in addition to an account of the Institute's acquisition of RCA Laboratories in 1987.

---

[2] Appendix C lists the members of two early SRI Boards.

The marketplace also had its influence on what SRI was to become. Though created for the benefit of Western U.S. industry, SRI's client base immediately expanded to include U.S. government research entities. Its first contract, in fact, was for the Office of Naval Research to look into alternative sources of natural rubber. Work for governments would continue, and over the years SRI's client base was apportioned on the order of 60% government and 40% commercial. Moreover, with the blessing of its Board, SRI broke away from serving only a Western U.S. industry client base and started to undertake international work as early as 1950—a move that would eventually give SRI a worldwide presence.

SRI's core business is contract research and development. While other forms of income have been and are being explored, working for clients on a research problem has been SRI's enterprise engine for more than 55 years. The spectrum of the Institute's contracts is extremely broad, defined primarily by the expertise and predilections of its staff and by opportunities in the research marketplace.

But contract research is not necessarily a lucrative business. Work from the federal government is normally constrained in regard to fees—ranging from nothing on research grants to negotiated cost-plus-fixed-fee arrangements prescribed by federal guidelines.[5] Commercial contracts are often characterized by tasks that are not only limited in scope, but ones the client also expects SRI to execute frugally. Over the years, some exceptions to this way of building revenue and income have occurred, but not many. Since the U.S. Bayh-Dole Act was passed in 1984, nonprofits have been able to retain the intellectual property developed under government contracts. That stipulation clarified SRI's ability to leverage such property into selected commercialization activities to supplement its normal income from contract fees. Accordingly, in recent years SRI has turned to the formation of equity by spinning off start-up companies and by licensing intellectual property for royalties.[6]

---

[5] "Fee" in this case is viewed as profit, which, in the case of a nonprofit institute, forms a pool of funds that is reinvested for a variety of capital and business development needs.

[6] Appendix D provides a more complete discussion of SRI's business model and the growing importance of intellectual property commercialization. Some mention of that transition also appears in Appendix B.

The Role of SRI Staff

With a few exceptions, SRI's contract research operations are defined by the initiatives and expertise of the first two levels of its staff hierarchy—the program and laboratory levels.[7] These are the levels where choices are made about what to pursue in the field of endeavor and where hiring of qualified staff occurs. Programs consist of ongoing collections of similarly oriented projects, run by a program manager, and laboratories (or centers) are made up of a family of similar programs. The laboratory or center is SRI's first level of fiscal accountability. The present organizational taxonomy includes only two higher levels: divisions, which are aggregations of laboratories and SRI's highest level, its president. But from perhaps the 1960s through much of the 1990s, when the Institute was larger, the divisions were consolidated as Groups in Engineering, Sciences, Business, and Education and Policy. All of these organizational elements will be repeatedly referred to, either generically or specifically, in the project descriptions presented in the following chapters.

The roles played by SRI staff depend, logically, on their position in the above research hierarchy. As mentioned, the preponderance of research ideas and contract sales occurs in the programs and the laboratories. Within those levels are cadres of qualified support staff, who usually divide their time among multiple projects. At the program level and above sit research managers, whose job it is to monitor the quality of work, assess client satisfaction, budget and track the fiscal performance of the various laboratories and programs, and decide when to close or initiate programs. Most of SRI's seats of innovation lie within the laboratories and centers. Individual researchers in the laboratories help advance the state of their chosen discipline and provide clients with solutions that are realistic and innovative and that will stand the test of time. Because of the diversity of talents and disciplines among this set of professionals and their sheer number, they collectively represent a stable marketing and sales force for the Institute as a whole. When SRI was at its largest, their—not always coordinated—marketing efforts produced roughly 2000 new projects a

---

[7] Appendix E provides a more extensive account, based on the author's own views, of the roles of research staff and managers.

year. Some of those projects bring several years of consistent and focused research and thus offer their type of operational stability; but even the most transitory projects, if plentiful enough, offer another, more aggregated stability.

Some people are uncomfortable with such dynamics. When interviewing people for a position, I would sometimes ask them how they would feel being in a laboratory that was often less than a year away from going out of business. That was, after all, the nature of much of the work. But, given the ability of the staff to be both innovative and adaptive and given enough different projects to even out the revenue flow, laboratories and sometimes programs can be quite stable. It's just that at any given moment, some subset of staff may not feel that way.[8]

But the uneasiness created by the transient nature of SRI's contract research is often supplanted by the feeling of independence it provides individual staff members. An SRI project leader has great latitude in the area he/she chooses to address. In a real sense that leader has complete control over the technical and financial aspects of each project. His supervisors are there mostly to encourage an adequate backlog of work, to provide the environment needed for conducting the work and, as mentioned, to occasionally check on the quality of the work when a leader is new or a project entails some unusual risks. Managers are also there to help an innovative researcher engage other insights or skills when an interdisciplinary solution best satisfies a client need.

This type of environment has a distinct quality to it. Though immersed in a large organization, the researcher is, in a very real sense, working directly for the research client. If the work done pleases both the client and the responsible research leaders, other judgments about the work become secondary. On the other hand, when a researcher is not meeting the obligations expressed in the contract,

normally little external motivation is needed for the marshalling of supplementary effort. The scientific ethic and the self-imposed expectation of performance quality have created an atmosphere of integrity and objectivity at SRI.

The Allure of Innovation

It is hard to conceive of a research organization, either basic or applied, that doesn't encourage and reward fruitful innovation. Such applied imagination results in fresh solutions to a problem or advances in the state of an art. For researchers, it is also the most important ingredient of self-satisfaction—the exhilaration that comes from doing something for the first time. It doesn't have to be of Nobel Prize caliber at all, but it should capture the acclaim of peers and the client.

Of course, not all such innovation needs to be individualistic. In today's technical world, a lot of innovation lies at the intersections of existing disciplines and is, by nature, a collaborative effort. But no matter how many collaborators are involved, there is an intrinsic joy in discovery, and everyone in a research organization strives to cultivate an atmosphere that fosters such discovery—even in the somewhat constrained environment of contract research. Those who have spent their careers at SRI invariably know that feeling.

These two attributes, innovation and noteworthy solutions to a clients' problems, go a long way toward defining the pride and motivation the SRI staff feel about their place of work. While administrative and support staff participate in that general feeling, the pride of individual researchers is often influenced, perhaps dominated, by their own perceived contributions. In support of these contributions, many mid-level managers at SRI believe their most important job is to build an atmosphere where important and fruitful innovation can unfold. After all, innovation comes from original and creative thinking in a conducive and receptive atmosphere.

The personal drive required of principal researchers at SRI is, quite expectedly, very akin to the motivations of an entrepreneur. To be responsible for all aspects of getting and executing a project, both technically and financially, is to exercise the rudiments needed to create a business. And many of those who

---

[8] Clearly, a finite pipeline or backlog of work is simply the nature of most service businesses including law firms and medical clinics. Within contract research, some areas may provide more opportunity than others. As a case in point, in my nearly 24 years as a laboratory and division director in the field of communications, computer networking, and computer science, in only one brief episode when a large, longstanding project was not renewed, did we have to lay staff off for lack of work. Some SRI laboratories have been in continuous operation for four or even five decades.

have "cut their teeth" at SRI have decided to leave to found companies or more individual business pursuits. Because SRI has not kept a record of such departures, the list in Appendix F is a very partial one. Nonetheless, the creation of the more than 80 companies listed can be viewed as another facet of the culture at SRI, the kind of people it attracts, and the ideas it engenders.

The SRI "Diary"

Another way to gain an appreciation for the character of SRI is to travel through what might be called its "diary"; that is, the chronological collection of considerably more than 50,000 individual projects that serves to communicate just what SRI has been and continues to be. This logbook of thousands of researchers, all heading into usually uncharted territories of every imaginable description, is a highly dimensional, eclectic journey that is nothing short of amazing and certainly tantalizing to the curious. Each project's tale begs to be told, and, having dipped in just a bit, it is clear to me that a huge number of project tales are worth telling. Therein lies the inevitable frustration in being able to address but a relative few.

Just the first pages of the log reveal the vast diversity of SRI's work over the years. The very first project in 1946 was an exploration of a new source of natural rubber to relieve the great shortage evidenced during World War II. Another early effort was a campaign by the Western Gas and Oil Association to understand the constituents of what came to be called smog in the Los Angeles Basin. SRI held the first nationwide conferences on identifying the constituents of smog. Later, carbonation in beverages was studied for Pepsi-Cola, and not long thereafter, for the American Chicle Company SRI examined why peppermint flavor waned too quickly in Chiclets. Soon Spreckels Sugar wanted to know the optimum conditions for storing concentrated raw juices, and the port of Richmond, California wanted a review of its harbor operations.

Examples from 1950 include measuring the demand for cotton textiles along the Pacific Coast, researching ovarian cancers for the American Cancer Society, finding means for reducing brush foaming of paint for W.P. Fuller & Company, testing antennas for Douglas Aircraft, conducting work for the Bank of America that would revolutionize how banking

was to be done, and designing pulse transformers for the Army Signal Corps. SRI's 342nd project brought its first overseas work, an economic study of Cuba and, one project later, a study of the revitalization of the war-torn Italian mechanical industries for the Italian Government. In November 1956, SRI, in partnership with the University of Arizona, held the world's first major conference on the capture and use of solar energy. Over 5 days, approximately 500 energy scientists and engineers, industrialists, and government officials from around the world heard about solar furnaces, photovoltaic cells, solar space heating and cooling, solar stills for making drinking water, and even algae and higher plant cultures that were potential energy storage systems. Some 29,000 members of the public and press toured the technical exhibits and saw how India, Africa, Europe, as well as the immediate U.S. Southwest, were interested in developments in this field. It was a landmark event.

Also in the 1950s, there were sugar beet hydration methods, ultra-high-frequency antennas for Learjets, diversification studies for the Rohr Corporation, project "Mickey" that helped found Disneyland, a study of Israel for the U.S. Foreign Operations Administration, an exploration of the psychological factors of using colored hair rinse, the design of wooden boxes for who else but the Wooden Box Institute, the solution of problems in the manufacture of phonograph records for Capitol Records, creation of printed circuit countermeasure antennas for the Air Force, and the development of Hydracushion railcars for Southern Pacific that ultimately changed how most railcars would be built.

The variety of SRI research is staggering: the development of quick-drying ink that prints on vinyl for Plastic Fabricators, the study of the absorption patterns of salicilate, evaluation of instant mashed potatoes for the American Potato Co., examination of high-temperature oxidation and nitridation of niobium in ultra-high vacuum, and a toxicology analysis of muscatel wines for the State of California's Wine Advisory Board.

While vague research titles often mask detailed investigations, some projects can still be quite general in nature: conducting a market analysis for the Asparagus Board; structuring complex man-machine systems for the Air Force project in 1961, which led to the first development of personal computing; assessing manufacturing opportunities for the Ethyl Corporation; analyzing command, control, and communications for the Army Signal Corps; and undertaking the ubiquitous "technical service" projects, which were usually both small and very directed. SRI even undertook studies for the U.S. Congress when in 1959 it assessed those fields of science and technology that might affect how the Senate Foreign Relations Committee made foreign policy decisions, and in 1960 made recommendations concerning the U.S. balance of payments.

Among projects in 1969 was work for NASA: building simulated lunar rocks, developing tactile feedback for teleoperations, and studying the noise characteristics of jet turbulence. Also, in that year SRI forecast Iowa's long-term airport needs, developed a fire retardant for polymers, figured out how to clean and debark wood chips for the U.S. Plywood Association, and formulated post-attack survival and recovery strategies for the Office of Civil Defense.

The 1970s saw a study for the Colorado Legislature of that state's Department of Education, the development of a saline removal process called reverse osmosis for the Department of the Interior, a small project in denying bank vault penetration for Diebold, a sensory evaluation of Oreos for the Keebler Corp., an auroral radar installation in McMurdo Sound for the National Science Foundation, a 911 emergency number system design for the Miami Police Department, an evaluation of the air quality impact of a proposed winter resort north of Lake Tahoe for Walt Disney, and determination of the fluency of speech over packet-switched communications systems (now, called Internet speech or Voice-Over-IP) for the Navy. In the wake of the reactor accident at Three Mile Island in Pennsylvania, the U.S. Nuclear Regulatory Commission called on SRI to evaluate various ways to cool the reactor core. In a related vein, the Wisconsin Electric Power Association asked SRI to examine its needs for future nuclear power plants. SRI not only didn't find any need, but that finding coincided with the end of nuclear power plant construction starts in the United States.

As you might expect, undertaking some projects has been open to question. SRI decided not to conduct studies for the Nevada Gaming Commission but it did look at the transportation options to bring more people to Reno to gamble. SRI did undertake a project in 1978 for the Edgar Cayce Foundation in exploring archaeological sites in Egypt, a small project for astronaut Edgar Mitchell's Institute for Noetic Sciences, and several paranormal investigations for both private and government sponsors.

The diary, of course, goes on and on. Today, SRI is studying projects like miniature fuel cells to power laptops and cell phones, techniques to develop magnetic levitation, wearable polymer batteries, and power generators imbedded in the heels of soldier's boots. In the case of the latter, a company has recently been formed to pursue the broad applications inherent in the SRI technology called electroactive polymers. On the other hand, SRI is also investigating age-old phenomena such as how deep ocean waves intersect with a shoreline. The stream of projects is as exciting as it is endless. If you are at all curious, watching this flow is very much like viewing a fantastic, eclectic parade that you can't quite leave. But those who work here, those who find themselves inside the parade, get to see only that which is immediately around them.[9] I claim even that limited view has been exciting. Regrettably, from the continuous flow of projects and the incredible concentration required by researchers toward their own endeavors, most SRI staff do not have the time to publicize their part in the parade or even to watch much of it pass by. That is just one reason for this book.

As another comment on SRI's work, I have the distinct sense that it has never been sufficiently credited for its contributions. Contrary to the public exposure the Charter suggests, much of SRI's work goes unheralded. Of course, that must be the case for projects that the sponsoring agents consider proprietary and for classified work for the U.S. government. Other reasons are less clear. They include insufficient money at the end of a project to write articles about its innovative aspects, as well as the pressure of moving on to new

---

[9] One personal experience that shows the unannounced skills that exist in our colleagues occurred in a 1998 meeting of the U.S. Air Force Scientific Advisory Board of which I was a member. Each year they recognize a single Air Force researcher for his or her accomplishments. That year it was given to a young biochemist who, in the introduction of his invited talk, mentioned that none of what he had accomplished would have been possible without the help and inspiration of Ron Spanggord of SRI. "But that's my tennis partner!" I uncontrollably blurted out, knowing but vaguely the kind or significance of his work.

projects that leaves little time for such announcements. Nevertheless, some of SRI's technical laboratories have policies that encourage the use of discretionary money to publish any advance in the state of the art they practice. In my division, an explicit management goal was to publish and, with that policy in place, we easily achieved on the order of one professional paper per researcher per year. Although in recent years SRI is paying much more attention to publicity, over most of its existence it has chosen not to publicize its work. This is yet another reason for writing this book.

One final feeling the "diary" may suggest is that with all of its breadth and diversity, defined as it has been by the initiative, instincts, and insights of its legion of project developers for over 50 years, SRI is truly an uncommon, perhaps unique, place to be. Without belaboring the truth of that feeling, its acceptance by the staff can only help to make it so.

SRI's Dominant Character Traits

Though shifts in the research marketplace require SRI to adapt over time, there is an unchanging essence that those who have spent meaningful time here come to know. To experience it requires your having been "in the trenches," so to speak: having lived with the excitement of forming a new concept, solution, or vision; having struggled to find the needed support; and having known the euphoria of bringing an idea to realization. Some of the magic of SRI is the creative atmosphere that pervades the Institute and becomes intensely personal for all principal investigators and those who support them. Even many who leave SRI under less than ideal circumstances, can't shake the feeling engendered by that creative or innovative process. In the image painted up front in The Setting, creativity is seen as an ethereal quality, something that you know when it has visited you but are uncertain as to how to make it appear. Here we can simply attribute it to a happy confluence of the right people and a supporting atmosphere or culture.

One of the most important traits of the early years of SRI was the freedom people felt. Within the scope of a researcher's skills, almost any honorable endeavor was not only allowed but supported. One retired leader mentioned that during the 1960s, some staff who discovered they could realize their passion only outside the Institute were given, in the most positive sense, encouragement and even financial assistance to do so.[10] The atmosphere seemed oriented toward individual fulfillment, always tempered, of course, by the necessity of finding sponsorship for whatever that fulfillment might entail. To that atmosphere, add the opportunity to affect the future, where creativity is not wasted. Fortunately, SRI has been attractive to innovative people who feel invigorated by that kind of environment. Perhaps that is as much as one need say.

As one brief example of the kind of forward-looking, creative thought evidenced at SRI, notice the figure below of a person enabled to work at home through the use of a computer terminal, in this case, in his living room. The remarkable thing about the figure is that it is from a SRI promotional brochure called *Investments in Tomorrow* issued in 1974! Such an arrangement was seen at SRI at that time as a network-enabled, multitasking environment for the work of a specialist lending his talents to a variety of projects centered at different times and locations.

Few know of such prescient visions. Many SRI researchers have such visions of their own,

"What! Coffee time already?"

[10] Conversation with former SRI COO, Charles Cook (Feb. 23, 2000). He mentioned that some SRI people were even known to dip into their own pockets to help someone realize his or her goal on the outside. Often, SRI has also allocated time or money to help in relocation.

visions from which they are not easily distracted. As a consequence, most SRI staff members know little about the individual projects and accomplishments of their colleagues. What, in fact, has SRI done that made a difference? Some who are familiar with SRI will easily cite the mouse or perhaps the world's first computerized banking system but in all likelihood that may be as far as they get. Well, this book is intended to help correct that. Here, you will find plenty of examples of how other SRI researchers, by doing what SRI people do every day, with some serendipity, have changed the world.

Endnote

[A] "The Story of SRI," *SRI Journal*, Feature Issue 4, December 6–11, 1966 (a review of SRI's first 20 years).

Chapter 2
Innovations in Computing

Computing Research at SRI

Because of its importance to SRI and the world, research into computers, including their interconnection and some of their underlying technologies, will comprise the next three chapters of this book. SRI has been engaged in various aspects of computing research since 1950 when the design of practical computers was in its very infancy. SRI involvement began at that time with an enormous challenge: to build a reliable, real-time, transaction-oriented, error-free computer that could input checks and update bank account statements. The successful completion of that work over the ensuing five years also led to two other notable SRI computer research

activities that will also be described in this chapter: automatic handwriting recognition and computer technology. To appreciate SRI's contributions to computing also requires the depiction of its role in the conversion of computing from a detached, batch-oriented convention to an interactive, highly responsive one that now dominates nearly all of computing. Rounding out this Chapter will be the important story of SRI's work in automatic speech recognition, including its entry into the commercial marketplace. All of this work, including that covered in the following two chapters, has left an important impact on the inevitable influx of computing power into our lives.

ERMA—The First Banking Computer

The Genesis

SRI's involvement in electronic banking began almost accidentally.[A] In the spring of 1950, SRI Vice President Weldon "Hoot" Gibson and a couple of colleagues were promoting SRI at the San Francisco headquarters of the Emporium retail stores. When the meeting ended early, Gibson decided to call on S. Clark Beise, an acquaintance at the Bank of America (BofA). He told Beise that although it was a "shot in the dark," he thought the Bank ought to be looking at possible electronic banking applications. He also expressed doubt about whether the BofA would ever get what it needed from IBM or other providers of banking equipment. What Gibson didn't know was that the BofA was already laboring under the rapidly growing volume of checks that, handled manually, was threatening to prevent completion of daily

account updates.[1] Gibson gave Beise the telephone number of the head of SRI's

---

[1] In the late 1940s, then BofA President Mario Giannini, the founder's son, scoured the banking equipment industry to find help managing what in 1950 came to be 4.6 million accounts. He found no one ready or willing to meet his challenge. When Senior Vice President Clark Beise informed him of the SRI alternative, he authorized Beise to secretly contract with SRI. When Giannini died in 1954, Beise became President, ensuring the continuation of ERMA at SRI. ("The ERMA Chronicles," Bank of America Technology Magazine, 156, June 2000.)

Engineering Group, Dr. Tom Morrin, and then left. A few days later BofA contacted Morrin to initiate the innovative partnership with SRI that resulted, over the next 6 years, in development of automated check handling, the first computer for banking applications, and a magnetic ink reading system still in use today.

In 1950 BofA was the largest bank in the world, and Beise was a senior vice president and one of the few members of the Bank's upper management actively leading the search for machine-based innovations. He also was unique among senior management in realizing that check handling, not creating new business accounts, would be the major factor limiting growth. Automation was essential to keeping pace with the Bank's growing business, and the business equipment manufacturers Beise had talked to were not interested in the investment needed to create a whole new electronic banking system. But SRI could act as the Bank's R&D arm to show the manufacturers such a system could be built and perhaps to sell them the prototype.

At that time the BofA's checking accounts were growing at a rate of 23,000 per month, banks were being forced to close their doors by 2:00 PM to do the proofing and processing necessary to finish daily posting, and the situation was only going to get worse. As a measure of the cumbersome process, consider that unless a check was deposited at the bank branch where it was drawn, it had to be sorted by hand and individually entered into an adding machine at least six times during the clearing process. Business machine companies were unwilling to invest in new bookkeeping machines that might hurt sales of existing equipment, and the few computers that existed were viewed as calculators rather than record-keeping and accounting systems.

Assessing the Feasibility

The first meeting of SRI and BofA staff took place in June 1950, when the Bank's Frank Dana arranged through Morrin for Oliver Whitby and Joseph Lovewell to visit the Palo Alto Branch to view banking procedures in action and to assess the magnitude of the check-handling problem. This visit was followed by a number of meetings between SRI and the Bank wherein they agreed that together they would address the following basic functions: credit and debit all accounts,

maintain a record of all transactions, retain a constant record of customer current balances to be printed as needed, respond to stop-payment and hold orders on checks, and notify the operator if a check caused the account in question to be overdrawn.

Of course, strict accuracy was mandatory. Errors in arithmetic or in the integrity of an account simply could not go undetected. Also, the bookkeeping system had to be fast enough to make sure that all accounts were posted and reconciled each day. The system was not intended to assume the role of proofing the checks and sorting them by account or for distribution to the bank of origin. Operators would key in the values of the checks, and the system would then compute the new balance.

In July SRI was asked to embark on a feasibility study of an electronic bookkeeping machine to handle the five functions mentioned above, stressing the following performance attributes: speed, as dictated by the banking time schedule; handling of all the information needed for storage, processing, and printing; and the ability to provide up-to-date balance information for customers. The work was designated as "client private" so that only SRI and BofA staff members working on the project would be aware of it.

Thus the "whiz kids," as the BofA called the SRI project team members, went to work weighing the requirements of the new bookkeeping system against the available technology. Recall that only a few computers existed anywhere, and they had nothing to do with accounting. Transistors were just becoming available but were very unreliable, and the only magnetic media that would be large and fast enough were magnetic drums. But new available technology was always a point of discussion. From the BofA's perspective, the nature of the check should be changed as little as possible because checks were the interface between the bank and its customers, about whom the Bank was solicitous. But SRI immediately noticed that the blank checks of the day had no identification on them and were, in fact, passed around for anyone to use. Because accounts were kept alphabetically, opening a new account required an awkward reshuffling of the account list. At SRI's urging, the Bank agreed to require checks with preprinted account numbers. Each new account, then, would simply be added to the end of an account list, leaving all preceding numbers intact. The BofA's acceptance of this approach made it possible to combine the formerly separate processes of proofing and bookkeeping.

In September 1950 SRI completed a written report on the feasibility study. The report stated that an automatic bookkeeping system could be built that would satisfy the BofA's requirements. SRI called the proposed system an electronic recording machine, or ERM, and Morrin suggested a three-phase approach to system development:

- Study the banking procedures external to the machine

- Create the general logical design

- Build the system and test it.

The last step would not be done by SRI, but by an equipment manufacturer. In mid-November 1950, the BofA awarded SRI $15,000 over 6 months to complete the first two phases. Even with a $5,000 payment added in April 1951, the compensation seems minimal for such a large undertaking. SRI's interim report was delivered on 30 April, as promised.

The ERM was outlined as a large computer-like system for bookkeeping only. Checks would be proofed and sorted at the branches and then sent to the ERM for posting to individual accounts identified by numbers that would be optically readable on each check. All transactions would be recorded and printed by account number, and a statement reflecting them would be sent to customers once a month. The following numbers reflect the ambitious goals: Each ERM would handle 32,000 accounts and on the average process about 48,000 items per day. (ERM processing begins after the amount of each check has been added at the bottom in machine-readable form.) SRI's estimated cost for each machine ranged from $530,000 for a minimal configuration to $830,000 for a complete one.

After the numbers were refined a bit, the BofA took the bookkeeping system descriptions to a number of manufacturers, but only Burroughs expressed any interest. Because of existing product lines, Burroughs suggested that it convert its bookkeeping machine to an ERM and also offer a proof machine and a printer. After a few meetings, however, Burroughs withdrew its interest, saying the costs would be double SRI's estimate of about $1 million.

Whether this interplay was just a test of the SRI estimates, as Morrin suggested, will never be known, but Beise soon asked SRI to proceed with an ERM prototype to give the manufacturers evidence that such a system could be built for about the amount that SRI had estimated.[2] Although building prototypes was usually outside the role of a research institute, Morrin reluctantly agreed to proceed through design and construction. In January 1952 SRI signed a contract for $875,000 to develop the prototype.

SRI's Reluctant Continuation

The working relationship between SRI and the BofA was very close. SRI was responsible for the technology and worked with the Bank to examine the banking process and discover how it might be modified commensurate with what the equipment could or could not do. One of the most important contributors from the Bank was Charles Conroy, Assistant Vice President. He worked daily with the SRI designers formulating the essential compromises between what the banking system needed and what technology could deliver at a workable price. The BofA had also brought other people on board, not directly part of the ERM team, to help it prepare for the advent of computers, be they ERM or not. The need was becoming evident to everyone.

The next few years brought a whirlwind of innovation and yet a continuing dilemma. The SRI team wanted the performance potential of new technology but had to use components that were proven reliable and affordable. For example, transistor-implemented logic, though fast, small, low power, and potentially reliable, could not be used because the early manufacturing methods left them quite unreliable. Even the keyboard circuits that encoded each key had to be built. High-speed printers, needed for statements, were both experimental and preponderantly mechanical. In addition, magnetic tape drives for large-scale

---

[2] In a letter to the authors of the Harvard case-study (Op. cit.,[A]) leader, SRI's Tom Morrin wrote the following: "Mr. Beise told me...after his retirement...[that] in making the decision about Burroughs, et al., he called David Sarnoff at RCA, for whom we had done lot of work in color television, transistor circuitry, special tubes, etc., and was told that SRI was the only one to do the job, but to double our cost estimates. He knew, of course, that in advanced research there are no really good ways to estimate costs. One has to decide, as Beise did, as you go along whether it will pay out."

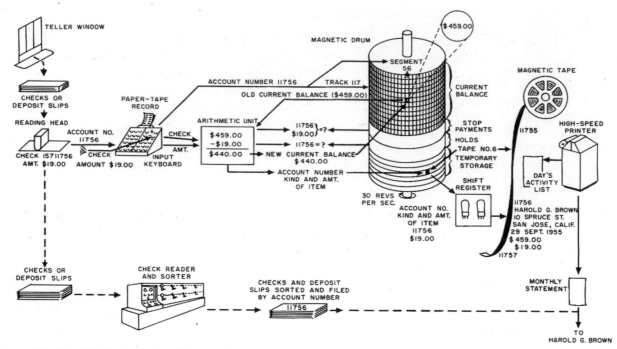

Figure 2-1. The ERMA check handling and accounting process.

storage had to be specially developed (in this case, by ElectroData, a subsidiary of Burroughs).

As it developed from 1950 through 1955, the ERM used magnetic drums and tapes for storage and vacuum tubes, silicon diodes, and relays for logic. Unlike other (batch-mode) machines of the period, the ERM made account data available on line to validate inputs and to respond to inquiries about account status. To understand the chronology of ERM, we must appreciate that stored-program computers were only a few years old and still in a laboratory state when SRI began its work. The first real-time computer, the MIT "Whirlwind," was also being assembled at MIT. It used magnetic core memory, but that technology was not available to SRI. Clearly, no existing system was close to the functionality needed by the ERM...it was simply a whole new machine! As the machine evolved, so did its name. ERM was difficult to say and the Bank wanted a name more easily communicated. As a result, "accounting" was appended to ERM and it acquired its more familiar and approachable title, ERMA.

To understand the rudiments of ERMA, it helps to view it in terms of the trajectory a check takes through the system. In Figure 2-1 the lower dashed line shows the path of the physical check and the accounting relevant to the check is depicted along the upper route. Here a number of tests are made against the account, including its present balance. A report

of transactions and the canceled checks are returned once a month to the holder of the account.

One of the early technical obstacles was the check reader/sorter. According to Bill McGuigan, then an assistant director of Engineering at SRI, Beise made it clear to Morrin that the BofA did not want to have to deal with punched cards.[B] Transferring all the check's information onto another medium would just encumber the process. Thus the check or deposit slip itself had to be read, at least for the account number and perhaps the check number. Because they were handwritten, the amounts stated on the checks required human entry. SRI was then faced with building a check reading and sorting system that would be infallible. The check-reading task was addressed by Ken Eldredge, Fred Kamphoefner, Phil Merritt, and others, while the mechanical design of the sorter was done by Alonzo W. "Bill" Noon. Noon's team produced a sorter able to handle about 10 checks per second with errors of less than 1 per 100,000. (see Figure 2-2) The early success of this sorter showed that Beise's request for a cardless system could, in fact, be met.[3,4]

---

[3] According to project supervisor Jerre Noe, when Thomas J. Watson of IBM visited the project and saw the high-speed check sorter working so well, he became noticeably concerned about this alternative to his punched-card realm.

Figure 2-2. The check sorter for ERMA with Ken Eldredge, the creator of MICR.

Figure 2-3. The ERMA that SRI demonstrated to the BofA in September 1955. (The control console is at upper left and the input machine is at mid-left. The SRI staff are (from the left) Dr. John Blickensderfer, Joyce Trainer, Mari Watson, and Maury Mills.)

The final ERMA computer, part of which is shown in Fig. 2-3, contained more than a million feet of wiring, 8,000 vacuum tubes, 34,000 diodes, 5 input consoles with electronic reading devices, 2 magnetic memory drums, a check sorter, a high-speed printer, a power control panel, a maintenance board, 24 racks holding 1,500 electrical packages and 500 relay packages, 12 magnetic tape drives for 2,400-foot tape reels, and a refrigeration system. ERMA weighed about 25 tons, used more than 80 kW of power, and had to be cooled by an air conditioning system.[c]

Following the successful demonstration of ERMA at SRI, the BofA engaged General Electric Corporation (GE) to manufacture 40 machines for installation in California. SRI worked with GE to transfer the basic processing algorithms

to the new architecture. The GE version of ERMA used transistor logic and magnetic core memory, both still in the experimental stage when the SRI machine was being designed.

Creating Readable Magnetic Fonts

A second major innovation in the project was the preprinting of checks with individual account numbers that could be read automatically with great fidelity as well as by humans. Solutions such as fluorescent ink that was invisible to the eye were initially considered, but they to be too vulnerable to pen and pencil marks that would produce reading errors and, more importantly, would require that banks change many of their bright check cancellation inks. During the project, the BofA also considered an optical reading system from a company in Arlington, Virginia, that offered one of the first optical character readers. But both fluorescent and non-fluorescent optical methods were too prone to errors from overwriting.

By about mid-1952, SRI had decided the solution was to create a machine-readable font using magnetic ink. By late 1952 the check owner's account number was being imprinted on the back of the check in both magnetic barcode and optical characters so that the number would be readable by both humans and

[4] According to Fred Kamphoefner (personal communication, February 10, 2001), Watson also said his "engineers told [him] that it wasn't possible!" At the time the SRI sorter was sorting stacks of used checks that varied by up to two to one in length, width, and thickness, plus an occasional IBM card and an old dollar bill.

When the BofA chose September 1955 for a final demonstration of ERMA, SRI's project team began working multiple shifts to create a minimal but working version of an automated bookkeeping machine. But the check sorter continued to have problems right up to the last moment. The appointed "ERMA Day," September 22, 1955, was carefully managed by BofA. The demonstration was held at SRI in Menlo Park, and reporters were bused there from San Francisco to prevent leaks. Beise of BofA and Morrin of SRI, without mentioning either organization, described the great contribution this system would make to banking. But before the demonstration, and because of the tenuous reliability of the check sorter, a cue from the SRI engineers to Morrin was needed to show the sorter was indeed working. After a slight delay, the sign was given, and the demonstration went perfectly, and the reporters left to file their stories. That evening, at a private showing for SRI employees, the sorter spewed checks all over the room! (*IEEE Annals of the History of Computing*, 1993, op. cit.)

machines. The account number was also preprinted on the front bottom of the check for convenience. This technique was used throughout the remainder of the SRI project, including in the prototype demonstrated in September 1955. The days of the barcode were numbered, however, partly because of esthetics but mostly because of a realization that magnetic-based Arabic characters could be made machine-readable. This innovation was to arise out of a companion SRI project from the Bank having to do with traveler's checks.

While traveler's checks didn't have an account number, they did have a unique serial number. Traveler's checks were processed in much smaller volumes than conventional checks, and the BofA's processing method involved first creating a punched card to be processed. The ability to automatically read the check serial number was helpful and would, incidentally, solve the identical reading problem faced in ERMA. To avoid the optical problems in reading both checks, Eldredge, by then director of SRI's Control Systems Laboratory, devised several test patterns and magnetic-ink fonts that proved to be reliably read by both humans and machines. (see the traveler's check font in Figure 2-4) Phil Merritt, then a graduate student at Stanford University, built the recognition circuitry. By applying some new matched filtering techniques he had picked up, Merritt designed and tested a second, more normal looking font (the left font in Figure 2-4). The third and final font is the stylized one that now appears on all checks, consisting of the 10 integers plus a few ancillary characters. Given a readable Arabic font, the account number could

be moved to the front of the check, where it remains today on all checks. Figure 2-4 shows the three different fonts:

- SRI's traveler's check font is shown in the upper righthand corner of the check (partially obliterated by a purposeful stain) and, in draft form, in the top center of the lower portion. Immediately below that is a profile of the sum of magnetic flux in a vertical slit scanned across the character.

- The first SRI font for ERMA is shown in the left inset, along with traces that represent the derivative of the sum of a vertical slit scanning each magnetic character.

- The final ERMA font that became the

Figure 2-4. Evolution of machine-readable fonts for checks.

international standard is at the bottom.

The third font, shown at the bottom of Figure 2-4, was, as it appears to be, the work of a committee, specifically the Bank Management Committee of the American Bankers' Association (ABA), which began deliberating about the font in July 1956. Several manufacturers offered input into its peculiarities. SRI called the font MICR, for magnetic ink character reading, but after the ABA's acceptance, it also became known as the ABA Common Machine Language. It has since evolved into an international standard. Fortuitously, and perhaps because of its implied importance, the U.S. Patent Office awarded SRI and Eldredge Patent No. 3,000,000 for a magnetic-ink-based character reading process. The magnetic ink character reading worked so well that it was common to demonstrate its resilience by marking and then wadding up a check, unraveling it, and putting it through the reader to show that it still could be read.

Traveler's checks were easier to work with than commercial bank checks because they were all the same size and were issued in only a few denominations. So-called normal checks of that day might vary as much as two to one in length, width, and thickness.[5] The MICR font for checking account numbers, while more difficult than other fonts for humans to read, has been extremely reliably read by machines. The BofA's Al Zipf, who was quickly becoming the Bank's best expert in data processing, helped transform MICR into an ABA standard. He later led the transition of ERMA from prototype to production.

The Production of ERMA

Once SRI had proved the feasibility of processing checks directly without creating any surrogate paper, it was time for ERMA to go into production. According to Jerre Noe, 24 companies had at least some interest in bidding on the job, in contrast with mild interest from Burroughs alone before SRI demonstrated the prototype. In the interim, technology had advanced, SRI had proved the existence of a working system, and probably

most important, a clear market for such machines had emerged.[6] GE won the competition to produce the system commercially.[7] When GE's Industrial Computer Section began to consider the potential market for ERMA in mid-1956, it asked SRI's business group to examine the banking and other industries to estimate the total market for a system such as ERMA. This examination was necessary because ERMA was GE's first venture into the computer field. After the award, SRI provided technical support for ERMA production design at GE until 1957 or 1958. The total cost to the BofA for ERMA was about $10 million, including the cost of many large components billed directly to BofA to avoid markup. SRI billings to GE over the transition totaled less than $1 million.[D] That total included a $5,500 contract awarded to SRI in August 1957 to "dispose of the Mark I ERMA equipment."

The BofA installed the first production ERMA system in its Foxworthy-Plummer Branch in San Jose in January 1959. The units included a sorter/reader, a computer, magnetic tape units, and a high-speed printer. Over the next 2 years, 32 systems were installed, and by 1966, 12 regional ERMA centers served all but 21 of the Bank's 900 branches. The centers then handled more than 33,000 accounts each hour and 750 million pieces of paper each year, about the number they were predicted to handle by 1970. Without such a system as ERMA, the BofA would clearly not have been able to meet the demand for account updates, no matter what assumptions were made about manual check processing.

The SRI ERMA Team

In almost every respect the ERMA project was a team effort, in part because so many different

---

[5] Fred Kamphoefner, personal communication, June 8, 1999. The BofA at first wanted to preserve its clients' freedom to choose the kinds of checks they used, including one in the shape of a fish. Although the Bank soon started to compromise, the SRI sorting machine was made to handle checks that varied two to one in width, length, and thickness.

[6] SRI conducted two studies for the BofA on the commercialization potential of ERMA. The reports on these studies, submitted on 1 April and 18 July 1955, looked at the market nationwide (estimating a market of about 600), suggested several marketing options, and stated criteria for evaluating the bidding manufacturers.

[7] According to Oliver Whitby (personal communication, August 2000), SRI helped to evaluate the four main bidders: IBM, RCA, GE, and Texas Instruments. SRI and BofA technical people liked TI, but GE's size and attractive financial proposal persuaded the BofA's decision makers. Curiously, GE's upper management was not in favor of entering the computer business and didn't learn of the arrangement until it was time to sign the contract. The proposal had come from GE's Palo Alto laboratory.

critical skills were needed. Morrin had overall project responsibility and interfaced with BofA. Noe, then an assistant director of SRI's Engineering Group, assumed technical leadership of ERMA. Eldredge, Whitby, and Dr. Byron Bennett played supervisory roles. Their collective job was to make the many components of the system "play together."[E] Most project participants shared the feeling that the effort was historic, although no one could foresee the exact shape or pace of computer applications and computer research. The technology was raw and in flux. Design decisions had to be taken with great uncertainty about the future of new hardware devices, and there were no tools for logic design or programming. Project team members had to experiment with new devices and develop their own design techniques, and yet preserve commercial security throughout the project. All these factors made ERMA an exciting experience for young engineers and fueled the effort that was needed for its success.[8]

---

[8] The principal participants in the ERMA project and their roles were:

Overall Direction	Tom Morrin (SRI) and Clark Beise (BofA)
Technical Direction	Dr. Jerre Noe (SRI) and Charles Conroy (BofA)
Major Supervisors	Drs. Byron Bennett,. Oliver Whitby, and Ken Eldredge (all SRI)
For the Computer	Richard Melville (manager of construction), Milt Adams, Dr. Frank Clelland, Howard Zeidler (all SRI)
Logical Design	Bonnar Cox, Jack Goldberg, Dr. William Kautz (all SRI)
Physical Wiring Design	Roy Amara, George Barnard, Dr. John Blickensderfer (all SRI)
Quality Control	Bruce Clark (SRI)
Other Engineers	John Boysen, Rolfe Folsom, Alfred Fuller, Keith Henderson, Robert Leo, Maurice Mills, Robert Rowe, Dennis Finnigan (all SRI)
For Paper Handling/ Reading	Fred Kamphoefner, Paul Wendt (all SRI)
Mechanical Design	B.J. O'Connor, A.W. Noon (all SRI)
Electronic Design	Mendole Marsh, Phil Merritt, C.M. Steele (all SRI)
Magnetic-Ink Development	Sam Graf (SRI)
Other Engineers/ Technicians	F.C. Bequaret, John Boyson, Tom Drewek, Bernard Elspas, Rolfe Folsom, Al Fuller, Ken Gardiner, Willard Guthoerl, Keith Henderson, Tatsu Hori, A.E. Kaehler, Mitchell Matovich, Ron Presnell, and Benjamin Wolfe (all SRI)

The ERMA Epilogue

ERMA was the first computer used for commercial check processing and the first system in which the actual check was the input medium. Because of SRI's system insight and because the BofA was large enough to establish a convention, banks began, after ERMA's introduction, to preprint individualized checks for each customer and to identify customer accounts by accession number rather than alphabetically by customer name. ERMA gave the BofA a leadership position in the banking industry's use of computers and allowed GE to enter the market for computers for data processing.[9]

A few later developments provide footnotes to ERMA. In a 1960 report to BofA's Board of Directors, Zipf noted that in 2 years ERMA had cut BofA's check processing costs almost in half, a savings of about $6 million a year.[10] The last GE ERMA machine was unplugged in June 1970. Many years later, an ERMA that had been relegated to a warehouse in Livermore, California, was refurbished to operating condition by BofA volunteers and placed on permanent display in Concord, California.

Over time the BofA has collected some of the accolades regarding ERMA. Examples include the following:

- Federal Reserve - "Bank of America established the dominant design of modern electronic banking."

- Professor James L. McKenney, Harvard University - "The development of the MICR line, which enable checks to be sorted and processed at high speeds, has been recognized as one of the great breakthroughs in banking."

- *American Banker*, 1984 - "I don't know how we would have gotten on without MICR. It was one of the enormous leaps in technology that preserved banking."

---

[9] According to Dan Evans, BofA, (series of articles in BofA's *Technology World*, issues 156-159, June-September 2000), two other major banks were looking into automation. Chase Manhattan was working with MIT, and First National City Bank had a partnership with ITT Labs in Belgium. Neither of these materialized. Also, unknown to the BofA until after the fact, the bid from GE was unsanctioned by GE's leadership, who wanted no part of the data processing industry. When GE won, management reluctantly agreed to support the BofA contract. The company did abandon the computer field 14 years later, when the relevant division of GE was sold to Honeywell.

[10] Dan Evans, op. cit.

RONALD REAGAN

May 6, 1992

Dear Friends:

⋮

I remember with much fondness, the nationwide press conference we staged in 1959 to announce ERMA to the world. How proud everyone was -- B of A, SRI, and GE. When you unveiled ERMA to the world you literally saved the banking industry from drowning in paper. The technology was revolutionary; you paved the way for the use of computers in every business in America. Your achievements are lasting.

⋮

A lot has happened in the last 33 years. I've done a few things since 1959, and so have you. MICR and I were both working in 1959. I see on my checks that MICR is still working, but now I'm retired from political office. I refuse to draw any conclusions from that.

With hearty congratulations and best wishes for continued milestones.

Sincerely,

Ronald Reagan

Figure 2-5. Excerpt of a letter from President Reagan on the occasion of the thirtieth anniversary of ERMA going online.

- President Ronald Reagan, who knew of ERMA from his days with GE - see the letter in Figure 2-5.

Beise became an SRI Board member in 1959[11], and SRI went on to help the Federal Reserve System specify, purchase, install, and verify ERMA-like machines for its huge check processing needs. Bonnar "Bart" Cox was instrumental in this assistance, and by 1959 he was leading the testing of the first installed Federal Reserve systems for accuracy and capacity. The check reading and processing systems developed under ERMA, by then available in the marketplace, were up to the task. Finally, at a celebration in March 2001 honoring the SRI ERMA team with SRI's Gibson Achievement Award, a representative of the BofA, retired Senior Vice President Duncan Knowles, revealed an important fact. The power of machine processing, specifically as evidenced by ERMA, gave the BofA the encouragement it needed in 1958 to start the first nationally accepted credit card system, BankAmericard. Later renamed Visa, it is used worldwide, with over 1 billion cards issued.

---

[11] Clark Beise was one of several SRI Board members who deliberated over the terms of the SRI separation from Stanford in 1970.

Automatic Handwriting Recognition—The Signature Pen

The genesis of SRI's so-called signature pen occurred in the fertile mind of Hew Crane in the waning days of the ERMA project in the late 1950s. Knowing that most of the important information on an individual check is handwritten, Crane thought there must be a way to automatically encode that information so that computers could understand it. He also considered the possibility that the idiosyncrasies of handwriting that made it difficult for a machine to read it might give computers a means to identify who was writing a particular check. Crane also reviewed the issue of whether the pen or the writing surface should contain the instrumentation needed to gather the data from which information could be processed. Nearly 50 years later, the automatic recognition of handwriting has traversed both of these approaches but, with the appearance of small personal digital assistants (PDAs), it is the pad and not the pen that has become the critical information-gathering component. We will briefly see how that course transpired at SRI.[F]

It was the late 1950s and though a rudimentary digitizing surface existed (the RAND Tablet), Crane first concentrated on the pen. This choice left the writing surface quite arbitrary and so it could include checks or forms. SRI's first demonstration system was centered on a direction-sensitive shaft or pen, programmed for the recognition of the digits 0 through 9.[G] It was built with the help of George Eilers and it simply sensed four cardinal directions used in the sequence of writing a digit.[12] As long as the pen was held in the prescribed orientation and the same sequence was used, it did a reasonable job. Those stipulations, however, proved to be unacceptable limitations.

In the context of check writing, Crane also saw the value in being able to record the dynamics of the pen's use to recognize not just what was written, but to identify the pen's user as well. While the potential interest centered on checks, barely over the horizon lay an even more important signature verification need, the ubiquitous credit card slip. But it was still early, not just in the growth of credit card use but also in the development of small powerful, but more importantly, affordable processors. Those reasons, plus the lack of a sponsor to help perfect the pen, would relegate its exploration to the shelf for over a decade.

In the early 1970s, a large supplier of paper forms began to worry about the ushering in of the "paperless society." Having seen an IRE paper by Crane, they called to learn the status of the so-called signature pen. The company was interested in online form input, and while that contract didn't result in anything significant, it did rekindle interest at SRI in technology of using handwriting as a means of computer input.

By the mid-1970s SRI had built a new version of the pen that used an array of strain gauges to measure the writing force in three dimensions. Xebec Systems sponsored an exploration of the pen for recognition of all alphanumeric characters. But, again, the design was impractical for recognizing characters because it imposed too many restrictions on the user in terms of writing directions (e.g., left-handers).[13] However, that approach did enable the measurement of how the pen was held and so this second version of the pen shifted toward its potential as a signature verification system.[14] By then, the burgeoning use of credit cards was expected to provide an excellent reason for such verification and it was easy to imagine using such a pen at every point-of-sale (POS) terminal. VISA and others became clients about this time but again the SRI pen effort would be stalled by the economics of the credit card world. One reason was that the generalized cost of the signature verification, including false rejections, was too high in light of the vast majority of credit card drafts being of low value. It also turned out that credit card forgery was but a small increment on the marginal costs.[H]

---

[12] SRI received a patent in 1964 for the character recognition circuit used in this system. A number of other pen patents would follow in 1975, 1977, and 1978 as the detection and recognition systems advanced.

[13] One could imagine a recognition system that learned a given users writing style but processor and memory costs were so high at that time that the per user equipment cost would have been prohibitive.

[14] Besides Crane, others working on this improved version of the signature pen were Dan Wolf and John Ostrem.

Figure 2-6. Hew Crane using the kanji handwriter recognition pen and (right) demonstrating it for CBS's Dan Rather in April 1976.

But another area of potential use arose, driven by the influx of computers into Asia. Their written language, Kanji, consisted of a huge number of characters that was next to impossible to represent on a normal-sized keyboard. A handwriting recognition system thus seemed a promising opportunity for the emerging East Asian market.

According to accounts by Crane and Earle Jones, an SRI division director, Crane's team obtained a combination of internal SRI support and project funding from the Taiwan Ministry of Telecommunications to build a trial system that could recognize a few hundred Kanji characters. This time the device was primarily a tablet digitizer and they called it Handwriter (see Figure 2-6).[15] Japan was chosen as the target market because of its use of Kanji and its phonetic kana alphabet. Through a chance meeting between Don Scheuch, then Senior Vice President of Engineering, and a business acquaintance, an experienced Chinese-American entrepreneur named James Dao was identified and offered the chance to form and lead a new company. After considering the intellectual property and traveling to Japan to evaluate interest there, he agreed to license the Handwriter technology in exchange for 25% of the initial stock of the company. The company, called Communications Intelligence Corporation (CIC), was formed in 1981 with Lester Hogan (of Motorola and Fairchild Semiconductor) as Chairman of the Board.

About $2 million was raised from individual investors and venture capitalists in the Bay Area, and once the new company had some money, several SRI staff members left to join CIC.[16] Contracts were to be sought from large Japanese corporations, and Jones was selected to join CIC and seek orders from Japanese companies such as Seiko, Mitsubishi, and C. Itoh. Part of this effort also involved CIC's manufacture for Apple of the SRI/CIC Handwriter, calling it, naturally, MacHandwriter. It was sold only in Japan but, surprisingly, the Japanese market for handwritten Kanji input simply did not develop.

At CIC development work on more general handwriting recognitions systems continued throughout the 1980s with ultimately over $10 million in investment capital being raised. A shakeout of handwriting recognition companies in the early 1990s initially weakened CIC and it filed for Chapter 11 in 1994. But its new leadership downsized the company, chose to abandon hardware development, concentrated on software for the PDA market, and eventually created some of the industry's best handwriting recognition software. As increasingly capable PDAs began to appear, CIC was able to secure licenses for its Jot™ recognizer from Microsoft in 1999, for use with its small computer operating system, Windows CE, and from Palm for the Palm Pilot. Jot is still licensed by Palm including its use in PalmOS 5.2 and in a new PDA-phone combination called pdQ.

---

[15] The wire shown in the figure is the lead to a pressure sensor inside the stylus.

[16] Included were John Ostrem, Peter Edberg, and David Foyt with Hew Crane participating part time.

CIC has become a successful company and over the years has licensed its handwriting recognizer to over a dozen companies including Microsoft, Casio, Hitachi, Handspring, Palm, HP, IBM, Compaq, Nortel, Ericsson, Mitsubishi, Fujitsu, NEC, Symbol Technology, and Telxon. Not to forget signature verification, earlier in May 1998, CIC also licensed its Sign-it™ signature verification software to Microsoft for use in Word 97, to Adobe for Acrobat in 1999, and in the fall of 1999 shipped the first biometric signature verification system for Palm organizers. Since President Clinton signed e-signature legislation in 2000, CIC has become an industry leader in handwritten e-signatures.

SRI's road to success for handwriting input and signature verification was a bit long and troubled but ultimately worth it. SRI sold its shares of CIC in 1992 and 1996 for a combined value of just over $4 million, some of which went toward defraying expenses when CIC was housed on the SRI campus.

The Origins of Personal Computing

Though he left SRI not quite 30 years ago, Douglas C. Engelbart is, almost without question, still SRI's most famous talent. His vision, played out over his nearly 2 decades at SRI, helped revolutionize the way people viewed the purpose and utility of an emerging new class of machines called computers. His stay at SRI was both enabling and at times frustrating to him. In both interviews and various books written about him and his contributions, he has spoken openly of both those conditions. In this account, you will find an SRI perspective of his story, including some detailed insight on those conditions. Doing so will require more detail than other projects described in this book, but I will endeavor to tell it fairly and accurately, including those frustrations he faced and his sometime awkward relations with his managers.[17] By concentrating on his SRI world, some of the wondrous and ubiquitous consequences of his work will be left to others who are relating his impacts on the world.[1] Just to be clear, I confess an enormous respect for how he changed the face of computing.

The above "section" title would almost certainly not be Engelbart's choice, since it reflects only part of and probably even a diversion from what he was seeking during his years at SRI. The tremendous changes that personal computing has brought seem to blind us to a greater good that he sees. He believed that personal computers, to the extent they remained "personal," were contrary to what he was trying, above all else, to show: that the computer could provide the basis for a set of tools that would raise *organizational,* not just personal, effectiveness.[J] Though what he and his laboratory showed the world were the first truly comprehensive and intimate ways that computers could serve their users, they were but a way station on the road to Engelbart's vision. Engelbart saw how computers could not just aid individuals, but in fact alter or, he hoped, profoundly alter the way we work together. That was his quest when he began

Figure 2-7. Dr. Douglas Engelbart

---

[17] So as not to detract too much from the evolution of Engelbart's ideas and their outcome, his interactions with SRI management, including the ultimate demise of his SRI group, is detailed in Appendix G.

almost 50 years ago and it remains his quest today. But as it has turned out, the responsiveness he and his people designed and demanded from a computer could not help but foster the power of what personal computing meant, no matter how subordinate or incidental that power was to his vision. Their innovations were so commodious that they have benefited both individuals and in most cases the groups to which they belong. Engelbart and too few of his SRI associates are now belatedly receiving the acclaim they deserve.

The Genesis

Engelbart (see Figure 2-7) started his professional life in a fairly ordinary way. He graduated as a good student from Oregon State University in 1948 with a degree in electrical engineering and moved directly into the application of his acquired skills by delving into a wide range of electrical and electronic problems for the National Aeronautics and Space Administration (NASA) Ames Research Center (then NACA) in Mountain View, California. He was to get married while working there and unfolding before him was the conventional path of job security and family. But even at 25 Engelbart soon came to burn inside for some larger contribution he might make to society. Through deliberate effort, he landed on the notion that people needed some way to deal more effectively with the increasing complexity in their lives. With that general goal and in a stroke that can only be called prescient, he imagined that we could individually and collectively enhance our intellectual pursuits and solve more complex problems through a continuous, almost intimate interaction with computers.

Never mind that computers were hardly in existence in 1950. Even those creators trying to bring them into being, saw them as enlarged calculators or mathematical problem solvers to which were brought periodically very specific and well-formulated programs. Engelbart's vision revealed them as few others' did, as the means to facilitate our thinking in a responsive and interactive way. While he was aware of the very few others in the country that were probing, philosophically, the nature of human-computer interaction, his take on the roles of the user and the machine were his own. In

retrospect his vision was truly a defining concept for the information age, which was still nowhere on the horizon. He would come to learn just how unorthodox his concepts were.

If Engelbart had an epiphany on that December day in 1950 when he began to see how computers could give wings to his dream, it was influenced greatly by his earlier absorption of a 1945 article by Dr. Vannevar Bush, the preeminent Massachusetts Institute of Technology (MIT) scientist.[K] Bush had a vision of a means by which information could be organized associatively to make more naturally retrievable the rapidly expanding body of man's knowledge. Engelbart found Bush's concepts appealing and consistent with what he was thinking. By 1951, he could also see a way to get there. [L]

His now focused journey began with Engelbart quitting his job at NASA in 1951 and going to the University of California, Berkeley, largely because a computer was under construction there. At first he was a part of the research staff, but soon realized that he needed to again enroll in classes to better his understanding of what was developing. By 1955 he had received his doctorate, and the Berkeley computer was still not running. Engelbart stayed on as an assistant professor until 1956 and then had a brief fling at starting a new company to produce some of the digital devices he had developed at the University. He became President and Director of Research at Digital Techniques. But the company never got off the ground. Its failure was due in part, ironically, to an investigative report that a potential investor, at the recommendation of Engelbart, had commissioned at SRI. The plasma devices that Engelbart was pursuing, the report said, would one day be eclipsed by semiconductor devices. Though Engelbart wasn't necessarily in disagreement with that outcome, he was trying to use his Berkeley device patents and the company to ultimately finance his augmentation dream. This turn of events just meant he had to find another avenue to get there.[M]

Engelbart and SRI

Engelbart was not unfamiliar with SRI. He had heard about a computer that had been built at SRI for the banking industry. Jerre

Noe, the division head of the group to which Engelbart would ultimately come, recalls that he met Engelbart at a lecture he gave in Berkeley, while Engelbart was still there. But according to Engelbart's own recollection, he saw at SRI the freedom to define a goal and pursue the means to reach it.[N] So, he called on SRI and then waited for about 3 months before receiving an offer. The group he joined in September 1957 was, interestingly, involved in the aftermath of the huge ERMA banking computer project described earlier. That is what had earlier called his attention to SRI, but by the time Engelbart actually joined the group, it was not at all certain what lay ahead for its members.[18]

Characteristically, Engelbart dived into his new job with verve and creativity. He began designing electronic components, and his work later resulted in SRI receiving a series of patents in the areas of magnetic cores and electronic discharge devices. In 1958, just a year after coming to SRI, he was promoted by his boss, Reid Anderson, to a Senior Research status in recognition of his contributions.[O] Perhaps his earliest evidence of information retrieval at SRI appeared in the *SRI Journal*.[P] With colleague Charles Bourne he wrote about the challenges presented by the deluge of technical information being published. The article was not very revealing of his vision, but it asked a lot of questions, in fact, no fewer than 123 questions, many thoughtful, without suggesting a single answer.

In a series of internal SRI memoranda from January to December of 1960 we can see the vocabulary and consequences of Engelbart's vision unfold. He was exploring his emerging vision in a number of petitions to his management for investment money. His first request, on January 21, 1960, had a telling theme: "The dynamic utilization of automatic information-handling equipment for everyday personal use." He spent a bit over $10,000 on that first exploration of issues surrounding personal rather than group use. In May 1960, however, he switched directions a bit and suggested that SRI become involved in teaching machines. In July he authored a request that zeroed in on his pet project, "seeking to improve the

intellectual capability of humans." It was a request to develop a Stanford seminar, in collaboration with staff members in the SRI Economics Division, and a request for $1,500 in capital funds.

In September 1960 Engelbart offered a long treatise on the notion of teaching machines, directed at building physical skills through sets of cognitive linkages. On December 5 he wrote an informal summary of his earlier writings on "Augmented Human Intellect." This summary became Exhibit A in an otherwise short proposal to the Air Force Office of Scientific Research (AFOSR) requesting $27,000 to match equal SRI funding for an exploration of his ideas.[Q] The proposal was entitled, "Augmented Human Intellect Study." The seemingly futuristic title was not particularly unusual. For example, J.C.R. Licklider, who was recruited to head an information technology office at DoD's relatively new Advanced Research Projects Agency (ARPA), in 1962 launched the long-running ARPA Project MAC, which stood for machine-aided cognition. Licklider had been writing about man-computer symbiosis in 1960. Another example was the theme of the 1961 Joint Computer Conference in Los Angeles: "Extending Man's Intellect." Yet in the AFOSR proposal, the difficulty even Engelbart had in describing his research aims is evident in this vague excerpt from the proposal's Brief:

> The vocabulary doesn't seem to exist with which to communicate briefly the subject range involved in this multidisciplinary study. The best summary of the proposed research would seem to be a statement that we are going to try to determine what the range of subject matter must be within which to give rational, overall consideration to the problem of making humans more effective as problem solvers, and to try to provide perspective for a coordinated attack upon this problem.

In any case SRI was awarded a grant. As far as I can tell, this gave Engelbart his first external money to refine his vision unbridled; to try to express for others the passion he had inside.[19] A condition of the grant was that SRI

---

[18] While that uncertainty may sound ominous, it is commonplace at a research institute where securing new projects is part of life. In this case, however, the end of a large, long-term, and ground-breaking project presented an unusual challenge.

[19] Research in Individual Information Handling Problems, SRI Project 3578, Contract No. AF 49(638)-1024, March 1 1961 to March 31 1962, $26,924. It is curious that 1

had to match the amount with its own internal funds. So from 1960 through 1962, SRI spent discretionary investment money of about $60,000 to meet that condition and to pay for the writing of the requisite proposals.

By fall 1962 Engelbart had finished the project and written the now famous AFOSR report that offered his first augmentation concepts and described the role the computer could play in them. While not a blueprint for the future, it was a crown of conceptualization. Here are some of the early concepts:

- For the most part our intellectual effectiveness is not limited by our intelligence.

- Humans, together with personalized artifacts such as computers and their attendant information handling displays and storage, form a powerful system for the solving of complex problems.

- In various ways our intellectual activity can be directly aided by the capabilities and offerings of a digital computer, which can provide:

  - An ability to supplement human memory with that of a computer

  - A work environment with visual access to that memory as well as other libraries and processes, forming whole new kinds of encyclopedias

  - Associative linking possibilities between processes and documents

  - Devices that enable the user to interact effectively with a displaying computer for document generation and modification faster than a typewriter can achieve.

- Problems are more easily solved if they are decomposed into a hierarchy in which each layer has a defined capability.

- A systems engineering approach is appropriate for this human-machine and human-team integration.

- This augmentation of intellect does not have to await an understanding of mental processes; we can begin at once, adapting and building as we go.

Perhaps it was his familiarity with radar screens from his Navy days that helped Doug see a medium for this new human-computer interaction, and he imagined that computers would one day have enough power to aid an intellect. In the report he openly acknowledges the influence of and insights from the earlier-mentioned article by Vannevar Bush, "As We May Think."[R] What Engelbart saw that Bush could not see was the potential of the computer as the means to deliver what Doug came to think of as supplementation of the intellect: ways that humans, quite generally, could rise above their intrinsic intellectual and collaborative limitations.

In June 1961 Engelbart had sought and received an additional $27,000 from AFOSR for a second year of work.[20] As his ideas were maturing, it is instructive to look at how he expressed his continuing need for SRI to fund his concept development. His 1962 petition for Internal Research and Development (IR&D) funds was titled "Program on Human Effectiveness." It "proposed research…aimed at refining and developing in greater detail the initial conceptual framework for augmenting the human intellect." This proposal expressed his vision in the most general terms. For 1965, his last year of SRI IR&D support (at least for a while), he received $17,468 for something much more specific: "To develop and evaluate an experimental computer-aided text-manipulation system suitable for a wide range of applications…." This specificity was no doubt a result of the crystallization of at least one tangible means to achieve the goals he sought.

Engelbart used the AFOSR report to introduce his ideas to other potential funding agencies and was fairly successful at ARPA and NASA. But while he was receiving both internal SRI and client support during the early 1960s, he still didn't have a computer.

---

month before this contract was awarded to Engelbart, SRI was awarded $30,634 for another AFOSR project entitled "Structuring Complex Man-Machine Systems" (SRI Project 3546). The AFOSR contracting agent (not technical monitor) for both projects was Rowena Swanson. In spite of the connotations its title implies today, SRI Project 3546 dealt only with systems analysis, not man-machine interaction.

[20] This amount, with the SRI matching funds, would cover between one and two people for the year.

The first money from ARPA in 1963 wasn't enough to buy one and still have enough left over to do appreciable work. At ARPA Licklider insisted that Engelbart link up to a timeshare machine at the Systems Development Corporation (SDC) in Los Angeles via what Licklider wanted to call the California Net.[21] Though that option was limiting and frustrating to Doug, he had little choice and therefore needed at least a minicomputer in Menlo Park to make the connection and the associated interaction experiments run as best they could. According to Dave Brown, a friend and acquaintance of Doug's at Berkeley and later SRI, Engelbart had become a friend of Finley Carter, SRI's president at the time. Brown relates that Doug used that access to Carter to obtain a computer funded by SRI capital investment. Unfortunately, Doug doesn't recall this happening.[22] By whatever way it was acquired, the first small computer he used was a $100,000 CDC 160A. Early proposals had requested money to lease that specific machine, and project files show its costs were shared among the active projects using it. Though shared, it at least enabled Engelbart to begin experimenting on the human-machine interaction methods he wanted to create.

Over those formative years of 1960–65 and in addition to whatever external money was forthcoming, SRI invested about $120,000 of IR&D funds in Engelbart's ideas. A portion of this money may have gone toward the $54,000 in required AFOSR matching funds. Noe, Engelbart's SRI division director in Doug's early years at SRI, commented recently that he personally

believed in the future Engelbart espoused and therefore approved his requests for internal funds. In any case, Doug received enough investment money from SRI (1960–65) and in contracts from Harold Wooster at AFOSR (1961–62), Licklider at ARPA (early 1963)[S], and Bob Taylor at NASA (in 1964)[T] to eventually win a place at the revered table of ARPA contractors funded by the Information Processing Techniques Office (IPTO). That position meant years of continued support as ARPA moved aggressively into this new field of computing.[23]

This aggregation of support should not be misinterpreted, however, for it took an enormous amount of proselytizing and selling by Engelbart to make all this happen. But it was a propitious time at ARPA. It was beginning its revolutionary venture into computer sharing and networking. For more than a decade the internal and external funding was sufficient for Doug to pursue his vision and to increase his laboratory to a truly talented team of over 40 people. The Human Effectiveness Program was renamed the Augmented Human Intellect Research Center in 1969, which became the Augmentation Research Center (ARC) by 1971.

Though SRI's internal support was an important enabler to this growth, during 1963–64 Engelbart encountered what he saw as resistance from his manager within SRI. From the comments of one of his contemporaries, it seems that his managers, and to some extent his clients, understood what he was trying to do only in some general sense. This lack of precision was likely due to some combination of their lack of vision and Doug's inability to explain what he was trying to accomplish (see Appendix G).[U, 24] Though in Engelbart's

<hr />

[21] While that moniker of "net" today sounds pedestrian and may imply a switching fabric, it was, in fact, nothing of the sort—just a long distance link to a timeshare host in El Segundo. Also, according to SRI's Dave Brown, Engelbart's trip to Project MAC let Engelbart understand the importance of having one's own machine. From letters and visits between DARPA and SRI in the February–March 1963 time frame, Doug's manager, Roy Amara, and John Wensley who Amara had assigned to work with Doug, both were responding to Licklider's remote connection preference rather than supporting Doug's need for a dedicated machine.

[22] Douglas Engelbart, personal communication, February 22, 2001. On the other hand, a conversation with SRI's Bud Rorden on July 13, 2004 revealed that he had used the 160A for a totally different project dealing with satellite data. If this had been a dedicated project-provided machine, that kind of sharing wouldn't have occurred.

[23] Engelbart had tried to obtain funding from NASA, National Institutes of Health (NIH), ARPA, and other agencies before MIT psychologist Licklider, who appeared at ARPA in October 1962, the same month that the AFOSR concept report was published, would fund Engelbart beyond just paper studies. Licklider formed the new office in information processing called IPTO. But it was Bob Taylor, who had funded Engelbart earlier at NASA and who came to IPTO under its next director, Ivan Sutherland, who would buy Engelbart and his group their first state-of-the-art, dedicated timesharing computer in 1966, an SDS-940. Sutherland became head of IPTO in 1964 and Taylor in 1966.

[24] In fairness, the notion of augmenting knowledge work is intrinsically vague. But as a 1963 ARPA contract was winding down and SRI was seeking an extension, Licklider, in a March 1964 letter to Doug's supervisor,

recollection this was a trying time, it didn't seem to appreciably affect his internal financial support or his eventual ability to grow to laboratory size. Not until the mid 1970s, when the external support began to erode seriously, did SRI management again choose to intervene (more on this later).

Figure 2-8. A June 1965 version of an SRI workstation.

The Evolution of the NLS Workstation[25]

Though the software underlying a computing system carries most of its critical functionality, perhaps the clearest embodiment of the course being pursued by Engelbart and his laboratory lay in the NLS workstation. How best could the promise of real-time interactive computing be realized? Uncommon in this use at the time, a cathode-ray screen was clearly a good way to present dynamic information but the burning question was how to interact with it. Let's look briefly at the evolution of the workstation.

Although ARPA was the first to provide serious funding for workstation implementation in early 1963, it was NASA money a little over a year later that helped provide a critical mass. For some time those two contracts plus the ongoing AFOSR grant

provided the resources to explore these first facets of real-time human-computer interaction.[26] Much of the first ARPA money had gone to modifying the CDC 160A, both to provide interaction tools such as a cathode ray tube (CRT) display and to manage the link to SDC. But the goal of improving user productivity, at least in the beginning, didn't actually require the link and its distant resource. Because Engelbart always wanted his own timeshare machine, the link to SDC was always a costly inconvenience and distraction for him. While not large, the 160A would be the first platform for exploring a more intimate interaction. The final report on the first NASA project reveals the state of development at that time and here are some reflections from it.[V]

The major workstation implementation goal surrounded the question of how best to view the information residing within or accessible by a computer and how such information (in the early stages just text) could be generated and manipulated. While the CRT was the early and probably only

---

Roy Amara, made it clear that more money was conditioned upon SRI being able to demonstrate what was happening. Engelbart's proposal for that extension contains both vague phrases like "bootstrapping my own work" and "computer-aided work" and specific concepts probably not then adequately appreciated. Where specific, it mentioned aspects of text editing in a 10-page document (the first widely used, interactive text editor, EMACS, was still more than a decade away) and "associative linking" whose enormous significance probably was not yet recognized outside Doug's fertile mind. Also, at this point, the interactive tools were not yet settled on and there was no mention of the mouse as a pointing device. All was in flux and concepts common today, not yet formulated.

[25] NLS was the software that gave life to functionality in the ARC. Since the thesis of the work was online interaction, as opposed to the dominant practice of off-line or batch computing, NLS was simply an online System.

[26] This claim, of course, applies to that type of interaction that has the general utility we now associate with virtually all computers. Another, detailed and chronologically oriented account can be found in a book reporting on a 1978 conference held in Palo Alto on personal workstations: Adele Goldberg, ed., *A History of Personal Workstations*, ACM Press and Addison-Wesley, 1988.

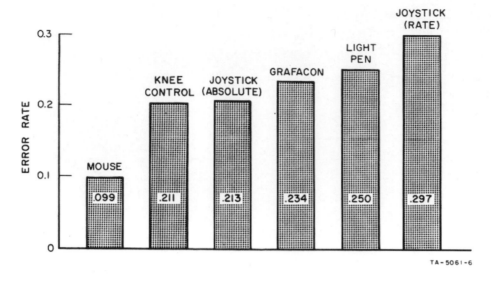

FIG. 11 ERROR RATE FOR "INEXPERIENCED" SUBJECTS, "CHARACTER MODE" OPERATION

Figure 2-9. Results of one phase of the testing of pointing systems for a computer display.[v]

possible choice for a display, adapting it to textual material with comfortable viewing conditions took some engineering. The tube shown in Figure 2-8 as part of a 1965 workstation gives some idea of the cumbersome state of displays for this kind of environment. The working part of the display consisted of 16 lines of 63 characters when it was under normal use, but shifted to 13 lines of 40 characters each when taking photographs or movies.

The mouse at the right was manifested on the screen as a small, character-sized "+" that is not visible in the display in Figure 2-8. Explaining the rest of the workstation shown is best done through an excerpt from the report:

> 2b4 Within comfortable reach of the user's right hand is a device called the "mouse," which we developed for evaluation (along with others, such as a light pen, Grafacon,

joystick, etc.) as a means for selecting those displayed text entities upon which the commands are to operate.

> 2b4a As the mouse is moved over the surface of the table, its position is constantly being monitored by the computer, which displays a special tracking cross, which we call the "bug," on the screen in a position corresponding to that of the mouse on the table.

Figure 2-10. Engelbart holding the first working version of the mouse.

March 1964

March 1965

June 1965

March 1967

1968

Figure 2-11. Evolution of the ARC Workstation during the 1960s

2b4b A user soon finds it very easy to keep his eyes on the screen and cause the bug to move about upon it as quickly and naturally as if he were pointing his finger (but with less fatigue).

The paragraph headings used in the above quotation are direct evidence of the group's use of bootstrapping. The entire report was composed, edited, and printed using the workstation described, and the headings were part of the accounting system used in the text editing system built into NLS. That the mouse was selected over the other pointing systems mentioned is evident in just one of a number of results in the NASA report shown in Figure 2-9. The mouse was not only used for selection of text in word processing but also for a variety of other functions on the screen. The first working version of the mouse is shown in Figure 2-10.

Workstation command or "operator" selection could be performed in one of two ways. The keyboard could be used to enter one of a set of commands relevant to the task immediately at hand. The 14-button control box on the left was a shortcut for the most frequently used operators or editing commands. This device was later replaced by the five-finger, chordal keyset that was more flexible but also required a steeper learning curve. Its five keys could, using straight binary representation, input any of the 32 characters in the standard Teletype alphabet. While the keyset never caught on, Engelbart still swears by it and uses it to this day. Many other devices had been tried to help perfect the interaction, but in the ARC it ultimately came down to the standard keyboard, the keyset, and the mouse. The evolution of the workstation at SRI from 1964 to its first public debut in 1968 is shown in Figure 2-11. In Engelbart's mind the concepts behind this development involved a partnership between the tools created for augmentation and the newly acquired skills of the user. The new tools were not intended to ease the user into decreasing states of cognitive involvement. Bootstrapping was consistent with this partnership.

As mentioned at the outset, this second partner, the user, was expected to evolve too. Engelbart used the diagram in Figure 2-12 to explain this partnership during a 1986 talk.[w] Notice that the left-hand side is not just a

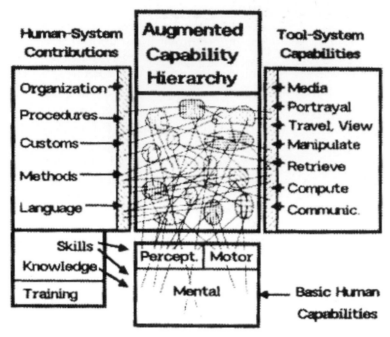

Figure 2-12. Engelbart's conceptual diagram of the roles of the human and his or her machine.

system with its cultural underpinnings. The middle or interaction space is where the consequences of the partnership arise. The failure of the human side to develop as quickly as the tool side gave Engelbart considerable concern. By the time of this talk he had begrudgingly accepted that desirable changes in the human side might take

Figure 2-13. Bill English, architect of much of the ARC online hardware and interactive systems.

generations, and that timely co-evolution of the two would be unlikely.

A Culminating, Watershed Event

In late 1968 a demonstration of huge significance in the development of computing took place. Any lingering doubt in the minds of the few who knew what Engelbart was pursuing would soon evaporate as a part of Doug's vision assumed striking clarity. Computer-aficionado Alan Kay, now at Hewlett Packard, said that it not only changed the way he viewed computing, it changed his life. Charles Irby, a software engineer not at SRI at the time, said it was one of the most impressive things he had ever seen. The place was San Francisco's Civic Auditorium and the occasion was one of the largest computer conferences of the day, the Fall Joint Computer Conference for 1968.[27] On this first day of the conference, December 9, Engelbart had requested a special hour and a half session not just to describe their work but to demonstrate NLS, the ARC's online system. Given that the very large room was filled to overflowing with perhaps 2,000–3,000 people, the courage of his decision was evident. After several months of preparation, his group had set up a live demonstration of what they had created, a system that connected two remote collaborators to an extent never seen before.

Remember this was a time of punched cards, batch processing, and the equivalent of priestly sentinels that kept common folk at arms length from the expensive computing machines that executed their programs. Engelbart was in the Civic Auditorium giving the world its first glimpse of the mouse, a five-fingered keyset, and a CRT as an interactive display. Don Andrews, Jeff Rulifson, and Bill Paxton were taking turns at an identical station at SRI in Menlo Park, where the computing resources were. A large and touchy light-valve projector was used to show everyone in the auditorium Engelbart's

[27] Held twice a year the Joint Computer Conferences were sponsored by the Association for Computing Machinery, the IEEE, and the Computer Society.

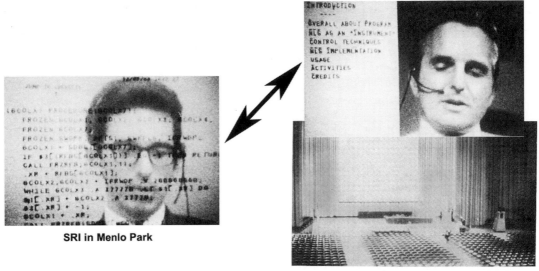

SRI in Menlo Park

Civic Auditorium in San Francisco

Figure 2-14. Images from the 1968 demonstraton: Rulifson (left) at SRI and Engelbart in San Francisco. (*A History of Personal Workstations*, Edited by Adele Goldberg, ACM Press, 1988.)

NLS screen. Since the normal telephone network couldn't handle the communications capacity needed, a special microwave link was established with a relay on Skyline Drive to cover the 35 or so miles between the sites. Bill English (see Figure 2-13) deserves special credit for his inventive abilities to make all the functions work, both in the evolution of the NLS workstation and particularly here in this prodigious undertaking. He was backstage in San Francisco pulling all the strings.

There, for the first time publicly, Engelbart displayed and explained what NLS and real-time, personally responsive computing could do.[X] He demonstrated online editing and hypertext jumps from a word to its supporting or ancillary information; opened a visual-plus-audio window with colleagues at SRI; and opened a cooperative session in which two separated people could read and edit the same document at the same time, each looking at an identical screen (see Figure 2-14). The crowd was at once mesmerized and sat or stood in stark disbelief.[Y] But at the end, there was a standing ovation for what was truly a watershed moment in the history of computing.[28]

---

[28] For 2 days after the demonstration, the ARC operated an open house in specially set up rooms in the Civic Center. Some 2,000 visitors came during this period to learn more about the concepts and actually use one of the two consoles connected to the SDS 940 at SRI (*SRI Intercom* 105, January 29, 1969).

Other Innovations in Computer-Aided Knowledge Work

While the San Francisco demonstration offered a glimpse into a new world of information and communication technology and would become world famous in that development community, that shouldn't imply its recognition or acceptance by a world not yet ready for such capability. Nevertheless, the ARC continued to operate another 9 years. Innovations in NLS continued, and the Center, committed to Engelbart's guiding vision, produced many of the functions we now consider essential to computing. As mentioned, during the first half of the 1960s the group built a startling array of interactive computing features. Moreover, they wisely used these features each day to test and refine them. As mentioned, Engelbart called this practice bootstrapping and it was likely the first instantiation of this approach in computer development: Use the tools you are building to perfect the tools you are building. Engelbart's biographical sketch at the Bootstrap Institute's web page (www.bootstrap.org) provides the following compilation of innovations developed in the ARC:

- The mouse

- Dimensional display editing

- In-file object addressing, linking

- Hypermedia
- Outline processing
- Flexible view control
- Multiple windows
- Cross-file editing
- Integrated hypermedia email
- Hypermedia publishing
- Document version control
- Shared-screen teleconferencing
- Computer-aided meetings
- Formatting directives
- Context-sensitive help
- Distributed client-server architecture
- Uniform command syntax
- Universal "user interface" front-end module
- Multi-tool integration
- Grammar-driven command language interpreter
- Protocols for virtual terminals
- Remote procedure call protocols
- Compiled "command meta language"

While this list is imposing, for Engelbart these accomplishments were just the beginning, just the means toward the all-important end of collaborative or group problem solving. Workers at Xerox Palo Alto Research Center (PARC), including a sizable contingent of expatriates from SRI's ARC, added features such as the desktop metaphor, the bit-mapped graphic display, and the graphical user interface (GUI). An important difference was that the thrust of the work at PARC veered somewhat away from Engelbart's conceptions. At PARC the strategy was to make everything easy for the user and to let the machine do whatever it could to enable that. In contrast, as mentioned earlier, Engelbart's philosophy expected the user to change, too. He was always looking for the optimal combinations of human and machine, even if the human had to train substantially to get there.[Z] This difference in philosophy cannot be overemphasized. As these two main branches of the tree of personal computing continued to grow, one

could be labeled user-friendly and the other the growth of human-machine proficiency. That schism also existed for a time within PARC between those SRI expatriates who wanted to continue NLS running on a network of minicomputers and those who focused on individual machines and a newer, easier language, called SmallTalk. The latter group won out, but some of them had to move to Apple to see their dream played out.[AA]

The Mouse, Its Acceptance, and Licensing

Between about 1972 and 1987, when the patent expired, SRI licensed the mouse on a nonexclusive basis to perhaps as many as a dozen different mouse purveyors and manufacturers.[29] The term "mouse purveyors" must be used because many of the computer supply houses such as Apple bought their units rather than manufacturing them. Licenses were all nonexclusive and early ones were offered for a $500 initial fee and 2% of the net selling price. By the time that personal computers were hitting the street in serious numbers, however, SRI's mouse patent was nearing the end of its life. For example, the Macintosh was introduced in 1984, 3 years before the SRI patent expired. Thus, Xerox and then Steve Jobs of Apple Computer each bought a paid-up license for $45,000. The known licensees are listed in the following table, roughly in the order in which they were licensed. According to Bonnar Cox, who was handling this licensing at the time, these licenses produced, collectively, about $150,000 for SRI over perhaps 5–6 years when returns were noticeable.

Others who considered licensing but whose participation is uncertain are Logitech (1983) and Televideo (which used Mouse Systems' optical mouse). As a measure of the ubiquity of this ergonomically effective device, Logitech announced on its web site in September 2003 that it had shipped its 500-millionth mouse![BB]

Networking

One aspect of the ARC's work receives less publicity than its other contributions is

---

[29] The mouse patent, No. 3,541,541, was issued November 17, 1970 and ran until that date in 1987.

Nonexclusive Licensees of the SRI Mouse and Approximate License Issue Date			
Computer Displays, Inc. (later Adage) Boston, MA	1970	Apple Computer Cupertino, CA	1981
Cybermex Stanford, CA	By 1972	Kinetronics Arlington, MA	1982
Century Tool San Carlos, CA	1977	3G Company, Inc. Gaston, OR	1982
Tymshare, Inc. Cupertino, CA	1978	Mouse Systems Corp. Sunnyvale, CA	1983,4
Alps Electric Co. (for Microsoft, Tandy, Wang, etc.) Yokahama, Japan	~1980	WICO Corp. Niles, IL	1983
Hawley Labs (Mouse House Division) Berkeley, CA	1981	Fujitsu Limited Tokyo, Japan	1985
Xerox Corp. Palo Alto, CA	1981	Product Associates* Redwood City, CA	?

*(Martin Hardy, ARC alumnus)

computer networking. This topic is discussed in greater length in Chapter 3, but a bit more deserves to be related here. Bob Taylor was hired at ARPA in about 1965 to help create networking among computers. Though a number of small individual networks of computers had arisen, he was frustrated by the number of different terminals he was forced to have in his Pentagon office to use this collection of networks. Taylor clearly saw the benefits of a single-access terminal and persuaded Larry Roberts, who had done similar networking at Lincoln Labs, to join him. Roberts soon became one of those pivotal players at ARPA who saw the advantages of computer networking and worked tirelessly to bring it to life. In the periodic meetings of his ARPA contractor community, Larry would remind those gathered of the natural benefits of connecting computers together. One of the biggest reasons was something called resource sharing. Bob Kahn, a member of that community and later a director of IPTO, was an important advocate, suggesting that good connectivity between time-shared hosts would let major sites each specialize in some important aspect of computing. Some would have elaborate programs in graphics, others in simulation or data processing. The concept seemed economically sound: each time-share host would need only enough expensive memory to serve one chosen specialty, and all users on the network would gain remote operational access to those programs. Users

who had a graphics problem would simply log in at the University of Utah, regardless of where they were working.

In this new world of interactive computing and remote, cross-network access, the ARC was a unique site. But at that moment there was another reason to attach it to this new network. Early in the discussions of networks at ARPA, the need became apparent for a place on the network that knew where all the resources resided. There was also a need for a central repository of the common, correct software to be used to obtain access and other functionality on the network. That place was called the Network Information Center or NIC. The concept of such a place surfaced during the 1967 ARPA principal investigator meeting where these networking concepts were first discussed. Probably because the NIC didn't sound "researchy" enough and because they resisted sharing their machines with remote users, other contractors seemed reluctant to volunteer to run the NIC. But Engelbart saw the NIC differently, as a meeting ground for a family of network users, and volunteered SRI for that role, even though no one in the ARC had an appropriate background.

In these early years of networking, Engelbart's initiative had some profound consequences for his group and SRI:

- The first though temporary leadership of the Network Working Group and a design role in many of the earliest networking innovations, such as:

- The network virtual terminal—This innovation reduced complexity by enabling network access terminals to use a single interface specification rather than a different one for every type of host on the network. The same concept also benefited the network hosts.[CC]

- The network virtual circuit—The circuits freed packet traffic from the need to follow a consistent or *a priori* route.[DD]

- Some of the early designs of communications protocols—Telnet, the ARPANET's remote terminal access protocol, was first advanced in RFC 97 in early 1971.[30]

- The receipt from ARPA of the second packet switch, called an IMP, in early October 1969.

- The first computer-computer communications, with the University of California, Los Angeles (UCLA), in October 1969.

- The operation of the NIC, a network protocol repository and the point of issue for network names and addresses for the ARPANET, then Internet, a role it held for 21 years.[31]

- The first network locator directory, called WHOIS.

The diagram in Figure 2-15 indicates the conceptual state of networking in the ARC. This sketch was taken from an internal administrative presentation made by Engelbart in June 1973. The free flow of information, access to central repositories, and network-wide services are evident. The diagram could depict the Internet today, 30 years later.

One of the Internet's earliest and most notable contributors spent a portion of his networking days in the ARC. His name was Jon Postel, and he was in the ARC from September 1974 to March 1977. He was an early critic of the internet protocol, TCP, as originally specified.[32] While at SRI he saw the need for two protocols instead of the single TCP version. Within 6 months after leaving SRI, Postel's advocacy helped spawn the simpler IP protocol, which was faster and eliminated the end-to-end reliability negotiations of TCP. Postel became one of the Internet's true pioneers, the principal architect of many of its functional protocols, and a pivotal contributor to the domain-naming concept that gave all hosts a text-based name along with their numeric network addresses. Most of Postel's best-known contributions were made at USC's Information Sciences Institute after he left SRI, but he got some of his early grounding in the ARC. He died in October 1998 from complications in a heart operation, and his contributions to the Internet were acknowledged worldwide.

The "ARC" Develops a Leak

One problem faced by people who are way ahead of their time is being cast as irrelevant. Since truly dramatic visions are by nature not widely held, Engelbart and his Center began to lose their sponsorship in the early to mid-1970s. The NLS software that embodied the concepts of the ARC was idiosyncratic; that is, it was not easily mapped into operations different than those found in the ARC. In addition, and perhaps most importantly, it was a moving target. Continual change is not uncommon at SRI or any research site. Nevertheless, when government agencies such as the DoD were unable to adapt NLS to their own world or their world to NLS, it became harder and harder for them to continue their sponsorship. Even ARPA must at some point transition its innovations to its DoD "clients" or abandon them for other pursuits.

---

[30] Several ARC people contributed to Telnet development, including Richard Watson, John Melvin, and Jim White.
[31] Richard Watson provided the early guidance for the NIC but for most of the two decades that it offered services to first the ARPA and then the general Internet community, it was under the leadership of Elizabeth Feinler, known throughout her world as "Jake".

[32] See the Chapter 3 on computer networking for a discussion on SRI's own specification of TCP.

OPERATION AND EVOLUTION FOR SPECIAL COMMUNITIES

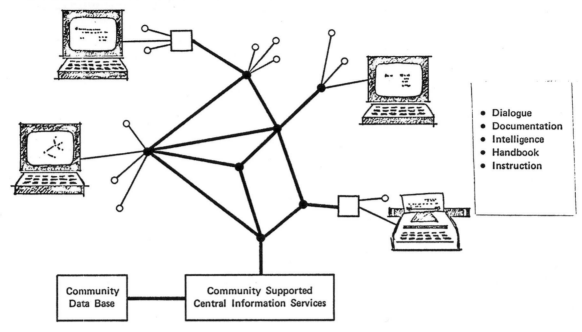

- Dialogue
- Documentation
- Intelligence
- Handbook
- Instruction

Community Data Base

Community Supported Central Information Services

Figure 2-15. Conceptual network functionality from an SRI internal presentation by Engelbart dated June 13, 1973.

Another reason for atrophy may have been a decrease in innovation at the ARC caused by the departure of key staff members. In a real sense the 1968 demonstration proved to be an emotional pinnacle for what the system could do. A revolutionary research system had been built and demonstrated, but neither its continued incremental improvement nor its transition to new hardware was as exciting to some as starting anew with some other opportunity. In addition, the technology was changing, and Engelbart, in the opinion of some ARC staff members, was not. Smaller machines that started to appear affordable for one person seemed on the way. But Engelbart thought it best to continue to rely on large time-share machines, in particular the soon to be released DEC PDP-10.

For all these reasons, around 1971, many of the key ARC staff members started to leave for Xerox PARC. There a number of bright people, some of whose lives had been altered by the 1968 demonstration, had assembled under Taylor, the former head the ARPA information technology office that had funded Engelbart. Bill English, Bill Duvall, Jeff Rulifson, Charles Irby, Bill Paxton, and Don Wallace were among those who carried at least the functionality of the Engelbart vision to PARC where the next significant

milestones in the development of personal computing would occur.

In spite of these departures, Engelbart and his ARC would continue for several more years. By 1972 the Center had grown to over 40 people and the administrative load that Doug deplored got only worse. With the encouragement of management and for the first time, he appointed two assistant managers. While that helped administratively, by the mid-1970s there were more troubling signs on the horizon, in particular, the rising inability to get or retain contracts that would fund the research that in his mind he had only begun to explore.

One clear evidence of this decrease in sponsorship occurred in late 1975 as Engelbart submitted a SRI budget that requested some relaxation of the ARC's financial goals so that some of his new, but unsponsored ideas could be developed. This act was essentially a request for other labs in his division to partially subsidize his operation and, as it turned out, they were willing to do. But the coming year, 1976, wasn't a particularly healthy one for the division as a whole and not only weren't the subsidies fully forthcoming, pressure arose on the entire division to reduce costs. Such pressure, plus the ARC's existing turnover problems, meant that by the end of 1976 the professional count was down to perhaps 15 plus a smaller number of programmers and research analysts providing NIC services. The ARC was trying to retain revenue by selling NLS-centered services on its time-share hosts. The revenue stream from such subscriptions and their associated expenses were enough out of the mainstream of SRI's accounting system that the Center's financial performance was consistently in doubt.

For better or for worse, these are the times when research managers are compelled to act. Engelbart was asked to step down from the leadership of the ARC in late 1976. How all this played out is given in more detail in Appendix G, but in this instance, management, faced with the ARC's falling income stream and potential market value in its software and services, decided to sell it to the growing Tymshare Corporation at the beginning of 1978. Some ARC staff, including the NIC, transferred into the communication activity at SRI but the sale of the ARC and its intellectual property meant that Engelbart, along with many of his remaining staff, opted to move to Tymshare and thus end his two fruitful decades at SRI.

An Epilogue: Legacies of the ARC, Intended or Not, Accepted or Not

Although personal computing originated at SRI under Engelbart's vision, he still believes that personal computing, whatever that term means, was only a piece of his dream, just one necessary milestone along the way. But in the 7–8 years from his early work at SRI to the spectacular demonstration at the 1968 Fall Joint Computer Conference in San Francisco,

Engelbart, English, Rulifson, Paxton, Duvall, and many other members of the ARC defined, for the first time anywhere, what we think of today as personal computing. Their collective accomplishments forever changed the way computing was viewed. Though he clung perhaps too long to the behemoth time-share computers, Engelbart also saw back in 1959, before it became evident in Moore's Law, that computing resources would one day become affordable enough that time-sharing would no longer be necessary (see text box). Perhaps unwittingly, Engelbart's cost-benefit notion of micro-miniaturization would be advanced by our predilections simply to own things, including our own computer. In any case the stage is now set to go beyond simple affordability or ownership into a world of rich networking where we can truly be indifferent about where the actual computing takes place or the information resides.

While it may seem a fine point, Engelbart in effect worried that personal computing, as he saw it, for example, in the developments at Xerox PARC, would result more in subrogating or automating intelligence rather than *augmenting* it. Certainly, it can't be detrimental to hide the arcane complexities of our interactions with machines, for they can only detract from some higher purpose to which the man-machine combination can aspire. I have always believed that it is the first role of a personal computer's power to bring about a more natural interaction. While that is not likely to appear until speech understanding is perfected, we have come a long way. But what illuminates Engelbart's vision best is what is still missing. Doug is right in that all this deference to the human does not, in itself, lead to the tackling of more complex and meaningful problems, and it certainly does not necessarily demand more from the user. The direction that personal computing is taking is to help make us more versatile in what we can do easily, but no where is there a staircase of computing sophistication that takes a user to a higher effective plane of thought—which is, after all, what augmenting intelligence really means.

This is a story still unfolding. Though it may take concerted effort to confirm it, Engelbart's concept of how computers can truly augment our own intellect is probably developing around us. One only has to look at the young people of today, who are comfortable in gaining benefit from a personal computer and who have little trouble with a computer-stimulated intuition, to see how important the gravitation of computer power toward the individual has been. To them the means, the machine and its associated networking, are becoming transparent to the services available. And it is often the use of computer models that opens a more complete understanding of many complex processes such as the human genome and its proteome.

But what of Engelbart's Holy Grail, elevating computer-empowerment groups toward unprecedented accomplishments? That too is arriving. While he remains discouraged by society's blindness to his vision, there are plenty of examples, probably countless ones, of computers enabling groups to function in ways unachievable before. Consider just one case. In the field of product development, the time to market or to break-even is today's yardstick of choice.

Figure 2-16. Engelbart Wearing the National Medal of Technology for 2000

Competition has demanded this time urgency and, since time is money, more rapid development sets the stage for lower costs. Rapid prototyping is a process whereby teams, representing the talent needed to bring a product to market, are now joined together through computers and their supporting networks to cut the time and cost of product development. Production engineers, market specialists, profitability managers, and life-cycle maintenance people all join the early-stage designers to shorten the product development cycle. And their physical location is virtually immaterial. Development durations that used to be measured in years with sequential handoff are now measured in months or weeks. These are nothing more than Engelbart's envisioned groups, collaborating through networked computers, across space, to accomplish what would have been impossible before. Such acceleration is the *sine qua non* of today's successful companies and good evidence to support his thesis.

Other examples veritably flow from the Internet. When we have the tools to locate what we seek more efficiently, it will become a true extension of our awareness and our individual and collective capabilities. The groundwork for that extension was laid in the online access system started in the ARC. Today, scientists from all over the world can link to the Hubble telescope in space. One of the world's largest and most sophisticated ionospheric research radars, soon to be built by SRI, will be reachable from any Internet site. That kind of collective, real-time access, together with the rapid sharing of information, promote great insights, extend collaboration, and offer a continued acceleration of man's quest for knowledge. Engelbart's desire for the co-evolution of both humans and machines, in their interdependent partnership, is still valid, however, man's preference will continue to place the greater change in his machines than in himself. Nevertheless, in this man-computer partnership, our *collective* abilities and knowledge will continue to accelerate just as his vision portrayed.

Recognition for Engelbart's Achievements

Although neither Engelbart nor SRI ever gleaned much compensation for the innovations mentioned in this story, Engelbart has received some individual recognition. Over the last decade or so Engelbart has been honored with over 30 awards, including:

- The MIT-Lemelson prize with its $500,000 award for innovation

- The Turing Award, the highest honor in computer science worldwide

- The IEEE Von Neumann Award for contributions to information technology

- The National Medal of Technology, the highest U.S. award for innovation (see Figure 2-16)

As evidence of the respect I have for what Doug and the ARC accomplished in the last half of the 1960s, I had a major hand, with

Kinney Thiele, in his nomination for the last two awards on this list.

In addition to Engelbart's personal laurels, the major professional computing society, the Association for Computing Machinery or ACM, did acknowledge two others. ACM gave its 1990 Software Systems Award to Engelbart, English, and Rulifson for the development of NLS, a full quarter-century after it was created.

Though appreciative of this worldwide recognition of his achievements, Engelbart continues to believe that the honors are somewhat misplaced. He still fights for the principles of group, organizational, and societal enablement and problem solving that he voiced almost 40 years ago. Perhaps it is enough to say that, without question, there is much to be honored and respected and yet much left to do.

Computing Science at SRI

It was late in 1954 and the incredible excitement and stress of building one of the world's first real-time computing systems, ERMA, was in full swing.[33] But in spite of that preoccupation and the newness of computers like ERMA, there was growing realization that they were emerging as broadly useful, general-purpose tools. As evidence, Jerre Noe, then Assistant Director of Engineering at SRI, decided to start a Computer Laboratory and named Byron Bennett as its first head.

Some members of that new lab had been responsible for designing the logic circuits of ERMA and then, as the project was winding down, could see the need for more rigor and formalism in computer design. Jack Goldberg, Bonnar "Bart" Cox, and Bill Kautz had handled most of the logic design of ERMA and, according to Goldberg, their work had been all technology and no science. It seemed to them that there should be better ways to approach the design of these new and increasingly capable digital tools. Also, since the individual logic components were so unreliable, the design would somehow have to take those failures into account. So, in 1956 Kautz started an SRI program to try to define mathematical methods for computer design.

By 1957 the new program, part of what was by then called the Computer Techniques Laboratory, was concentrating on computer hardware design and reliability. This work continued for at least a decade or so, and in March 1969 the group gained a stronger identity under Goldberg's leadership (see Figure 2-17). Around 1970 the research focus began to

Figure 2-17. Jack Goldberg, first director of the Computer Science Lab.

---

[33] See the first section of this chapter.

shift to software, in which the lab would eventually make its greatest contributions. Though the group continued to grow, it didn't achieve laboratory status as the Computer Science Lab (CSL) until 1977. Given that the CSL is still a vibrant, technically excellent laboratory, if its history is measured from its start in 1957, it is one of the oldest continuously operating groups at SRI. Of great consequence, however, is the dedication of its staff to becoming a world-class software laboratory. This quest often means trying to arrive at not just a narrow, specific result, but, where possible, defining whole new classes of engineering approaches or solutions. This competency, in a field that is still very vital and expanding, has enabled CSL to also be one of the most financially successful labs at SRI. From its wide range of contributions to computing science and technology, only four areas will be presented here: magnetic logic, fault-tolerant computing, software formal methods, and information security.

All-Magnetic Logic

In the 1950s there was an increasing realization that computers would serve well in control and switching systems such as for telephones. But the unreliability of the logic elements of the day, including vacuum tubes and early semiconductors, led to a perceived need for a

highly reliable logic element. Hew Crane believed, from work he had done at RCA Labs, that he could build a computer using only magnetic elements. Except for the wire itself, they were the most reliable components in a computing system at that time. If a logic system that used only magnetic cores and copper wire could be built, it would be essentially trouble-free.

The first major problem facing the designers of an all-magnetic computer was the need for a two-state element that was also capable of inter-element gain; that is, a binary element that could be used to control the state of a similar element without the need for an intermediate amplifier. Some major computer manufacturers, such as Burroughs, had tried magnetic elements but, in the end, all opted for much less reliable vacuum tube diodes. The answer attempted at SRI was something called a multi-aperture core. By the late 1950s Burroughs and then AMP Inc. began supporting SRI's work. With SRI assistance AMP built and delivered many all-magnetic logic systems to handle critical functions. For example, all-magnetic logic systems were used to control one of the largest railroad switching yards in the world for the National Railroad in Toronto. These systems seemed to find a role wherever reliability was paramount, including in aerospace applications. The AMP logic systems were used in, for example, the docking radar for the Gemini capsule, a flight programmer for the Agena rocket, and communications satellite access control. Parts of the New York subway system also used such units (see box).

The SRI work culminated in the early 1960s in a project under U.S. Air Force sponsorship that resulted in the all-magnetic arithmetic unit shown in Figure 2-18. Even though the reliability of semiconductor devices would soon improve, this unit attracted a lot of attention.[EE, 34] According to an estimate retired AMP vice president Sweeney gave to Crane, AMP sold, in today's dollars, in the vicinity of $300 million worth of magnetic logic devices and systems.[FF]

Figure 2-18. Bill English (seated) and Hew Crane with the world's first and perhaps only all-magnetic-logic arithmetic unit (about 1961).

[34] Others participating in the all-magnetic computer were Jim Baer, Doug Engelbart, Bill English, Herb Heckler, Ed Van de Riet, and Joe Hunt. SRI recently donated this system to the Computer History Museum, Mountain View, CA.

Fault-Tolerance, Distributed Systems, and Formal Software Methods

The role of fault-tolerance in increasing the reliability of a logic system probably had roots at SRI in the late 1950s, when researchers were confronting the unreliable building of monolithic circuits. The device population in such circuits was increasing dramatically and the failure of one logic gate or memory cell could render the whole integrated circuit useless. To compensate for failures, could circuits be "overbuilt" and then self-organized to provide some guaranteed level of performance? That line of reasoning would take SRI innovators along two notable directions, one in the direction of artificial intelligence (see the opening of Chapter 4) and a very different one that we will briefly delve into here. This second approach directly explored the concept of a new field in logic and computer design called fault-tolerance. Though the subject had been under discussion for some time, it was the early 1970s before the first project to deal comprehensively with fault-tolerant systems was undertaken by the Computer Science Group for ARPA and the Office of Naval Research (ONR).[GG]

The purpose of this first study was to assess the state of the art in fault-tolerance for ARPA and estimate its effectiveness in the design of new computers. Evaluations were made of existing systems, concepts, and theory along with any new approaches that might be in the offing at SRI or elsewhere. This kind of project is excellent in helping form the solid base on which new, more promising concepts can be built, and that is what happened at SRI. The study considered both hardware and the emerging software approaches to fault-tolerance. It concluded that fault-tolerance theory and technology could significantly improve system reliability without dramatically increasing system cost. There were, however, important gaps in the art of designing and implementing software that would support fault-tolerant hardware. These included a lack of real time system diagnostics and the inability of the operating systems of the day to provide the hardware-software integration that rapid system restoration demands. The study also examined the role in reliability of a more formal approach to system specification. Finally, the authors advanced a novel approach to hardware-software unification using reconfigurable computer memory, which would be much cheaper than massive redundancy.

That latter insight was simultaneously being explored elsewhere within CSL as its staff began to investigate the question of highly dependable computing for NASA. Part of NASA's mission in the early 1970s was to promote the technologies that would make both aircraft and spacecraft more reliable. It was clear by then that computers would find their way into aircraft; the question was whether they could be designed and built to be continuously available. About 1973 NASA asked SRI to use all it knew about fault-tolerant computing and build an experimental computer that could control the safety-critical functions of airplanes. An ultra-dependable controller was vital. What happened next is a hallmark of a truly competent research organization.

The need for ultra-reliability could have been met in more than one way, of course. One possible approach was to use redundant computers, some of which would operate in "hot" standby mode in case the principal machine failed. (Tandem Computer was founded on that principle in 1974.) But the staff of CSL took another, more lofty approach to the reliability question; namely, to integrate a number of separate processors (in this case five) tightly networked together. It was called a software-implemented fault tolerant computer, or SIFT for short (see Figure 2-19).[HH] Again note that the emphasis was deliberately not on duplicate hardware and software running in the

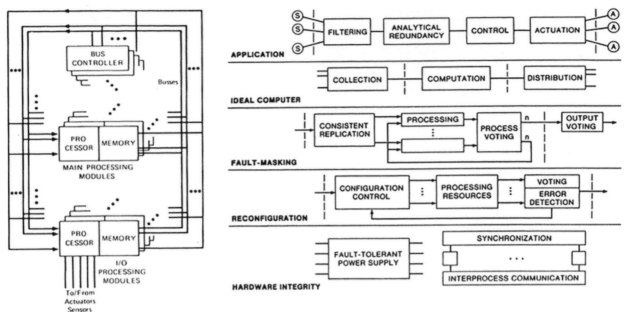

Figure 2-19. The physical (left) and the logical (right) structure of SIFT. (Notice the hierarchical form of the logical structure.)

shadows, but on gaining the requisite reliability from more richly redundant hardware and, especially, highly accurate and resilient software. This integrated multiple processor approach was a beachhead in an emerging field that came to be known as distributed computing.

This focus on tightly coupled processors plus the fact that the Lab was immersed in the notions of provable software correctness ensured that the problem of fault-tolerance would be tackled fundamentally. There were no rules for how multiple processors would even determine their individual role with respect to the instantaneous load, let alone assess their individual or collective health. In exploring this new ground, the CSL decided that each task would be multiply (redundantly) executed, and a vote on correctness would be taken before a task was invoked. As a result, the separate processors needed to be only loosely synchronized. Given that approach and the need for correctness, one of the first decisions to be made was whether any of the processors could or should believe the professed state of another.

So, in pursuing the SIFT design, CSL's Dr. Robert Shostak and Marshall Pease conducted one of the first forays into the question of consistency in "distributed systems." They both formulated the issue and provided a general solution for how to deal with it.[II] The issue was popularized by the Lab's Dr. Leslie Lamport when he called this potential for inconsistency in distributed systems the Byzantine Generals Problem.[JJ] The name refers to a condition in systems with multiply redundant processors where states that should be identical have been computed or communicated inconsistently. The implication is that to be able to detect the presence of a faulty processor, due either to its own error or that of its communications channel, requires a certain minimum number of like participating devices. By first tackling and then solving the more general problem of inconsistency, the CSL researchers laid new and fundamental ground for distributed systems, an expanding field in information science.

The other consequence of taking the SIFT design along a higher developmental path was the use of software formal proofs. Most people are unaware that software can be written to a certain level of uniformity using so-called specification languages that make it possible to prove that the resulting code will execute exactly as specified. This approach to software design is seldom used because the processes are difficult to understand and the proofs required to show that the code complies are computationally intensive. The hope has been that the computers would become powerful enough to absorb this complexity and computational intensity or that the provable languages would become closer to a natural, readable language that mere mortals could use. Neither of these states has been achieved, but CSL has contributed as much as or more than

Figure 2-20. John Rushby, one of the world's leading authorities on formal methods.

any other group in the world toward achieving these goals for software. In hardware design, formally based analysis techniques are now commonly used to analyze digital circuits before they are fabricated.

The purpose of formal software methods, of course, is to improve the reliability of software. Reliability is beneficial for all software, but critical for contexts in which software malfunctions endanger peoples' lives. Furthermore, since software now accounts for the bulk of digital system costs, reducing its almost ubiquitous bugs would be a huge cost advantage. John Rushby, one of CSL's most distinguished researchers, loves to point out that because software doesn't wear out, the only software errors are design errors (see Figure 2-20). He reasons that, like other engineering disciplines, software development needs a mathematical basis for its design. Other engineering disciplines have long ago developed beyond a trial-and-error approach but, alas, virtually all software development finds itself still in that stage. Rushby's colleague and the current (2004) director of CSL, Pat Lincoln, expresses the need similarly: "Bridge designers use finite element analysis and computer-aided design tools to test their intended structure before they ever begin construction. Software engineers, more often than not, build systems without knowing if they will, in the end, collapse." Lincoln believes there are underlying mathematical principles of software, just as there is a physics of bridges, and eventually software engineers will be able to know at design time if a software system will

work correctly. He asserts that, "Formal methods will one day be applied to all software. It will be embedded into compilers. Standard engineering practice will include mathematical analysis of designs, at every stage."

Even given current technology, applying formal proofs to all but the simplest of programs has been daunting. The SIFT computer was complex enough that, given the power of machines at that time, its software was never completely proven. Yet for more tractable problems, such as the guaranteed synchronization of multiple system clocks, formal methods have worked. They have also been successfully applied to the aforementioned, complexity-driven technology, integrated circuit hardware. In the end the SIFT work established the basis for what is now called the "state machine" approach to fault-tolerant systems, and the SIFT computer, built by Bendix, was installed at NASA Langley's Airlab in 1982, where it ran for about a decade. Not all of the original SIFT design features were realized, however.[KK] Tasks had to be randomly assigned to processors rather than dynamically by need. Voting also had to be scheduled rather than being transparent to the application programs.

One powerful concept in software design that can make a program amenable to verification is the use of functional hierarchies. This concept is actually one of decomposition, of structuring functionality so that by a series of layered abstractions one can go from simple or atomic operators whose functionality can be easily verified, to increasingly comprehensive operators that directly and unambiguously depend on that same lower level functionality. This concept was used in SIFT, for example (see Figure 2-19). But an obvious difficulty in this approach is defining each step in the abstraction with enough rigor to ensure verification as the abstraction increases. In security, for example, the hierarchies must span from the lowest level operator that can be ensured to what usually amounts to a higher-level, but still unambiguous security policy.

Using this approach to software construction, CSL developed two of the most recognized and useful tools in the verification of software programs: Hierarchical Development Methodology (HDM) and PVS. HDM and its successor, Enhanced-HDM, were among the first programs anywhere for the formal specification and verification of software. They used the powerful concept of formal abstraction and relied on hierarchies in the software design process. Also, behind HDM is a specification language called Special (and, subsequently, E-Special). Reflecting a continued need for innovation in this field, the evolution between HDM and its successor was radical. Because of the need for the inviolability of critical national security software, development of both these programs was sponsored by the U.S. National Security Agency.

Development of PVS, on the other hand, was supported by several hundred thousand dollars of SRI internal funds. Although Natarajan Shankar, John Rushby, and Sam Owre began work on it 1990, PVS is still a current expression of the state of the art in program specification and verification. The acronym originally stood for, among other things, the "Peoples" Verification System to indicate the desire to broaden the usability of such programs. But it has come to be known, like SRI itself, only by its acronym. The goal in building PVS was to create and make available a more usable specification and verification system than, say, E-HDM. PVS also includes a necessary software specification language and a theorem prover. Today, with the participation of Leonardo DeMoura and Ashish Tiwari, a suite of utilities has also been built around PVS. These include some automated decision procedures and something called SAL, which stands for Symbolic Analysis Laboratory. SAL performs the abstraction needed in the formal characterization of concurrent systems and has been applied to such different areas as automobile control systems (GM cruise control) and a biological model of diabetes. Finally, PVS is unusual in being licensed in a LINUX-like way, essentially free to anyone under terms that any improvements they make will be fed back to SRI so that configuration control can be maintained and the package will evolve to everyone's benefit. With this kind of accessibility, PVS has very likely become the most widely used formal software creation program in the world.

In a somewhat related vein, CSL researchers such as Joseph Goguen and Jose Meseguer have been the instigators of research into what they call modern ultra-high-level software languages. These are languages that can express functionality and variables in a manner much closer to a specification than can ordinary languages such as FORTRAN or the C family.

"High level" in this case means that functionality comes from more expressive statements that avoid most of the detail of more common languages. They reflect a belief that detail is a hobgoblin of accurate software, and the less the author has to deal with it the better. The first ultra-high-level language developed by CSL was called OBJ. It was intended to bring together several advances in programming style: logic programming with its equational form,[35] a declarative approach to execution,[36] and object-orientation for the simplicity of equivalent representation of a wide range of variables, constructs, and functions. OBJ and its descendent, MAUDE, now the responsibility of Carolyn Talcott and Steven Eker, have been licensed for research and development use in hundreds of laboratories worldwide. They are part of the search for the next generation of more accurate and easily programmed software languages.

As evidence of the general utility of the CSL work and as a peak at the future, lab director Pat Lincoln and some of the above CSL staff are now applying formal methods to new disciplines including molecular biology. Here one of the great benefits of a diverse research institute comes into play. With the collaboration of SRI biologists,[37] formal methods are enabling a new approach to understanding biological systems. Using some of the above automated reasoning tools such as PVS, SAL, and MAUDE, CSL has integrated them with a number of other analytical tools to form BioSPICE.[38] This collection is another open-source platform being made available to molecular biology labs worldwide.

---

[35] This means that statements lend themselves to replacement by equivalences, and functionality can thus be verified.

[36] Software languages can be usefully grouped into two types: imperative languages such as FORTRAN, C, Ada, and Cobol, wherein all actions to achieve an outcome are explicitly programmed; and declarative languages such as Prolog and LISP, wherein a computational goal is specified but the method for achieving that goal is left to the language. For a variety of reasons declarative languages are still not accepted for "industrial" or critical uses.

[37] Including Keith Lauderoute, Merrill Knapp, Larry Toll, and Analisa D'Andrea.

[38] This term is an intentional analog to the integrated circuit characterization program, SPICE, built at the University of California Berkeley, which stands for simulation program with integrated circuit emphasis.

Information Security

Perhaps the second greatest shortcoming of software systems, after poor reliability, has been their vulnerability to outside influence. This flaw applies not just to programs themselves, but to the data that surround them and the accessibility of both to unauthorized people. The Internet and the broad and simplified access it offers to users, regardless of their location, has underscored a problem that has been part of software from its beginning, particularly since the creation of time-shared, remotely accessible machines. The rush toward innovation in and employment of computers has never been able to wait for the fundamental conventions and constraints that are necessary for secure systems. Even worse, once the systems are in place and pervasive, both hardware and software, there are no practical ways security can be retrofitted. Remarkably, this lack of focus or discipline in the manufacture of general computing systems has to this day prevented the introduction of a system capable of holding multiple, independent levels of secure information guaranteed to remain separated. The two major aspects of security are protection against (1) unauthorized access to or modification of information and (2) denial of a computing or communications service.

The first major initiatives into computer security, both at SRI and elsewhere, can be tied to the introduction of a number of time-share computing concepts in the late 1960s. Machines were expensive and sharing them among many users was a way to spread costs. But multiple users on a single processor obviously raised questions of privacy, even if memory was somehow segregated. These concerns were of particular interest to the military, with its multilevel conventions of secrecy and the corresponding need to prove that one level of secure access on a machine couldn't compromise information at a higher level on that same machine.

With this motivation and a repertoire of tools and knowledge about formal software specifications such as HDM, CSL created one of the first provably secure computer system designs, the Provably Secure Operating System (PSOS). PSOS had a hierarchically structured, highly regulated (strongly typed), capability-based hardware-software architecture.[39, LL] Computing systems based on PSOS's notion of strongly typed objects were eventually implemented by Honeywell in the 1970s and by its spinout, Secure Computing Corporation, in about 1985.[40] But because the computing market was growing faster than these specially configured systems could be sold, they fell outside the mainstream, and as a consequence, their overall cost remained high. In addition, people's ability to rationalize away even known system vulnerabilities in favor of more rapid and less costly implementation, has retarded growth in the market for secure systems and stalled the necessary standards work needed to make them pervasive.

Beyond multi-user hosts, one of the next most vulnerable points in the landscape of software systems is a database. Securing a database requires controlling access, and a primary issue is whether it is possible to isolate certain information from some users who might have authorized access to different or limited segments of that information space. In 1984 Dorothy Denning, a staff member of CSL at the time, started a long-term project for the US Air Force Rome Laboratory on the design of a multiaccess database called "Secure Data-Views." The goal was to build a relational database that could meet the criteria for the National Security Agency's highest security level, Class A1. Again, an attempt was made to create a mathematical model that defined the behavior of the database, particularly with respect to its security properties. From this model would come design specifications that could be verified, thus ensuring that only certain parts of a database could be accessed. As the name implies, controls were applied not to individual data elements per se, but to the views of the database that were authorized. A simple example would be a database of employees in which their salaries were viewable by only selected parties. This approach to database security was taken over by CSL's Teresa Lunt and came to be called SeaView.[MM] The SeaView security model is used today in research settings and in the design of multilevel

---

[39] CSL researchers Goguen and Meseguer, under the NSA-sponsored PSOS project, defined the highly influential "noninterference" standard for multiple levels of security on a single computer system.

[40] Honeywell's offering was the Secure Ada Target (SAT) and Logical Coprocessor Kernel (LOCK). The division of Honeywell that produced the system was spun out as Secure Computing Corporation, whose main secure system offering today is a firewall known as Sidewinder.

secure databases for both the military and commercial sectors. It is capable of providing the highest government security classification, Class A1, when implemented over a Class A1 operating system kernel.

The third and final area of computer security to which CSL has made notable contributions is in the real-time detection of unauthorized computer or network access. In comparison to the upfront designs mentioned earlier, proposed solutions for this problem, intended to fit over a wide range of multiple-access systems, are still very complex but of a different type. This complexity has at least two dimensions: (1) the variation in the hardware and software systems that are already in existence but need an overlay of access monitoring and control, and (2) the variety of procedural models for access authorization within the normal office or company workflow.

CSL's work on real-time access detection began with a project in 1983 for a nameless government agency that wanted to explore the computing wanderlust of internal as well as external people. The solution involved statistical profiling of users to enable a system to sound an alert whenever significant departures from those profiles were detected. This work was also conceived and led by Denning. Building on this effort and the advent of expert systems technology, SRI designed a new scheme called Intrusion Detection Expert System (IDES). The easily expressible rules of that technology made it adaptable to a wide variety of administrative procedures in which security policy was expressed. It was intended to run in the background of host computers, monitoring the access to important open processes that defined machine operation. The intention was to detect unusual behavior in the machine that might tip off the presence of unauthorized access. From this monitoring IDES would also adaptively learn normal user behavior patterns to provide a basis for the statistical detection of abnormal events. Such real-time insights could both record relevant process information and alert human operators. The rule-based nature of IDES could also permit easy modification as experience with the program suggested the need.

Work on IDES continued for almost 9 years under sponsorship of the Navy and Air Force. A second-generation system called NIDES extended the audit-record capability of IDES and improved interfaces for a security officer

and the maintainer of the rule-base. In related efforts NIDES was used to extend real-time observations to the profile software applications rather than just user descriptions. This program was installed for service testing in several machines around the United States, including an experimental phase on the main computers of the FBI.

The current and state-of-the-art embodiment of unauthorized access detection programs at SRI is EMERALD (a somewhat stilted acronym for Event Monitoring Enabling Responses to Anomalous Live Disturbances).[NN] The EMERALD development program, created and led by Phil Porras, applies many of the techniques developed in NIDES to the area of communications networks. SRI was issued a patent in 2002 on the underlying event-monitoring technology in EMERALD and is now seeking to package it in a form releasable as a commercial product.[41]

CSL also created one of the first means to establish private links between arbitrary points on the Internet, requiring only that the end terminals have the appropriate encryption and other security software. This system, called ENCLAVES, was demonstrated in 1994–5. This general capability is now quite common under the name of virtual private networks.

One additional CSL effort in the area of security and reliability should be mentioned. The burgeoning of computer use is bound to have consequences that are not all beneficent. Everyone experiences negative impacts that, given human nature, get more attention and linger longer in the memory than the positive ones. One member of the CSL has done more than any other person anywhere to chronicle those unfortunate occurrences: Peter Neumann, who joined SRI in 1971. Neumann has been near the center of the research, advocacy, and controversy surrounding computer security ever since. In about 1985, as a personal endeavor and under the auspices of the ACM,[42] he began what has come to be called the Risks Forum, an online, broadly participatory collection of computer mishaps. Because the foibles of computer use touch so many lives, the Forum became one of the most popular sites on the

---

[41] U.S. Patent No. 6,484,203 covers computer-automated hierarchical event monitoring and analysis within an enterprise network, including the deployment of monitors. It also covers detection of events through the analysis of a variety of network traffic data.
[42] The Association for Computing Machinery.

new Internet. Thousands of contributors, from disgruntled neophytes to Nobel laureates, have eagerly related their frustrations or their observations on computer misuse or mishaps. The collective account in the Risks Forum comprises perhaps the single most comprehensive anthology of computer-related mishaps in existence. As such it is also the best harbinger of the risks we face in future computer use.[OO] Though these Neumann archives are sometimes overly inclusive, thousands of relevant accounts are given: from the pranksterish commandeering of the Rose Bowl scoreboard by California Institute of Technology students in 1984[PP] to countless, more catastrophic events such as the illegal 1989 intrusion into the California Department of Motor Vehicles computer to retrieve the address of an eventual murder victim. In spite of all this collected awareness, progress toward achieving security in the rapidly emerging information infrastructure is still slow.

One addendum to this review of computer and system security centered in CSL actually lies nearly totally outside it. The business consulting groups in SRI began to conduct security evaluations of companies in about 1970. By spring 1987, largely under the leadership of Donn Parker, some 85 companies had been reviewed and some 1,600 cases of computer abuse had been logged. Parker has also written several books on computer crime and its prevention. That experience base enabled SRI to begin at that time a large multiclient service it called the International Information Integrity Institute (I-4).[QQ] "Integrity" has a broader implication than security alone, including such mishaps as accidental destruction or misplacement. Focus on that larger topic has had broad appeal, and I-4 continues to this day. However, as a result of some organizational turbulence involving the demise of SRI's Business Group,[RR] it is now operated by a separate company housed on the SRI campus.

The Ability of Machines to Listen

Humans have a propensity to talk, and speaking is a more developed need, perhaps, than listening. Speech is overwhelmingly our preferred mode of interacting with other people. But that entire predilection is interrupted when we face a machine. For centuries we have not been able to expect much in this regard from a machine, but that expectation has already changed. Machines in the new class we loosely call computers are creeping more deeply and completely into our lives. Our somewhat misguided tendency to grant them anthropomorphic skills is abetted by their extraordinary processing capacities, and they will become better and better at listening to us. [43]

Whether you love it or hate it, the recognition of speech by machines is now with us to stay. Though computers that recognize speech may often seem impersonal and unresponsive, because they save their owners a lot of money, time, or convenience, they will only become more prevalent. Like most technical achievements, the arrival of speech recognition seems much more rapid

than was actually the case. Finally, for reasons that will become evident, this section could be subtitled "The Benefits and Risks of R&D Commercialization."

SRI's Entry into Automatic Speech Recognition

Perhaps the first time serious money was expended for research on automatic speech recognition was in 1971 when DARPA funded a program of Speech Understanding Research (SUR). Cordell Green, a former member of SRI's Artificial Intelligence Center who had been called to active duty, initiated the program at DARPA. About half a dozen organizations, including SRI, participated in the research to learn whether a computer could recognize perhaps a thousand words, spoken by a limited set of speakers, under calm and quiet conditions. At the end of 5 years several of the recognition programs were tested, but under some unanticipated rules; that is, rules not established at the outset of the research. None measured up, and SUR was terminated.

SRI also made an excursion into speaker identification in the early 1970s. For the Law

---

[43] This section has been modified from the first printing with the help of Patti Price, Mike Cohen, and Hy Murveit.

Enforcement Assistance Agency of the Department of Justice, SRI looked into the use of so-called voiceprints for identifying the person speaking.[55] SRI built a prototype system and acted as an advisor to Rockwell when it received a contract to produce a commercial version of the SRI prototype. While the system was semiautomatic and worked in some uses, it had to be operated by a trained person, a phonetician.

Speech research resumed at DARPA in 1984 as part of an ambitious artificial intelligence (AI)-centered program known as the Strategic Computing Program. Many of the SUR research centers, such as Carnegie Mellon University (CMU), Bolt, Beranek, and Newman (BBN), SRI, and MIT renewed their efforts under this new program, along with both industry and European researchers. This time evaluations were conducted each year and the better techniques were quickly propagated among the participants. This effort continued into the late 1990s and was pivotal in the development of commercial-quality speech recognition systems that have made their way into the marketplace.

In this second round of funding SRI became one of the top-tier organizations developing what would emerge as unprecedented and successful recognition techniques. Whereas in the earlier SUR program SRI's Artificial Intelligence Center (AIC) worked with SDC to build a recognizer based largely on language properties, the second speech recognition effort was centered in the Sensory Sciences Research Laboratory (led at the time by Hew Crane), which had no AI expertise at all. Before 1984 the lab's research interest in speech had concentrated on the exploration of the physical models of the vocal tract and other elements of speech phenomenology.

As it turned out, the second technical direction that automatic speech recognition took didn't favor an AI approach anyway, at least initially. SRI's approach became much more statistical and followed an approach called hidden-Markov modeling (HMM). Here word recognition is based on the previous one or more words spoken and the likelihood associated with various word sequence transitions. As computer power increased, this approach enabled greater word-transition flexibility and thus ever-greater

vocabularies.[44] Prosody, the intonation and duration patterns of speech, was also modeled. The speed and simplicity of this overall approach, plus the advent of more powerful workstations, led to the commercial systems in use today.

The Second Venture into Speech Recognition

The leader of the second SRI speech program was Don Bell. Beginning with the arrival of Dr. Hy Murveit from the University of California, Berkeley, Bell gathered a world-class group of researchers in the Sensory Sciences Lab. Their innovations in the intricate algorithms enabled speaker independence, vocabularies that climbed toward 100,000 words, continuous uninterrupted speech, and tricks for computational acceleration helped them perform repeatedly at or near the top of the annual competitions that DARPA held to promote the success of speech recognition technology. The difficulty of meeting DARPA's goals is hard to overestimate, and the climb was not easy. It would take about a decade before the collective DARPA community would produce sufficient recognition accuracy for a usable product.

The development of a more accurate recognizer required that a number of linguistic and speech modeling research questions be answered:

- How could models of grammar, words, phonemes etc., be efficiently and robustly combined?

- Could natural language grammars help constrain word sequences and still handle the ungrammaticalities of spontaneous speech?

- Would the successes in English generalize to other languages?

- Could other pattern-matching techniques or hardware accelerators improve speed and/or accuracy?

To determine not just the words spoken but also their meaning, SRI's AIC collaborated

---

[44] The term for this difficulty in speech recognition tasks is perplexity, and its definition is related to entropy from information theory. It is approximately the geometric mean of the word branching factor after the application of a language model.

with the Sensory Sciences Lab in a new effort integrating speech and natural language. The natural language (NL) understanding research had gone on in the AIC for years, but had to be modified considerably because people don't speak the way they write. SRI's resulting system was developed in the air travel planning domain and was called ATIS (Air Travel Information System). The other DARPA-sponsored sites then adopted ATIS as a benchmarking task. One innovation of the new technology was a "progressive search" that allowed the same system to use the most detailed contexts (slow but accurate) or to back off to fewer, less detailed models when speed was necessary. SRI won the last ATIS competition held by DARPA, and Hy Murveit bought trophies for the SRI team.

By late 1992 the SRI HMM recognizing program, DECIPHER, was working well enough that Bell began to explore its commercial utility. In that regard, he consulted several specialists and began to look at the market in a number of speech recognition applications. In 1993 a new lab director, Patti Price, selected one of those consultants, Ron Croen, to help continue the quest for commercialization, including licensing.[45]

But the overly optimistic promises and subsequent failure of earlier recognition systems made for dictation had soured the commercial world on the subject, and SRI was unable to sell a license to the technology. A few small companies were already in the business, but the new DARPA technology was not yet in commercial practice, although it soon would be.

Then, a number of researchers at the Lab, including Murveit and Dr. Mike Cohen, began to assert that the best way to commercialize SRI's speech technology was by starting a company focused on telephone-based applications.

The Commercialization

Also at this point, and totally coincidentally, new upper management at SRI decided that commercialization of technology was to be important, perhaps dominant, in SRI's future

(see Appendix B), and the Lab and division-level entrepreneurial efforts got caught up in this new corporate emphasis. Consequently, after reviewing the results of a market study or two, the chairman of the SRI Board, Paul Cook, decided in late 1994 that SRI should start its own company in speech recognition. For the first time in its history, SRI invested serious money, $1 million, to start a commercial enterprise, the Corona Corporation, to which SRI transferred:

- A worldwide exclusive license to its core technology in speech recognition, including demonstration systems based on DECIPHER

- A toolkit for the rapid development of commercial applications

- Four key personnel

- An obligation to transfer future research results exclusively

- A reputation for high-quality benchmark results in the DARPA tests

- The commitment of time and personnel to achieve the transfer of the technology.

Three key technical personnel, Murveit, Cohen, and Peter Monaco, together with Ron Croen, founded the new company with Croen as president. Cohen continued half-time at the SRI lab for the first year to help with technology transfer and to ease the transition. (The turmoil of the spinout resulted in the loss of two or three other people who chose neither to remain at SRI nor to join Corona.)

The founding team moved into a separate building on the SRI campus and carved out a new area for speech recognition: call-center telephony. In 1994, speech recognition was nearly exclusively used for dictation. The call-center strategy allowed the fledgling company to grow a new market without going head to head with IBM and Dragon Systems, who dominated the dictation market. Ten years later, it is call-center applications that now dominate speech recognition.

In its first year the new company gained first-round financing from the Peninsula's ripe venture capital world, increased in size, and changed its name to Nuance Communications, Inc. Subsequently, second- and third-round financing became available, the company moved off the SRI campus, and

---

[45] Dr. Price also reorganized the lab as the Speech Technology and Research Laboratory (STAR), which is its present name.

as of this writing in 2004 has perhaps 300 staff members.

To gauge the quality of the recognition software that Nuance produced, consider its first major client and deliverable. SRI's Business Group had persuaded Schwab Discount Brokerage to examine the ability of automatic speech recognition to reduce the cost of Schwab's telephone quotation system. SRI, Nuance, and Schwab explored and eventually built the first over-the-phone stock quotation system. As a measure of its performance, it could (and still can) respond automatically to oral requests for any of 11,000 stocks listed in Schwab's catalog, which can be expressed in 3 million different ways, with an accuracy exceeding 95%. By the end of 1996 this system was saving Schwab about $1 million per month. Since then Nuance has provided similar systems to a dozen or more other commercial clients. More recently, the company has gone public and become one of the leading suppliers of speech and speaker recognition systems, speech synthesis, and development tools.

While Nuance represented a commercialization success for SRI, the STAR Laboratory, which had made it all possible, faced a struggle. Spawning Nuance had some severe negative consequences that became an object lesson for subsequent spinouts:

- In the formation of the spinout or its associated turmoil, the lab eventually lost all but one of its senior staff and several other talented engineers to Nuance or other employers.

- The SRI license to Nuance was so broad and exclusive that it prevented the lab from engaging in any commercial marketing with the exception of nonexclusive licensing in language training. With very few exceptions, only projects with government sponsorship were available after the license, although the lab could use Nuance technology in the nonexclusive area.

- The commercial outlet for the STAR Lab as the long-term research arm for the new company never materialized.

- Some new technology, such as speaker identification, noise mitigation, and recognition models for other languages, continued to flow from the lab, with no

remuneration for SRI, and most often with the continued loss of people as the technology was transferred to Nuance. In the years after the spinout, the president of SRI at the time and his equity manager were focused on making their first large commercial investment, and dismissed attempts to mitigate internal difficulties the spinout process created.[46]

- The long-term drain of people from the Lab to Nuance became an ongoing challenge, abetted by the government's continuing de-emphasis of speech research. Although new Lab leadership and a new user interface program were formed, retaining personnel became more difficult. Ironically, the license's foreclosure of new commercial opportunities also became a disincentive to some new Lab hires.

To continue to maintain a vital group, Price focused the Lab on the language education carve-out, an area initiated much earlier by Jared Bernstein. She convinced Broderbund, a northern Bay Area software company, to partner with SRI in a government-sponsored dual use (government and commercial) Technology Reinvestment Program (TRP) in language education.

Broderbund had shown early successes in some of its educationally oriented products. But this arrangement faltered badly when, halfway through the several-year product development, Broderbund abandoned its role in the program. Strangely, in a downsizing intended to support the company's stock price, its leaders showed they were oblivious to the existence of Broderbund's obligations under the alliance even though it involved millions of dollars. The Lab, however, was able to revise the project toward an even stronger result: rather than one speech-enabled language education product with Broderbund, the effort would produce tools to make it easier to speech-enable language education software by the government and by anyone licensing the tools. The resilient

---

[46] That indifference to the technology-generating laboratory in the course of commercialization is now completely gone under the more equitable policies of the present SRI administration.

Laboratory also launched a special recognition engine for computer-based education tools as the term of the Nuance license agreement was expiring. Under the current lab director, Dr. Kristin Precoda, the STAR Lab has also found a new area in which to excel: speech translation. The war in Afghanistan created a desperate need for soldiers to be able to speak to Afghans. The lab has built bilateral translation software that effectively translates one of the leading Afghan dialects, Urdu, into English. Under Precoda's and Dr. Horacio Franco's leadership, about a dozen stalwarts still offer world-class speech technology.

Regarding Nuance, it initially concentrated on telephone-based speech recognition applications. But at one point it broadened its efforts to include voice-activated Web interaction. Because of the ubiquity of the telephone and the burgeoning use of cell phones, Nuance foresaw a speech-enabled, browser-like interface that could become not only a means to retrieve information from the worldwide complement of online sources, but also a communications device that can enhance all telephone voice traffic. The company calls this product Voyager, and the telephone-accessible part of the World Wide Web, the "Voice Web." Nuance has since retreated a bit from this initiative to return to its most successful area, voice-based servers and their accompanying service and support.

All in all, Nuance Communications has done quite well in building a leading position in the telephone-based speech recognition market. It has delivered, both directly and through a growing number of industrial partnerships, a large number of recognition and speaker identification systems worldwide.[47] While SRI's stake in the commercialization of Nuance has yielded a large financial return, it came at the expense, perhaps unnecessarily, of diminishing SRI's research base for at least the duration of the license agreement. The STAR Lab and the Nuance spinout, two different worlds, with very different objectives and reward systems, have intersected with important consequences.

Watchwords for Commercialization at SRI

Given that SRI remains a nonprofit research institute, it is useful to recall that its commercialization ventures are intended first to strengthen the research base and, if possible, to enrich SRI's compensation package so it can compete successfully with other recruitment efforts in Silicon Valley. But some serious questions need to be answered to safeguard SRI's interests in the commercialization process:

- Does the technology to be commercialized represent most or all of that practiced by the inventing lab?

- What are the consequences if key personnel of the lab participate in the startup at the outset? What happens if they stay with the startup?

- Does the license leave the lab with adequate latitude to pursue continued funding in its research specialty?

- Does the license permit, encourage, or require an ongoing relationship between the lab and the startup, one that is beneficial to both?

- Do the managers with authority over both the lab and the startup have the best interests of both organizations in mind?

These questions are obviously posed from the perspective of the research organization. Left on its own, the startup will, by its nature, have little concern for the continuing success of the enabling laboratory. It has investors to satisfy. And if the lab continues to be technically strong and advances the state of its field beyond the technology licensed to the startup, then new licensing ventures with others can become aggravating competition that threatens the startup. How is this thicket to be negotiated?

The answer to these questions depends on why SRI wants to become an incubator of technology that can be commercialized and what fraction of its operation that effort represents. The announced reason for such efforts is, in the long run, to strengthen the research base at the Institute and thereby provide greater benefit to the public interest it is chartered to serve. That cause, derived from its nonprofit status, means that all excess

---

[47] In 2005 Nuance merged with competitor ScanSoft to form a more powerful market presence.

income is reinvested and in some instances into labs that have the potential for commercializing their output. It is hoped that this cycle of innovation would grow with increasing ability to help all parts of the Institute.

If the work of an inventing lab is narrowly defined and the intellectual property to be commercialized cannot avoid encompassing everything that the lab and its staff members do, care is needed to design a licensing agreement that leaves the lab viable. Possible options are to 1) restrict the field of use of the licensed technology, 2) restrict the time of exclusivity, and 3) require a flow of funds back to the lab for longer term R&D.

If none of these are possible, then the lab personnel should all be given the opportunity to transfer to the licensee, and SRI should abandon work in that area rather than leaving researchers without continuing opportunities.

If the technology to be licensed is only a part of a laboratory's work, then the license conditions can be more flexible, but care must be taken to preserve the lab's ability to remain viable. If researchers do transfer, then the structure of the equity offerings to those that leave and those that stay should be sufficiently equal to make it difficult to decide which path to take. This approach seems fair, and SRI tried to follow it as Nuance was being created. It is now clear, however, that persistently equitable arrangements can be difficult to achieve.

Endnotes

A Some of the material presented here is drawn from two sources: Fisher and McKenney, The Development of the ERMA Banking System: Lessons from History, *IEEE Annals of the History of Computing*, 15(1), 1993; James L. McKenny, *Waves of Change*, Harvard Business School Press, 1995.

B William D. McGuigan, personal communication, May 27, 2000.

C SRI's *Research for Industry*, 7(9), October 1955.

D Tom Morrin, personal letter to Prof. James L. McKenney, Harvard Business School, June 26, 1992.

E SRI's *Research for Industry*, 7(9), October 1955.

F Some of this story was taken from autobiographical material of Hew Crane entitled: "*Reflections on a 50-Year Career*" dated October 12, 1997.

G H.D. Crane, "Sequence Detection Using All-Magnetic Circuits," *IRE Trans. on Electronic Computers*, Vol. EC 9, 155-160, June 1960.

H Earle Jones, personal communication on August 2, 2004.

I For the most recent and complete record, see Thierry Bardini, *Bootstrapping*, Stanford University Press, 2000.

J Douglas Engelbart and Harvey Lehtman, Working Together, *BYTE*, page 245, December 1988.

K Vannevar Bush, As We May Think, *The Atlantic Monthly*, 176 (1), 101-108, July 1945.

L Ken Jordan, "The Click Heard Round the World," *Wired Magazine*, 12(1), January 2004.

M Stanford oral history interview found at www-sul.stanford.edu/depts/hasrg/histsci/ssvoral/engelbart/engfmst2-ntb.html

N Ibid.

O See Chapter 3 on Reid Anderson's own entrepreneurial exploits.

P Charles R. Bourne and Douglas C. Engelbart, Facets of the Technical Information Problem, *SRI Journal*, 2(1), 2-8, 1958.

Q SRI Proposal No. EU 60-251 to the Air Force Office of Scientific Research, December 13, 1960. The contract technical monitor was Harold Wooster.

R Vannevar Bush, op cit.

S Research Aimed at Computer Augmentation of a Programmer, SRI Project 4385, Contract No. SD-163, $195,000, February 1963 to February 1964.

T Computer-Aided Human Control of Computer Display, SRI Project 5061, Contract No. NAS1-3988, $85,626, June 1964 to July 1965.

[U] Personal email communication from Jack Goldberg, November 15, 2001.

[V] W.K. English, D.C. Engelbart, and Bonnie Huddart, *Computer-Aided Display Control*, SRI Report to NASA, July 1965.

[W] Adele Goldberg, ed., *A History of Personal Workstations*, 187–232, Addison-Wesley for the ACM Press, 1988.

[X] Douglas C. Engelbart and William K. English, A research center for augmenting human intellect, *AFIPS Conference Proceedings - Fall Joint Computer Conference*, San Francisco, December 9–11,1968.

[Y] Ken Jordan, op. cit.

[Z] Thierry Bardini, op. cit. Contains extended coverage of this transition of ideas and the attainments at PARC. The notion is also mentioned in Adele Goldberg, op. cit.

[AA] Ibid.

[BB] Michael Kanellos, CNET News.com, September 18, 2003 or www.logitech.com as of July 9, 2004.

[CC] Richard Watson, personal communication, December 9, 1998.

[DD] Implicit in the "transparent pipe" mentioned in: Elmer Shapiro, *A Study of Computer Network Design Parameters*, SRI Project for ARPA, December 1968.

[EE] Hewitt D. Crane, A High-Speed Logic System Using Magnetic Elements and Connecting Wire Only, *Proceedings of the IRE*, 47(1), 63-73, January 1959 and D.R. Bennion, H.D. Crane, and D. Nitzan, *Digital Magnetic Logic*, published by McGraw-Hill, 1969. Also from 1997 autobiographical material of Hew Crane entitled: *"Reflections on a 50-Year Career."*

[FF] Hew Crane, personal communication, January 24, 2002. The sales estimate was based it on material Crane received from retired AMP Corporation vice president, Joe Sweeney.

[GG] P.G. Neumann, J. Goldberg, K.N. Levitt, and J.H. Wensley, *A Study of Fault-Tolerant Computing*, SRI Final Report to ARPA and the Office of Naval Research, July 31, 1973.

[HH] J.H. Wensley, Leslie Lamport, Jack Goldberg, Milton W. Green, Karl N. Levitt, P.M. Melliar-Smith, Robert E. Shostak, and Charles B. Weinstock, SIFT: Design and Analysis of a Fault-Tolerant Computer for Aircraft Control, *Proceedings of the IEEE*, 66(10), October 1978.

[II] Jack Goldberg, email communication dated July 30, 2004.

[JJ] L. Lamport, R. Shostak, and M. Pease, The Byzantine Generals Problem, *ACM Transactions on Programming Languages and Systems*, 4(3), 382–401, July 1982. According to Goldberg, this paper set off a rash of technical papers and interchanges that lasted for more than a decade.

[KK] Daniel L. Palumbo and Ricky W. Butler, A Performance Evaluation of the Software-Implemented Fault-Tolerant Computer, *J. of Guidance, Control, and Dynamics*, 9(2,) p. 175, March–April 1986.

[LL] Peter G. Neumann, Robert S. Boyer, Richard J. Feirtag, Karl N. Levitt, and L. Robinson, *A Provably Secure Operating System: The System, Its Applications, and Proofs*, SRI report to the National Security Agency, May 1980.

[MM] T. F. Lunt, D. Denning, R. R. Schell, M. Heckman, W. R. Shockley, The SeaView Security Model, *IEEE Trans. on Software Engineering* (TOSE), 16(6), 1990.

[NN] P.A. Porras and P.G. Neumann, "EMERALD: Event Monitoring Enabling Responses to Anomalous Live Disturbances," *Proceedings of the Nineteenth National Computer Security Conference*, Baltimore, MD, 353-365, October 22-25, 1997.

[OO] Peter G. Neumann, *Computer-Related Risks*, Addison-Wesley/ACM Press, 1995.

[PP] According to the Computer Risks Forum, the radio control of a computer, previously spliced into their scoreboard control circuits, caused the UCLA-Illinois game score to be replaced with a CalTech-MIT score of 38 to 9.

[QQ] I-4 Is Underway, *SRI Journal*, 7(1), Spring 1987.

[RR] See Appendix B.

[SS] SRI's *Investments in Tomorrow*, No. 9, Autumn 1973. The voiceprints, called "sonograms," essentially plotted acoustic energy as a function of frequency and time.

Chapter 3
Advances in Communications

AT SRI:

1969
First Computer Network Connection
–With UCLA–

1976
First Internetwork Connection
–Two Dissimilar Networks–

1977
First Internetwork Connection
–Three Dissimilar Networks–

Communications is a broad and immensely critical part of our existence. In this chapter we will examine only the technical side of this huge preoccupation we have to talk to one another and to learn the state of our world. SRI has been engaged in some form of communications research almost from its beginning but here we will cover just three important aspects that have had significant impact on our lives and certainly upon mine, for this is my chosen area of work.

Computer Networking

Rossotti's had been a well-known Mid-Peninsula "watering hole" since the days when it was a stagecoach stop between San Francisco and Monterey. It was in the second bank of foothills west of San Francisco Bay, had a casual atmosphere and some outdoor seating—a good place for a special event. It would be all right to park SRI's "bread truck" van alongside and run a few wires to one of the tables in the courtyard. It was far enough from SRI to look remote but close enough to have good radio contact to SRI through the Stanford University field site repeater. That's why this venue was chosen to mark the occasion of the first internet transmission on August 27, 1976.[1]

The van was an SRI-outfitted mobile radio lab that contained the equipment to make it a portable node on the emerging Packet Radio Network (PRNET), sponsored at SRI by the DoD's Advanced Research Projects Agency (ARPA) starting about 1973. Placing a terminal on one of the wooden courtyard tables and connecting it to the van, a number of SRI people who had gathered for the celebration filed a weekly Packet Radio Program report,

representing all the Program's contractors, to ARPA. Although the testing of such a connection had been going on for several months, this long email report was, in a ceremonial sense, the first internet transmission; that is, the first formal use of the internet protocol called TCP.[2] That protocol convention was designed to carry information over dissimilar networks, in this case the PRNET, through a gateway at SRI, across the wire-based ARPANET, to a set of hosts distributed around the United States. This small, understated but deliberate episode is indicative of but one of SRI's early contributions to the field of digital communications. But let's return even earlier to the beginning of computer networking itself.

---

[2] TCP is the acronym for Transmission Control Protocol, network software that establishes, operates, and closes a reliable virtual circuit across dissimilar networks. Although it is still in use today, the overhead for this type of connection was deemed excessive for some types of traffic. This recognition soon led to development of a companion transaction protocol called the Internet Protocol (IP). Together they comprise the transport system of today's Internet.

---

[1] In the formative days of computer networking, terms like internet and intranet were in common use with their respective meanings. The lower case usage here purposely reflects that language, with the Internet arriving some undefined time later.

The First Computer Network Connection

SRI's first computer network involvement arose when the notions of such networking were first being created. Accounts of that creation and the people who worked to develop computer networking at organizations like ARPA, the University of California, Los Angeles (UCLA) and Santa Barbara (UCSB), the University of Utah, Bolt, Beranek, and Newman (BBN), and SRI can be found in *Casting the Net*,[A] *Inventing the Internet*,[B] and other books on the history of the Internet. Although the early formulations of networking were carried out as part of other ARPA programs, in the spring of 1968 SRI was awarded the first contract under a new program area at ARPA specifically called ARPANET.[C] It was given to SRI engineer Elmer Shapiro to study the "design and specification of a computer network." The report of the 4-month study mentioned rudiments of concepts that today are part of the lore of packet networks.[D] Figure 3-1 from that report defines a few network nodal terms and shows the three types of links for which protocols had to be written: IMP-IMP, IMP-host, and host-host.[3] From the flexibility of using any workable set of switches in host-to-host communications, and its transparency to the end user (Shapiro called it a "transparent pipe"), came the term virtual circuits. Messages passing through the network had various compartments, some relevant to switches and some to hosts. This convention evolved into protocol layering. Protocols were discussed, but packets per se and the concept of a network virtual terminal, a specification

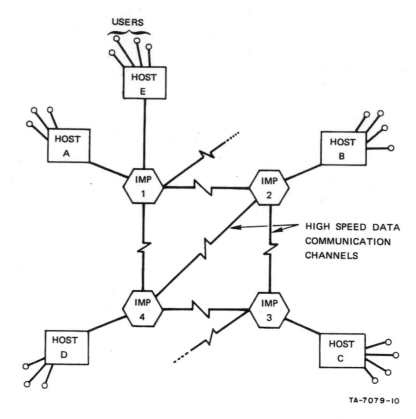

Figure 3-1. Network nodal terms as shown in Shapiro's early network study. (E.B. Shapiro, op. cit.)

allowing the many different types of terminals to meet just one interface standard, were adopted later. Hosts were assumed to be of the timeshare nature, permitting many simultaneous users not all of which were local. Because Shapiro was under contract to ARPA, ARPA program manager Larry Roberts asked him to get the relevant interface and packet transport software going. Shapiro had also suggested to Roberts that a more formal group be established to govern the design of the new network.[E]

Accordingly, in mid or late 1968 a meeting was called of people from what were to become the first four ARPANET sites and posed the problems to be addressed. Shapiro chaired that first meeting of what was to become the dominant voice in the technical design of the network, the Network Working Group (NWG). That first gathering also included Steve Crocker (UCLA), who would soon become the chair and formative leader of the NWG; Steve Carr (University of Utah); Ron Stoughton (University of California, Santa Barbara); and Jeff Rulifson (SRI). Crocker described the occasion as a "seminal" meeting.[F] But it was undoubtedly the fortuitous absence of established conventional

---

[3] The term IMP, used in Figure 3-1, stands for Interface Message Processor. It was the host computer's access point and the ARPANET's basic packet switch. Although initially each site had to interface its own host to the IMP, the first standard interface software was soon developed by Bolt, Beranek, and Newman (BBN) as defined in their so-called 1822 Interface. The building of the IMPs was awarded to BBN in December 1968.

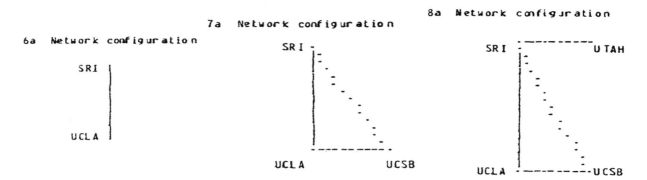

Figure 3-2. The first three ARPANET configurations—actual text images from RFC 4.

network professionals that allowed the tabling of fresh new ideas. This now respected meeting set the stage for the high level at which this totally new networking world would be pursued.

The medium of interchange between these pioneers and the place where concepts were hammered out came to be called Requests for Comments (RFCs), a name and process still in use in the Internet with nearly 4,000 RFCs having been issued. That unassuming name, suggested by Shapiro to Crocker,[G] seemed to look for and await more professional guidance. As it turned out, the professionals these young pioneers awaited didn't exist, and RFCs became the process for setting network standards and remain so to this day.

It is worth noting that RFCs 2, 4, and 5 were written by SRI people: two from Douglas Engelbart's lab and one, by Shapiro, from the Information Systems Lab. Bill Duvall outlined, in RFC 2, the initial procedure for host-host interaction. These first awkward network interactions were patterned after a regular terminal-to-host dialogue and became the basis for the first connection between two networked computers. Shapiro wrote RFC 4 in March 1969, an implementation schedule appropriate to his ARPA contract and his leadership role in the NWG. This RFC showed the first three configurations of this evolving network, which are reproduced in Figure 3-2 just as they appeared there. Rulifson of SRI wrote RFC 5, the definition of a language called DEL that was to be the first, albeit rudimentary, realization of a host-independent computer language.

On October 1, 1969, SRI received the second ARPANET packet switch or IMP. UCLA, in its capacity as Network Measurement Center, had received the first IMP a month earlier. Its arrival offered the important opportunity to create, with UCLA, the first linkage on a general-purpose digital network, which occurred in October 1969.[4] These first sites had to build their own host-to-IMP interface, a major effort that took several weeks. The next task was to develop the host-host connection software. For background there was Duvall's link-level terminal-host protocol outlined the previous April in RFC 2. The first such program was a simple procedure, limited to one character at a time, and as a result there was a brief "hiccup" in that very first interaction. It was late at night when the SDS Sigma 7 at UCLA and the SDS 940 at SRI could be unloaded. The natural first step was to have a terminal on one host log on to the other, connected but distant host. To complicate things a bit, the machines used two different operating systems, SEX at UCLA and GENIE at SRI. Therefore each machine had to convert each character received to its local equivalent, meaning the programmers watching had to convert the hex to an equivalent alpha letter. After correctly receiving an *L*, an *O*, and a *G*, the SRI machine, as was its custom for its attached terminals, automatically returned a *GIN*, thus violating the one-character-at-a-time rule of that first interplay. This caused the UCLA machine to respond with a *?*, to which the SRI host automatically also returned a *?*. This loop continued until one machine crashed or was shut down. Duvall couldn't remember which.[H] The multi-character correction was made and the network was off and running.

An SRI Quarterly Progress Report to ARPA for the period indicates the matter-of-fact meaning of the new connectivity:

---

[4] The exact date of the first transmission is unknown, but it was certainly in October 1969. Charles Kline, then at UCLA, finds in his notes that it occurred before 29 October (see *San Jose Mercury News*, front page article by David Plotnikoff, September 9, 1999).

"The Interface Message Processor (IMP) and communication terminal for the ARPA Computer Network have been installed and the hardware interface between the IMP and the 940 is complete and in operation.

Under control of EOM instruction from the 940, the interface will transmit and receive Network messages directly to and from buffer in 940 core. Interrupts signal the 940 when transmission is complete. The interface was designed to operate with either 940 core or external core, and…..

Test programs have been developed to check out communication with the IMP and with other Network host computers by "looping" messages. A preliminary operating system that allows one remote user to log in to our system over the Network and simultaneously allows us to log in to any other available system on the Network has been written and is in operation."[1]

In truth this interim report reads like thousands of others at SRI, where doing things for the first time is simply taken for granted. But to their credit, these people were seeking the fundamentals of networking, concepts and practices that would provide not just an ad hoc solution to two computers talking, but a foundation for the best evolution of this new technology. That the work of these pioneers, represented in general by the NWG, should seem compelling is mostly the consequence of some talented young researchers being given some new resources, some workable deadlines, and, most important, a clean slate.

The SRI people became involved, I believe, because the program managers at ARPA saw that the visionary computer-based, distributed collaboration work being developed in SRI's Augmentation Research Center (ARC) anticipated rich computer networking (see the following box and Chapter 2). Perhaps the most

important reason that the second IMP came to SRI was Engelbart's willingness to host the Network Information Center (NIC). Participation in this effort was certainly consistent with his notion that the ARC was an information-creating and -wielding resource and… there were apparently no other volunteers. Thus the NIC became part of the ARC and, through the initiative of the first NIC director, Dick Watson, helped motivate and, in some cases, contribute technically to the evolving network protocols and higher level services. The NIC also became responsible for distributing, both online and physically, the technical designs and procedures for joining this first-ever packet network. It also began to assign and distribute network host names and addresses. These service roles came together in the NIC's practice of writing and distributing three formal documents:

- The ARPANET Directory, which listed the network address and telephone number of all registered users

- The ARPANET Resource Handbook, which was a compendium of the hardware and software of each host and the research interests and procedures and policies of its owner

- The DoD Protocol Handbook, which contained all the standard network protocols as well as relevant reference material.

The NIC performed these roles for about 22 years, from 1970 until October 1992, long after the creation of the Internet. Elizabeth "Jake" Feinler led the NIC over most of that time. The NIC also borrowed an idea from the Massachusetts Institute of Technology (MIT) for an informal geographical locator program and built the first online directory service, WHOIS. This innovation, developed by Ken Harrenstien and others, enabled visitors to obtain from the NIC server the network-related addresses and particulars of any registered host user. In its first year, in the mid 1970s, WHOIS received over

In the early 1970s, an SRI editor, Shirley Hentzell, worked online with Douglas Engelbart on a proposal that was also being composed jointly and simultaneously at two separate locations; that is, the same text was viewed at the same time by those at SRI and by a Purdue University professor in Indiana. The terminal showed the text in one window, with suggested insertions being made as we watched, and the other windows showed comments from Engelbart at SRI and the professor at Purdue. It was not only magic, it was a type of collaborative interaction only now coming into commercial development thirty years later.

28,000 visits from a still embryonic network.

But these anecdotes are getting ahead of the story of the network's genesis. Shapiro recalled a very interesting aspect of its early use.[J] The first few sites had been connected together. Utah had been chosen so as to develop, with the California sites, an interstate configuration that would ensure AT&T's participation in the network. But after some initial experimentation, the network wasn't being used very much, to the disappointment of Larry Roberts, the ARPA manager leading the ARPANET implementation. The network functionality was confined mostly to file transfer (FTPs) and some terminal access (TELNET) traffic, but even their collective affiliations through ARPA weren't enough to cause much traffic between the contractor sites. Certainly, computer resource sharing, the initial prime motivation for the network, was not materializing as an important need. Roberts, in a very pragmatic ploy that looks brilliant in retrospect, suggested that traffic between the contractor sites might very well be a condition for continued contract funding. Moreover, the amount of traffic might influence the amount of future work. Clearly, Roberts's pressing people to explore the utility of the new network not only now seems justified, but is also evidence that can only be called visionary.

By most appraisals, the first serious and widespread demand for networking came with the almost cavalier introduction of cross-network electronic mail by Ray Tomlinson of BBN in 1971.[5] It should be mentioned, however, that electronic messaging and file exchange, with symbolic addressing, was a fact of life within the SRI ARC as early as the fall of 1970. It was a feature of the NLS Journal system and when network addressing came along, the expansion to other machines was as natural as specifying a person and the machine on which their mailbox program resided.[6]

As for the continuing design of the ARPANET, SRI's role receded as the 1970s wound down. Shapiro, who had been recommended to ARPA by Engelbart, participated only temporarily. He had helped ARPA (Roberts) write its first bid invitation for network hardware (the IMP), helped evaluate the proposals, helped set up the NWG, and then turned to other pursuits. Members of the ARC such as Watson continued to help demonstrate the efficacy of packet switching and the new network, often through the use of applications.[K] But the ARC would elect to play a relative minor role in developing network technology except for that centered in the operation of the NIC. The NIC had an important role in the issuance of network host names and addresses and as the repository of the RFCs and other standards for network connection, access, and interchange. With this important exception, SRI largely withdrew from the later technical evolution of the ARPANET itself.

The First Internet Transmissions

The second notable area of computer networking development at SRI arose within a couple of other Engineering Research Group laboratories during the 1970s. Several visionaries at DARPA,[7] most notably Roberts and Bob Kahn, had seen the military need for a mobile, wireless version of the embryonic ARPANET. SRI and DARPA had discussed the possibility of a transportable, possibly handheld terminal or switching node for such a network rather than the massive, steel-encased IMPs of the early fixed network. Some researchers in SRI's Information Sciences Division attempted to develop a conceptual design for such a device, but they weren't able to convince DARPA that they were up to the task, in part because they had little radio experience. In response, SRI moved the project to the Telecommunications Sciences Center, which had splendid radio capability. By that time DARPA had formed a team of contractors in what came to be called the Packet Radio Program, which was created to develop a wireless adjunct to the evolving ARPANET. Its resulting network would be called the Packet Radio Net (PRNET). Members of that DARPA

---

[5] Like so many internet innovations, electronic mail has many fathers. It was present on some time-sharing systems by at least 1970, but Tomlinson's program, including its "@"convention, set the stage for network-wide rather than host-wide email.

[6] As a component of the NLS Journal, a generalized email was a natural tool of the community of users in SRI's ARC as early as August 1970. When the ARPANET attachment came, extending it outside the ARC was a simple modification carried out in 1970 (Doug Engelbart, personal communication to the Stanford University History Department, available at www-sul.stanford.edu/depts/hasrg/histsci/ssvoral/engelbart/main4-ntb.html). A rudimentary form of mailboxes was

implemented on Multics by Tom Van Vleck in 1969 (see www.multicians.org).

[7] With the addition of "Defense" to its name ARPA became DARPA in 1972.

program were BBN in Boston, Collins Radio in Dallas, Network Analysis on Long Island, UCLA, and SRI. Because of a good understanding of radio and some background in high-frequency (HF) networking, SRI was chosen as system engineer and technical director (SETD) and integrator for DARPA's packet radio effort, a position it maintained for over a decade. (A comprehensive description of packet radio technology can be found elsewhere.[L, M])

The introduction of a radio segment to supplement the ARPANET was a natural outgrowth of the military context in which a great deal of U.S. research is done. Ultimately, military use of this new, interactive digital technology would depend on adaptation to the reality that the military is inherently mobile and may be deployed to any point on earth. Thus a radio network, particularly one that served a mobile population, was needed, and it turned out to be intrinsically different from the existing fixed, wired one. This clear difference, along with the need for the two networks to work well in tandem, led to the notion of a communication software structure that would effectively bind these disparate networks together as though they were one.

One technical insight needs to be inserted here to help understand how disparate packet networks can still function together. In most communications networks only the source and destination terminals are visible to network users, and all resources that lie in between are normally of little interest to users as long as they fulfill their role. In circuit switching, common to the telephone networks of the day, once a physical pathway was chosen, the same route is maintained for the whole session. When such circuits are leased, the connections may even be "hardwired;" that is, never changed. In packet switching, where subunits of a message may travel entirely different routes from source to destination, the exact role of intervening resources would not even normally be known. Thus, there arose the concept of a virtual circuit, where the only defining network nodes lie at the ends and the intervening ones are neither specified nor known by either the users or the network providers. This switching concept had been part of the basic ARPANET design, and it was to be extended to this amalgam of wire and radio networks, and thus to the world of internets.

The clear differences between the wire-based ARPANET, the mobile radio-based PRNET,

and eventually satellite networks led Kahn, then leading the networking efforts at DARPA, and Vint Cerf of Stanford to design the first end-to-end protocol that could span dissimilar packet networks. The essence of such a construct began to emerge as Kahn attended a seminar held by Cerf at Stanford in the summer of 1973 and mentioned the existence of these dissimilar networks.[N, O] After some airing in the internet working group and elsewhere, the first encapsulation of such a protocol came together for them over a weekend in October 1973 at Palo Alto's Rickey's Hotel. They continued to rework it through 1973 and published the protocol in May 1974.[P] They named it the Transmission Control Program, or TCP, even though today the "P" is always referred to as protocol. With modifications, some of them very important, TCP is still in use today as the basis for packet transport in the worldwide Internet.

Following the introduction of TCP, DARPA let contracts for three separate implementations: one to Stanford University, one to BBN, and one to University College, London. The first, clearly "buggy" specification appeared in December 1974, when Stanford produced RFC 675. BBN had an in-house version working reliably about a year later and began exchanging TCP traffic with Stanford on an intranet basis. Jim Mathis, a student of Cerf's at Stanford, started to implement the Stanford group's protocol in 1975. In summer 1976, Mathis joined SRI, where he completed a version that would run specifically on the much more modest hosts of the PRNET (Digital's LSI-11 microcomputer). In the meantime Cerf, now a program manager at DARPA, was trying his best to inculcate the DoD with the virtues of packet switching and TCP for its future data networks.

Some of Cerf's effervescence led to an independent effort to implement TCP in a new DoD network called AUTODIN II, which was intended to be an upgraded version of an ancient paper tape system that had none of the desirable attributes of the ARPANET. The Defense Communication Agency (DCA) contracted with SRI in 1975 for yet another specification of TCP for AUTODIN II. Jon Postel,[8] Larry Garlick, and Raphael Rom

---

[8] Jon Postel was a member of SRI's ARC until spring 1977. Later, at USC's Information Sciences Institute, he became one of the most important and influential designers of the Internet.

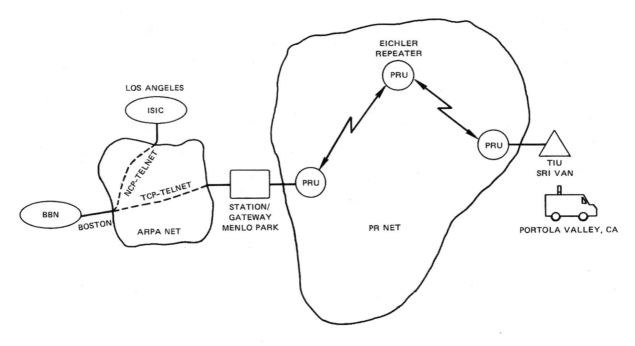

FIGURE 1   FIRST WEEKLY REPORT BY RADIO

Figure 3-3. The network map and site of the first two-network internet transmission on August 27, 1976.

submitted that design in July 1976.[Q] During this work, some of the limitations of TCP became apparent, and the critical need for a less reliable or datagram protocol was conveyed to DCA.[9] For a variety of reasons, including the accommodation of packet speech, this concern was later addressed by the internet community, and the datagram, or transactional Internet protocol (IP), was separated out from TCP in 1978.[10] The standard to which TCP and IP were to subscribe was issued by Postel in RFCs 791–793 in September 1981.

With this background, we can revisit SRI's role in the first truly *internet* transmission. As mentioned at the outset, the first testing of TCP across dissimilar networks started in late summer 1976. The first trials stayed one radio hop from the Packet Radio station (the PRNET's controlling node) where the bidirectional ARPANET gateway software, built by Ginny Strazisar at BBN, was located. During July and

August the SRI team tested and tuned Mathis's version of TCP for better accuracy and speed. In August 1976 a terminal attached to an LSI-11 "host" running TCP, which was in turn attached to the PRNET, which was in turn connected to an ARPANET gateway, first accessed an ARPANET host. This trial was the first time, at least in any formal sense, that dissimilar networks were bridged by TCP and was thus clearly a two-network internet connection. That specific network configuration is shown in Figure 3-3, taken (as Figure 1) from a packet radio progress report written at that time.[R] Figure 3-4 shows the aforementioned demonstration using TCP to convey the lengthy weekly Packet Radio Program report. Other TCP connections would soon follow.[11]

To fulfill the assumed need for a network of global reach, DARPA next moved to include a

[9] Raphael Rom, personal communication, February 10, 2000. Also, a pressing need for a less than infallible protocol was to convey speech over such packet systems. In other ways, too, the need for a low-delay, best-efforts protocol became clear.

[10] According to Abbate (Janet Abbate, *Inventing the Internet*, MIT Press, 1999, p. 130), Cerf, Cohen, and Postel decided to create IP during a meeting in January 1978. Cerf (personal communication, January 15, 2002) attributes most of the IP initiative to Cohen and says that packet speech was an important justification. IP was to be a best-efforts, no end-to-end retransmission protocol, and therefore to have smaller delay variance.

[11] An expected part of the DARPA work was to demonstrate progress and give evidence of this new networking capability. Therefore, TCP, spanning the PRNET and the ARPANET, would be demonstrated in May 1977 between the SRI van and hosts at ISIC and the SRI-KL host. Also, on August 11, 1977, a TELNET connection would be established between the van and the Naval Ocean Systems Center in San Diego for Admiral Stansfield Turner (Director, Central Intelligence Agency) and William Perry (DDR&E). On September 19, 1977, a single LSI-11 microcomputer, containing TCP, connected four independent terminals through a packet radio to four different ARPANET hosts, essentially all of the ones that were running TCP servers at the time.

Figure 3-4. (left) Participants in the First Two-Network Internet Transmission (From the left: Don Cone, Army observer Mike Berishinski, Nicki Geannacopulos, Dave Retz, Ron Kunzelman, Jim McClurg, and Jim Mathis.) (right) Nicki Geannacopulos entering the packet radio weekly report. (Don Nielson took the pictures.)

third packet network, one that was satellite-based. Within a year, DARPA was ready to test all three networks together. On November 22, 1977, what has also come to be regarded by many as the first internet transmission was sent from the SRI mobile packet radio van to a host computer at the University of Southern California (USC) by way of London! The route is shown in Figure 3-5.[S] The SRI van, used as a mobile test node throughout the Packet Radio Program and now a historic vehicle, is shown in Figure 3-6.[T]

Two interesting demonstrations were used repeatedly at the time to illustrate the robustness of this new concept of networking. To illustrate the flow of traffic between the mobile van and some distant network host, a character generator would grind out continuous alphanumeric sequences that formed patterns on a CRT in which errors would be obvious. While this source was moving at high speed in the SRI van, the signal would sometimes be interrupted owing to shielding of the radio signal (for example, when the van passed beneath an underpass). The flow would stop momentarily and then resume with no errors being observed. Error-detection using cyclic redundancy checks, applied at the end of each transmitted packet, was used to verify reception accuracy. These checks, along with the end-to-end ordering and retransmission properties of

TCP, would not permit delivery of altered packets even though packets were frequently lost. A similar procedure was to withdraw from the packet radio its critical synthesizer card. This would terminate the character flow, but reinserting the card would restart the flow. Thus, for a variety of reasons, the traffic would stop or could be interrupted, but no errors were ever observed. Those demonstrations were splendid evidence that each packet could have sanctity, even in a tough environment of intermittent propagation and noise. This exciting capability was certainly foreign to those circuit-oriented engineers who saw reliable mobile radio data systems as some sort of oxymoron.

SRI's final contribution to the development of TCP came as the protocol was being incorporated into Berkeley UNIX, the host operating system that was dominating the research-oriented Internet in the early 1980s. Bill Croft, a member of the Telecommunication Sciences Center at SRI, faced the problem of installing networking software on a number of PDP-11 minicomputers at SRI and elsewhere. In porting the Berkeley UNIX TCP/IP software from the VAX to the PDP-11, he found and repaired "dozens of bugs" in the original UNIX code. Croft's corrected version of TCP/IP, now an integral part of UNIX, became an important vehicle in the rapid spread of networking.[U]

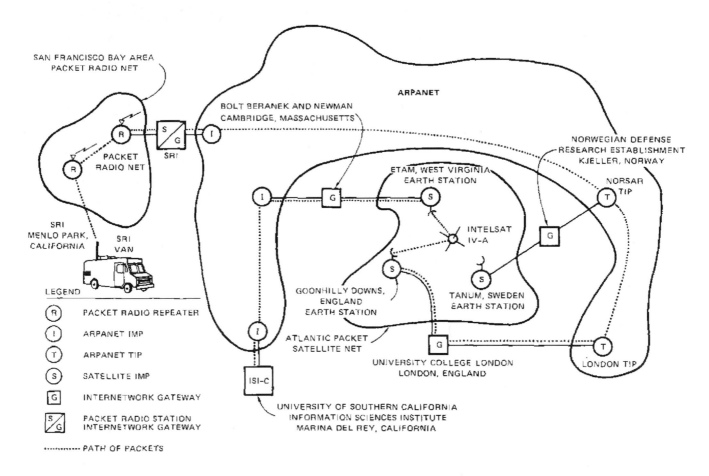

Figure 3-5. Route of the first three-network internet transmission on 22 November 1977.

Thus, the beginnings of internetworking, driven by the needs of the U.S. military for both mobile and longer range digital radio systems, were the result of broad collaboration both within and outside SRI.[12]

The Introduction of Packet Speech

When the ARPANET was perhaps 5 years old and before the development of internet protocols, Kahn at DARPA requested that a group of contractors explore how the new network could handle normal telephone traffic.

Given the initial focus on reliable data transmission, it was not clear whether the variability in interpacket delay would permit

Figure 3-6. The SRI packet radio van. Inset shows two packet radios, an LSI-11 microcomputer containing TCP plus terminal interfaces, and a DataMedia terminal.

---

[12] Other than project leaders Donald Nielson and Ronald Kunzelman, important SRI contributors to these early internet efforts were Jim Mathis, Stan Fralick, John Leung, Don Cone, Dave Retz, Jim McClurg, Russ Wolfram, Mike Placko, Keith Klemba, Janet Tornow, Don Alves, Bud Sargent, and Vince Sherville. With the advent of other PRNET and internet design issues and a range of internet services such as speech, these SRI staff members were joined by Earl Craighill, Nachum Shacham, Jan Edl, Jose Garcia-Luna, David Beyer, Barbara Denny, Diane Lee, Mark Lewis, Raphael Rom, Andy Poggio, Bill Zaumen, Andy Poggio, John Hight, Richard Ogier, Ed Kozel, and Zaw-Sing Su.

the smooth flow required by a voice call. In 1974 because of the narrow bandwidth of the initial circuits comprising the net, Kahn initiated the Network Speech Compression Program. This program resulted in the choice of some speech compression algorithms, and these were first tried over the ARPANET. In 1976 SRI's Earl Craighill and Tom Magill, both of whom had been working on the speech program, convinced DARPA to let them try speech on the Bay Area PRNET. By this time the internet protocol, TCP, was also being tested, and thus speech experiments also began on an internet basis.

Because the SRI van was an easily outfitted facility in which packet radio and internet equipment had already been installed, it became the first mobile node for packet speech experiments (see Figures 3-7 and 3-8). In addition to the challenges of mobile data transport, transporting natural-sounding speech focused on the importance of delay variance. Innovations were needed in variable rate encoding, new buffering strategies, and rapid rerouting of packets whenever the route-in-use failed. All these techniques were needed to help smooth the flow of speech. Thus, internet speech connections were being made as early as 1977–1978, about the same time as the Internet itself was becoming a reality. It was mentioned earlier that the handling of packet speech was one reason for wanting a less-than-reliable or transaction protocol. In packet-based speech a wide variance in the delay of individual packets, stemming from repeated end-to-end packet retransmissions, is worse than the occasional loss of one. Thus, packet speech, anticipated to be a common future internet service, became a motivating factor in the creation of IP.

Taking Packet Radio to the Field

In the 1980s SRI continued its leadership in the development of packet radio systems. Through a variety of new network terminal devices and a larger supply of packet radios, SRI placed packet radios aboard ships, airplanes, and helicopters to demonstrate that this technology could fit into the operational environment of all of the military services. Several concurrent and concatenated programs at DARPA continued such development as much larger, more dynamic, and more survivable military networks were envisaged. In 1983 DARPA began a mobile digital network effort called the

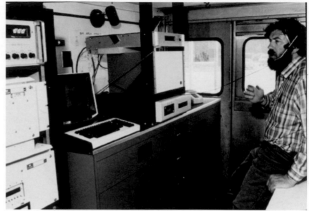

Figure 3-7. SRI's speech packet project leader Earl Craighill in the SRI Van (which housed the speech encoding and packet-forming equipment).

Survivable Radio Network Program or SURAN. SRI continued as the integrator and technical director in this new work, which again involved many contractors. Over a period of 7–8 years development continued on robust algorithms and protocols for routing amid node failures, more secure network access and management procedures, improved adaptation in larger and larger networks, and finally methods of implanting those changes on available hardware. The packet radio equipment became smaller and more portable; such devices included lower cost packet radios from Hazeltine Corp. and new, smaller terminal-network interface units designed and built at SRI. In addition to conducting large and expensive field tests, SRI also operated a large laboratory testbed to accomplish the same kind

Figure 3-8. SRI's Jan Edl demonstrating speech transmission over the internet. (The Mickey Mouse phone was deliberately used to illustrate that the speech equipment hardware and software were designed to accommodate a "standard," off-the-shelf telephone.)

of evaluation.

Another related area of work unfolding in the 1980s consisted of applying these new digital network-based systems to the information needs of military operations. SRI's role in networking also came to include developing and demonstrating how to use such a network. Demonstrations occurred as early as 1980 at Ft. Sill, Oklahoma, where a packet radio network was used in Army fire control exercises. The topological clarity of the packet radio connectivity made the PRNET control station the focal point for observing much of the entire operational exercise.

But the largest and most influential use of both packet radio and the ARPANET in military operations began at Ft. Bragg, North Carolina, in 1979. With mainly DARPA funding and under the leadership of SRI's Mike Frankel, SRI undertook activities there that showed, for the first time, the power of interactive computing and digital messaging systems in military exercises. In a team effort, SRI and military personnel explored, on a limited scale, the utility of these computer-based networks in relation to existing military communications and information processing systems. Because of a lack of encryption, packet radio, like its DARPA hosts, was limited to unclassified roles. A collaborative effort between the Army and DARPA to test interactive computing and digital messaging went on for over 7 years and clearly affected how the Army approached its information needs. The first phase of the program was called Army Data Distribution System (ADDS).[13] A continuing exploration of how the online digital network could offer new and better capability was called ADDCOMPE. Its specific objective was to explore new concepts in command and control. Could emerging digital systems actually increase the availability of critical information even as a battlefield became more decentralized? More flexible and robust packet-switched communications, enabling new distributed information processing technologies, in fact,

did just that and SRI was leading the military through that change.

In a concurrent program, appropriately called TACTICS, SRI also introduced a set of military-required application programs that expressed these new ways to view and move information. Application programs such as SITMAP, an online, dynamic depiction of the military situation in map form using standard symbols, showed the Army how to keep much more apprised of a situation. New messaging and a new Tactical Reporting System were also developed and used in normal operational exercises. All these new capabilities made the power of distributed information technology evident and started the Army down a revolutionary path in its information systems that continues to this day. Prompted by power and miniaturization of this technology, now so well illustrated by the Internet, all military services are rapidly moving toward modern communications and information systems that can support the increased mobility and effectiveness demanded of a worldwide deployable force (see box on Accommodation.)

Another good example of how the new technology changed operational capability came from SRI's presence among the airborne units at Ft. Bragg. Since their mission was to be ready to fly anywhere on short notice, the ability to rapidly identify the correct materiel to take with them was crucial. SRI staff members working on site at Ft. Bragg noticed the time-consuming and precise practice of loading military transport aircraft. Realizing that new software methods might speed up this task, SRI suggested a method that led to a totally new airload planning system. Using SRI expert-system technology and working closely with highly experienced Army and Air Force loadmasters, the SRI team wrote a new program. SRI designed and built a new software expert system that was orders of magnitude faster than existing methods and accurate enough for widespread military use, for example, in the 1991 Gulf War.[14]

The last of the packet radio initiatives at DARPA was a 5-year program that sought to increase the available bandwidth of the network to accommodate the digital distribution of essential military information such as imagery. Begun in 1995, the Global Mobile Information

---

[13] ADDS had unclassified roles in many Army and joint field exercises in the United States and overseas. Domestic examples were Solid Shield '81, Gallant Knight '82-'83, Gallant Eagle '82, and Brim Frost '83. Overseas examples were demonstrations with the British at the SHAPE Technical Center in the Netherlands linked to England and at U.S. headquarters in Heidelberg. Both of these used packet radio networks that linked to existing European military networks in ways that showed the true flexibility of internetting (Douglas Hagan, SRI International, personal email communication, May 26, 2002).

[14] The program was called the Automated Air-Load Planning System (AALPS), also mentioned in Chapter 4 on artificial intelligence. Its project leader was Debra Anderson.

TECHNICAL ACCOMMODATION BY THE MILITARY

As one might expect, the introduction of new information technology to the military is no easy task when time-tested methods have become standard operating procedures. However, with skepticism came some willingness to try as long as.... The two images below depict first reluctance and then accommodation. The picture on the left is a veteran Army colonel gingerly exploring the utility of some of the earliest programs at Ft. Bragg in 1981. On the right is a marine corporal with a completely mobile, handheld computer that enables a continuous account of his situation and those around him. SRI also designed and built the latter in its ongoing exploration of the equipment and software that increases the awareness and capability of our soldiers or any collaborating group. That current system is called INCON, a wireless automatic information distribution system now undergoing field-testing. The accommodation period between these two images is about 20 years.

Systems Program, or GLOMO, delved broadly into the functionality needed in wideband distributed systems. On the radio side this effort included new antennas and CMOS digital radios. On the software side, it required new distributed file systems. The most visible change was the replacement of special-purpose, quasi-milspec hardware by equipment from the rapidly evolving commercial sector. In the area of terminal equipment, commercial products included conventional laptop computers, then miniature laptops, and now wireless personal digital assistants (PDAs). SRI was DARPA's lead technical director and integrator of the demonstrated technology for GLOMO, playing the same role it had played in similar communications programs for over 30 years.

Attempts at Commercialization

In the 1980s, when packet radio was a working, demonstrable system, SRI called on a few commercial organizations to test their interest in its technology. One application, easy to envision, was the use of packet radio technology as a telephone and data

communications overlay on the deteriorated or non-existent telephone systems in underdeveloped countries. Another was its use in oilfields or other places where distributed monitoring and control were critical. Control of a fleet of mobile trucks was another. Although SRI suggested all these applications to companies such as Motorola, none aroused interest. Today, of course, wireless is an exploding technology that enables, for example, a customer to track a FedEx package from pickup to delivery.

The first company to venture into the world of commercial, area-coverage, wireless networking was Metricom. With money from Paul Allen of Microsoft and leadership from Paul Baran, one of the originators of packet transport, the company was formed in 1985 and grew during the early period of the dot-com surge. But its offering began with a paltry 28 kilobits per second (kbps) bandwidth (not upgraded until 1999) and a high $75 per month fee. Also, because Metricom targeted consumers over vertically integrated businesses, customer growth was slow. More important, by ultimately extending its scope of operations to

17 cities nationwide and incurring the associated high capitalization costs, Metricom eventually outran its inventory of paying customers, slightly more that 40,000 at the beginning of 2001. With a billion dollars in debt, it filed for bankruptcy in July 2001 and offered its Ricochet Network assets for sale a month or so later. Other than having created similar technology, SRI had no role in Metricom.

In 1995 a number of former SRI packet radio engineers, led by David Beyer, banded together to form another packet radio technology company, Rooftop Communications.[15] Its aim was to provide residences and businesses with wireless, broadband access to the Internet. Like packet radio, each node was both an access point and a relay station that helped form a more accessible network; that is, every node did not have to have line-of-sight connectivity to a high, prominent, centralizing node. Unlike Metricom, which had a half-dozen or so company-owned nodes per square mile, Rooftop nodes exist only at each subscriber's site and act as both network routers and access points. By 1998 Rooftop had developed the first commercial self-configuring, multi-hop wireless IP routers.[16] Self-configuring in this case means that each router (switch) determines which other routers to use for a given packet address. Rooftop's routers are also able to change their routing neighbors dynamically as environmental conditions change. According to Dave Beyer, the Rooftop protocols were designed from scratch but arose out of the "deep experience" he and other company staff members had gathered at SRI. Protocol issues like the hidden terminals, the density of nodes required for full connectivity, the ability to scale the network to a much larger size, and supporting real-time traffic all drew on SRI experience. Software development methods built and used at Rooftop also drew on SRI experience, as did the staff's ability to gain an overall system architecture view similar to that required for the role as system engineer for the DARPA packet radio project.

Recognizing the value of this informed approach to wireless system design, Nokia Telecommunications purchased Rooftop in September 1999 for $57 million in cash and stock. SRI as an organization had no stake in Rooftop.

Recently, however, SRI has built a software system called "PacketHop" that embodies much of what packet radio offered 20 years earlier. PacketHop:

- Builds a radio-based infrastructure that is self-forming, self-organizing, and self-healing

- Offers true peer-to-peer communications

- Has multi-hop, multiple-path algorithms that reroute around problem areas

- Applies to a wide range of transmission media

- Is scalable to thousands of nodes

- Offers guaranteed packet delivery through packet management functions.

As of this writing the technology has been licensed to three concerns. Speedcom Wireless of Sarasota, Florida has a worldwide non-exclusive agreement that extends for 6 years and gives SRI some equity in the enterprise and a seat on an advisory panel. Associated with this licensing is a reminder of the lag time of new technology. In about 1974, before SRI received its first Collins-built packet radios in about mid-1975, SRI handcrafted a set of radios itself and took them to Hawaii to run over the same links as the radio-based University-based Aloha Net. Recently, an article in the Hawaii Business Magazine[V] indicated that a Hawaiian company called Landmark Networks (now called FireTide) is the second licensee of SRI's "PacketHop mesh technology." The company will work with the University of Hawaii to create in the Honolulu area what is perhaps the most flexible wireless network yet. Almost 30 years has elapsed between initial use and commercial application. The third licensee is SRI's own spin-off company Packet-Hop.

Yet another company emerged in 2000 using packet radio technology. It is called SkyPilot and two of its earliest members were a former SRI researcher and manager, Mark Rich, and researcher Bernadine Yetso. It also uses the mesh network technology inherent in packet

---

[15] Besides CEO David Beyer, other members of the 20-person firm who once worked at SRI were Thane Frivold, Darren Lancaster, and John Hight. JJ Garcia-Luna-Aceves and Bich Nguyen worked part time and Ed Kozel served on its board of directors.

[16] Others exploring this multi-hop routing were the radio amateurs, Tetherless Access Ltd., whose products failed to reach the market because of technical and management failures, and Metricom, whose routers were not commercially available.

radio. As of this writing, SkyPilot is in a beta-testing phase and completed a $24 million second round of financing.

A final startup using the Packet radio mesh technology was an SRI spin-off called PacketHop. Ambatipudi Sastri and Michael Brown transferred to the new company in 2003. It has a developing role in public safety networks.

A Concluding Perspective

SRI was clearly in the forefront of the new networking age. As with most technical "revolutions," the deployment of this new digital technology took time. Important factors in that wait were the decreasing price-to-performance ratio of electronic equipment and acceptance by the military and the public of real-time online operations. When the technology was developed 25 years ago, almost no one, at least among companies serving the consumer community, was interested in digital radio systems even when they offered the characteristics of the internets and intranets of today. But the revolution was coming. In 1985 SRI researchers helped define the methods for multimedia electronic mail.[W] In the late 1980s and early 1990s the SRI NIC's host-counting measurements were the first to verify the exponential growth of the Internet. Those measurements continued until well beyond the millionth connected host. In spite of attempts by standards bodies to create a replacement for TCP/IP, it remains, after almost 25 years, the protocol for all Internet traffic.

Today, one can easily see and feel the growing communications revolution. With functionality that was already available in the packet radio networks at the genesis of the Internet, you can now, in examples of pervasive alacrity, establish instant messaging, send email, teleconference, co-edit drawings, examine medical records, or obtain comparative prices or order goods on wide variety of wired or wireless Internet terminals, including cellular phones. Even the recent acceleration in the exporting U.S. jobs overseas is abetted by these high-speed digital communications networks, which from the beginning included purposeful design attributes such as "distance- and location independence." The savings in labor far outweigh the costs of very complete and capable computer-based communications systems.

With the recent explosion of wide-bandwidth (now called broadband) wireless services, enabled by a profusion of widely and frequently distributed network entry points and a bevy of wireless-equipped portable computers, there seems to be another, perhaps over-exuberant "land rush" for ubiquitous connectivity encompassing both the Internet and new kinds of interpersonal communications. "WiFi" is marching in as the medium of choice for the frequent traveler; it is also esteemed for its ability to rid the home and the workplace of unsightly and tethering wires.

Though the change around us is abundantly evident, this new way of communicating is so fundamental that its collective capabilities and uses are impossible to predict. After almost 3 decades, it is still an expansive and wild frontier. What is clear is that with its burgeoning capacity, broad connectivity, and innovative services, the boom in both Internet and personal communications will forever change the way we conduct our business, civil, and personal lives.

Communications Aids for the Deaf and Blind

Helping the Deaf to Communicate

In the late 1950s the director of SRI's Communications Laboratory, Ray Vincent, received a telephone call from the director of the University of California's Lick Observatory, located atop Mount Hamilton east of San Jose. The observatory needed a device to work with its cameras that would help take the atmosphere-induced scintillation out of photographs of heavenly objects. The observatory director also suggested that a

physicist by the name of Bob Weitbrecht would be a good person to work on it. Weitbrecht was a tall, lanky man with a shuffling gate. He had some practical technical skills, and just happened to be deaf. He joined the SRI Communications Laboratory in 1958 and, with others in the lab, successfully built and demonstrated a control system for an imaging plate that moved quickly and accurately enough to compensate for the apparent movement of the position and size of a star (see

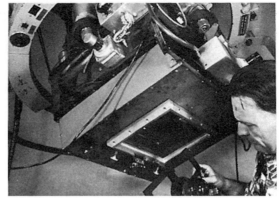

Figure 3-9. Bob Weitbrecht and his Lick Observatory camera.

Figure 3-9). The concept helped extend the useful life of telescopes in many of the world's observatories.[17] But rather than astronomy, it is Weitbrecht's and SRI's contribution to communications for the deaf that we wish to recount here.

Until the 1960s members of the deaf community had no means of interacting with each other or others except through face-to-face signing or lip reading or the use of third parties as interpreters. The ubiquitous telephone system, so useful to others, became a taunting symbol to the deaf. In some instances and at considerable cost, teletypewriters, often surplus equipment from the telephone companies, were connected to leased-direct (i.e., nonswitchable) lines to enable deaf people to link up for a "conversation." In 1964 a deaf orthodontist in Los Angeles, Dr. James C. Marsters, shipped a teletype to Weitbrecht and asked him to create a way to use such a machine over the normal switched telephone system. Resourceful person that he was, Weitbrecht saw that two such machines could link through a telephone if they could simply "whistle" their signals rather than using the hard-wired, direct current pulsing they were designed for. Devices that do such signaling are called modems, standing for the modulation-demodulation task they perform.

These teletypewriters used a five-level character code called Baudot, and so it was natural that Weitbrecht, using such machines, would design his audio signaling system to use those same five levels. SRI applied for a patent

for the new device in August 1966, and the patent was issued in two versions in 1970 and 1973. These modems were then made and sold by a small company Weitbrecht started, Applied Communications Corp., in Belmont, California. Using Weitbrecht's modem along with the widely available free teletypes, a deaf person could be in communication for about $300. These connections were then as easily made as any other telephone call. Eventually, Weitbrecht left SRI to devote himself full time to providing this important service through his company. Also, to expand the availability of teletypes, a national organization, Teletypewriters for the Deaf, Inc., now Telecommunications for the Deaf, was formed in the Washington D.C. area. As many as 40,000–50,000 of these machines were in use in the deaf community by the 1980s, and the teletype museum indicates that up to 1 million may be in use today.[18]

But other technologies were being developed in the computer access world that would one day become inimical to the Weitbrecht modem. Ironically, some of the strongest evidence of that conflict would become apparent within SRI as staff members tried to adapt computer-related devices to deaf communications. In the 1960s Bell Laboratories was developing its own modem to help meet the increasing need for access to new time-shared computers using what were essentially modern electronic versions of teletypewriters. The new signaling standard for this modem, however, adopted the eight-level ASCII character set, rather than the five-level code, and used full-duplex rather than half-duplex

---

[17] The camera was installed on Lick Observatory's 75-year-old, 36-inch refractory telescope in 1961. There it would be used for very long exposures on very faint stars as dim as 19th magnitude that would not have been possible before. The SRI camera was also being designed into a new 60-inch Navy telescope in Arizona.

[18] This information was first accessed on www.deafexpo.org/tty_museum.htm on July 29, 1998. The TTY Museum is now owned and operated by CSD, a nonprofit deaf organization (see www.c-s-d.org).

Figure 3-10. Functional demonstration models of small, portable terminals for the deaf (1980).

signaling; that is, both ends could be sending and receiving at the same time. This major new standard, eventually called the Bell 103 standard, was issued in 1967, and it was, of course, incompatible with the Baudot convention.

Another staff member, John Crandall, who joined the SRI Communications Laboratory after Weitbrecht's departure, had a deaf child and, with his wife, cared for other deaf children. Crandall's views on the need for communications among the deaf were welcomed by some other Laboratory staff members who were trying to design and build a portable, handheld digital radio-terminal combination for remote and wireless access to computers (hosts) on the ARPANET. A number of Lab people[19] began to consider the notion of a very small, equivalent teletype, but one that would "speak" both the new Bell 103 standard and the Weitbrecht convention. Their strategy was clear: make a highly portable device that would double as a computer access terminal *and* as a teletype-compatible communications device. They believed the new device would lead the members of the deaf community into the developing, commodity world of inexpensive computer terminals, familiarize them with the emerging uses of computers, including email, and, it was hoped, introduce them as well to the emerging job markets in the computing industry.

The Communications Laboratory staff members knew they could build a small, portable terminal for the deaf, and to help

demonstrate that opportunity, the Lab Director, Donald Nielson, had a mockup built. After about 2 years of using the mockup and putting the idea forward, SRI won a contract from the Department of Health, Education, and Welfare's (HEW) Office of Education in 1977 to build several demonstration models.[X] The results are shown in Figure 3-10.[20]

These devices helped illustrate to both the deaf community and the government agencies that served them the need for portable and compatible communications terminals. Ultimately, two SRI staff members, Nielson and Ken Harrenstien, testified before the California State Public Utilities Commission (PUC) about the need for such terminals to use both the new Bell standard *and* the Baudot convention. This exposure helped lead to the subsidization of terminals for the deaf through a small state tax on telephone usage. Unfortunately, the affirmation of the SRI recommendation by the PUC meant that Weitbrecht's company, which restricted its products to the five-level standard, would ultimately face a weaker market.[21]

---

[19] These included, in the beginning, Stan Fralick and Donald Nielson. The later, more fully developed designs and implementations shown in Figure 2, were created by Dave Fylstra, Bill Ross, Roy Stehle, Russ Wolfram, and Jim Gaddic.

[20] In light of present-day communications technology, perhaps the most striking aspect of these innovative terminals was that they were acoustically or inductively coupled to the telephone. Today they would have modular jacks and would plug into any telephone outlet. It was not until 1968 that the Federal Communications Commission (FCC) issued what was called the "Carterphone decision," which for the first time sanctioned the direct electrical (rather than acoustic) connection of communications device to the phone line. Because such direct connection by consumers had been prohibited by the telephone companies, when these terminals were developed there was no electrical or signaling standard.

[21] To the credit of Weitbrecht and those backing his company, now Weitbrecht Communications, Inc., it is still a successful company over 20 years later. After Weitbrecht's death, the company moved from Belmont to Santa Monica, California (www.weitbrechtcom.com). But the new digital

Once a highly portable terminal had been built, the next step was to introduce the deaf to the benefits of email that had been evident on the ARPANET since the early 1970s. Therefore, in 1977 SRI began developing the concept for an email and conferencing demonstration system called Deafnet. Deafnet started as an attempt by HEW to make the deaf population aware of the advantages of email. Ultimately, its goal would expand to introducing pilot email systems to be operated by deaf organizations and individuals themselves.[Y] Funded in 1978, the SRI project first built a demonstration system that was installed at Gallaudet University in Washington D.C., the nation's university for the deaf. The email system offered service to both ASCII and Baudot terminals, as well as direct conferencing for up to four clients or end terminals. Handling both types of modems was made possible by the clever engineering of SRI's Russ Wolfram, who designed an "intelligent" modem that automatically determined the type of signal being received at the server. The email software was a modified version of that in use on the DoD's ARPANET.[Z]

The number of users at Gallaudet and in surrounding Washington D.C. amounted to about 250 enthusiastic clients. Given that small user base and the operating cost of computers of that day, the service, without subsidy, began to look too expensive. Again, taking advantage of the emerging ARPANET, the network and email coverage was expanded to include mail hosts at Boston and SRI as early as September 1979. Later in the project, smaller, more affordable computer systems were designed that would better fit the budgets of the deaf community. To control costs and to obtain a broad support network for the email servers, a RadioShack TRS-80 computer, shown in Figure 3-11, was selected as the server. A lot of work went into porting the Deafnet program to this smaller machine. Though it worked, a nationwide email and conferencing system was still predicted to cost each user between $50 and $75 per month for moderate usage, and amount considered still too expensive. A larger population was needed to share the capital and operating costs, and there was simply no way to make that available at the time.

To ensure success of the email service in the deaf community, those involved in the project considered it essential for the businesses to be owned and operated by deaf people. The government primed each service by providing the equipment and paying SRI and other organizations to train staff members and help keep the service running for a while. Those who volunteered to start and operate the service were for the most part enthusiastic and were truly pioneers in this fledgling email technology.

SRI, under HEW sponsorship, assembled systems for 9 of an initial 20 metropolitan areas around the country in a so-called dissemination phase of Deafnet. As it turned out, the demonstration project was successful, but the dissemination project was not—only Minneapolis-St. Paul was still in operation a year later. Several factors contributed to the lack of great success in the dissemination phase: the requirement by the federal government that the

---

communications and computer technologies are also

Figure 3-11. TRS-80, the email computer server chosen for dissemination to metropolitan areas.

system become self-supporting before there was a sufficient user base; the high variability and poor reliability of the old teletypewriters as computer peripherals; the requirement for continuous 24-hour service; some high marginal operating costs; and the surprisingly unenthusiastic adoption of the service by the deaf community at many sites. Many deaf people were just not ready to accept the new technology. Beyond technical aversion, many individuals in the deaf community at the time did not see the need for a large email community when the number of people they interacted with was, intrinsically, quite limited. The intelligent modem that could communicate in either Baudot or ASCII was technically successful but less commercially successful than it might have been, largely because of the displacement of the need for it by the rapid acceleration of personal computing and the ASCII code.

To this point, around 1980, all the initiatives in SRI's work for the deaf community had come from the technical or engineering side of SRI. During the dissemination phase of Deafnet, an SRI staff member from the social

---

SRI'S ROLE IN THE DEVELOPMENT OF ACOUSTIC MODEMS

SRI and its staff made at least three contributions to the development of the telephone-based modulation/demodulation devices called modems. Out of a desire to serve the needs of the deaf community or to support the impending revolution in computer access, three SRI staff members designed, built, and demonstrated modems for which SRI received patents or were involved in new ventures to produce them. Bob Weitbrecht, the deaf engineer mentioned in this section, was probably the first person to conceive of an acoustic modem, and SRI filed his patent in August 1966. Only 6 months later, with almost no interaction with Weitbrecht, SRI's John Van Geen also filed a patent for a Teletype Communication System. Both patents were first issued in 1970.

Van Geen's modem design bore little resemblance to Weitbrecht's. Born of the frustration of costly nation-spanning TWX lines, Van Geen's patent centered on dialup connections and the emerging Bell 103, 300-baud standard for computer access. Modems had existed for a few years, but all were housed within a terminal, which was permanently wired to a set of phone lines. To link to a remote computer required the purchase of a "permanent" telephone connection. More important, at that time it was illegal for anyone but the telephone companies to directly connect anything to their lines. These constraints were severe. Long lead times and high costs set difficult thresholds of use. Van Geen saw the advantages of being able to use any phone and take advantage of the switching system to connect from any phone to, in this case, one of the first timesharing hosts at Dartmouth University. His patented design enabled error-free connections over very long distances (as much as 6,000 miles), well beyond the capabilities of existing modems. To explain how this design and its contribution found fulfillment, a third person must be introduced.

In June 1958 J. Reid Anderson came to SRI from Bell Laboratories to work mainly in the area of magnetic materials. After about 5 years at SRI, seeking relief for his entrepreneurial itch, Anderson started a company called Scientific Products, Inc. One of his first products was an electronic metronome. After a time, and quite incidentally, he met John Van Geen and learned about his modem. Seeing the opportunity, Anderson, with an accountant named Ray Jacobson, formed Anderson-Jacobson in January 1967. The new company's mission, approved by SRI, was to build acoustically coupled modems following Van Geen's design. Van Geen received shares of Anderson-Jacobson stock, and he and SRI received 1% and 3% royalties, respectively, on all their modem sales. Note that this happened long before SRI formally encouraged such arrangements.

During the late 1960s, pressure was mounting to remove the restrictions on the direct connection of "foreign" equipment to the phone lines. In 1968 the FCC permitted the first such connections, although only through a telephone company interface. Since Anderson-Jacobson modems could be acoustically coupled, they were not subject to the restrictions, and they would come to lead the modem industry. Modems, directly connectable after 1977, would become the universal umbilical cord that tied computers to their networks. For some years Van Geen consulted for Anderson-Jacobson, and he was designing a 1200-baud FSK modem and a 2400-baud PSK modem when Anderson and Jacobson had a falling out.

Anderson then left the company along with most of its technical talent. Van Geen departed as well. Anderson later founded Verbatim to manufacture computer diskettes. Anderson-Jacobson was sold in 1988 to CXR Telecom of Fremont, California, and its modem products were incorporated into the offering of the acquiring company.

sciences, Teresa Middleton, whose daughter was deaf, became its project leader. The later stages of the handheld terminal development effort and the majority of the Deafnet projects benefited enormously from the talents of yet another deaf SRI staff member, accomplished computer programmer, Ken Harrenstien, who had been hired by Elizabeth Feinler as a member of the ARPANET's NIC. His technical talents gave him great insight into the terminal project, and because of his particular expertise in the major timesharing software systems of the day[22], Harrenstien became the lead technical person on the design of the Deafnet email system.[23]

It was clear that the deaf community couldn't receive the benefits of a handheld terminal unless some company would accept it as a product. Toward that end SRI ultimately gave demonstrations to about 10 potential commercial manufacturers, hoping to interest them in manufacturing a small, portable terminal resembling the one SRI had built. Although a couple of companies proceeded with their own devices, including Plantronics, none chose to license SRI's technology. The market size was not impressive until the California PUC mandated a price subsidy, which led a few manufacturers to venture into the field. But clearly the general market for small terminals would eventually prosper, particularly with the advent of small microprocessors. Indicative of the era of the SRI models, every LCD character on one of our models cost $40, so 16 characters seemed quite enough. A number of portable terminals for the deaf were developed after the SRI device had been publicized, one of which is shown in Figure 3-12.

Clearly, the largest impact of these projects was raising awareness within the deaf community of the emergence of new technologies from which they would benefit. Even today email is fulfilling only a fraction of its potential, so imagine the difficulty in accepting it in the 1970s. SRI and HEW clearly had an impact. In the earliest days, when the SRI Communications Laboratory director was

Figure 3-12. An early portable terminal built commercially for the deaf community.

just beginning to seek funds for the development of the portable terminal and carrying a mockup to help convey the concepts, the President of the National Association of the Deaf literally embraced Nielson when he saw the communications and mobility that such a device offered deaf people.

Finally, apart from the deaf community, there is the matter of modems and their impact on the world. Because the world's telephone systems are ubiquitous, they became the natural points of departure for the digital highways of the future. By enabling the network connection of computer terminals and their hosts to existing networks, modems accelerated the explosion of computer networking. Today, modems are a necessary part of all computers with network access. The box on page 3-20 and Figure 3-13 recount the important modem developments at SRI.

Helping the Blind to Read— The OPTACON

The Optacon is a device that permits the blind to read arbitrary text. It does so by translating the image of textual characters into magnified tactile images conveyed through a set of vibrating reeds felt with one's fingers. As depicted in Figure 3-14, the user moves a wand, containing a light source and a set of optical sensors, across a printed page. This movement by one hand generates a flow of enlarged characters across the index finger of the other hand. Blind people can be trained to "read" such a character stream at speeds as great as 60 words per minute. "Optacon" is an acronym for optical-to-tactile converter, and the first Optacon was designed and built at SRI and Stanford University in the late 1960s.

---

[22] A measure of Harrenstein's talent came when, in the 1981 conversion of the ARPANET's communications protocols (from NCP to TCP), MIT couldn't get their large timeshare hosts working. Harrenstien was called back to Cambridge and had them up and running in a few days.

[23] Other major contributors to Deafnet were Earl Craighill, Hal Huntley, Dan Allan, Raphael Rom, and, of course, the dissemination project leader, Teresa Middleton.

Figure 3-13. The Anderson-Jacobson acoustically coupled modem (upper left) and Reid Anderson (right) and John Van Geen (below) using it (about 1967).

The idea came to Dr. John Linvill, a professor at Stanford, in 1962 when he was traveling with his family in Germany. He had visited an IBM research center near Stuttgart and had seen a high-speed printer in which carbon traces were accelerated against the rapidly moving paper by a line of vibrating pins. His perspective on this new printing method was influenced substantially by its implications for his daughter, Candy, who had been blind since she was 2 years old. He wondered whether Candy could actually feel the impulses of the carbon ink against the paper. Could something be made that converted text into impulses, and could a blind person be trained to "read" them? If so, such a device would vastly increase the printed material accessible to the blind and improve their employability. More immediately, it

would clearly ease his wife Marjorie's burden of spending 4 hours each day preparing material in Braille for Candy, who attended a regular school. Linvill began mulling over the possibilities and filling up notebooks of ideas about vibrating pins.

Jim Bliss was enrolled in a Master's program at Stanford in 1956 and working at SRI. He graduated in 1958 and went to MIT to study circuit theory. Because of his advisor there, he soon became interested in devices that would aid the blind. As a thesis he explored whether our kinesthetic senses would support some reasonable level of communications. He had built a sort of reverse eight-key typewriter in which the keys vibrated in three dimensions in response to a symbol input. Bliss also met a blind person, John Dupress, who would help him obtain funding when he graduated from MIT and returned to SRI. At SRI Bliss formed a small group doing research in tactile communication and vision. In 1961 he met John Linvill by chance at Stanford. Linvill started the conversation by asking, "Well, what are you up to?" Bliss answered, "Well, I'm making a gadget to teach reading to blind people. It's a Times Square display."[AA] Over the next 5 years, with SRI funding from the Department of Education (DoEd) and the National Aeronautics and Space Administration (NASA) and the Office of Naval Research (ONR) at Stanford, Bliss and Linvill developed the Optacon.

The Optacon had two custom integrated circuits, one for the 144-phototransistor light sensor and one for the vibrating reeds. The former was the first integrated circuit to be built in Stanford's new Integrated Circuits Lab. From Stanford also came the piezoelectric method of causing an array of tiny metal rods to vibrate in patterns that could carry information. At SRI Bliss and Hew Crane were developing a general-purpose, computer-controlled tactile matrix capable of transmitting static or dynamic tactile images to potentially any part of the body.[BB] The goal was to explore the best methods of

Figure 3-14. Candace Linvill using the Optacon to read a text (about 1968).

Bliss became the first president of Telesensory Systems and led its expansion into a variety of products for the sensory disabled. By 1991, Telesensory Systems had sales of $30 million, 200 employees, and a worldwide market. The original Optacon sold well for about 15 years, and then it was redesigned. By the end of 1996, when Telesensory announced its discontinuance of the Optacon, nearly 20,000 Optacons had been sold in over 30 countries. It helped people on all continents find better access to the workplace, the ultimate rehabilitation. Like in all important advances, the uses of the Optacon couldn't all be anticipated. Take the case of a blind author by the name of Deborah Kent Stein. Here is her account of getting an Optacon in summer 1977:

Without a doubt reading with the Optacon was slow. Through steady practice I built my speed to about 100 words per minute, compared with my Braille-reading speed of 250 words per minute or more. But reading speed was not the issue. What mattered was access, and the Optacon provided that. Books, newspapers, magazines, catalogues, bills, record jackets, and the recipes on boxes of cake mix—the barriers were down, and suddenly everything was within reach. For the first time friends lent me their favorite books, sent me clippings, and dared to share their private thoughts in typewritten letters.

'So what's the first thing that machine helped you do?' my aunt asked when I brought the Optacon home from Philadelphia. 'I cleaned out my purse,' I told her. It was true. I didn't plunge straight into the latest bestseller. I emptied my purse onto the couch and sorted through several weeks' accumulation of receipts, theater programs, ticket stubs, and random scraps. In the past I would have had to wait for the opportune moment with some patient friend or paid reader who could help me weed out the debris. Perhaps I might simply have taken the

tactile or electrical expression to determine the "channel capacity" of various dermal surfaces. This work was sponsored in part by NASA because of the difficulty in voice communications under the high noise of liftoff.

SRI was using computer-generated character streams to explore the question of how well a blind person could learn to read the flowing characters as they moved across the array of reeds. The 12-year-old girl in Figure 3-14 was able to read 5 words per minute after about 90 minutes and 20 words per minute after about 30 hours, where the rate leveled off. Those rates are slow compared to rates of reading Braille with its compressed characters, but the approach had the advantage of working over a wide range of symbols.

The first Optacon emerged from these efforts in 1966, and about 10 units in all were made in the SRI and Stanford laboratories. But then the DoEd requested 50 Optacons for a field trial, and neither SRI nor Stanford was prepared to produce them on that scale. They tried to interest local manufacturing companies but found no takers. Therefore, in 1970, Bliss joined Linvill and two others at Stanford to form Telesensory Systems, which built the 50 units at $5,000 each (see Figure 3-15).

Figure 3-15. A blind SRI programmer, Bob Stearns, using the Optacon (about 1974).

exceptionally large—all call forth the maddening message: 'Page too difficult, may be upside down!' Pages with more than one column may be read accurately, as long as the space between the columns isn't too narrow. Italicized words often turn into strings of 'unrecognized characters.' And anything handwritten, no matter how clearly, is totally out of bounds.

With the Optacon, on the other hand, the only limits are my time and patience. With a bit of both I can read virtually anything. Cursive handwriting is the only holdout; I can usually read handwriting if people print. I can also examine charts and tables and can puzzle out simple line drawings and maps. The underlying fact is that the scanner interprets what it perceives, often in its own idiosyncratic fashion. The Optacon shows me what is on the page and allows me to interpret for myself.

When I got the Optacon twenty years ago, I believed it would be available to blind people for as long as civilization endured. I never imagined that the company that created and marketed this extraordinary instrument would one day renounce it as obsolete. But by the mid 1980's TSI (the descendant of Telesensory) had moved on to other, more lucrative products. It promoted the Optacon, even the newest model, with waning enthusiasm. In 1996 came the dreaded proclamation. The Optacon would no longer be manufactured. Old machines will be serviced 'until the turn of the century,' unless the parts run out

matter into my own hands, dumping everything into the wastebasket and hoping I wasn't losing some crucial phone number or appointment slip. Now, with the Optacon, I could check each questionable paper and dispose of it as I saw fit, on my own time, without having to let anyone else glimpse the rat's nest my purse had become.

I have had a Kurzweil scanner since 1990. I no longer use the Optacon for reading full-length books as I often did in the past. But the scanner has never replaced the Optacon in any other regard. They are both tools for accessing print, but each has its own unique strengths and limitations. The scanner can read quickly through large blocks of standard print. It enables me to store material on diskette for future reference, thus building up a small library of books and articles. But the scanner has strong views on what standard print really is. Poor to moderately well-xeroxed copies, most newsprint, all faxes, print that is unusually small or sooner. The Optacon is an essential part of my life. In my work as a freelance writer I turn to it a hundred times in the course of the day—to check a page number for a footnote, to make sure the margins are correct on a printed page, to check whether my printer needs a fresh ribbon.

Beyond my working life the Optacon is just as important. I can browse through gift catalogues before Christmas and birthdays. I can sort the mail and read the pieces that are addressed to me. I can use the dictionary, the encyclopedia, and even the Yellow Pages. Without the Optacon I could not do any of these things independently. Each of these small but necessary tasks, plus dozens and dozens more, could be done only with another person's assistance.

The Optacon has given blind people a level of autonomy and flexibility unparalleled in history. Yet that gift is being withdrawn. That sense of freedom, that knowledge that print poses no barriers, may be lost to future generations. As a devoted Optacon user I belong to a minority within the blind community. We spend a lot of time worrying, raging, strategizing, and mourning. We stockpile used machines, buying them up at every opportunity. With renewed hope we pursue each rumor that another company will buy up parts, will service old machines, will build new ones. We tell each other that something has to be done. We try to carry that message to the world.[CC]

As time progressed and the general population aged, low or poor vision became a much more common problem than total blindness. Telesensory introduced products for people with poor vision, too. The Optacon itself also faced the relentless advance of technology in two ways: the introduction of automatic optical character recognition (OCR) hardware and the increased availability of online (as opposed to printed) information affected the market for the Optacon. Telesensory sold the rights to the Optacon in 1998 to another company with products for the blind, Blazie Engineering of Maryland. Bliss left Telesensory in 1994 and started another company, Sensory Technologies, which later became JBliss Imaging Systems. This company concentrates on bringing low-vision software to the personal computer.

Two other derivatives of this SRI effort are worth mentioning. In 1970 the SRI lab used the camera portion of the Optacon to capture and transmit a digitized image of printed characters over the phone to a remote computer that would convert the letters to words and speak them back over the phone to the blind reader. SRI also developed a two-finger version of the Optacon for HEW. Sometime later, in 1975, SRI's Jim Baer led an effort for NASA to design a wrist-worn pager or alarm device that would alert a deaf-blind person. Because of an internal government conflict, it was never released for commercialization.

And what of Candace Linvill (Figure 3-14), the person for whom the Optacon was invented? Today, she has a PhD in psychology from Stanford University and works in a hospital in Redwood City, California. She is proof of the potential of blind people, of the fulfillment that can come to those who work in their behalf, and of the promise of technology to help.

Postal Automation

Americans' appetite for mail has come a long way since 1639, when Richard Fairbanks' tavern in Boston was named the repository for overseas mail. For hundreds of years, up to the mid-1960s, mail was handled essentially the same way as in colonial days. But beginning in the 1950s and for at least the past 40 years, the U.S. postal system has been under continual siege by the voluminous and overwhelming demand for mail services. When the Post Office Department underwent reorganization in 1971 to emerge as the more independent U.S. Postal Service (USPS), it had reached a point of precarious inability to handle the nation's mail. Since then, and even with the family of new, private mail carriers to handle urgent mail and packages, pressure on the USPS has continued. This independent government agency now delivers about 200 billion pieces of mail a year, over 40% of all the world's mail.[DD] As one indicator of its size, in its effort to maintain steady delivery times under the onslaught, the USPS has become the dominant U.S. air cargo shipper, accounting for nearly 45% of all domestic shipments in 1998.[EE]

Meeting this challenge and trying to change a history of labor-intensive pricing clearly required automation. If the USPS has been able to meet its obligation, and it marginally has, its success has been due to an almost continuous commitment to automation, at least in the interior of its mail handling practices. The ends, the pickup and delivery parts, are still costly and historical vestiges that the USPS has seemed unwilling to touch.[24]

SRI has been an active technology developer and supplier to the USPS since the early 1980s, performing basic research, studies, and system design and prototype development. These efforts have drawn on and integrated a broad range of SRI technologies, including imaging, optical character recognition (OCR), artificial intelligence, computing and network architectures, electromechanical control, and design for ease of manufacture. This section describes a few SRI technologies that have given the Postal Service more efficient, cost-effective, and novel postal and intelligent materials-handling services.

The Automatic Machine Reading of Zip Codes

The zip code was clearly an attempt on the part of the USPS to speed the sorting and handling of all types of mail. But unless that code was amenable to repeated automatic machine reading along its journey, its impact would be modest. In the early 1970s the Postal Service (the Post Office until 1971) issued a request for proposals for a high-speed, non-contact method to imprint on letters some form of machine-readable address. Since the zip code was normally written on the envelope by hand or machine, that first machine reading of such varied text was anything but reliable, particularly after it suffered the vagaries of mail handling. The USPS sought a way to read a zip code once, then encode the destination address in binary form and print it onto each letter. At SRI Fred Kamphoefner's Engineering Sciences Laboratory had been working on nonimpact

---

[24] It was about 1975–76 and the Post Office was drowning in red ink. Postmaster Benjamin Bailar was asking for another postage increase. As a researcher in information technology, I saw a way for the Post Office to become more capital intensive rather than labor intensive; to attack the most expensive part of mail handling. The notion was to place printing terminals in homes and offices that could act as sources and receptors of mail. The reality was that transaction mail (bills, etc.) was the only profitable segment of mail and the most displaceable; that is, the most eligible for a complete bypass of the postal system. I pointed this out to the director of Strategic Planning for the Post Office. A combination of an inexpensive ($50) printing phone and the cooperation of the phone companies to deliver (with verification) transaction mail to these terminals at night was either a threat or perhaps an opportunity if the Post Office wanted to go into that business. He dismissed me with the conjecture that I didn't understand letter carrier unions. Their then current notion was to open envelopes, scan their contents, electronically transmit them to a destination post office, print and re-envelope them, and in doing so ignore 84% of the cost of handling mail, which, of course, lies at the ends of the process.

printing methods since the mid-1960s,[25] so it submitted a bid for this work and won the contract.

SRI's ink jet technology had been used to imprint machine-readable bar codes on a variety of objects, including the backs of checks and credit card sales slips. Once the readable code was imprinted, it enabled the rapid automatic sorting of such transactions and, for both checks and credit slips, became widely used. In each case it was necessary at the first handling to lift the relevant information from the check or sales slip, either by hand or by OCR. For the USPS, this meant reading the zip code. Within a short time and using its ink jet printing technology, SRI delivered an experimental system that was successfully demonstrated at the USPS engineering facility in Washington D.C. The Postal Service, convinced of the utility of this approach to automatic handling, awarded a contract to A.B. Dick to build and install printers across the postal system. As it turned out, A.B. Dick had been developing a production version of the same SRI ink jet technique, which it had asked SRI to review in mid-1972. Although it would then not be involved in USPS hardware for some time, SRI continued to develop inks for such printers for both the Postal Service and A.B. Dick. The ink jet-barcode process is still in use on mail today.

As an aside, after the USPS contract ended, SRI tried to convince several major mailers of magazines to print the address directly on the cover itself, not on a label that had to be attached. This approach would have displaced another SRI printing technology, the high-speed, label-printing Videograph, (see Chapter 7). As it turned out, no one was interested at the time, although the practice is common today.

Address Processing and Recognition Technology

The total automation of mail handling begins with the absolutely essential task of finding and

Figure 3-16. The RCP and its designers: Greg Myers, Talia Shaham, and Wayne Cruz.

reading the address of the intended recipient. Over the years SRI has developed methods for the location and interpretation of addresses and bar codes on letters, flats (flat mail pieces larger than letters), and parcels. SRI postal address reading technologies include the novel use of gray-scale image processing and contextual constraints in the OCR process to successfully locate and read mail-piece addresses in spite of poor-quality printing, extraneous advertising, and background interference. SRI's research efforts have resulted in real-time systems that locate the address block and recognize its words. These recognition modules are part of the USPS Recognition Coprocessor (RCP), a system that was deployed nationwide in 1997 (see Figure 3-16). The system, which is implemented as a networked array of Pentium-class computers and processors, processes letter mail at up to 15 mail pieces per second and when first deployed demonstrated a 7% to 12% improvement in the correct interpretation of addresses. Each percentage point improvement in the processing rate leads to annual savings of $9.5 million per year by the USPS. SRI's contribution directly accounts for about one-

[25] See discussion of SRI's relevant contributions to high-speed printing in Chapter 7.

half of those savings or approximately $50 million per year.

The RCP system augments the processing of existing mail sorting equipment by first identifying the location of the destination address and separating the address into lines of text, words, and characters. These characters are then "read" by OCR software and compared against directories of valid postal addresses. The result of the comparison is a delivery point code (11 digits consisting of the ZIP+4 code and 2 digits identifying the specific delivery point), which, just as in the case of zip codes described above, is sprayed onto the mail piece as a bar code. A closer look at the components of the RCP will clarify how it works.

Figure 3-17. A challenging address to identify.

To process a scanned image of a mail piece, an automated system must first locate the destination address and then perform OCR, using existing address directories to interpret the recognized characters as an address. SRI's methods for address block location (ABL) automatically find the destination address on the mail piece and segment it into individual lines of text. Algorithms can distinguish the address from background patterns and lines preprinted on forms and labels, extraneous advertising, and speckle noise. The ABL technology was implemented as an all-software module in the USPS RCP for letter mail; it has also been implemented in a combination of digital hardware and software for processing images of flat mail. The module has been tested and tuned at the USPS facilities for the last 7 years. SRI has also added the ability to distinguish machine-printed from hand-printed and script addresses, information that can be used to automatically select the appropriate OCR module for each individual mail piece. Figure 3-17 provides an example of the challenges faced in address identification.

To help read the characters in the address, SRI has developed a novel binarization technique for extracting text from gray-scale images of scanned mail pieces or other documents. Conventional binarization methods may perform poorly if the background is non-uniform, or if the contrast between the

foreground and background is small or variable, or if noise is present in the image. SRI's technique, specifically designed to work with images of text, can accommodate local variations in intensity without picking up extraneous interference. In addition, it can detect printed characters with poor contrast. This technique has been implemented in software as well as in custom digital hardware that operates at 40 million pixels per second. Figure 3-18 shows the use of the SRI technique on address text printed on patterned backgrounds.

To gain high reliability in character and word recognition, the SRI technique uses contextual knowledge about addresses. This context-based OCR technique combines the characters recognized by the OCR engine into words that are part of an intelligible address, thus taking full advantage of the interword contextual constraints inherent in an address. This SRI approach is much more powerful than conventional recognition methods and has been implemented and deployed in the USPS RCP.

As an example of context-based "word" recognition, Figure 3-19 shows a poorly printed address line on top. Just below is the character hypothesis produced by the OCR subsystem. Subsequent arcane numbers reflect processing steps and the correct city-state-Zip combination is found at the bottom. It could not have been found so quickly and reliably by examining combinations of characters alone.

As pointed out earlier, mail is imprinted with zip addresses encoded as barcodes. SRI developed a Wide-Area Bar-Code Reader

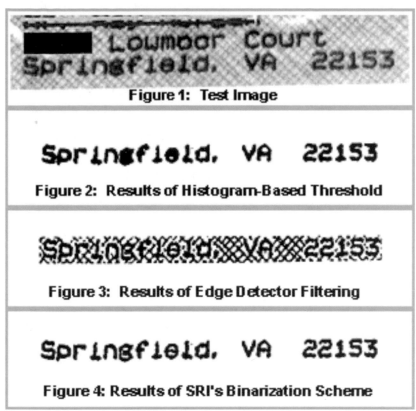

Figure 1: Test Image

Figure 2: Results of Histogram-Based Threshold

Figure 3: Results of Edge Detector Filtering

Figure 4: Results of SRI's Binarization Scheme

Figure 3-18. Results of SRI binarization technique for extracting text from patterned backgrounds.

techniques to locate and interpret the bar code. The system demonstrates an improved immunity to the presence of text and background interference; the gray-level processing also gives the system a high tolerance for poorly printed and skewed bar-code patterns.

The Processor Horserace

Throughout the development of computers, and perhaps even today, a race is under way whose outcome is starting to be clear, at least for a time. The race is between special-purpose hardware and software, designed that way to meet some real-time or complex computational need, and the relentless march in the capabilities of commodity processors such as the Pentium. The difficult and demanding tasks of the USPS

(WABCR) system for letter mail that reads the so-called POSTNET bar code (which contains Zip code information). Based on a charge-coupled linear-array scanner, the WABCR can locate the bar code anywhere on a letter mail piece. Thus, bulk mailers can print the bar code as part of the address block, which can be variously positioned on the envelope. Since the bar code pattern may also be printed over advertising and patterned backgrounds, extracting it with traditional processing methods, such as with fixed thresholds, is not reliable. To make such reading possible, SRI developed gray-level image processing

were witness to this race in countless ways. During the development of the RCP mentioned above, several design directions were pursued to meet the timing or difficulty demands of the automatic handling of mail. In the early 1980s the only way to automatically find and read an address was to employ a VAX minicomputer from DEC. Even then each piece took an incredible 20 minutes! That totally useless outcome might have been grounds for discontinuing the pursuit of automated mail handling unless you had faith in Moore's Law and thus believed that processing power would someday be adequate. After the VAX, several

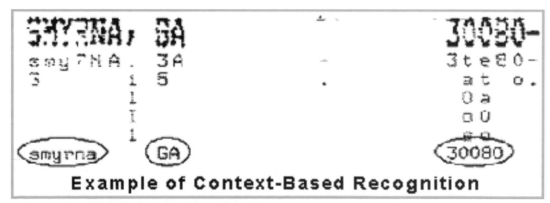

Example of Context-Based Recognition

Figure 3-19. An example of context-based address recognition.

A SORTER...SORT OF!

One of the sorting tasks in mail handling is to separate letters from so-called "flats," which are large, oversized, sometimes-stiff envelopes. SRI had been working on an automatic system for this type of sorting. The input was a continuous flow of vertically standing envelopes and flats of all sizes. To estimate the size of the piece first in line, a light source was placed to one side of the stream so that shadows from the individual pieces of mail were created. An image recognition system was built that was able to determine the size of the next piece to be sorted. To physically move the piece for sorting, a vacuum system attached to the end of a robotic arm was created. Its vacuum interface to the piece could be adjusted in area and vacuum power to match the size of each piece of mail. The entire process was controlled by a microprocessor. One Saturday, Greg Myers, one of the engineers on the project, was bringing some friends by SRI to show off the sorter. Without first checking the software state of the machine, he switched it on in what turned out to be a random state left from the last person who was modifying it. To his embarrassment and the glee of his visitors, the sorter proceeded to throw letters and flats all over the room. The invisible hand of software governs both success and failure.

special-purpose machines were built using the 6800 or 68000 microprocessors common at the time. In this case the struggle for adequacy has been won by the commodity processor. Today, in 800 USPS locations across the country, the RCPs are sorting 15 pieces of mail each second. The processor consists of 10 Pentiums running in parallel, all controlled by an eleventh. It is an enormously powerful and reliable system for which SRI designed and built the software and Northrup Corporation built the hardware shown in Figure 3-16.

Given the tremendous number of letters that are handled by the USPS every day, it seems aggressive, if not presumptuous, to say that an SRI address processing software recognizes and parses the address on every one of them. It just happens to be true.

Over at least a couple of decades SRI has undertaken a wide variety of tasks for the U.S. postal system. Almost all of them are difficult and the progress toward a successful outcome is not always linear. The box depicts a small, humorous example along the way.

Endnotes

[A] Peter H. Salus, *CASTING the NET—From ARPANET to INTERNET and Beyond*, Addison-Wesley, 1995.

[B] Janet Abbate, *Inventing the Internet*, MIT Press, 1999.

[C] Peter H. Salas, op. cit., page 25.

[D] E.B. Shapiro, *A Study of Computer Network Design Parameters*, Final Report to ARPA, SRI Project 7016, December 1968.

[E] Peter H. Salas, op. cit., page 28.

[F] Internet RFC 1000 and the ARPANET Completion Report.

[G] Janet Abbate, op. cit., page 74.

[H] William Duvall, personal communication, May 10, 1999.

[I] Douglas Engelbart, SRI Quarterly Progress Report 5 Covering the Period 8 August 1969 through 7 November 1969, SRI report to ARPA and Rome Air Development Center, November 26, 1969.

[J] Elmer Shapiro, personal communication, December 7, 1998.

[K] Richard Watson, "Notes on a Conversation with Bob Kahn on the ICCC," RFC 372, July 12, 1972.

[L] R.E. Kahn, Steven Gronemeyer, Jerry Burchfiel, and Ronald Kunzelman, Advances in Packet Radio Technology, Proc. IEEE, 66(11), 1468-1496, November 1978.

[M] Barry Leiner, Donald Nielson, and Fouad Tobagi, eds., Special Issue on Packet Radio

Networks, Proc. IEEE, 75(1) 1–176, January 1987.

[N] Janet Abbate, op. cit., page 127.

[O] Vinton G. Cerf, personal communication, January 15, 2002; additional comments by Cerf are available at www.wcom.com/about_the_computer/cerfs_up/qa/answers.phtml.

[P] Vinton G Cerf, and Robert E. Kahn, A Protocol for Packet Network Interconnection, IEEE Transactions on Communications, Comm-22 (5), 637-648, May 1974.

[Q] Jon Postel, Larry Garlick, and Raphael Rom, *Transmission Control Protocol Specification*, SRI report to the Defense Communications Agency, July 15, 1976.

[R] Ronald C..Kunzelman, Michael A. Placko, and Russell T. Wolfram, *Progress Report on Packet Radio Experimental Network*, SRI Quarterly Technical Report 5 to DARPA, September 1977. This report also documented multiple PRNET terminals communicating simultaneously with multiple APRANET hosts.

[S] R.C. Kunzelman, V.D. Cone, K.S. Klemba, J.E. Mathis, J.L. McClurg, and D.L. Nielson, *Progress Report on Packet Radio Experimental Network*, Quarterly Technical Report 10 to DARPA covering the period from November 1977 through January 1978, February 1978.

[T] Don Nielson, "The SRI Van and Computer Internetworking," *CORE*, a publication of the Computer History Museum, February 2002.

[U] Bill Croft, personal communication, December 12, 1999. Bill Joy led the installation of TCP/IP in UNIX (v4.2 and v4.3) while still at the University of California, Berkeley. Croft eventually left SRI to work for Joy one of the founders of SUN Microsystems.

[V] Kelli Abe Trifonovitch, Plans for a Wireless Waikiki Could Put Hawaii on the Technology Map, *Hawaii Business Magazine*, December 2, 2002.

[W] A. Poggio, J.J. Garcia-Luna Aceves, E.J. Craighill, D. Moran, L. Aguilar, D. Worthington, and J. Hight, CCWS: A Computer-Based, Multimedia Information System, IEEE Computer Magazine, 18(10), 92-103, October 1985. (The first two authors were guest editors of this special issue on multimedia communications.)

[X] David J. Fylstra and William C. Ross, *A Communication Device for the Deaf or Mute Person*, Final Report on SRI Project 6964 with the Dept. of Education's Office of Special Education and Rehabilitation Services, August 1980.

[Y] Dan Allan, Earl Craighill, Shuel Oreu, Charles Jackson, Susan Russell, Harold Huntley, and Jane Wilson, *A Nationwide Communications System for the Hearing Impaired – Strategies Toward Commercial Implementation*, Final Report to the National Telecommunications and Information Administration, October 1981.

[Z] Kenneth Harrenstein, Earl Craighill, David Fylstra, Harold Huntley, William Ross, and Susan Russell, *Deafnet: A Distributed Communications Service for the Deaf*, Final Report on SRI Project 7883 to the Dept. of Education, May 1982.

[AA] *San Jose Mercury News*, August 14, 1988.

[BB] James C. Bliss and Hewitt D. Crane, Touch As a Means of Communications, *SRI Journal*, Feature Issue No. 5 on Human Senses and Systems, 2-15, January 1969. This article reflects how extensively Bliss and Crane had been looking at the various means for tactile sensing and control.

[CC] The web site of the National Federation of the Blind: http://www.nfb.org/bm/bm98/bm980506.htm.

[DD] According to Hoover's Online business information source (www.hovers.com).

[EE] Colography Group, an Atlanta-based research firm that specializes in the airfreight and air-express business, (www.colography.com).

transitions and small enough that just two levels of management are needed and that a single area of interest can be pursued. In the discussion that follows, we relate how a group of this size has made its impressive way in the helter-skelter world of contract research.

How AI Began at SRI— Learning Machines

The possible utility of this nontraditional engineering approach to problem solving came to Charlie Rosen around 1959 when he was head of SRI's Applied Physics Laboratory. For an early electron-beam machining technique, SRI had conceived of an approach to manufacturing electronic circuits by using huge arrays of field-emission triodes.[1] Because each triode was about a micron (10^{-6} m) in size and because there were thousands of them, it became clear that, given the fabrication methods of the day, not all of the triodes would work. Given the high numbers of these emitters, was there a way to make them self-organize to work around the imperfect ones that were sure to occur?

A staff member from Cornell Aeronautical Research, Frank Rosenblatt, a psychologist by training, visited SRI about that time and described to Rosen and Ted Brain the principles of a new concept he called *perceptrons*. These were elementary "learning machines" whose architecture and logic units grossly imitated the brain's neurons and their functions. He claimed that his perceptron systems could learn, by being presented with many samples over and over again, to recognize many different patterns automatically; the system's internal connections were thus being adapted or trained until the system "learned" to identify each pattern. Perceptrons (and, at Stanford, Bernard Widrow's analogous Madeline systems) were pioneering systems that formed the basis of an important class of "intelligent" machines that came to be called *neural networks*. Rosenblatt visited SRI seeking help in developing inexpensive logical elements (threshold logic units) needed for the proposed construction of a large perceptron. It was conjectured that, to do anything worthwhile, a very large parallel-operating machine would be necessary. (At that time, digital computers with the power and speed required to simulate such a large system were not available.)

These new ideas were immensely stimulating. Supported by Division head Jerre Noe, Rosen and Brain began promoting this project and within months had secured initial funding from the Office of Naval Research (ONR). Active staff recruiting ensued, resulting in one of the first groups anywhere working in AI. The group included Nils Nilsson, Dick Duda, John Munson, George Forsen, David Hall, and Dick Singleton—some of whom went on to become well-known in this field. Soon, with additional funding from the U.S. Army Signal Corps, the U.S. Air Force, the U.S. Navy, and others, SRI became the largest research group in the world working on perceptron-like systems. A highlight of this research was the delivery to the Signal Corps in the mid-1960s of a system called MINOS II,[2] a large self-contained learning machine developed and built at SRI (see Figure 4-1). The logic units, which were based on ferrite multi-aperture cores, invented by SRI's Hew Crane, served as variable analog weights that effectively changed the connectivity between logic units during training.

MINOS II also included a novel optical preprocessor, consisting of 1024 lenses that could replicate as many optical images from a TV screen or projector. The 1024 images were then sampled in parallel using masks to extract one important feature from each image. These features were then combined into 100 elements that delivered a state of +1, -1, or 0 depending on whether the signal exceeded a threshold or not. The preprocessor output, then, made up the input to the trainable part of the perceptron system. That part of the system used a matrix of 6600 magnetic weights to identify objects about which it had been trained.

These early "learning machines" were essentially used as pattern-recognition systems. They were applied to the recognition of military targets shown, for example, in aerial photographs, and to the classification and recognition of the salient features in time-varying signals such as radar, sonar, spoken words and phrases, hand-printed isolated characters, faces, and the like.

---

[1] This is the same technology of field-emitting devices described in Chapter 7.

[2] In this particular setting we have chosen not to define the acronyms associated with individual software/hardware systems. They are simply too numerous and in many cases would be meaningful only to those in the AI community.

Figure 4-1. MINOS II preprocessor and Ted Brain (circa 1964).

in November 1968. Papers describing its capabilities in context-based, hand-written code recognition and other areas were published.[3] However, perceptron-like work took a backseat to emerging digital processors, and sponsorship simply dried up. Nonetheless, continuity for an operating group such as the AIC is essential, and a contract research lab demands no small amount of anticipation of such changes in funding.

The funding for learning machine research began to slow drastically in the late 1960s, partially because influential MIT researchers claimed they could prove that these neural nets were "a blind alley," and that mainstream AI work should be based on digital computing. More recently, their "proof" has been shown to be valid only for the earliest of the perceptron architectures, and neural net research has regained some interest. At that time, however, SRI researchers and others in the field were unable to overcome an important barrier to progress for such machines: the need to automatically and adaptively train the elaborate architectures needed for more complex tasks, particularly those with more than two layers of logic units.

During the development of the MINOS family of analog-based learning machines, a curious but meaningful transition occurred. To better predict what MINOS might do under a given set of teaching patterns, simulations of the analog system were written on emerging general-purpose digital computers. This was done in part because of the inordinate time it took to set up and operate the MINOS machines. But early on it was recognized that the simulation was running faster than the machine it was simulating. That was just one of the many indicators of the growing power of digital machines. The last of the MINOS series, MINOS III, thus became partly digital. The overall MINOS III package, consisting of an SDS 910 digital computer, the MINOS II analog learning machine, and the 1024-lens preprocessor, was delivered to the Signal Corps

Entering into Robotics

So, in the mid-1960s, Rosen and Nilsson initiated an in-depth, internal study at SRI to define a new AI program to replace the fading perceptron work. After 3 months, the concept of an intelligent mobile robot system was developed and formed the basis for a new SRI program. This "intelligent" machine, later named *Shakey*, was to serve as an R&D test-bed for key AI subsystems; namely, machine vision and scene analysis, natural language, theorem proving, planning and problem solving, and—because the machine was a mobile automaton—navigation and obstacle avoidance (see Figure 4-2). SRI promoted the program at the U.S. Department of Defense (DoD) for 18 months and finally succeeded in obtaining sponsorship from the Advanced Research Projects Agency (ARPA).

---

[3] John Munson, Richard Duda, and Peter Hart, "Experiments in the Recognition of Hand-Printed Text, Parts I and II," ACM Fall Joint Computer Conference, December 1968, San Francisco. The MINOS III system was "trained" to read handwritten FORTRAN code and, with the introduction of context-based reasoning, it did surprisingly well. *SRI Journal*, No. 19, March 1968, stated that when averaged over many writers, it could recognize about 85% percent of instructions correctly. If trained on a single writer, it had accuracy as high as 97%, even though the printing was untutored and constrained only by a standard code sheet.

Figure 4-2. Shakey the Robot and Charlie Rosen.

Shakey and its environment proved a fertile ground for new concepts in AI. It had obvious needs for things such as sensors and navigation approaches and for not-so-obvious elements that would give it a measure of autonomy. Sophisticated planning systems, capable of entertaining hierarchical goals (performing a mission expressed through hierarchical sets of subtasks and in the process not destroying itself) were also required.

The Center took a sophisticated approach to the capabilities needed by a wandering robot. For example, advanced problem solvers were built that employed some of the world's first automatic theorem provers. Fortuitously, these had been developed in 1963-64 using a new technology in logical systems brought to the AIC from Stanford by Cordell Green. The technology influenced the design of STRIPS, the SRI problem solver used in Shakey's navigational system, and in hierarchical

planning systems like NOAH[4] that were intended to help Shakey consider and successfully satisfy multiple goals. This work continued to evolve, becoming a logical basis for both reasoning problems and planning systems and with more than 25 professionals participating in the program for more than 10 years. Perhaps the most significant contribution from the Shakey era was a search algorithm that became the basis for the huge literature on optimal search, including present route finding systems such as MapQuest. All this helped establish SRI as a world-class center in AI research.

In the early 1970s, Rosen resigned as head of the AIC and turned over supervision to Bert Raphael, who was later followed by Peter Hart, Nils Nilsson (see Figure 4-3), Stan Rosenschein and Ray Perrault. Rosen wished to see some pragmatic results from AI and initiated a new SRI program aimed at transferring some of the technology learned in the Shakey work to industrial automation. He believed that recently introduced industrial robots could be greatly improved by incorporating sensors, computer controls, and new training methods, and that these machines could then act as "smart" material-handling systems and perform simple assembly tasks and inspection. After a year's promotional activity, a joint National Science Foundation and SRI Industrial Affiliates program was started to develop industrial robot systems that would increase productivity and quality in manufacturing. This program grew to include over 25 major industrial firms, including General Electric, Westinghouse, General Motors, Ford Motor Company, Unimate, 3M, Digital Equipment, Lockheed, and others. For a decade SRI's program in robotics was a model for cooperative research by government, universities, and industry. Furthermore, SRI's program was enormously influential as a source of technology in this field and as a convenient center where key people in industry could meet three to four times a year and share experiences to their mutual advantage. Many industrial research groups had their start by participating in these exchanges and by viewing the periodic laboratory demonstrations at SRI and at the various participating companies.

---

[4] NOAH was an early hierarchical planning system that derived from work on a Stanford thesis on robot problem solving that Earl Sacerdoti had done while at SRI. Unfortunately, NOAH was developed about the time ARPA was losing its interests in robotics.

Figure 4-3. AIC Director Nils Nilsson (right) and Daniel Sagalowicz.

one hand was equipped with a proximity sensor. As part of a robot for package handling, a two-sweep method for reading any-orientation bar code was developed by John Munson and patented by SRI, but SRI never pursued infringements on that patent. Later, package-handling machines led to the long series of mail-handling research projects pursued by the then separate Robotics and Mechanical Engineering Laboratories.

Another reason for adopting a more commercial bent in robots at SRI was that in the early 1970s ARPA, the prime sponsor of much of AIC's robotics work, went through one of its periodic "relevance" transitions; desiring more practical solutions from its programs, it discontinued robotics research. Consequently, it was time to redefine the Center's future. Searching out new technology and who can build it, understanding the changing intent of a range of sponsors, and relying a bit on serendipity are common approaches SRI research labs take to stay in business. The best research labs make sure that new, trial research areas not only have open and challenging vistas, but also lend themselves to solving important client problems. Only then will they obtain significant levels of funding.

Because much of the SRI work done in the early days was not patented but, in fact, widely reported, subsequent research around the country on unmanned vehicles still incorporates ideas and devices developed in the work on Shakey. In its November 20, 1970 issue, *Life Magazine* carried an article by Brad Darrach whose headline, "Meet Shakey, the first electronic person," provoked much teasing. The article in the July 1971 issue of *Fortune* was more circumspect, saying "The Stanford machine, a similar one at M.I.T., and the mobile robot Shakey...are actually all experiments in solving problems through the techniques of scene analysis."[5]

Rosen's group developed the vision system first used with Unimate industrial robots and developed several end-effectors or "hands" equipped with tactile, force, and torque sensors;

---

[5] Shakey now enjoys a permanent home at the Computer History Museum in Mountain View CA and was recently "elected" into the Carnegie Mellon University's Robot Hall of Fame.

Further Marketplace Adaptation—Moving Toward Language- and Knowledge-Based Systems

Thus, the resourceful AIC leadership and staff adapted by entering two new areas of work: one concerned the creation of programs that captured, then supplemented human knowledge; and the other sought to get machines to understand natural human language. These initiatives resulted in SRI's first participation in:

- The machine embodiment of knowledge or expert systems.
- Automatic speech recognition and understanding.
- Text-based natural language understanding.
- Understanding the content of photographic images.

The early to mid-1970s saw the blossoming of these new fields, rich with unknowns and research opportunity. The work on expert systems grew out of an AIC attempt to finesse ARPA's departure from robotic systems by shifting to the design of software that might ultimately control robots. Thus was born the notion of a computer-based consultant (CBC) that would serve as an "expert" on assembly or disassembly of electromechanical equipment. The CBC could be used either as a training aid or real-time helpmate for military personnel or in actually programming a robot. ARPA bought into the idea...at least for a while.

The AIC's work in natural language understanding grew out of a new program that had been initiated at DARPA in 1972 by a former AIC researcher, Cordell Green, then on active duty there. ("Defense" was added to ARPA in 1972 but its mission didn't change appreciably and the two terms are interchangeable here.) The program was called Speech Understanding Research (SUR). Don Walker led the SRI work, which attracted a host of outstanding people in language, including Barbara Grosz, Jane Robinson, Bill Paxton, Gary Hendrix, and later Ray Perrault. Though DARPA would terminate the speech program by 1976, it did continue work in areas such as natural-language interfaces with databases. The limits of natural language understanding continued to be extended with the arrival at AIC of Bob Moore and Doug Appelt with their notions of *reasoning* about knowledge.

Concurrent with these two new programs came another initiative from the Center's Marty Tenenbaum and Tom Garvey to help automate photographic analysis. They saw the job of photo interpretation as one ripe for automation and were anxious to apply new ideas in vision research. They began to do so in 1976, but the problems were sufficiently complicated that they are still being addressed today. DARPA was interested in this work and later created a long-term program in "image understanding," We return to this program later.

Expert Systems

DARPA did not renew the CBC project, and Government-sponsored robotics work at SRI was truly dead. But the leaning of CBC toward the encoding of human expertise and a new attempt at Stanford to create an expert system for advising on bacterial infections (MYCIN) led Peter Hart and Dick Duda to wonder about other applications. A secondary goal was to try to avoid the funding vacillations the Center had experienced with DARPA. This new area of knowledge-based systems produced one of the world's first examples of an expert system, with a system that provided consultation services on mineral deposits. Naturally, it was called PROSPECTOR. Using production rules and semantic networks from the natural language efforts, it was completed in 1977. PROSPECTOR represented a significant advance in the state of the art of expert systems because of the data structures used, the techniques for updating probabilities, and the extensive geological application models developed. The program housed information on more than 20 types of ore deposits. A similar number of experts were interviewed for approximately 50 hours each. One of the types of deposits was molybdenum and, using this segment of the program, a large extension to a previously sampled but unmined bed of molybdenum was predicted and found on Mt. Tolman in the state of Washington. Unfortunately, the bed lies under an area used for tailings from a smelting process and thus cannot be exploited economically. Major participants in PROSPECTOR were Hart, Duda, John Gaschnig, Rene Reboh, Nilsson, and Kurt Konolige.

Though not many complete software systems have emerged as purely expert systems, the evidence/rules concept they are based on has become an important tool of computer science and is embedded in many programs. One, a heavily used expert system that emerged in another applied AI group at SRI, was the Automated Air-Load Planning System

(AALPS).[6] From their extensive work with the

---

[6] AALPS was created in SRI's Information Telecommunications and Automation Division around 1984, and the prototype version was completed 2 years later. The project leader there was Debra Anderson.

Army's 82nd Airborne Corps at Ft. Bragg, North Carolina, SRI staff recognized the critical need for moving matériel rapidly. Using expert system techniques, SRI was able to capture in AALPS much of the knowledge the military air-lift loadmasters used to load air cargo, including correct weight distribution and order of egress. Because AALPS also contained the size and weight characteristics for all airborne matériel and cargo aircraft configurations, the program was able to compute loading plans in seconds to minutes, whereas previously used manual approaches required days or weeks. Manifests created using AALPS eventually were accepted by the Army and the Air Force Military Airlift Command. AALPS saw extensive use in the Gulf War and is still used throughout DoD.

Not all expert systems are as successful as AALPS in correctly modeling known criteria or events, however. Many situations can occur where the input information is incomplete, inexact, and uncertain. To cope with this uncertainty, a new reasoning method, developed by John Lowrance and Tom Garvey, was invented to deal with more realistic evidence that doesn't fit nicely into the framework of the rule-based algorithms on which all expert systems were then built. The pioneering method, which was called evidential reasoning, drew on the various representational forms of uncertainty.[7] These were embodied in a program called GISTER that has been used by many other SRI expert system applications as well.

Another outgrowth of the AIC's expert system work was a slightly different problem orientation called "procedural reasoning." This method of imparting supplemental expertise in problem solving addressed problems in which a strong set of procedures or sequences had to be followed, often in real time (e.g., to meet safety concerns). To tackle this type of problem, Mike Georgeff created the Procedural Reasoning System, which had a role in the Space Shuttle and the paper describing it was recently honored by the AAAI, two decades after it was published in 1987.

Natural Language Understanding

The other technical initiatives begun in the early 1970s were research into both natural language and image understanding, research that proved to be enduring at SRI. The natural language work was first vectored toward database query and how such systems could be more easily and quickly built. Part of the desired capability was enabling domain-independent transport; that is, the ability to move the processing engine from one subject area to another with a different associated vocabulary. First, Hendrix developed LIFER, a system for English access to databases based on semantic grammar. This was followed by Hendrix's, Sacerdoti's, and Daniel Sagalowicz's LADDER, an English interface to a distributed database, under which began the development of DIALOGIC, a large grammar of English implemented in an augmented context-free grammar framework. DIALOGIC then became the basis for TEAM, another English interface with databases that provided a new and easier approach to tailoring interfaces to new domains.[8] The Knowledge Learning and Using System (KLAUS) and Parsing and Translation system (PATR) were used for parsing and generating natural language based on constraints using a method called unification. Developed by Stuart Shieber, Fernando Pereira, and Lauri Karttunen, they were the predecessors of the Core Language System (built at SRI's Cambridge Centre in England), of Gemini, the Air Traffic Information System (ATIS), and of several other systems worldwide.

In 1983, the AIC's natural language program and SRI joined a research consortium dedicated to exploring the fundamentals of language and the information it and machines shared. Joining such outside consortia has not been common at SRI, but since the Institute had an excellent reputation in this small and growing community, the collaboration with other local campuses was natural. The consortium included SRI, Stanford University, and the Xerox Palo Alto Research Center; the new organization was called the Center for the Study of Language and Information (CSLI). Its seed funding came from the required passing of

---

[7] Although the distinction between representational forms or models of uncertainty may be open to debate, the ones handled were normal probabilities (often Bayesian), the Dempster-Shafer model, and fuzzy logic.

[8] The main authors of DIALOGIC and TEAM were Barbara Grosz, Jane Robinson, Jerry Hobbs, Bob Moore, Paul Martin, and Fernando Pereira (see Figure 4-3 from the *SRI Journal*, 2(6), August 1982).

Figure 4-4. Jane Robinson, Barbara Grosz, and Bob Moore of the Natural Language Program.

can then, for example, operate in a provably time-bounded way; an ability important in situations where it may endanger itself.

Another branch of natural language understanding work at SRI was text extraction, which searches normal newspapers, books, or compendia for information about a specific topic. In this case the opportunity was presented by DARPA in 1984 and the AIC was prepared to respond. The collegial approach that DARPA often took—that is, letting several different universities or research centers work collaboratively on different parts of a difficult problem— was modified in this case. The contracts in this program required a periodic "bake-off" or competitive demonstration of the performance of each contractor's systems. These were the so-called Message Understanding Conferences or MUCs. SRI participated in this program from its inception and created FASTUS, one of the most capable systems to date. FASTUS performs a semantic search through textual forms such as the *Wall Street Journal* and automatically completes a user-defined information template. Because of FASTUS's relevance to information search systems fostered by the Internet, SRI is now exploring the commercialization of the system.

In a related vein, the 1980s saw a return by DARPA to the problem of automatic speech recognition.[9] Computers were becoming increasingly capable of meeting the intrinsic real-time requirements of speech recognition, but it was also an opportunity to explore new algorithms. This second entry into speech would become more important to SRI and is discussed elsewhere (see Chapter 2). SRI's participation in this new program began in another laboratory, with the AIC participating because of its continuing interest in natural

funds to the public interest by the nonprofit to for-profit conversion of the System Development Corporation in 1968. The Center is located at Stanford, and with the three members contributing directly and sharing other, non-CSLI results, a serious research agenda began that continues over two decades later. The CSLI not only offered new opportunities for fundamental work but also attracted new talent to the AIC.

The AIC contributed important research to the CSLI areas of unification grammars and situated automata. Unification grammars are a type of formal specification of a language wherein grammatical units (words, phrases, sentences, etc.) are given complex formal descriptions such as sets of attribute-value pairs. They are called "unified" because they permit the representation of grammatical knowledge independent of the language-processing algorithm used. Situated automata do not constitute a natural language concept, but involve a method for defining the behavior of automated objects such as a robot. In situated automata, an agent is specified in declarative terms (e.g., performance norms or limits or protective conditions). This specification is then compiled to machine operations that exactly support the specification. The digital machine

---

[9] The first speech program at DARPA, SUR, had run its intended 5-year course by 1976 and had been terminated. This new program at DARPA was not a continuation of the earlier work.

language understanding. Not surprisingly, the structure and vocabulary of natural language systems can also play a potentially important part in speech recognition. For this reason, Gemini was built at SRI as a parsing and semantic interpretation system to supplement the already existing speech recognizer. In this way and others SRI has continued to advance the state of the art in natural language understanding for more than two decades.

SRI-DEVELOPED HUMAN-COMPUTER INTERACTION TOOLS	
Available Capability	**When**
Pointing devices, predominantly the mouse	From about 1965
Automatic handwriting recognition	From about 1978
Automatic speech recognition	From about 1990
Natural language understanding for text and speech	From about 1977

Human-Computer Interaction

But clearly not all convergences of technology pan out, even when they appear made to order to do so. In early 1988, another research opportunity seemed at hand and it stemmed in part from unique capabilities (see table) that SRI had already developed—a set of computer interaction tools. Given these capabilities, it seemed a propitious time to create an environment in which many of these advances in information technology could be integrated to build better and more complete approaches for humans' interactions with their computers. Computers were gaining so much power that a goodly part of their processing resources could be used to improve the ability of the machines to understand what their users were trying to do. Arguably, the dominant mode for future human-machine interaction is speech, and SRI had one of the best laboratories in the world for automatic speech recognition.

Accordingly, an informal computer dialog laboratory was formed to bring some of these modalities together and to explore experiments in machine interaction. While the lab never met its promise, a few things did emerge. A semiconductor fabrication process control system with natural language input, called Shoptalk, became one of the first systems to automatically determine context as part of its natural language component. Another outcome was a closer relationship between speech recognition and natural language understanding, then housed in two separate laboratories. From this foray into human-machine interaction came a simple but powerful notion, arrived at experimentally: if a computer user is seeking an object such as a piece of information and sees a means of securing it on-screen, the easiest thing for humans to do is to point to it, whereas if the means isn't displayed, the easiest thing to do is to ask for it. This simple finding explains the importance of speech in human-machine interaction, particularly if such interaction is to be natural for the human and not simply convenient for the machine.

Most humans are quite flexible in how they approach a task, particularly one with which they are not familiar. Part of that flexibility is the way we can easily adapt to different communications modalities. That trait, then, should be reflected in the design of human-computer interactions. To match machine capability with different human modalities, the notion of software agents was suggested. Nevertheless, although a useful construct for such a functional communications inventory, it didn't catch on in the field for another 4 years or so.

Software Systems Employing Agents

Given the multiple modalities involved in human-machine interaction, some of which are complex for a machine to recognize, a specialized piece of software was created to handle each mode. To convey that modularity and independence, each module was called an agent. An agent could represent almost any capability or functionality such as speech recognition, email, handwriting recognition, or natural language understanding. In 1993, the AIC's Adam Cheyer created what is known as an Open Agent Architecture (OAA), a framework within which different functional agents can collaboratively or competitively vie for completing a task. Figure 4-5 shows an early family of agents that supported a computer user. The facilitator is but another agent that knows agent capabilities and can adjudicate which agent gets assigned which task. That assignment is flexible, however, in that if the preferred agent is unavailable, another may be eligible and assigned. This approach represents one of the most flexible and sophisticated approaches to the use of software agents, and it has formed the basis for dozens of applications at SRI in which human-computer interaction are important. These applications have ranged from controlling and processing video streams, spoken-language interfaces with simulators, to the control of semiautonomous robots using speech and gestures.

Nor are these agents confined to operation within a single machine. In our increasingly connected world, agents in one location need to negotiate with those in another location to carry out users' requests. One example is the smart refrigerator that was built at SRI. The "fridge" was programmed to have a certain complement of food inside. For tracking purposes, the food items were bar-coded so that by noting their comings and goings, the fridge was aware of what it did and didn't have. The agent in charge of that accounting, then, was free to communicate with an agent in the family car to notify the occupant that

something was needed from the store. It was the agents, not the processors, that had a functional relationship that was intended to satisfy some high-level user need.

This flexible concept came to be used widely across SRI, both in the AIC and in other labs. As many as a dozen different programs with important human-machine interaction used OAA. Whether the term "agents" will survive in the evolution of software systems is open to question, but there is no doubt that the concept of a software entity, programmed to be aware of a context reflective of its owner's interests, will grow in some fashion under some rubric.

Image Understanding

One evolutionary line in the AIC's map of technology migration (shown toward the end of this chapter) is computer vision. Progress along that line requires a computer to be able to identify the objects that make up a given scene. "Image understanding" is the term used to define the ability of a machine not just to identify objects or conditions in two-dimensional (2D) or three-dimensional (3D) scenes, but even to deal with their roles, relationships, and activities. It means applying *a priori* and scene-derived knowledge to

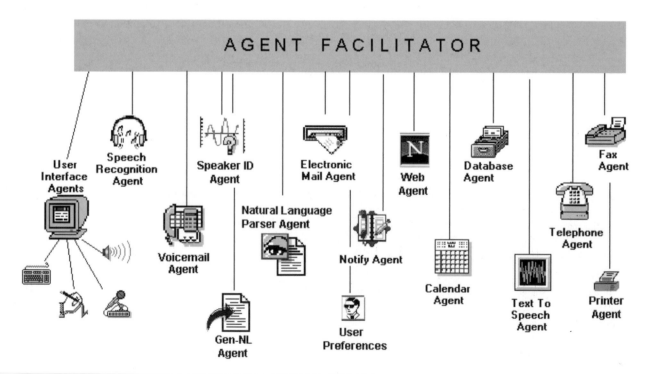

Figure 4-5. Organizational schematic of Open Agent Architecture.

automatically recognize objects of interest and what their presence implies. These are often very difficult tasks to perform and, like language, which humans take for granted, present enormous challenges to machines. A good example of image understanding is automatically finding and following a road in a photograph and then computing its exact location to update or upgrade a map; that is, making an approximate position on a map into an exact one. Automatically determining the location and dimensions of a building in a photograph is another. One of the earliest investigations into the field of image understanding was Garvey's Stanford Ph.D. thesis where he used the contextual relationships between objects to help identify and locate them. Other Center members involved early on were Marty Tenenbaum and Harry Barrow.

Somewhat akin to image understanding is the 3D construction of a scene from extracted information. The art of scene synthesis using a variety of available inputs such as digital maps, photographs, and objects extracted from photos or movies had begun in earnest at SRI by 1980. The chief architects of this work were Marty Fischler and Lynn Quam. The work began with programs that first employed the stereo pairs that were being derived from analog photographs and then the emerging digital terrain data sets. Programs were written that could form visual representations of terrain and its landmarks, and then view that scene from an arbitrary point. These were given names like IMAGECALC and TERRAINCALC, and they were photogrammically rigorous; that is, they derived all aspects of the computed scene from a precise knowledge of the location and perspective of the original source. After years of work and under the DoD-sponsored RADIUS program, Quam, Tom Strat, Aaron Heller, and others created one of the most sophisticated and accurate image manipulation programs anywhere. It is called 3DIUS.

Thus, over the 20 or so years of this program SRI has contributed:

- Methods for the top-down, goal-driven automatic exploitation of image content
- The generalized 3D derivation and representation of a scene from stereo pairs

- The extraction, modeling, and presentation of 3D objects within a scene using stereo algorithms, and a host of intrinsic characteristics such as shape, surface orientation, range or depth, and color or shading
- The construction of 3D topography from digital maps and photographs, with the ability to view the composite scene from any point
- Representation of natural scenes using fractals and a pliable, 3D, equation-based form called superquadrics
- Aids to autonomous navigation using image matching, plus scene analysis through the use of perspective changes due to lateral movement.

One of today's most sophisticated capabilities in this field is the ability to sense a 2D or 3D environment with enough precision for an autonomous vehicle to move safely within it. In 1987, the Center created a method that uses motion to discriminate the location of important objects. The processing has the arcane name of epipolar analysis. Other more conventional sensors such as those employing acoustics, laser rangefinders, and infrared detectors have also been used.

Another important product of image processing is that of visualization. With roots in the terrain representation programs discussed above comes a recently developed capability called TerraVision. TerraVision, created by Yvan LeClerc and others, is an interactive terrain visualization system that allows users to navigate, in real time, through a 3D graphical representation of a real landscape created from digital terrain elevation data and aerial images of that same landscape. The program is unusual in that it can deal with huge datasets (terabytes) that can be distributed over a wide-area network. From such a collection of sources, it can potentially produce a high-resolution model of the entire earth showing various types of imagery and cultural features. To enable TerraVision's wide use, it employs Virtual Reality Modeling Language (VRML) to store all of its terrain data, thus enabling users with a standard VRML plug-in to view TerraVision datasets over the Web.

Robots Revisited

Over the nearly two decades between the early days of Shakey and the mid-1980s, many advances were made that were relevant to mobile robotics. First, the power and affordability of computer workstations grew enormously, opening the way for a truly stand-alone and autonomous robot. Second was new software that addressed important needs such as real-time sensing, mapping, and, in particular, planning systems that enabled rapid decision-making. SRI was responsible for many of these advances, as mentioned above. The first, non-real-time planners emerged at SRI, including one of the first hierarchical and nonlinear planning systems. Folding in experience in rule-based and procedural expert systems like PRS, SRI developed a real-time, reactive planning system called SAPHIRA. Also, as mentioned, came innovations such as reasoning about uncertain knowledge or evidence. The Center has also done fundamental work in more esoteric concepts such as nonmonotonic (you-can-change-your-mind) reasoning, fuzzy logic, and reductions in the search space of certain theorem provers used in reasoning and planning. Then there is the flexible and resilient method of aggregating software modules already mentioned under OAA. All these helped lay the groundwork for the emergence of SRI's second-generation mobile robots.

In fact, several robots define the present state of mobile robotics at SRI. The most capable one was created first in the early to mid-1980s and became affectionately known as *Flakey*. Its name was a casual reflection to its being the sequel to the much earlier Shakey and, quite independent of its evolving reliability, the name stuck. In addition to its normal navigation sensors, Flakey has a number of human interface properties such as speech recognition and synthesis and stereovision (see the above box for an interesting account of their genesis). This suite of tools, assembled under OAA, lets it interact intelligently with its surroundings, including humans, and gives it perhaps the most comprehensive aggregation of features of any robot ever.

As mobile robots become increasingly sophisticated, robot competitions have been established to test both a robot's sensing and reasoning capabilities. Along with universities, some government labs, and a few commercial companies, SRI has entered a number of these friendly competitions. The first of these was the AI professional society's first Robot Exhibition and Competition held in San Jose, California in July 1992.[10] Here SRI's Flakey finished second to

---

[10] Sponsored by the American Association for Artificial Intelligence.

Figure 4-6. Some of SRI's more recent robot equipment (clockwise from upper left): Flakey, a vision module called "An Extra Pair of Eyes," Pioneer, and a gaggle of Centibots.

the University of Michigan's robot in a competition that consisted of navigating a cluttered environment, identifying objects in that environment, and following instructions to visit several sites in a specific order. Other competitions have been entered and some won. A 1996 event in particular revealed SRI's innovative spirit. The competition involved learning a complex space with many rooms of different purpose and performing a set of tasks, including reporting an appointment for a meeting to a "professor." All competitors used one robot, except SRI, which used two. The two diminutive Pioneers (see Figure 4-6(d)) were able to share the tasks, and won the competition, halving the completion time taken by the second-place robot. Obviously, the ability of the two robots to coordinate the tasks entailed both risk and, as it turned out, reward.

The latest notion in robot research in the AIC is teamwork. Figure 4-6(e) shows a working family of small mobile robots with two capabilities. One type has laser mapping tools, and the other, simpler ones move in the region the first robots have mapped to accomplish specific tasks collaboratively. The robots, which are called Centibots, perform a kind of surveillance and tasking role in otherwise hazardous environments. As of early 2004, the

SRI Centibots, 100 strong, have successfully mapped and performed tasks under a DARPA competition and in a building environment never seen before. Charles Ortiz and Regis Vincent have led this new effort.

Under more recent DARPA field tests, Curt Konolige, Bob Bowles, and their SRI colleagues have won competitions where their SRI robot found its way fastest through unmapped outdoor terrain.

Bioinformatics and a New Concept for Databases

Although AIC projects generally entail substantial derivative innovation, here is an example of how an absolutely new initiative can take wing. Born of necessity and of the creative talents of computer scientist Peter Karp, a different kind of database has been evolving over the past decade or so. As is often the case in fields touched by AI, ways have been found to build representational or symbolic forms that in effect encode human knowledge and make it more amenable to computer processing. Such representation can be applied to imprecisely known or evolving fields of work or, as we have seen earlier, even to language itself. To be successful, however, it is critical for the chosen representation to model the target system with high fidelity and also be able to be read and understood by the specialists who deal with it, if not by laymen. In the accelerating biology research field, where new functions of cells at the molecular level are constantly being revealed, a means to record such progress is needed. Traditionally, such records take the form of published papers, but Karp and his colleagues are building another, more efficient and revealing way to define progress, by depicting ongoing discoveries in the way a specific cell functions. The first cell chosen is *Escherichia coli*, or *E. coli*. Scientists use this widely studied cell to understand cell workings in general, and now that the observed metabolic processes in the cell have been supplemented by its genomic sequencing, there is much to depict.

Karp's and colleagues' representational mechanism is called a pathway database, and the resulting functional picture it constructs describes the numerous biochemical reactions and enzymes that constitute *E. coli's* life. These reactions involve molecular transport, cell metabolism, and the complex networks that regulate cell function. Which cellular proteins accelerate a given chemical reaction? Which chemical compounds inhibit or activate those enzymes, and by what physical mechanisms? If done well, the representation not only accurately depicts what is observed but also helps explore possible but unconfirmed pathways in the cell's metabolism.

But even the simple, one-celled *E. coli* is complex. It has a metabolic network that involves 791 chemical compounds involved in 744 enzyme-catalyzed reactions. Small wonder that its complexity needs some type of model and an understandable representation of it. But this complexity also underscores other reasons for a consistent symbolic representation: first, because no one person can assimilate all that is going on, such a dynamic database helps convey less precisely known or related aspects of an evolving model; second, such a representation permits the expression of qualitative theories about how and why certain functions exist; and, third, it enables the creation and use of a formal, precise ontology.[11]

Given the development of symbolic processing in the AI world, this model can also be computationally exercised to test the different theories advanced. New genomic sequences for *E. coli* can be used to predict new pathways and their relative importance. Last, to help biologists interact with the database, an online interface brings the model and its representation into more standard English. This new pathway database program is called EcoCyc and it has been followed by MetaCyc and BioCyc, two collections of computationally-derived metabolic pathways and enzymes for hundreds of organisms. These may be the harbinger of what is needed to understand infinitely more complex biological systems as they become defined.[B]

Attempts at Commercialization

Given AIC's leading edge developments, history should be marked by examples of commercial impacts from its work. Since the early 1980s that has indeed been the case. Commercialization forms have ranged from the outright sale of individual software packages to licensing. At the same time, some individuals chose to follow their entrepreneurial instincts elsewhere. In light of SRI's current emphasis on commercialization, we briefly review the AIC's history in this area.

Though not always with concerted effort, the AIC has been exploring the commercialization of its software for the past 20 years, with about 30 products involved. Figure 4-7 shows the magnitude of the return on these efforts. Though the curves don't reveal the details of how successful individual products were, as normally the case most of the income has been attributable to just a few packages. In fact, 90% of the total of the nearly $11.5 million income shown in the curve came from just four software "products."

The software placed for commercialization had several important characteristics. Three of the four successful products were written and proffered by just one person, Dave Kashtan, whose software design efforts were *not* derived from the AIC's research efforts *per se*. Kashtan was an excellent systems programmer in the AIC who understood the operating systems of

---

[11] An ontology is a catalog of the types of things that are assumed to exist in a domain of interest from the perspective of a person using a language to describe and talk about that same domain.

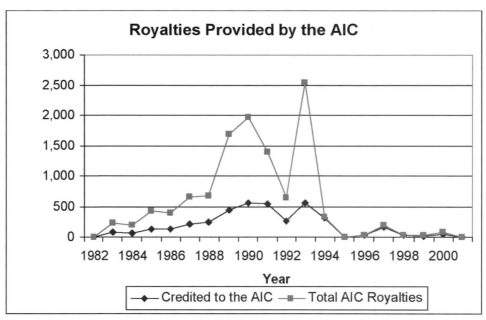

Figure 4-7. The AIC's royalty history since 1982.

the day. The widely used VAX series of computers from Digital Equipment Corporation served essentially two communities. The commercial sector used VMS as its operating system, and the other, dominated by the research community, favored UNIX. Because a lot of software was being written for the UNIX system that wouldn't run under VMS, Kashtan wrote a version of UNIX that would and called it EUNICE. EUNICE and another utility program called MULTINET, which took several of the communications protocols emerging in the government research world and made them operate under VMS, became popular. But they had nothing to do with research in AI. The next most popular software, the IMAGECALC/ 3DIUS/CME series mentioned earlier, accounted for perhaps 6% of the total return and was based on reasoning about imagery.

The third characteristic of the most profitable software was that it was eventually taken outside SRI to become the centerpiece of a new company called TGV,[12] where normal maintenance and other product services could be offered with fewer distractions. Thus, the most lucrative software from the AIC was utilitarian, both in what it did and how it was supported.

The fourth characteristic of the commercialization income stream in the AIC is that it did not correlate well with the SRI administration's press for commercialization as

conveyed under the added impetus from Chairman Cook and President Sommers. The ability to increase commercialization opportunities naturally depends on just what research or other offerings are extant *within SRI*. That occurrence is somewhat problematical and the ability to forecast subsequent success is even more elusive.

Having said that, one commercialization effort has emerged since the new SRI emphasis that has a good chance of success. The new start-up is called Discern Communications, and its product is an outgrowth of the natural language understanding program and the years of DARPA sponsorship. Discern is addressing the need people have for product or service support from sources ever more devoid of human interaction. Whether through the telephone or online, these information sources are increasingly large, complex, and, in the case of technical subjects, arcane.[13] The frustration level can be excruciating, and people become desperate to talk with someone.

But economics have favored the use of automation to human inquiry. So, without human response, interaction, and convergence, what can be done? Suppose that the automated responder could let people ask for what they need in more natural terms and, at the same time, unambiguously understand what has been said. Both natural language understanding

---

[12] TGV stood for "Two Guys and a Vax" and was eventually bought by Cisco.

[13] According to Discern, by 2006 corporations will be creating 200 terabytes of information per day, of which 80% will be unstructured data.

algorithms and the speed of processors now offer that potential. Discern has built the best system to date for interpreting a phoned or online question and finding direct answers from multiple data sources. Gone is the overbearing cascade of menus, both verbal and visual. Discern dynamically understands the context and syntax of the question in terms of the enterprise's information sources and generates sentences "on the fly" containing the answer.

The new company gained seed round funding from SRI and first round investments from Spanlink Communications. Its browser-based product was chosen as "Product of 2002" by Technology Marketing Corporation's *Interaction Solutions Magazine.* As of May 2004, Discern has been integrated into Spanlink in return for stock considerations to SRI.

As a final note on the commercialization area, considerable effort must be expended to market each SRI "product." Although some of these efforts are accounted for in tracking development costs, most are not. Even less accountable are the extra hours principals devote to making research prototypes presentable and reliable. In most cases, the real economic and opportunity costs of commercialization will never be known.

AIC Alumni

What of those that left the AIC to seek their equity fortunes elsewhere? In all, nine companies have been founded at some point by leaders from the AIC. One of the earliest, Symantec, is still going, albeit not with the AI orientation with which it began. Kestrel Institute is also in business, as is the more recent conversion of Discern into Spanlink. TGV, Teleos, and Interop were bought out by larger companies, and the remaining three failed—not a bad batting average in this particular sport. While they did not start companies, many other AIC alumni nevertheless went to the commercial world at levels of high responsibility in AI-related or other companies. Others entered academia either here or in Europe. As evidence of the academic quality of work in the AIC, some became full professorships at institutions such as Harvard and Stanford.

A Recap—Maintaining Continuity in the Uncertain World of Contract Research

The preceding account shows in several ways how a vital and innovative lab, through deliberate initiatives and adaptation, can continue productive work for over three decades. Figure 4-8 summarizes the technical pathway with a "genealogy chart" of the various AI technologies the AIC has created over its history. The listing along the left-hand side shows in sequence the AI categories in which the AIC engaged from its beginning to the present. Note the first box to the right of the category represents a *new* initiative created both to expand the science and maintain the business aspects of the Center. A measure of the quality of the new initiatives has been their staying power, supported, of course, by adaptation. As the flow of what is technically possible changes with time and as new, and old, problems become solvable, new opportunities present themselves for those who are prepared.

Probably the most important requisite for such continuity is that the staff has what might be called "competent curiosity." It is not enough just to dream of a next direction for exploration; researchers must also have the skills both to understand the state of the art and to know how to extend it. Associated with all such advances are the degree of foresight involved and the quality of the foundation laid. Is the work incremental and predictable, or is it fundamentally different from what has gone before? The proof of how important a next step can be is often evidenced by the lab's technical reputation, which, in turn, is often defined by its publishing record. The AIC, through its adventurous advances in its field, has acquired an international reputation for good, fundamental work.

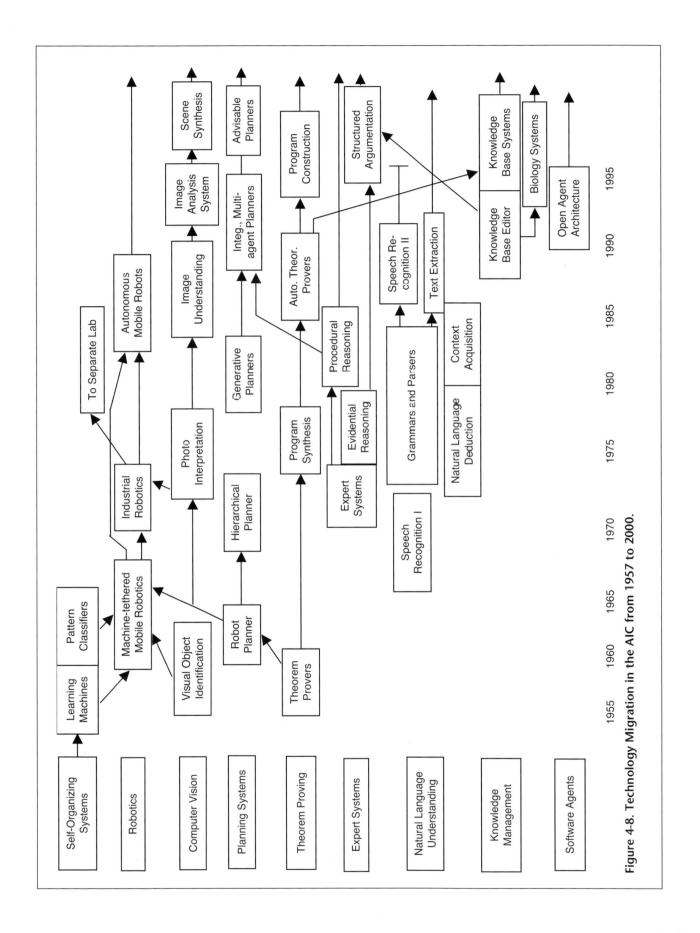

Figure 4-8. Technology Migration in the AIC from 1957 to 2000.

The next requisite for success at SRI is adaptation. We have related how the lab reacted to changes in the priorities of an important funding client like DARPA. When a program was to continue beyond one funding cycle, the lab came up with ideas about just what needed to be extended, reworked, or stopped. As always, a good, visionary researcher needs to understand what is important to the client in addition to trying to advance his or her own specialty. A good, long-horizon client permits such exploration. But many of SRI's clients have specific near-term goals instead. What does work is a deft adaptability that still leaves an interesting research problem on the table.

When a sponsored program first shows signs of winding down, it is time to lay new research agendas in front of a sponsoring agent, and in so doing try to determine or to influence the next likely course of work. Such adaptation is modulated, however, by the general progress of technology. What is now or predictably will be possible? With the dizzying advances in computing technology, what power is likely to become affordable soon? The advent of affordable automatic speech recognition was in part a result of a technical approach, but mostly attributable to the declining cost of powerful computing hardware.

SRI's adaptation may mirror a client's adaptation that comes partly through SRI's informal counsel and guidance. A good example is the approach to building the tools of automatic planning. Up to the mid-1990s, the approach sought by Government clients was an automatic planning system that, after considering all the inputs, produced an executable plan— sort of a black box approach. For realistic plans, this approach would often have required huge and

complex descriptions of possible resources and conditions. Under SRI guidance, the approach was modified to make plan generation more like human planning; namely, repeated human interaction with machine-generated options whenever the plan became uncertain or complex. This approach both produces better plans and keeps the ownership of the plan more defined. Creating this kind of trusted and involved role with a client is a big boost to project continuity.

Ray Perrault, the present AIC director and one with the longest tenure, added the perspective noted above (see Figure 4-9). He also indicated that the SRI staff often assumes a rather unexpected role in the *client's* community, that of bringing its organizational elements together where otherwise they might not be. Such isolation of client subunits applies mostly to the Government, but not exclusively. Fulfilling this amalgamator's role requires the respect of the separate client elements and the objectivity that is SRI's hallmark. The role is, of course, informal, but it can bring closure faster than would happen through internal measures, and it helps position SRI as a useful player acting in the overall client's best interest. This

Figure 4-9. Current and long-standing AIC Director, Ray Perrault. As with many group leaders at SRI, Ray also has a worldwide reputation, in this case in natural language representation.

integration happened often in the RADIUS program.

Finally, one additional point needs to be made regarding the lab's enviable continuity—a point that is not exactly self-evident: How can able researchers, driven by their individual interests to advance their art, provide the continuity and longevity the AIC has seen in a world where applied, rather than basic, science is increasingly demanded? One way has been to subordinate personal scientific interests for a time until they can be resurrected in later work. Another is to maintain those interests, but employ them flexibly as new projects and contexts unfold. Of course, it helps when the number of projects is large and overlapping and, perhaps most importantly, when the researcher is in a widely used, essentially inevitable area of technology.[14]

In July 2003, the Center won perhaps its largest single contract ever because of its willingness to assemble the requisite internal and external talent to meet evolving research opportunities. The new project, the Cognitive Agent that Learns and Observes (CALO), is rich in research potential and yet framed in a way that targets practical needs. CALO intends to draw broadly from existing knowledge about agent technology and about critical supporting components in machine learning, natural language processing, knowledge representation, behavioral studies, planning, and human-computer interaction. SRI will integrate knowledge in these areas conveyed by the best U.S. universities and companies in this field.[15] The sponsor, DARPA, is looking for revolutionary ways that computers can support decision-makers. This award is a solid affirmation of the value of research talent, the ability to draw a diverse team together to meet a client need, and, perhaps most importantly, the ability to provide a combination of both attributes. That combination has kept the AIC at the top of its field for nearly half a century!

By any SRI measure, therefore, the AIC is an outstanding research organization. It has built and maintained a reputation that attracts good people. It has also shown its ability to apply high levels of technical skill to problems of client interest, thus advancing science and meeting clients' needs simultaneously—a profoundly good prescription for success in high-quality contract research.

---

[14] In this discussion of volition in what a researcher works on, one aspect of being a lab or center at SRI needs mention: its relationship to other labs and their ongoing research operations. Since over this time period, artificial intelligence often seemed to pose a new and fruitful solution to chronic engineering problems, it was natural for other researchers to occasionally approach the AIC leadership seeking collaboration and commitments. Depending on the AIC leadership at the time and the specifics of the case, these requests were either rebuffed or accommodated. The reasons for denying such collaboration often lay in not wanting to defocus those who were trying to advance their art, to avoid classified work, or less defendable reasons. Such reactions are strongly influenced by the center director but also include the preferences of the staff directly affected by the request. One of the traits of a research atmosphere is to protect an engaged researcher from top-down direction on how his or her time should be spent. One such request for collaboration came in an exploration of new work and when denied led the requesting researcher to leave SRI in frustration. This struggle of when and how to conduct interdisciplinary work is endemic to a contract research organization and so is treated in a bit more depth in Appendix E.

[15] Among the 16 universities are MIT, Stanford, the University of Texas, and Carnegie Mellon; companies such as Boeing are also represented.

Endnotes

[A] Nils J. Nilsson, *The SRI Artificial Intelligence Center—A Brief History*, AIC Technical Note 317, SRI International, January 24, 1984.

[B] Peter D. Karp, "Pathway Databases: A Case Study in Computational Symbolic Theories," *Science*, Vol. 293, September 14, 2001, pp. 2040–44. As of April 2002, a dozen or so pathway/genome databases have been derived, the last being the sequencing of *Agrobacterium tumefaciens*.

Chapter 5
Medical Technology

Over its 50-year history SRI has made relatively few excursions into the world of new medical technology. But because of its passion for innovation and an ability to deal with fundamentals, it has made a number of significant contributions. Of those efforts, we concentrate here on telepresence surgery, eyetrackers, laser photocoagulation, ultrasonic imaging, and automatic blood pressure measurement. Each of these efforts has created unique capabilities, providing new and better approaches to medical diagnosis and treatment.

Telepresence Surgery

In the mid-1980s, Phil Green, a laboratory director and one of SRI's more prolific inventors, had a new idea that would extend the limited notions of telerobotics. In this case it would enable the capability of the human hand to access formerly inaccessible realms and make interactions there increasingly realistic for the human operator. Specifically, he saw how microscopic and endoscopic surgery, then quite limited in the range of functions they could perform, could be endowed with the natural dexterity of a surgeon's hands. He requested and received internal SRI funding to assemble a new system that would give surgeons the sensory perspective and manipulative ability they would have in a normal surgical setting.

The system would have many of the characteristics diagrammed in Figure 5-1.

SRI submitted a proposal to the National Institutes of Health (NIH) in October 1989 for support in building a prototype system for microscopic and endoscopic surgery.[A] Although that proposal was not accepted, Green continued building the limited prototype system with SRI funds. With the excellent control system design of John Hill and assistance from Yonael Gorfu and Lynn Mortensen, the working model they built closely resembled the notional drawing shown in Figure 5-1, except that the model was built for just one hand.

SRI UNVEILS A STARTLING APPROACH TO SURGERY

It is early 1995 and SRI's new surgical system is in place at the University of California Medical Center in San Francisco. SRI's concept has caught the attention of surgeons such as Larry Way. The machine has some startling features, such as removing the surgeon from direct patient access. Its telerobotic design, which anticipates the day when many kinds of surgery will be minimally invasive, makes it particularly exciting. Does the telerobotic design hamper or, given computer-assisted features such as those for microsurgery, enhance the surgeon's skill over conventional open surgery? The claim: Because of the system's intuitive nature, telepresence surgery will afford the surgeon essentially the same dexterity as regular surgery and, with computer augmentation, will eventually greatly increase the surgeon's hand stability.

The system has two major segments: the surgeon's workstation, which contains the grasping half of the telerobotic surgical instrument; and an effector station, where the other half of the instrument interacts with the patient. Anxious to test this new kind of operating system, Way, having set two clamps, grasps the surgeon station end of a scalpel and severs a small live bovine artery. Using normal open-surgery suture techniques, he proceeds to reunite the separated artery, and blood flows again. The surgeon has performed this feat with almost no specific training on the new system and at 10 feet from the operating site! Dr. Way recalls how the machine became "invisible" while he was using it, offering a tremendous advance over earlier laparoscopic techniques.

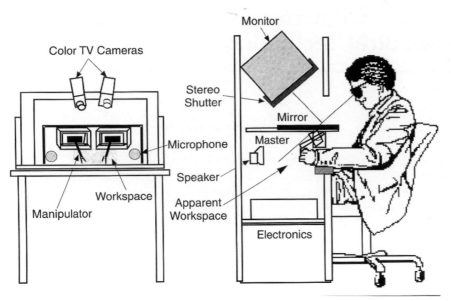

Figure 5-1. Schematic of the first SRI surgical telepresence system.

"I did the world's very first bowel anastamosis with [just a] one-armed version of telepresence. No manual. Very intuitive. We got some pig or sheep intestines and Rick [Satava] 'assisted' by holding the two cut ends near each other. I sutured with one armed telepresence dexterity. The significance was not lost on Rick or myself."

As the SRI version of the system was proceeding, Green began conversations with Col. Richard Satava, a surgeon from Ft. Ord (near Monterey, California) whom he had met at a medical conference. Satava suggested that the system would also be a splendid alternative to an increasingly widely used approach to gall bladder removal that employed a minimally invasive technique called laparoscopy. Figure 5-2 shows the basic approach for entering the chest or abdominal cavity; the internal manipulators shown are of SRI design. Laparoscopic surgery had been in development for several decades, mainly in Europe, and was becoming more widely used in the United States. However, the technique was awkward and difficult for surgeons to learn. Long hollow access tubes, called cannula, are inserted into the patient's inflated abdomen, and all internal viewing and instrument activity take place through the tubes. Coping with the fulcrum at the body entrance and axis-aligned movements imposed by the cannula, all guided by a television monitor that presented an often-disorienting perspective, requires many hours of training to attain even modest proficiency. A system could be designed, they reasoned, that would remove the contortions imposed by such a system and offer surgeons the access and perspective available in open surgery. That the SRI system was intuitively usable is evidenced by this account of Col. Irwin Simon, a colleague of Satava's:[B]

As the system progressed, numerous surgeons tried it out, and many wrote of their impressions. A letter from Carl Levinson to Green provides a good example:

"Truth be known, I expected to walk into your laboratory and have a hood placed over my head, after which I could fulfill my wildest endoscopic flights of fancy. Instead, I was treated to a remarkable exhibition of electronic and technologic know-how which brought to mind three virtually simultaneous thoughts: This is remarkable; How can I use this, or can I? There *certainly* is a place for this! These thoughts still run through my mind." [C]

In 1991, SRI submitted a second proposal to the NIH, this time emphasizing laparoscopic surgery. That proposal, too, wasn't funded, but Green was not deterred. He knew that the program managers at NIH had some discretionary money, and he believed in his system. By this time SRI's internal funding had exceeded $250,000 for his one-arm working system.[1] Green decided to make a video of the SRI system and take it to the head of the NIH

---

[1] It was interesting to witness the incredulity and chiding of my fellow managers when I petitioned SRI for internal funds for a "telepresence" system. Admittedly, the new name conjured up too many visions of an unachievable future, but it remains a good descriptor of what actually happens. Somewhat before I became aware of Green's notion, I had come up with a communication concept that I had also called telepresence. At one point I assembled some people to look at telepresence in general, and that's when I learned of Green's surgical concept.

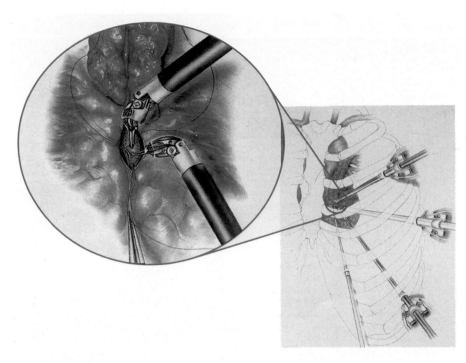

Figure 5-2. An illustration of how the new instruments are inserted into the body and used. (From William Leventon, Tech. Editor, *Product Design and Development*, November 1998, © by Cahners Business Information)

office to which he had submitted the second proposal. The video showed activities intended to verify both the feasibility and precision of the SRI system but, somewhat surprisingly, nothing directly to do with surgery. Green and Mortensen recorded several activities. First, Mortensen used the system to paint the small flower shown in Figure 5-3. Second, while she held an ordinary grape, Green used the system to slice it into almost transparent layers. The tape may have included some of the bead stacking that is still used in demonstrating the system's three-dimensional capabilities. The tape made the case well enough that the NIH

program office decided to fund the proposal.

In October 1991, SRI received a 3-year grant to design and build a more complete and capable demonstration system. The new system had essentially the same configuration shown in Figure 5-1. That same concept, consisting of workstation, viewing arrangement, and manipulation configuration first proposed in 1989, is still used in the commercial form of the system. The SRI project team that refined the next working versions was the same throughout, except for the addition of Joel Jensen. Figure 5-4, a picture from a special medical issue of *Time Magazine* in fall 1996, shows the new version.

As mentioned, several surgeons who helped foresee the surgical uses of the system were from Ft. Ord, Satava in particular. He became intrigued with the idea behind telepresence surgery, as well as with other surgical training concepts more akin to virtual reality. He visited SRI often to test the system and offer advice. In mid-1992, after showing the Surgeon General of the Army a videotape of the SRI system, he asked the Army for and received an assignment to the DARPA where he participated in its new program in medical technology. Part of this program would help fund the third-generation SRI telepresence system. The context for the DARPA work became battlefield casualties and exploring the relevance of remote surgery for the important "golden hour" for casualties; that is, the time immediately after sustaining a wound when emergency treatment is most efficacious. Several systems were built and demonstrations given, one just outside the Pentagon for the Secretary of Defense and his aides. The well-designed SRI system provided users with both stereovision and delicate tactile response. SRI delivered one system to the Department of Defense's (DoD's) joint medical training facility near Washington, D.C. SRI engineers Ajit Shah and Gary Guthart and

Created on June 13, 1991 by
Lynn Mortensen
the world's first Telepresence Artist

Figure 5-3. A sketch made with the first SRI telepresence system (done in color).

surgeon Jon Bowersox joined the team for this phase.

During SRI's development of surgical telepresence, more than 30 practicing surgeons were invited to try out the new surgical system. In addition, the equipment was taken to the University of California Medical School in San Francisco where surgeons gave feedback about the system after using it in trial operations on swine. Their experiences were important in the evolution of the system and, although procedures took slightly longer using it, the trials confirmed the concept and the intuitive and useful properties of the system. This exposure and the papers written for medical journals by the SRI staff and by surgeons Satava and Bowersox helped publicize surgical telepresence as a serious and important contribution to surgery.

In the meantime, Green began seeking investment money to commercialize the system. This effort went on during most of 1994 and 1995, but all of the major surgical instrument companies and the venture community turned him and SRI down. The concept was clearly sound and important to the future of surgical care, but a deal could not be struck.

One of the venture capital firms, in its due diligence pursuant to Green's inquiry, however, had retained Dr. John Freund, who was intrigued by the system. When the venture capital firm voted not to proceed, Freund came to SRI representing himself and a few other medical entrepreneurs and after negotiations obtained rights to SRI's system for all of surgery.[2] That was in September of 1995, and

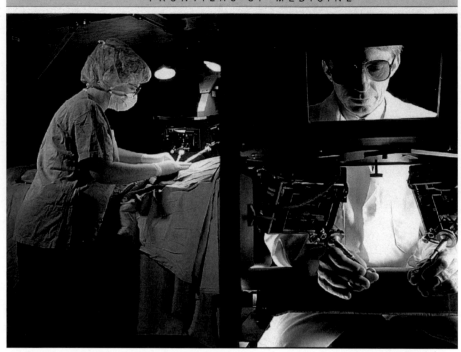

Figure 5-4. Examples of the surgeon's workstation and the effectors at the patient location. On the right is former military surgeon Jon Bowersox and the assistant on the left is Lynn Mortensen. (*Time Magazine*, Special Issue: The Frontiers of Medicine, p. 13, Fall 1996.)

Freund soon joined with others from the medical community to form Intuitive Surgical Devices (ISD) of Sunnyvale, California, to manufacture the system shown in Figure 5-5.

The utility and importance of this kind of surgery are likely to be monumental. Use of ISD's da Vinci™ surgical equipment began in Europe, where it was first used on human patients with outstanding results. This work proceeded while awaiting approval from the more conservative U.S. Food and Drug Administration (FDA).

ISD's Web page (www.intuitivesurgical.com) provided a number of early examples of use of the equipment:

- Starting on May 7 (1998), Professor Carpentier and Dr. Didier Loulmet of the Broussais Hospital in Paris performed six open-heart surgeries using the Intuitive da Vinci™ system. Broussais Hospital, Europe's first cardiac surgery department, is renowned for performing Europe's first successful heart transplant and aortic

---

[2] At the time, SRI lacked a valuable patent position and so received just 7% of the stock at the seed round. U.S. patents on the overall system and four component parts had been applied for, but none had yet been issued. The first system issuance would be several foreign patents in 1997, and U.S. patents would be received on the components beginning the same year. The U.S. patent on the overall system is still pending after several revisions.

aneurysm repair procedures. This facility is also recognized as a world leader in the development of advanced valvuloplasty techniques. Professor Carpentier and Dr. Loulmet performed all or part of five surgical procedures with the Intuitive system:

– Atrial septal defect repair

– Commissurotomy and prosthetic ring annuloplasty

– Papillary muscle shortening

– Coronary artery bypass surgery

• Carpentier described his experience performing surgery with the Intuitive system as a major advance in minimally invasive technique, and commented that "the Intuitive system will bring minimally invasive cardiac surgery another step forward. This technology brings something not available in the past: much better visualization and more precise maneuvers of instruments inside the heart." Commenting on the clinical study results, Dr. Fred Moll, founder and medical director of Intuitive Surgical said, "This is a key milestone for Intuitive Surgical. We're proud to unveil the technology that made it possible to perform the world's very first computer-enhanced open-heart operations."

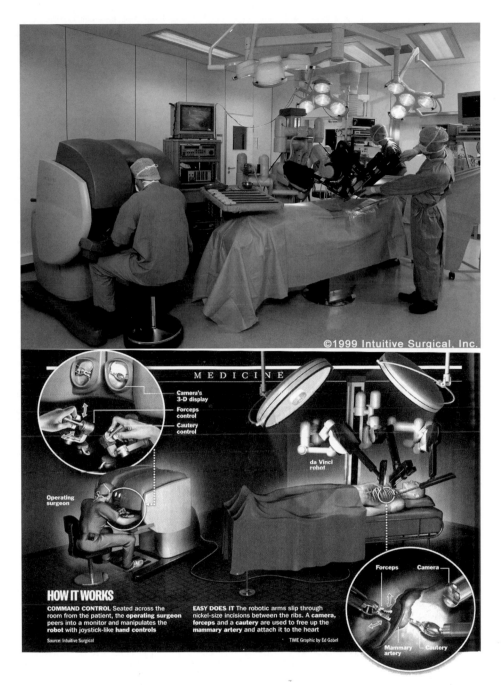

Figure 5-5. ISD's minimally invasive da Vinci™ surgery system as (top) installed in a Dresden operating room in 1999, and (bottom) depicted in *Time Magazine* in 2001 (Anita Hamilton, "Forceps! Scalpel! Robot!, *Time Magazine*, pp. 64–65, June 4, 2001).

• The first videoscopic coronary by-pass procedures were performed 23-28 May 1998 at the Leipzig Heart Center in Germany using the Intuitive minimally invasive equipment. Prof. Mohr said, "The computer-enhanced precision, high resolution 3-D vision system, and the dexterity of Intuitive's instruments allowed our team to perform the world's first videoscopic anastamosis." Dr. Falk commented on the surgeries by saying,

"We believe this technology will enable cardiac surgeons to perform coronary bypass surgery through tiny ports."

- In early January 2000 the Leipzig Center and the Cardiovascular Institute, University of Dresden, performed the first series of closed-chest, endoscopic beating heart cases earlier this month. The procedures were completed solely through 4-5 ports, each less than 1 cm in diameter: 3 ports for surgeon access, 1 port for the stabilizer, and in some cases, 1 port for the assistant surgeon. This is the first time in medical history that patients have enjoyed the clinical benefits of cardiac bypass surgery performed solely through incisions of less than 1 cm without being placed on cardiopulmonary bypass (CPB) during the procedure. The ability to perform this surgery through tiny incisions significantly reduces pain, trauma, and recovery time for the patient. The avoidance of CPB eliminates post-operative neurological complications and reduces the risk of stroke for older patients. The result of this combination of clinical benefits means a short hospital stay, quick return to daily activities, and lower medical expenses. To date the University of Dresden has performed more than 90 closed-chest CABG procedures including single and double TECABs using the Intuitive Surgical System.

- In March 2000 the world's first totally endoscopic mitral heart valve repair was successfully completed by a cardiac surgical team at the Deutsches Herzzentrum Munich. The morning after surgery, the 48-year-old patient was extubated and reported little to no pain, and the intra-operative trans-esophageal echocardiogram (TEE) revealed that her mitral valve was no longer leaking. Dr. Hormoz Mehmanesh commented: "This is a significant milestone in minimally invasive intra-cardiac surgery. For the first time, we were able to perform a mitral valve repair without a mini-thoracotomy or chest wall retraction. We happily report that the day after surgery, our patient had only minimal pain from the chest tube and the four tiny ports."

Thus, ISD began commercializing the da Vinci™ Surgical System in December 1998. In the United States, the FDA approved the da Vinci™ system in July 2000 for abdominal surgeries such as gall bladders and colons; in March 2001 for chest surgery, excluding the heart; and in July 2001 for prostate surgery.

More general permission has since been extended for laparoscopic and thoracoscopic (chest) surgery. As of the end of 2003, 200 systems have been installed worldwide, and more than 13,000 operations of approximately 200 different types, including cardiac, have been performed.

The importance of this SRI innovation seems almost impossible to overestimate. Though the system's capital cost is moderately high, about $1.25 million, it offers surgical advantages that are revolutionary:

- A less invasive, less traumatic means for an extremely wide range of surgical procedures
- A shorter operating time, reduced hospital stay or higher out-patient potential, and a more rapid healing process
- Intuitive operation that reduces or eliminates the need for specialized surgical training such as that required for laparoscopy
- A limited ability (defined by signal delay) to allow the surgeon to conduct procedures outside the operating location, thus enabling remote access
- Scale-up of surgery dimensions, including microsurgery, to allow the use of normal dexterity
- Stabilization of the surgeon's hand in delicate and dangerous situations.

Here are two brief observations on this subject. Curiously, only a few SRI people joined ISD, but none of those who invented the technique. One who did join ISD was Gary Guthart, now the Senior Vice President for Product Operations. Second, the market for this kind of surgical equipment is obviously young and open to competitive skirmishes. In May 2000, a month or so before ISD's IPO, its major competitor, Computer Control of Santa Barbara, California, filed suit for patent infringement. As the case dragged on for a long time and at great expense, the two parties decided that, rather than contesting such matters, they should merge under the ISD name. The resulting company is now the world's largest in this new and promising field.

The SRI Eyetracker

Its Genesis

Hew Crane is one of SRI's most prolific inventors. He has the uncanny ability to delve into the core of a technology and find the insight necessary there to open new horizons for its use. One such case was the SRI eyetracker, which is briefly described here. In the early 1960s, Crane had been working on a new means for automatically focusing a camera. At the same time, he had been looking into the "channel capacity" of various human sensory systems. He chose to concentrate on the human eye and found that, under certain circumstances, the eye oscillates slightly in its focal length. What if, he thought, those oscillations were the basis for the eye's ability to autofocus?

An opportunity to explore that hypothesis came when NASA expressed an interest in ascertaining whether the buffeting sometimes experienced in flight would affect a pilot's ability to focus. Such an inability to focus would be particularly troublesome in high-speed, low-altitude flight. SRI was awarded a contract to explore this condition, and its published findings—that a relationship existed between small, rapid movements of the eye and its adaptive focusing—caused excitement in the vision community. NASA continued funding SRI's work in the visual accommodation area and that funding led to SRI's development of an accurate optometer and the eyetracker. How the eye muscles focus in selecting different distances for viewing (a process called "accommodation") was known, but the neurological basis for the process was not.

A second and supplemental source of eyetracker funding came from an unlikely source that resulted from a chance meeting between Crane and Stanford social psychologist Leon Festinger (who eventually shared his National Science Foundation [NSF] grant on visual perception with SRI). Crane recalls how it occurred as a humorous, but not totally atypical, instance in research: Festinger, having learned of SRI's interest in vision research, paid a visit to Crane's laboratory. At the conclusion of a long, animated meeting where Festinger stated his need for an eyetracker, Tom Cornsweet, a vision researcher who had just joined SRI, said something like, "Well, one way or another, we could probably have something to demonstrate in at least crude form within a few months." When they were alone Crane exclaimed, "Tom, are you out of your mind? We don't have the faintest idea yet of how to build an accurate, noninvasive eyetracker!" But Tom did, and their competence prevailed.

The Approach[D]

The work on the eyetracker began in earnest in 1965, but to understand the approach it is necessary to back up a bit to SRI's study of how the eye focused. Their hypothesis was that accommodation depended on the axial position of a tiny area in the center of the fovea, the central, high-resolution part of the retina. To confirm that hypothesis, however, required a "means for stimulating and measuring eye focus in real time as well as the ability to place and hold a target image accurately within this small area." To do this required a major instrumentation effort that included the construction of:

- An accurate optometer to measure eye accommodation in real time

- An accurate eyetracker to measure the two-dimensional components of eye movement in real time

- A stimulus deflector that could, under the control of the eyetracker, stabilize a target at selected retinal positions.

The SRI team of Crane and Cornsweet quickly concluded that the only feasible approach to a noncontact eyetracker was to use Purkinje reflections, which are reflections from various layers at the visual entrance to the eye when it is exposed to a beam of light. It turned out that tracking the two-dimensional reflections from the surface of two particular layers could provide information on where the eye was looking. But because one of the important reflections (the one from the back of the lens) was weak, tracking it reliably was a challenge.

The two reflections used were known as the first and fourth Purkinje reflections—the first from the cornea and the fourth from the rear of the lens. The configuration of the eye, shown in Figure 5-6, produced virtual sources for these two reflected images, which separated from each other with eye rotation but not with eye lateral movement (or translation). Thus, the two-dimensional separation of the virtual sources was an expression of where the eye was pointed. This fact, then, became the basis for designing an eyetracker to monitor that separation continuously (see Figure 5-7).

As might be expected, years of work were involved in realizing the promise of this concept. System artifacts that unintentionally altered the relative position of the two Purkinje images had to be eliminated. SRI built five generations of eyetrackers, with each successive generation delivering better, more accurate measurements or greater ease of use. Development of the first generation lasted from 1965 to 1971 and, over the following 6 years, SRI built and delivered 30 Generation I, II, and III instruments. During that time and continuing through the development and sale of 11 Generations IV and V instruments, NIH's National Eye Institute provided additional funding, with the grants spanning about 12 years. Such manufacturing numbers were getting to be larger than SRI could efficiently handle and in 1987 the Institute licensed the technology to Fourward Optical Technologies on a worldwide basis. That company created a sixth generation with the following characteristics, which make it perhaps the most accurate eyetracker available:

- 400 Hz bandwidth
- 1 minute of arc accuracy
- Response time of less than 1 millisecond
- Slue rate of 2000° per second

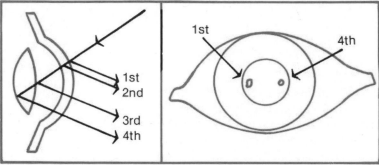

Figure 5-6. On the left are shown the four Purkinje reflections. On the right the virtual sources of the first and fourth reflections are depicted as being in the same plane (from Fourward Technologies' Web page, www.fourward.com).

- Less than 1 minute of arc resolution
- Enhanced auto staging
- Large two-dimensional field (± 20°).

Applications for the Fourward Optical eyetracker include:

- Image stabilization
- Analysis of visual perception
- Strabismus therapy
- Accommodation tracking
- Drug evaluation
- Reading analysis
- Vergence (binocular system)
- Stabilized photocoagulation
- Mapping retinal features
- Scotoma simulation
- Neurologic investigation
- Man-machine interactions
- Analysis of advertising material

Figure 5-7. (a) Laboratory complexity of the early eyetracker and (b) the present commercial product.

More than 80 of the instruments are in use around the world in eye research and other applications requiring an accurate knowledge of eye movement.

SRI also built a related instrument called an optometer about the same time.[3] It could instantaneously measure the plane of focus of the eye, and its speed enabled it to track the most rapid changes in focus. Because of it speed, it was capable of tracking the goodness of focus on a target as it moved closer or further away from a patient, revealing at what distance the eye ceased to focus correctly. This was an alternative to the normal method of overlaying different lenses and asking the patient for judgments about clarity.[E] But it would also be more costly so the use for the optometer remained as the sensor providing the third dimension (distance) to SRI's 3D eyetracker.

A final note about SRI's eyetracker work: In early 1979, the technology enabling this instrument to stabilize targets in the visual field was used to stabilize the instrument-eye relationship in the use of the laser photocoagulators, which are discussed next. Figure 5-8 provides an illustration of a prototype of that stabilization equipment. In addition to Crane and Cornsweet, other SRI staff added greatly to the development of the eyetracker—Carroll Steele, Lloyd Alterton, My Van Njuyen, and Mike Clark.

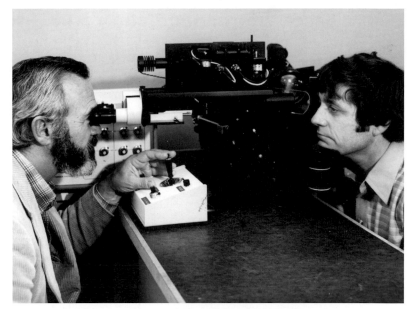

Figure 5-8. The prototype stabilization system for laser photocoagulation with Hew Crane and Mike Clark (right).

---

[3] The optometer measures eye focus with an accuracy of 0.1 diopter and with rapid response. Merging the optometer with the eyetracker resulted in a three-dimensional tracker. Other devices developed by Crane in conjunction with Carroll Steele can be added to the eyetracker including a stimulus deflector that the subject looks through and that can move the viewed scene horizontally, vertically, and in varying degrees of depth under rapid servo control, and a means for accurately simulating, in a patient with normal vision, a scotoma (a spot where the retina has ceased to function) of arbitrary shape, size, and position.

Laser Photocoagulation and Laser Eye Protection

It was at a local tennis club, but not one of your normal club tennis matches. Don Scheuch, then head of the SRI Electronics and Radio Sciences Division, was in the pool tossing a wet tennis ball around with his son. One such toss came at Scheuch from out of the sun and struck him directly in the eye. Dazed and hurt, he tried to brush it off, but a day or so later began to see the impact of the injury on the sight in that eye. He called his tennis friend and ophthalmologist, H. Christian Zweng, who urged him to come immediately to the Palo Alto Clinic where he worked. After diagnosing the injury as a torn retina, he showed Scheuch a brand new device that used a laser for retina repair. The treatment worked, at least temporarily, but Zweng took the opportunity to grumble about the many disadvantages of this handheld ophthalmoscope into which a ruby laser had been incorporated.[4] He was considering alternatives and looking for an environment in which to develop a more clinically useful device. Scheuch replied that SRI had very competent engineers and that if he wanted to pursue a better system why not come to SRI and explore that possibility. Zweng took Scheuch's advice, and in late 1963 a long and fruitful SRI relationship with Zweng and his fellow ophthalmologists at the Stanford Medical Center began. Some 5 years later that collaboration resulted in SRI building what was probably the first clinically useful instrument for laser photocoagulation.[5]

The transparent openings to the eye, the cornea and the lens, offer a natural entrance for visible laser light. The spherical inner backside of the eye, called the chorioid, supports the retina, a light-sensitive film containing rods, cones, nerve endings, and blood supply. Images falling on the retina are converted to electrical impulses that are interpreted in the brain as what we see. The center of the retina, that region responsible for our central vision is called the macula, and it is the most critical element in our visual field. When we look at an object and focus on it, we are positioning the image on the macula. When any portion of the retina detaches from the back of the eyeball, it loses its spherical shape and vision is disrupted in that area. Because the retina is so inaccessible, lasers offer excellent means to reach and treat the retinal area.

Since the early 1950s, powerful light sources have been used in a process called photocoagulation to repair injured retinas by binding retinal tissue together or cauterizing diseased blood vessels in the eye. The earliest approach was the use of a white-light xenon arc-lamp source. While a large and powerful source, it required an exposure between 0.5 to 1.5 seconds to produce a lesion. Therefore, to avoid injury, the patient's eye often had to be anesthetized. Nonetheless, lesions were often mislocated or proved too large to treat. Because the most critical areas of the retina are quite small, the inaccuracies of the white-light photocoagulator meant it was unsuitable for the most important operations. The coherent power of visible-wavelength lasers offered a new approach.[F] The first laser used was the low-power, handheld ruby laser mentioned above, but it was frustratingly difficult to use and somewhat dangerous.

When the program began at SRI, the leading cause of blindness in the United States was diabetic retinopathy, a disease for which the laser proved to be ideally suited and for which the treatment need was great. The procedure was noninvasive and simple for trained ophthalmologists. By choosing a suitable wavelength and exposure time, the ophthalmologist could readily cauterize the diseased blood vessels in the retina or reattach certain forms of torn or detached retinas. The laser's contribution has been enormous.

Soon after Zweng's visit to SRI, grant applications to NIH's National Center for Neurological Disease and Blindness were made through Stanford University to explore new uses of the laser in ophthalmology. In 1964, the group, which included some of Zweng's colleagues at Stanford, received initial internal funding[G] to look into medical applications of the laser. In 1966 a $1.5 million grant was awarded to Stanford, with appropriate funding

---

[4] The device, which was built by a local firm, Optical Technologies Inc., was one of the early laser photocoagulators. As mentioned in the preface of Zweng's book, *Laser Photocoagulation and Retinal Angiography*, Scheuch was the first patient on whom Zweng used the device, and he notes the date as Aug. 27, 1963. An important member of Optical Technologies staff, Norm Peppers, left there to become a member of the SRI project team with whom Zweng would work on a new laser photocoagulator.

[5] From comments by ophthalmologist Hunter Little, "clinically useful" means that it was powerful enough to be rapid and focused enough to be precise.

coming to SRI, and the two institutions embarked on a multiyear development program.[H] Figure 5-9 shows the SRI team, along with Zweng.

What impact has SRI's work had? As mentioned, out of this effort came the first clinically useful and commercially successful argon laser photocoagulator. This technology became the basis for an important local company, Coherent Radiation. It proved to be not only a highly successful clinical tool, but also a significant commercial asset for the company. Art Vassiliadas left SRI to join Coherent and helped transfer the technology. Today, Coherent, as it is now known, is a corporation engaged a wide range of laser applications and has revenues exceeding $400 million a year. Figure 5-10 shows its main ophthalmologic product.

This instrument can repair torn retinas or help prevent detached retinas by "welding" them back in place. The SRI team continued to work with the Stanford Medical Center in other ocular uses of the laser: puncturing a tiny hole in the iris to relieve the fluid overpressure in patients with acute glaucoma and coagulating hemorrhaging blood vessels in diabetic retinopathy. Other areas explored were the use of lasers as microprobes in the spectroscopic analysis of cells and dermatology. The laser even became important in the removal of tattoos—an improvement over existing methods, which involved incisions, scraping, or other trauma to the skin and which left broad scars or, in some cases, required skin regrafting. A higher intensity, Q-switched version of the ruby laser turned out to be not only effective in removing a range of tattoo pigments, but left minimal damage to the surrounding skin when the light energy density was correctly applied. SRI engineers designed and built a special excitation chamber for the ruby laser to gain the required power levels.[I] The treatment produced minimal pain but, because of the high cost of lasers at that time, treatments didn't catch on right away. One of those who volunteered to have a tattoo removed from his arm was the police chief of Menlo Park whose office was across the street from SRI.

Figure 5-9. The laser photocoagulation team at SRI. From left to right and front to back, Art Vassiliadis, Christian Zweng, Dick Honey; Norm Peppers, Ann Hammond, Lloyd Alterton; Earl Scribner, James Hayes, and Bob Myers.

Figure 5-10. Coherent 2000 Series photocoagulator.

In more recent years, SRI also obtained continued support for the development of nonlinear optical limiters that can automatically increase their opacity to protect the eye, or other sensors, from inadvertent exposure to lasers. The eye damage thresholds developed concurrently for the Air Force led to safety standards for Air Force personnel, and eventually were a major contributor to the American National Standards Institute (ANSI) laser safety standards adopted by all the armed services and industry.

Meanwhile, Scheuch's eye needed continuing attention as a result of his injury, and he became the first patient to use the SRI-developed system; a true pioneer, on more than one occasion he lent himself for tests as the development proceeded. Today, his eyesight is fine. To conclude this section of this phase of SRI work, two stanzas are presented of a poem written by a diabetic Lutheran minister who was treated in the testing phase at SRI and whose life was changed by the benefits of this collaborative work. Here is SRI meeting its chartered purpose.

Obviously, laser interaction with an eye can also be dangerous. Given the widening use of lasers in the workplace and the military, another concurrent effort was SRI's work on the eye's vulnerability to damage from lasers.[6] SRI wanted estimates of retinal and corneal damage thresholds, as well as a means to protect the eye from dangerous exposure. Retinal thresholds were measured for Rhesus monkeys and some humans, and corneal thresholds were determined using rabbits. Funding for this work came from the Air Force and the NIH. In parallel with the clinical program, and with support from the Air Force, SRI explored the thresholds for eye damage from a wide variety of lasers and laser pulse lengths.

---

[6] The work on laser vulnerability to the eye actually preceded that on photocoagulation, starting at SRI with Air Force sponsorship in 1965. (SRI Project 5571 July 1, 1965 for $91,368.)

Ultrasonic Imaging

Because of its safety and ability to image soft tissue, ultrasound has become a mainstay worldwide in medical diagnostic tools. Not only has it become the primary sensor for obstetrical and gynecological examinations, but it also has great utility in a variety of other soft-tissue imaging applications such as cardiac and vascular disease and breast cancer screening. In addition, it is the principal diagnostic tool used whenever X-rays are deemed too hazardous, such as in screening newborn infants with congenital deformations. The development of the technique has spread over decades and is global in its origins. While the use of sound for therapeutic reasons predates World War II, its use as a medical imaging modality began in the late 1940s, largely stimulated by the military development of sonar following the War. Contributions to its development came from Europe, the United States, and Japan. Though the 1950s and 1960s saw rapid increase in employing the real-time, intensity-modulated, two-dimensional imaging systems in use today, those early systems were static, and their sensitivity and resolution were poor.

Accordingly, work on more sophisticated acoustic sources and processing systems continued into the 1970s and 1980s. In the 1980s, the sale of ultrasonic imaging systems began to accelerate. Though SRI is not a visible part of today's marketplace in ultrasound systems, such as those from Picker, Siemens, and Diasonics, it has played an important role in the design of improved ultrasound imaging systems and in research into the biological effects of ultrasound. Let's see how.

Ultrasonics Begins at SRI

In 1967, when the utility of ultrasound was just becoming broadly appreciated, Earle Jones, head of the Electronics and Optics Group,

Figure 5-11. Phil Green, at the time director of SRI's ultrasonic imaging program.

brought in Phil Green (Figure 5-11) to open a new, exploratory SRI program in ultrasonic imaging. Green's goal was to make SRI a significant player in this developing field. Usually, such a statement was SRI administrative code-speak for an individual who had fresh ideas about how to develop a particular technology—and ultrasound, at that time, needed a lot of innovation to make it more clinically useful.

The first ultrasonic instrument to be built at SRI was a precision mechanical two-dimensional scanner that scanned a single transducer (i.e., an instrument that coverts input energy in one form into output energy in another) or opposed (facing) pair of transducers in a water tank containing the object to be imaged. The system permitted imaging in three modes: reflective, transmissive, and holographic.[7] A two-dimensional image was created by moving an acoustic detector in a raster pattern (as in a TV picture) that spanned the target. The output of the detector was then modulated onto an attached, point light source, moving in synchrony with the detector, that was in turn photographed as a time-exposure in the darkened room. This system produced exquisitely detailed transmission and reflection images, phase-contrast images, and ultrasonic holograms of a wide variety of objects,

---

[7] Acoustical holographic images detect a optical or acoustic wave interference field that is created by interaction between a plane reference wave and waves scattered from the target object(s). This lensless scheme can simultaneously acquire multiple image planes but has both sensitivity problems and image noise caused by artifacts characteristic of coherent wave interaction.

including excised animal organs. One of the images—that of an *ex vivo* human fetus—is shown in Figure 5-12(a). Its detail was unprecedented. It received widespread press coverage and dramatically raised the level of expectation for future diagnostic uses of ultrasound. Yet these images took many minutes to acquire, and true diagnostic ultrasound would have to show tissues and organs moving and thus be capable of real-time imaging.

An Ultrasonic Camera and Real-time Imaging

The next important development in SRI's pursuit of ultrasound systems was the building of an ultrasonic camera, which began in 1971. At the outset, this approach also used a tank of liquid but with an improved lens system and a highly sensitive electronic image detector. Figure 5-13 provides a schematic diagram, and Figure 5-14 shows a picture of the camera being used.

The camera system was sponsored by a 3-year grant from the NIH (subsequently renewed). At the heart of this instrument were two components. The first was a 192-element curvilinear piezoelectric transducer array with a curved plastic cylindrical lens. Each array element had an associated amplifier and detector that fed a multiplexer. The second component consisted of a large cylindrical chamber, whose faces were double-concave plastic lenses, 20 cm in diameter. Between the lenses was a pair of circular 15-cm-diameter, 4.7 deg. prisms, which were counter-rotated at a 15-Hz rate by a motor. The prism system, invented by Green, repeatedly swept the focused image field past the 192-element linear transducer array. The chamber was filled with a totally fluorinated hydrocarbon fluid. The 4:1 ratio of acoustic refractive indices of the fluid and plastic resulted in a very short focal length and a wide sweep angle. All of the computer-designed refractive surfaces were coated with quarter-wave impedance-matching layers for minimum reflection.[J] This flexible system had a number of advantages over then existing ultrasonic imagers:

- Real-time imaging, showing anatomical structures in motion
- High sensitivity with lower transducer power for equivalent depth of penetration
- High resolution of 0.75 mm

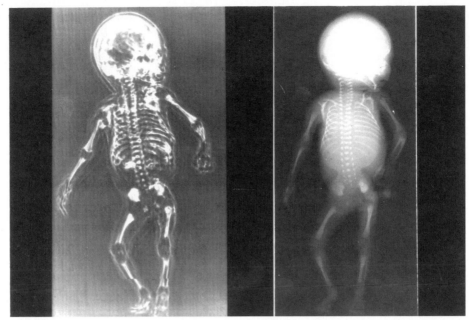

Figure 5-12. The (left) ultrasound and X-ray images of an ex vivo human fetus. The detail of the ultrasound image was unprecedented and markedly raised the awareness of what diagnostic ultrasound could do.

- A variable focal-plane position within the body
- Dual modes of operation—reflective as well as transmissive imaging.

But, as an instrument for clinical diagnosis, the camera also had significant problems:

- Images often contained spurious detail from diffraction by tissue outside the focal plane, which could be mistaken for real and valid structure. (In later versions, a more diffuse sounding source diminished this artifact.)
- Water-tank immersion was too inconvenient for most diagnostic applications.

The SRI ultrasonic camera was first presented in 1973 at the 5th International Symposium on Acoustical Holography, which

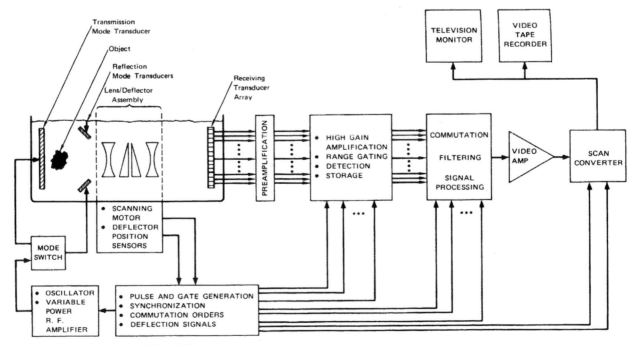

Figure 5-13. Schematic of the SRI ultrasonic camera.

Figure 5-14. The SRI ultrasonic camera in use.

SRI hosted.[K] It was acknowledged to be the most outstanding development in the field. A "water-pillow" version was also built that removed the need for the patient to be immersed in a tank; this version was intended mainly for abdominal imaging. This form of transmission imaging was successful in diagnosing several pathological conditions, including enlarged spleens, and large kidney stones or cysts. Late-pregnancy fetal imaging, earlier limited to extremities and torso, was also done. Several patents were granted on the camera systems, which were licensed to Picker, for which SRI did additional contract work. Picker chose to switch its interest to another SRI technology (see below), and the camera was subsequently licensed to Siemens, for which SRI built an elaborate clinical version that was used for orthopedic diagnostic studies at the University of Muenster. In collaborations with the Palo Alto Clinic and the Stanford University Medical Center, the camera was successfully used in depicting breast carcinoma *in vivo* and soft-tissue hand anatomy.[8]

While work continued on the camera, SRI began its first collaboration with the Mayo Clinic in 1977 under a major new contract secured from the NIH (also subsequently renewed.) The initial goal of this work was to develop and clinically evaluate a high-resolution real-time "B-scan" (pulse-echo, cross-sectional) imager designed especially to view tissue within the first few centimeters of the skin. Its major use was the examination of the site where the internal and external carotid arteries join in the neck—the site of arterial narrowing and clot formation that give rise to most strokes. With this work, an alternative was being sought to the use of X-ray angiography, the painful, sometimes risky injection of X-ray-opaque dye into the blood vessels of interest.

SRI developed a series of increasingly sophisticated scanners that operated at 10 MHz to provide the needed resolution. These instruments clearly delineated not only atherosclerotic plaque on arterial walls but its precursor—subtle thickening of those walls. Strikingly detailed images of the nearby thyroid gland demonstrated that high-frequency "small parts" scanning would have many other clinical applications as well. One SRI invention made on this project—a time-varied filter that compensated for variations in depth-dependent attenuation—proved later to be a major source of royalty revenue to SRI.[9] SRI licensed this system to Picker and developed a manufacturing prototype under contract to Picker. Picker produced and sold these systems as the *MicroView®*. In a special conversion made for the University of Düsseldorf's neurology clinic, SRI added a dynamically focused, annular-shaped transducer array and real-time Doppler blood-flow profiles that were superimposed on the image. Figure 5-15 shows a version of the SRI-Picker instrument. SRI and the Mayo Clinic continued collaborative research on arterial imaging for several more years, under a third NIH contract. This work

---

[8] Contributing significantly to the design and fabrication of the camera were John Holzemer, Jon Taenzer, Dave Murdock, Bill Mullen, Joe Suarez, Dave Ramsey, and Lou Schaefer.

[9] Because the attenuation of ultrasound in tissue increases linearly with frequency, the lower frequency components of a broadband pulse are stronger than its high frequency components at the same tissue depth. That action and the effective change in resolution with frequency suggested the introduction of a filter that varied as a function of depth, hence delay time.

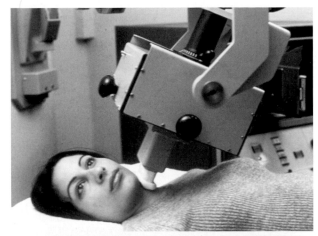

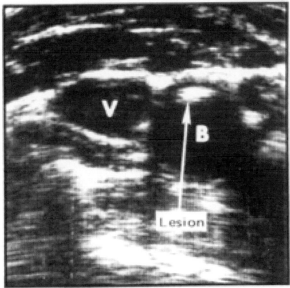

Figure 5-15. Ultrasonic examination of the cross-section of a carotid artery using the first of several such scanners developed at SRI. Atherosclerotic lesions (plaque) appear as a bright area within the otherwise dark interior of the carotid bulb (B)—the expanded region of the carotid artery just below just below where it branches. The jugular vein (V) is to the left of the artery.

resulted in a new system, operating at 4 MHz, that yielded images of deep arteries (to 5 cm) such as abdominal aneurysms.[10]

By the 1980s, ultrasound diagnosis was in widespread use, and concern began to surface over the possibility that this form of energy might have undesirable side effects, especially when used in first-trimester pregnancies. SRI's Ken Marich secured a major grant from the NIH for an extensive bioeffects study.[11] The

Ultrasonics Program, in cooperation with several laboratories in SRI's Life Sciences Division, conducted experiments in which pregnant mice and cellular suspensions were subjected to carefully calibrated ultrasound exposures and analyzed for short- and long-term effects, using a variety of analytical methods. These studies were carried out over many years and published in detail. Thanks to this program and to similar programs at cooperating universities, the mechanisms of ultrasound's interaction with tissue became better understood, and concerns over possible adverse side effects were abated. SRI made further use of its knowledge in bioeffects research and of its unique facilities by studying ultrasonic hyperthermia, then under consideration as an agent for cancer treatment.

Whereas SRI's "small parts" scanners showed anatomy in unprecedented detail, because of their high frequency (typically, 10 MHz) and high attenuation, they were limited to viewing only those tissues lying within a few centimeters of the skin. To extend this capability to organs lying deep within the body, SRI's James Buxton received a grant from the NIH in the late 1970s to develop a real-time ultrasound scanner with a transducer incorporated into the tip of a gastric endoscope—a device inserted into the esophagus, stomach, and duodenum to allow doctors to view those organs. Again, our clinical collaborator was the Mayo Clinic. A 3-cm-long, 64-element, lensed, piezoelectric transducer array was mounted within the tip portion of a 12-mm-diameter gastric endoscope, which retained all of its normal functions—optical illumination and imaging, forceps entry, suction, and irrigation; 64 subminiature coaxial cables conducted signals between the transducer elements and a novel, low-cost pulse generator, multiplexer, processor, and display. Multirange focusing ensured that the image was in good focus at all depths. The animal and human studies conducted with these systems at the Mayo Clinic showed, with great clarity, the ridges of the stomach lining and its thickness, the spleen and kidneys, abdominal blood vessels, and the heart's mitral valve. SRI also added a hand-held small-parts scan probe to the system to extend its utility (see Figure 5-16). SRI patented this technology and licensed it to Advanced Technologies Laboratories, which sponsored continued development at SRI. The

---

[10] Joining the team to work on artery scanners were Jim Havlice, Dave Wilson, Don Burch, and Dilip Saraf.
[11] While this work was initiated by Ken Marich, much of the bioeffects research was led for many years by Peter

Edmonds. Pepi Ross, Virginia Rimer, and Lynn Mortensen also participated.

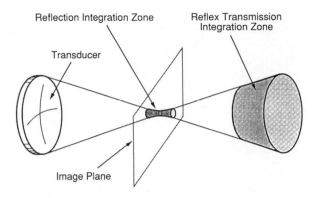

Figure 5-17. Basis for reflex transmission imaging. The large gray conic section on the right acts as a signal source for transmissive imaging.

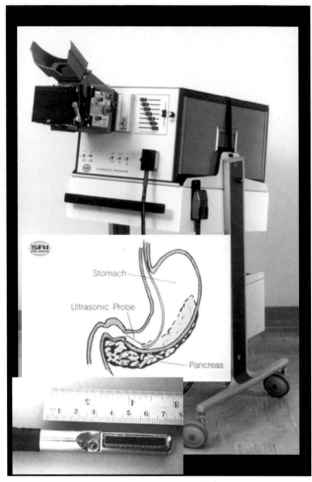

Figure 5-16. The SRI endoscopic ultrasonic imager showing the transducer at the bottom.

National Cancer Institute also sponsored SRI to explore the utility of this imaging endoscope to detect pancreatic cancer through the stomach wall.[12]

Reflex-Transmission Imaging

As noted, SRI's early transmission-imaging work with the ultrasonic camera did not migrate into common clinical use owing to the difficulty of adequately imaging large areas on both sides of a body part without inserting the part into a water bath. The small, hand-held probe used in B-scan imaging, which displays reflections only from targets lying in the plane of scan, proved to be more convenient.[13] But, some anatomy is better delineated using the transmission mode; that is, the detector lies on the opposite side of

the target or imaging plane from the transducer (see Figure 5-17). To incorporate transmission imaging into B-mode systems, in 1984 SRI devised reflex transmission imaging (RTI). In the RTI mode, a well-focused scanning transducer is used both to transmit energy into the body and to receive the echoes. However, in the RTI mode the echoes from a defocused (integrated) region beyond the focal plane become a source of sound waves directed back through the focal plane, thereby indicating the transmissivity of the tissue located there.[L] These sound waves are differentiated from the normal reflected image because they return to the receiver later. Thus, the displayed RTI image primarily depicts the variations in *attenuation* rather than reflection within the focal plane. SRI secured an NIH grant to develop a demonstration RTI system, which proved to be particularly effective for delineating kidney stones. RTI was licensed to Diasonics, Inc. for incorporation in its kidney-stone lithotripter, a noninvasive device for breaking up kidney stones using sound waves administered externally through water.[14]

SRI's Ultrasonics Program was active for more than 25 years. During that period, the Program also undertook many consulting and product-development projects for industry, including the development of a prototype ultrasonic eyescanner system for Asahi Medical, a prototype cardiac scanner system for Ansaldo Biomedica, and numerous design concept studies in nondestructive testing as well as in medicine using SRI's unique imaging systems.

---

[12] Other contributors were Jerry Russell and Helmut Mocssncr.

[13] B-mode or B-scan (B stands for brightness) systems show two-dimensional cross sections of tissue with the intensity of the return at any point in the image proportional to the strength of the signal received there.

[14] Contributors to the RTI development were Joel Jensen, Peter Schattner, Marcel Arditi, and Yonael Gorfu.

Over the course of its history, the Ultrasonics Program patented more than 30 inventions, with many licensed to medical equipment manufacturers worldwide and returning about $60 million in royalties to SRI. It is important to note that such royalties did not flow from up-front licenses. Instead, the substantial returns from SRI's intellectual property in ultrasound were due to Green's efforts. He determined which manufacturers were encroaching on SRI patents, and then tried to persuade them to sign royalty agreements with SRI, which most did. The largest sum, about $30 million, came in one of the very few lawsuits SRI has filed against an infringer of its patents. Without Phil's insight and determination, these returns would never have been achieved.

Few of the Program's staff members came to SRI with experience in ultrasound. But the experience they garnered at SRI enabled many of them to take key positions with Diasonics and Acuson, the two Bay Area medical ultrasound startups that grew to hold commanding positions in the industry. At its peak, the Program employed 18 people.

Blood Pressure Monitoring

High blood pressure is a pervasive problem across the United States. This fact, together with redefinitions that have lowered the threshold of high blood pressure (now anything above 80/120), leaves many Americans vulnerable. Blood pressure is becoming one of our more important medical measurements.

Traditionally, the measurement is made using the familiar cuff-enabled sphygmomanometer, which compresses the artery to a point where the blood flow stops. Then, noting the so-called Korotkoff sounds of the beating heart, blood begins to flow, first marginally and then completely as the heart sound disappears. Although this method is universally used, it falls short in at least three areas: First, it is somewhat labor-intensive, and when many such measurements are made in screening, the person making the measurement may get sloppy. Second, since it closes off the return of blood through the veins, the cuff-enabled method can cause peripheral edema, or swelling in the arm, with prolonged use. The issue of prolonged use brings us implicitly to the third area, the need for *continuous* blood pressure monitoring during surgical procedures or in lie detector testing. It is for this third reason that SRI began its investigation.[15]

SRI's involvement in this field started in the early 1960s. While most researchers were concentrating on the Korotkoff sounds, to SRI they seemed too indirect across the range of people and environments that would be faced. Instead, SRI concluded it was better to measure the pressure directly. Under contracts with NASA and the NIH, Gerald Pressman and Peter Newgard in the Control Systems Laboratory began looking into ways to measure blood pressure continuously.[M] Some work had been done in the field of tonometry, which deals with the medical measurement of pressures such as that of arterial blood or in the eye. While conceptually more straightforward, tonometry was subject to all the vagaries of individual physiology, automatic calibration, and, by no means least, the technologies needed to create a useful product. Seeing the value and success of ocular tonometry, SRI researchers became the first to develop arterial tonometry using a piezoresistive (i.e., pressure resistant) method to measure the pressure exhibited by the artery at a point of convenience, the wrist. When the radial artery here is flattened somewhat (but not completely), it becomes an easily accessible source point for the entire pressure waveform.

Having decided on this location, the next challenges for perfecting this noninvasive method were to position the pressure sensor at exactly the correct location over the artery and to apply only enough pressure, or flattening, to yield a good continuous measurement. SRI's first models had only one sensor element, which made placement difficult. In the early 1970s, Newgard invented a way to ease the problem of location by fabricating larger, multiple-element sensors from silicon. But that development in turn introduced the need for algorithms to compute which elements should, in fact, be used to yield an accurate measurement. In 1979, Joe Eckerle, Steve Terry (a Stanford student), and Newgard tested an eight-element sensor that not only determined

---

[15] Although some have mistakenly attributed to SRI the automation of the cuff method now seen in workplaces and drugstores, those devices obviously do not provide continuous monitoring and are not part of this story.

the correct elements to use but also the correct amount of pressure to apply.[N] In 1984 for the FBI, Eckerle built a multi-element tonometer for use in polygraph testing. It also helped rectify polygraph inaccuracies stemming from movement of the subject being tested.

Continuing with medical applications, SRI obtained a development contract from a Japanese firm, Colin Electronics. Over the course of this work Colin licensed a multi-element tonometer method from SRI in 1986 and by 1988 placed the monitor in the Japanese medical electronics market. Innovations in this unit continued, included a motorized positioning of the sensor and a completely automatic adjustment of the flattening pressure. But several factors required that the tonometer output be calibrated using a cuff measurement. A year later SRI helped Colin upgrade its sensor to 31 elements and eliminate the need for calibration. The resulting instrument, shown in Figure 5-18, became widely used in operating rooms in Japan and has belatedly received FDA approval in the United States.

But the vagaries of the commercial world have now appeared. Oddly, though the SRI tonometer approach represents the state of the art in clinical continuous blood pressure measurement, Colin has not been able to penetrate the U.S. market where cuff measurement, albeit automatic, is still in use even in operating room settings. This lack of market development, plus Colin's own costly but unsuccessful investigation into the use of tonometry as a noninvasive diagnostic for arteriosclerosis added to increasing competitive pressures in Japan, recently sent Colin into bankruptcy. Without a required performance clause in the SRI license agreement, this inactivity now threatens SRI's interest in medical field tonometry since its relevant patents expire in 2005. Outside the constraints of the license, SRI continues to explore the uses

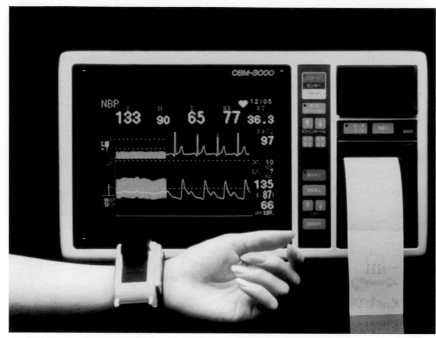

Figure 5-18. The Colin Electronics continuous blood monitoring instrument using the SRI sensor.

of tonometry including the continuous measurement of heart rate using a watch-like device.

Endnotes

[A] SRI International, *Telepresence for Microscopy, Microsurgery, and Endoscopy*, Proposal EDU 89-214, September 29, 1989.

[B] Col. Irwin Simon, personal communication, September 14, 2000.

[C] Carl J. Levenson, M.D., letter to SRI, April 21, 1992.

[D] Some of what follows can be found in Donald H. Kelly, Visual *Science and Engineering— Models and Applications*, Marcel Dekker, 1994. Kelly was an SRI employee in the same laboratory.

[E] *SRI Investments in Tomorrow*, No. 6, Winter 1972-3

[F] *SRI Journal*, 22, 11-20, October 1968.

[G] SRI IR&D Project 186531-107.

[H] SRI Project 6282 for $116,652, on October 1, 1966 from Stanford University under its Grant NB 06341.

[I] Richard B. Yules et al., The Effect of Q-Switched Ruby Laser Radiation on Dermal Tattoo Pigment in Man, *Archives of Surgery*, 95, 179-180, August 1967. (This explains SRI's Q-switched laser approach.)

[J] L. M. Zatz, Initial clinical evaluation of a new ultrasonic camera, *Radiology*, 117, 399–404, 1975; K. W. Marich, L. M. Zatz, and P.S. Green, Real time imaging with a new ultrasonic camera. I. *In vitro* experimental studies on transmission imaging of biological structures, *Journal of Clinical Ultrasound*, 3, 5, 1975; and L. M. Zatz, K. W. Marich, and P.S. Green, Real time imaging with a new ultrasonic camera. II. Preliminary studies in normal adults, *Journal of Clinical Ultrasound*, 3,17, 1975.

[K] Green chaired the conclave and edited its proceedings: *Acoustical Holography*, Vol. 5, Plenum Press, 1974. The volume also contained a paper about the SRI system by Green, Louis Schaefer, Earle Jones, and Joe Suarez, *A New, High-Performance Ultrasound Camera*.

[L] Philip S. Green, John S. Ostrem, and Todd K. Whitehurst, Combined Reflection and Transmission Ultrasound Imaging, *Ultrasound in Medicine and Biology*, 17 (3), 283-289, 1991.

[M] G. L. Pressman and P. M. Newgard, A Transducer for the Continuous External Measurement of Arterial Blood Pressure, *IEEE Transactions On Bio-Medical Electronics*, 73-81, April 1963.

[N] S. Terry, J. S. Eckerle, R. D. Kornbluh, T. Low, and C. M. Ablow, Silicon Pressure Transducer Arrays for Blood Pressure Measurement, *Sensors and Actuators*, A21-A23, 1070–1079, 1990.

Chapter 6
Transportation

Hydra-Cushion

In the 1950s, railroad boxcars and jolts just seemed to go together. Beyond the obvious noises were the more silent problems of broken goods and broken rolling stock as well as the often hidden costs of dealing with both. Even when insurance covered such costs, the cost of the insurance itself added up. At that time, damage to rail freight shipments

amounted to more than $100 million a year. Some of the railcars of the day had spring-based couplers, but they weren't very effective and an improved solution to such impacts was clearly needed. That need was augmented by the practice of forming trains by pushing them over the crest of a small hill into a "tree" of switches, a process called "humping." The down-slope speed of the railcar was 7 or 8 miles an hour and the in-rail braking systems of the hill often left a car vulnerable to impact from the car to follow. This practice of humping ensured that the jolt-at-coupling would continue.

One of SRI's long-time Board members was Don Russell, president of Southern Pacific Railroad (SP). Through Russell's awareness of the technical capabilities at SRI, the chief engineer at SP was asked to consider whether SRI might help with some of SP's more important technical challenges. Among the problems that surfaced in these discussions was the problem of high-impact coupling.

A cooperative project with the Southern Pacific began in 1954, with SRI undertaking the design of a new coupling system and the SP yards in South San Francisco doing the early, prototype fabrication. The work focused on the so-called "draft gear," a part of the coupler designed to cushion against the damaging high-energy impacts. The goal was to design an improved draft gear that was low cost, simple in construction, reliable, and maintenance-free. The new system also needed to be sensitive to the energy of the impact and to adjust the cushioning action accordingly. The SRI Hydra-Cushion was the result, and it was eagerly pressed into service in a large fraction of railroad freight cars designated to carry fragile loads.

The new impact-absorption concept was developed by William K. MacCurdy, who joined SRI in 1952 as a former naval architect with a background in shipbuilding, not railroads (see Figure 6-1). As he said, and this is important for a research environment, "the request came as a wide open question rather than a query for any specific solution...They described the industry's loss and damage problem and asked...if we could suggest any improvements in existing

Figure 6-1. SRI project leader and Hydra-Cushion designer, William MacCurdy.

practices. The Institute's practice is to examine a problem over-all so as to see where the real problems are."[A] SRI conducted a literature study and performed a survey of car-handling practices. The researchers found that cushioned underframes had been around for years but the "short travel" (the distance the coupler could move at impact) made it impossible to absorb the shocks they were experiencing. MacCurdy chose a more fundamental approach.

Ideally, the railroad car frame that supports the car and rests on the rolling trucks should not directly carry the pulling or stopping force to the adjacent cars. In the new concept, the train's load is transmitted from one coupler to the next by two sliding sills or beams whose movement is restrained by forces sensitive to their acceleration. Each coupler has an extended connection (sill) to a point in the center of the car where the Hydra-Cushion mechanism is located (Figure 6-2). The energy absorption starts with an interleaving of fingers on the end of each sill away from the coupler and some stationary fingers in the Hydra-Cushion unit. To make the restraint proportional to impact acceleration, a hydraulic piston increases the pressure on the interleaved fingers via a wedge attached to each sill.

The oil movement within the hydraulic piston is regulated in such a way that the braking effect is almost proportional to the magnitude of the impact.[B] To prove the soundness of the design, a railcar was modified in SP's Sacramento shops and quickly placed in

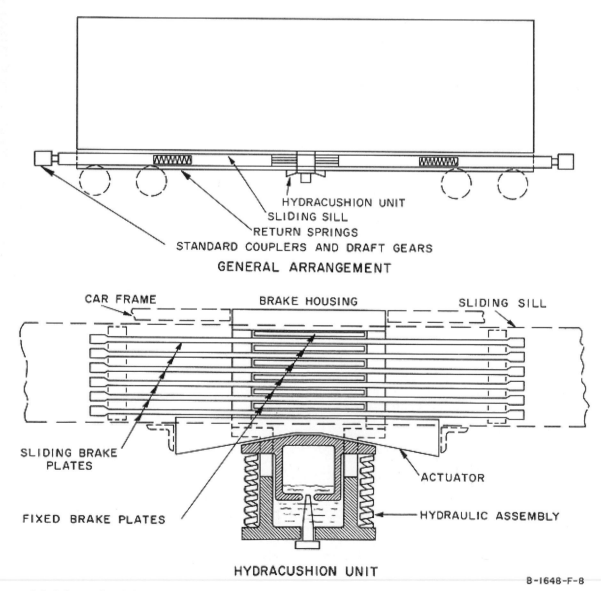

GENERAL ARRANGEMENT

HYDRACUSHION UNIT
SLIDING SILL
RETURN SPRINGS
STANDARD COUPLERS AND DRAFT GEARS

CAR FRAME   BRAKE HOUSING   SLIDING SILL

SLIDING BRAKE PLATES

FIXED BRAKE PLATES

ACTUATOR

HYDRAULIC ASSEMBLY

HYDRACUSHION UNIT

B-1648-F-8

Figure 6-2. Schematic of the Hydra-Cushion unit showing its location and its operating mechanism.

6–2

service for testing in December of that year. To give it a difficult test SP first put the car into "windshield service" from Detroit to the West Coast. The result was remarkable, with absolutely no claims for the first 6 months. The unit for that car was actually called "Hydra-friction." The second model, renamed Hydra-Cushion, was completed and introduced for in-service testing of fragile goods in April of 1956.

The benefits of the MacCurdy design can clearly be seen in the comparative loading or impulse traces shown in Figure 6-3. Not only is the peak initial load on the frame much less, the recoil is non-existent! The success of these models prompted 350 cars to be built and placed in SP service during the summer of 1957.[1]

These newly equipped cars were reserved for the more damage-susceptible loads such as canned goods, furniture, household appliances, paint, and glass. During their first year of service, the Hydra-Cushion-equipped cars made 1745 loaded trips. On 1425 of these, no damage to any goods was reported. On 445 shipments of canned goods, 70% were undamaged, whereas the rate in unmodified cars was only 48%. Most telling, however, was that the average value of the damage loss was reduced by a factor of 25.[C]

Though SRI does not show a MacCurdy patent in its database, SP gained some proprietary information on the Hydra-Cushion mechanism that it licensed in 1957. The license was to Evans Products Co. (where MacCurdy went after leaving SRI) for manufacture of the mechanism for all the railroad industry. SP also created a company, Hydra-Cushion Inc., in Chicago to profit from the innovation. By the beginning of 1963, over 6000 railcars on 20 railroads had been modified with Hydra-

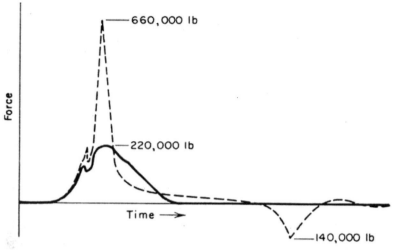

Figure 6-3. The change in the load on the under-carriage of a railcar with Hydra-Cushion given a 7-mph impact. The car was loaded to 169,000 lb.

Cushion and at least five other companies had sprung up with competing designs.[D] According to *Railway Age*, by 1967 over 125,000 railcars were equipped with underframe cushioning.[E]

In 1964 William MacCurdy received the Franklin Institute's annual George R. Henderson Medal. This gold medal was for achievements "in the field of railway impact control and associated car design, with resulting benefits in reducing lading and rolling stock damage." SP's William E. Thomford also received the honor, reflecting on the SRI tendency to work with, not just for, a client.[F] A final tribute from *Railway Age* in 1967 said this innovation made possible rail transport quality control programs that would have been previously "unthinkable." It concludes: "The 10th anniversary of the cushion-underframe…has to be one of the most significant anniversaries in the annals of the industry."[G]

The industry-wide benefits of Hydra-Cushion in reducing cargo damage, extending the life of the railroad car itself, and reducing maintenance costs were enormous. Considering that the Southern Pacific projects on which SRI first designed and tested Hydra-Cushion came to less than $20,000, this was a profitable investment indeed.[2]

---

[1] According to SRI's Bill McGuigan, the prototype Hydra-Cushion cars worked so much better than the existing stock that the test cars sent out for operational tests would never come back! He also recalled, during a discussion on June 7, 2000, that he also knew they were working well when he received an irate phone call from a manufacturer of existing shock-absorbing couplers. The caller wondered what SRI was doing in this business and McGuigan kindly told him that his company could have retained SRI if they had been on the ball.

---

[2] Project 1226 was for $7,000 dated September 15, 1954 and Project 1648 was for $12,473 dated February 10, 1956; both for the Southern Pacific Railroad. Other projects followed in 1960 and 1965 for continuing testing and improvements to the concept.

SRI did a lot of other work for the railroad industry, much of which was built on its relationship with SP. We will mention just a few others here, starting with the design of a more efficient train operation system that better classified, located, and used empty rail cars.

Managing the Flow of Railcars

Imagine that you own 10,000 boxcars that are distributed not only across the areas where your railroad's primary tracks are located, but on those of other rail carriers as well. Several operating and efficiency factors immediately emerge. First, you need to have your own empty railcars available when they are needed at the site where your shipping opportunities exist. Second, by arrangement, at least back in 1955, your company must pay $2.75 per day for each railcar owned by another company that sits on your own tracks. Reciprocally, every empty car of yours sitting idle on your tracks is a lost opportunity of $2.75 per car per day if it could be loaned to other carriers. These demands on railroad operations sent the Southern Pacific Railroad to SRI for help in 1954. How could SP govern the movement of its 10,000 railcars to best advantage?[H]

SRI immediately saw the complexity in managing such a system. The network on which the cars (yours and other carriers') can move is complex in itself, and it is complicated further by the need to allow for the effects of weather on track availability and the time variability of demand. For example, unusual weather conditions such as higher or lower than expected temperatures can move crop harvest forward or delay it. Such complexities and many more led SRI to a statistical, operations research model for the rail system.

For over three years, SRI mathematicians and engineers observed the sources and time movements of the various grades of railcars (important as to what they could carry) and modeled them. The model was used to characterize a given week's operation of car distribution for Southern Pacific's system. Most important, the system could forecast the holdings and movements required to meet the coming week's empty railcar needs. This prediction ultimately defined not only what empty cars should be moved each week between the SP's operating divisions to provide the most efficient flow of goods, but also how many empty cars should be ordered from connecting railroads.

The SRI model was implemented on an IBM punched card and data processing system and tested and put into use on Southern Pacific's Pacific Coast Line that extended 8,000 miles from Portland, OR to El Paso, TX.

Such models are of little use, of course, unless you first have some idea where the railcars are located in both time and space. Being able to form and reform trains also requires knowledge of where trains and their constituent cars are in the collective rail system. In the early 1950s, this information was typically gathered manually, either by men walking the tracks as trains paused at certain stations or by monitoring closed-circuit television cameras at points where trains were moving slowly. The manually gathered information was then telegraphed or phoned ahead to the next branching points. It was a slow and tedious process.

Around 1957-1958, the New York Central Railroad raised the problem with the A.B. Dick Company, a Chicago printing company that had an ongoing relationship with SRI. Was there a more efficient way the information could be collected and forwarded along the rail system so as to facilitate the rebuilding of trains or the management of empty cars? Since the cars were then identifiable only by the alphanumeric indicators on them, SRI quickly devised a high-speed imaging system that would capture the information as the train sped by. In this case, the image was of the entire train. The television camera imaged only a very thin vertical slice of the train at any instant, letting the movement of the train define the horizontal aspect of the image. The output of the camera was microwaved or cabled ahead where a version of the SRI Videograph would print out the image of the entire train (see Chapter 7). The printer was extremely fast, moving a two-inch-wide paper at something like 36 inches per second. Although the system went into use, it still left the reading of car numbers from the image to be done manually.[3] Later, car identification would be done using barcodes.

---

[3] Later the Denver & Rio Grande Western Railroad contracted with A.B. Dick for an SRI Videograph system to pass way-bills and other printed material much more quickly—in effect a very high speed facsimile system.

Other projects for Southern Pacific continued into the 1960s. For example, SRI looked into the old technology used in grade crossing warning systems. SRI, working with SP engineer A.C. Krout, replaced the long-used block system, one whose trigger activated when a train crossed into a certain grade-crossing zone and which required rails to be electrically isolated in that zone. SRI designed a better and more easily implemented system that was based on both the position and the velocity of the train and required no isolated sections of track. The objective was a system that could be fitted to any crossing and would provide a safe and minimum-delay experience for the automotive public.

The technique, designed by SRI engineer Carroll Steele, used the two rails as a transmission line, the reactance of which was indicative of the train's distance. SP conducted long-term tests on the SRI innovation. SRI's testing of the new crossing alert system began in 1961 and fail-safe features that checked the system every five seconds were integrated into a design that was in production by early 1963.[I] That production occurred at the Pomona Division of Marquardt Corporation who later sold it to Safetran, where it is still manufactured today.[J]

In another project for Southern Pacific, SRI built a journal infrared system that would detect the presence of high-friction wheel bearings or "hotboxes" as trains rolled by. SRI then designed methods for controlling the speed of the car at train-building hump yards to minimize coupling speed and reduce noise. Finally, SRI also determined why fires sometimes occurred in the shipping of cotton fibers and the role of railroads in restoring the civil infrastructure in the advent of a nuclear attack.

A Very Early Airline Reservation System

The year was 1956 and United Air Lines was getting behind in its ability to determine and schedule its available passenger space. United had conducted an internal study to look at the long range needs for controlling space utilization and determined that engineering consultants should be hired to design and implement a "space control system." In October of that year, United asked SRI for that help and

the following month signed a five-month, $85,000 contract to design a solution to this problem.[K]

At this time in the development of computers, stored-program general-purpose computers had only modest capability but were evolving rapidly. Reliability was an important issue, particularly to this client. So the question arose as to how far this system should go toward automating passenger reservations. To be conservative, United decided to go part way; that is, to build a system that kept track of the  available space, in this case seating, and make that information available to ticket agents. The ticket agents would then perform by hand the match between the available seat and the passenger. They would then pass back to the system the information needed to update the seat inventory.

SRI completed its work on time and issued a 182-page system design and information for United to use in making the appropriate hardware selection. The system was a hybrid of centralized and decentralized design, depending on the function in play. To have an unambiguous resource on the booked (ticketed) and available seats, there was one, centralized accounting of that data. Because of the repeated queries about the availability of seating without a booking, those data were decentralized to United's six metropolitan sites. Figure 6-4 shows a composite map of the system taken from the SRI design.

To meet the use specifications United had provided, simulations had to be done, including such factors as inquiry waiting time statistics. These simulations included modeling the frequency and types of various expected queries. The limit on a seat query was 3 seconds and for a booking was 15 seconds. These constraints boiled down to the design of both machine capacity and line traffic volumes. The specifications also called for 400 flights per day, 1000 ticketing agents, and 85,000 bookings or cancellations per day.

SRI also identified two implementers, Remington-RAND (UNIVAC) and Teleregister Corporation, and asked them to provide quotes

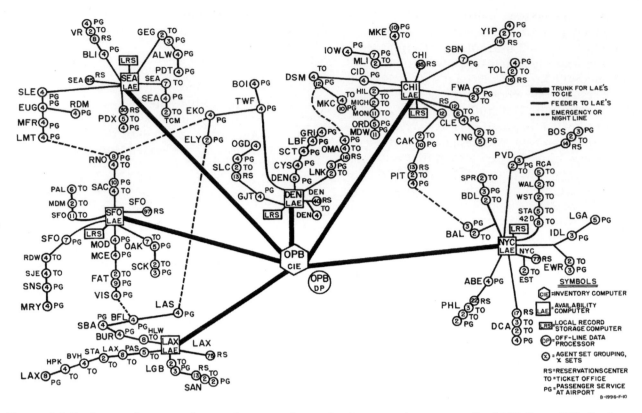

Figure 6-4. Equipment layout and map of proposed generic air reservations system for 1965 (from SRI's final report to United).

on the generic system design, costs, proof of capability, time to implement, and reliability. From these quotes, United chose Teleregister of Stamford, CT, as the implementer. Teleregister had made its name in the brokerage industry and for perhaps a decade Teleregister had been placing increasingly capable reservation systems in the sales offices of various airlines. Teleregister's reservation system, called Reservisor, consisted of relays, rotating magnetic drums, and some electronics. Teleregister was also one of the first companies to integrate completely the functionality of communications and computing. All this experience gave them a good understanding of the functionality needed by United.

This new system was not only a new, more intensely computer-based technology, it was also a much larger, distributed system, able to give 24-hour reliability. To gain that reliability, two computer systems had to be run in tandem so that when one failed the other would immediately pick up the task. Internally, Teleregister called it an Electronic Reservation System. Because of SRI's familiarity with the design, SRI was asked to help United monitor the fabrication and define the functional tests

of individual components and then the complete system. The design goals for the system were to meet or exceed the predicted 1965 traffic load, but SRI had laid out interim years and the capability the system needed to have. So, in a follow-on small contract, SRI also designed tests for traffic handling, response time, fault detection and attribution, and the overall reliability of the system as a space management tool.

By May 1961, Teleregister had installed the United system. United called it Instamatic. As the potential of the new system became apparent, United asked Teleregister to propose an integrated system that would go far beyond passenger reservations to other airline operations. These included freight, flight scheduling, pay, maintenance, profit and loss, and even load and fuel balance on each flight.[L] Teleregister submitted the proposal, and it was so well done that United used it as a basis for a competitive bid, which ironically was won in December of 1965 by Remington-RAND UNIVAC. This, I believe, ultimately evolved in part to United's Apollo reservation system, which is still an important player in the world of airline reservations.

So, what was SRI's net position in the rapidly evolving computerization of the airline industry? Unfortunately, not much. IBM was at the same time working with American Air Lines to build SABRE, which was in partial operation in 1960 after an investment of 400 labor-years and $40 million. Its first installations were of about the same size as the SRI design, but the system continued to grow. Its final cutover to operations was made in 1964. The SRI-defined system, then, had but a few years at United where it was a prominent part of the first airline reservation systems.

The Containerization of Ocean Shipping

One of the most obvious revolutions in the business of ocean-going cargo transport is the ubiquitous cargo container. Many ships are now made strictly as container carriers, and as they leave port, they seem to brim and even overflow with containers "pasted" to every flat spot. The larger vessels can now hold the equivalent of 6,000–10,000 containers, 8 x 8 x 20 ft in size. Not only does containerization enormously simplify and accelerate the loading and unloading of ships, but that ease of movement continues as other carrier forms, such as trucks and rail, cradle the same container aboard with hardly a missed beat. One of the pivotal aspects of such a flow of cargo is, of course, the need for standardization, both for dense nesting and for ease of transfer between various forms of so-called intermodal transport.

During the 1960s, SRI had a hand in the growth of this type of cargo transport. Much of the ultimate purpose of this work was to prepare the rationale for both individual maritime carriers and shipping ports in their transition to containerization. These studies required examining the adaptability of various kinds of cargo to a range of container sizes as well as estimating the cargo traffic that would justify the huge capital cost of conversion. With logistical specialists, naval architects, economists, and mathematicians on SRI's staff, virtually all aspects of the new containerization concept could be analyzed.[4]

SRI performed modular cargo handling and traffic studies for some of the world's largest cargo fleets, including the following carriers, ports, and passageways:

- Carriers
  - Johnson Line (Sweden)
  - Maersk Line (Denmark) (now includes Sealand)
  - China Overseas Shipping (Taiwan)
  - American President Lines (USA)
  - Columbus Line (Germany)
- Ports and Passageways
  - Tampa Bay, Tacoma, Portland, and the States of Alaska and California (USA)
  - Bahia Blanca, Rio Gallegos, and Santa Cruz (Argentina)
  - St. Lawrence Seaway Development Authority (Canada)
  - The Canadian Atlantic Development Board (Canada)
  - The Panama Canal Co. (Panama)
  - Al Aqabah (Jordan).

Most of this work was done in the 1960s when all carriers were struggling with the proper container configuration for their existing and proposed fleets, the routes over which containerization made sense, and the timing for transition. This work consisted of exploring appropriate container handling systems as well as elaborate simulations on where, when, and how transitions were best made.

One client on the list, The Canadian Atlantic Development Board, was a government board for whom SRI explored an interesting problem: the very seasonal uses of the Canadian ports of Halifax and St. Johns in spite of their being year-round ports.[M] Because of the summer opening of the St. Lawrence passage, ocean-going freight would bypass Halifax for the inland port of Montreal. Then, with the introduction of icebreakers, the seaway was kept open much of the winter. So, in the early 1960s even the cyclical use of the two coastal ports was dying. In 1964 the Canadian Atlantic Development Board asked SRI to look specifically at the containerization in the North Atlantic via Halifax and St. Johns.

---

[4] Some of the prominent SRI players in this work were Ben Andrews, Fred Witzel, Vance Miller, Robert Brown, Neal Houston, Beverly Taylor, Robert Hubenette, Phil Adams, and Ogden Hamilton.

Figure 6-5. Large container ship at Halifax (taken from the online version of the *Port of Halifax Magazine*, July/August, 1999)

In a nutshell, the answer was that Halifax could be a year-round port for the large container ships whose great circle route to New York passed close by. So investments were made and the first container ship docked in Halifax in the summer of 1969.[N] By the turn of the century, the port was serving more than 20 carriers and handling almost a half million containers per year. Both truck and rail transport then distributed them across Eastern Canada and the United States.

Several studies for the Panama Canal Co. were surveys of the future traffic it might expect, a basis for revenue prediction, and the configuration forthcoming ships might take as the containerization process matured.

SRI's early advocacy of containerization was indicated in a speech SRI marine engineer/naval architect Benjamin Andrews gave in San Francisco in 1967. There he outlined the trend toward specialty ships and away from the general-purpose cargo vessels of the past. He argued for the broad benefits of containerization including greater speed, lower shipping and insurance costs, and one of the biggest virtues, the ease of transshipment.[O] The revolution is still in full swing with about 25 million containers transiting U.S. ports each year.

The Maglev Project

Early in the 1900s, magnetic levitation (maglev) had been proposed as a way to decrease the friction of a ground vehicle. However, the various approaches proposed were so inefficient they were judged economically infeasible. In 1963, however, the field was reopened to more investigation with the notion of using low-loss, cryogenically cooled, superconducting magnets.

The late 1960s saw ongoing research and development work in Germany, England, Canada, and Japan and in special, non-transportation needs in our own Department of Defense. This DoD application explored using maglev to build extremely high velocity sleds, and SRI was involved.[P] So, in 1970 when the U.S. Department of Transportation decided to let a few research studies to explore the practicality of the concept for a rail system, SRI was ready and won one of those contracts in February 1971.[Q]

The purpose of the SRI study was to examine the technical feasibility of various methods of levitating high-speed ground transportation vehicles. SRI examined the use of permanent magnets, conventional electromagnets, and superconducting magnets. In work that continued for over three years, SRI physicists defined the theory, analytical models, and experimental outcome of maglev. Experiments were conducted on a 500-foot aluminum test track built on the SRI back lot. They used a 1 by 4 m sled to test levitation methods and to measure the control dynamics required to both lift and guide the sled in its track.

During the first year, the sled was not totally levitated but was used to measure a variety of levitating approaches. By 1972, the 300-kG sled was completely levitated and guided by magnetic forces. Levitation was achieved by four 28 by 32-cm magnets cooled to minus 450°F. Figure 6-6 shows the sled and track. Clearances in the track were purposefully set so that the sled could have 15 degrees of roll, pitch, and yaw without restriction. Thus, the vertical and lateral positionings of the sled were controlled by magnetic guidance and damping systems. Its forward motion, however, was defined by an endless cable and winch arrangement. Thus, the electromagnetic or other forward propulsion aspects of maglev were not explored at SRI.

The results of the work showed that all three types of magnets were capable of meeting the project design goal of suspending a 100,000-lb vehicle. However, when a host of considerations were factored in, such as estimated costs, ride comfort, and operating characteristics, the superconducting, repelling force, maglev, was the most favorable. Superconducting materials, in this case obtained by cryogenic cooling, approach zero resistance and therefore the induced current, in

Figure 6-6. The SRI maglev sled and test track located at SRI (Nov 1972) and its principal designer, Howard Coffey.

this case about 100 amperes, will persist as long as the temperature is maintained. These magnets can also use simpler continuous conducting-sheet guideways and are amenable to electromagnetic damping systems needed for ride comfort and guidance control. The superconducting magnets designed at SRI would allow a vehicle to clear the guideway by 8 inches at a speed of 300 mph. SRI's maglev work continued for about 3 years until the DoT terminated its interest in the area.[R,S]

Although the United States lost interest in this subject for a time, work continued in Europe and Japan through the 1980s and to the present. China recently fielded the world's fastest maglev train, having a 268-mph peak velocity and linking downtown Shanghai to its airport. The ride is smooth and each train can carry nearly 600 passengers.[T]

Endnotes

[A] This and other information for this story came from: Era of car cushioning began 10 years ago, *Railway Age*, February 27, pp. 34–35, 1967.

[B] William K. MacCurdy, *Comparative Impact Tests of the Hydracushion Underframe*, Final Report, SRI Project 1648, July 1956. Also SRI *Research for Industry*, 8(2), 10–11, January 1956.

[C] Softer Rides for Rail Freight, *SRI Journal*, 2 (2), 44-45, 1958.

[D] SRI's *Research for Industry*, 15(1), 10, January–February 1963.

[E] *Railway Age*, op. cit.

[F] A Research Accomplishment Acknowledged, *SRI Journal*, 2, 12 1964.

[G] *Railway Age*, op. cit.

[H] SRI's *Research for Industry*, 9(4), 1-3, May 1957.

[I] SRI's *Research for Industry*, 15(1), 14, January–February 1963.

[J] Email from Carroll Steele dated June 14, 2004.

[K] R. C. Amara, Bonnar Cox, George A. Barnard III, T. H. Meisling, and Oliver Whitby, *A Unified Electronic System for Passenger Space Control*, Final Report on SRI Project 1996, Contract No. 9001 for United Air Lines, Inc., May 1957.

[L] Dr. William Mitchell, Professor of Information Science, University of Arkansas, *The Genesis of NASA RECON*. Taken from www.ualr.edu/~wmmitchell/NASARECON.htm.

[M] SRI Project 5472 for $22,200 conducted from December 28, 1964, to August 14, 1965.

[N] The Magic Box, *Port of Halifax Magazine*, July/August 1999. (Mentions their contracting for two studies to address the plight of the port at Halifax.)

[O] Benjamin V. Andrews, The Changing Future of Marine Transportation, Speech to the San Francisco Traffic Club, March 15, 1967.

[P] T. W. Barbee, G. N. Bycroft, E. G. Chilton, F. M. Chilton, and H. T. Coffey, *The Hypervelocity Rocket Sled—A Design Analysis*, SRI Project PMU-7014, July 1968.

[Q] Federal Railroad Administration, Office of High Speed Ground Transportation, Contract DOT-FR-10001, $121,337, February 8, 1971, to January 7, 1972.

[R] *The Feasibility of Magnetically Levitating High Speed Ground Vehicles*, Final Report Task I, SRI Project 1080, February 1972, NTIS Report No. PB-210505.

[S] H. T. Coffey, Magnetic Suspensions for High Speed Vehicles, in *Advances in Cryogenic Engineering*, Vol. 19, p. 137, 1974, Plenum Press.

[T] Faster Than a Speeding Bullet Train, *IEEE Spectrum*, 30-34, August 2003.

Chapter 7
Printing and Imaging Systems

Modern Printing Systems and Their Inks—
New Approaches to an Old Art

For over forty years, SRI has repeatedly provided innovations to what has become a renaissance in the old art of printing. Linking much of SRI's motivation to the revolution in computer-generated text and graphics, virtually all these innovations served the need for faster, more flexibly programmed printing mechanisms and machines. The computer revolution that was supposed to have eliminated our need for paper has clearly done just the opposite: printed material is now more prevalent than ever.

SRI's work in printing began with the large Bank of America project known as ERMA (see Chapter 2). ERMA introduced the need for individual checks to bear an account number that would enable automatic posting and account maintenance. Before this change, checks could be literally written on anything. But because checks of even standard size could be written over with cancellation marks or handwriting, SRI decided that the most reliable method for printing and automatically reading checks was to use ink that included a magnetic pigment. Thus, for ERMA, SRI invented a font-ink combination that could be reliably read by both machines and humans. For this innovation, SRI's Ken Eldridge was awarded U.S. Patent No. 3,000,000.

Here we trace just a part of SRI's role in printing. First, we describe SRI's work in the 1950s and 1960s on the technology of printers: the Videograph printer for A.B. Dick and one of the first inkjet printers, built for Recognition Equipment, Inc. From about 1970 to 1983, SRI had a working relationship with the R&D arm of the Savin Business Machines Corporation of New York that would, over time, aggregate to research of almost $10 million. Three types of the projects for Savin are described here: a new fax machine, new office copiers, and early work on inks and toners. We then cover SRI's attempts in the 1990s to commercialize its breakthrough developments on water-fast inks and even the technology of the paper itself.

A.B. Dick and the Videograph

One of SRI's early and very long-term commercial relationships was with the Chicago printing company, A.B. Dick. In the early 1950s, A.B. Dick had a substantial worldwide market in mimeograph technology for duplication. That technique was, by the way, old enough to have been licensed by A.B. Dick from Thomas Edison, and thus A.B. Dick knew that this venerable product area would soon be challenged. SRI's first project with A.B. Dick came in September of 1955 to look into the feasibility of electronic duplication.[1] A.B. Dick was seeking a new generation copier but, along the way, became diverted by another process in which they were involved—something as mundane as mailing labels.[A]

Then and now, weekly magazines with very large circulation such as *Time* and *Newsweek* face a big problem in their huge weekly mailings. They can produce upwards of 10 million magazines a week because the magazines themselves are all alike, but the labels for their mail subscribers are necessarily all different. Moreover, the master mailing list changes significantly each week. In the 1950s, slow label printers just weren't coping with this problem.[2] How could they manage to print the millions of labels needed every week, each tailored to a new, valid customer list? To do just that, SRI engineers reoriented the technology

---

[1] In 1955 Xerox was still called the Haloid Corporation and Haloid's first successful copier, the 914 (called that because it could copy images as big as 9 x 14 in.), did not appear on the market until 1959.

[2] At the time, A.B. Dick was using more than 30 Addressograph-Multigraph printers, each operating 80 hours per week. And there was the formidable task of handling millions of embossed metal stencils each week, one for each subscriber.

they were exploring for A.B. Dick for electronic duplication into something called the Videograph.

Because of the speed requirement in this kind of printing, SRI did not pursue the selenium photoconductor approach Xerox was using. During the electronic copier investigation, staff of SRI's Television and Tube Labs had invented a cathode ray tube with an array of very small wires embedded in its face.[3] These wires were oriented in the direction of the scanning electron beam and perpendicular to the direction of the paper. In its raster motion, the electron beam would selectively deposit charge on the inside ends of those wires needed to form the desired character. Those wires, so excited, would directly transfer the charge to the paper that was in contact with the outside of the Videograph tube. The paper's charge pattern was then mechanically dusted with a black powder (toner) that clung to the paper in those regions of charge. The toner was then heated and pressed on the paper to make the print legible and permanent.

The Videograph printer, shown in Figure 7-1, could print as many as 50 labels per second and was completed in 1958. With it A.B. Dick captured a market for rapid printing and, with continuing upgraded technology, held that market for many years. In the late 1960s, A.B. Dick adopted inkjet printing for making labels and thus came its popular Videojet printer. According to A.B. Dick's company web page, the Videojet was the world's first commercial inkjet printer.[B] This printer came after some of SRI's own inkjet technology and so SRI helped develop the ink for the Videojet. But more on SRI's role in inkjet printing below.

Though briefly pursued, the technical approach to the Videograph should not be thought of as adequate for electronic duplication; that is, what we call today a copier. Because of the interwire capacitance in the wire-embedded face of the Videograph's cathode ray tube, there was a fundamental limit to its ultimate resolution.[C] However, this early electrostatic printing concept led to many uses and projects from A.B. Dick and others. For example, SRI explored that technology for computer output printers and reported to

Figure 7-1. Front panel of the SRI-developed videographic label printer.

A.B. Dick in 1957 that Videograph-like systems could theoretically print as high as 30,000 characters per second. In 1963 a facsimile-type printer was built that could print images of billboard size.

Inkjet Printing[4]

The pressure for greater flexibility and speed in the way documents were machine processed continued to increase in the early 1960s. Of particular difficulty was the "lifting" or reading of printed text by a machine. At that time optical character readers (OCRs) were much slower than other document processes such as searching or sorting. To circumvent the problem of rereading such text at each step in document processing, there arose the idea of creating from the first OCR scan a text representation that could be machine-read much faster thereafter. That way any later document processing step that involved rereading could be done more rapidly. One of the larger OCR companies of the day was Texas-based Recognition Equipment, Inc. (REI), which was building equipment for processing credit card transaction receipts. To meet the needs of this equipment, REI was looking for a faster-read, higher quality, intermediate form in which to carry forward the details of the transaction. SRI suggested a bar-code system of character representation and a corresponding

---

[3] The principals were Phil Rice, Wayne Crews, John Papacosta, Jack Kabell, Howard Murphy, and Howard Borden, with Bob Tobey and Bill Barnes making the theoretical assessments.

[4] A review of early inkjet work can be found in Fred J. Kamphoefner, Inkjet Printing, *IEEE Trans. on Electron Devices*, ED-19(4), 584-593, April 1972. This became one of the most cited papers during the 1970s and helped stimulate the field, even in the later dot-on-demand inkjet techniques.

fast bar-code printer that would convert the output of the OCR system to this new intermediate form. So, in 1965 REI embarked with SRI on a three-phase study to develop a bar-code printer.

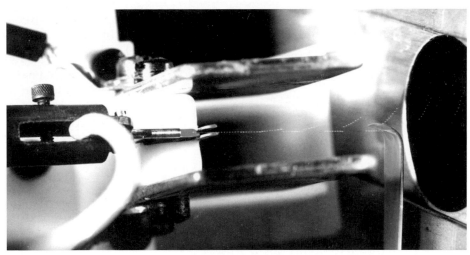

Figure 7-2. One of the first inkjet printers, built by SRI for Recognition Equipment, Inc. Shown are a droplet source, electrostatic deflection plates, and a stream of deflected ink droplets (1966).

In the meantime, Richard Sweet, a member of Stanford's System Techniques Laboratory, had invented an electrostatic inkjet technology for printing the output of an oscillograph. He had won an Army contract with three phases.[D] Phase I showed the feasibility of building such a printer, and Phase II developed a fast-drying, fluorescent ink and a satisfactory barcode-sensing system. The printing system used in Phase II was the original experimental apparatus constructed by Sweet, which had been designed for different ink. Phase III was to generate an experimental model of a printer that would print a simulated bar code using the fluorescent ink as well as meet the client's required level of operating performance. This entailed the redesign of the nozzle, flow modulator, valving system, drain, and controlling circuits. These changes were done at SRI and the result was a printer with a different, axially modulated drop formation system.

SRI developed a method that formed a reliable and synchronized ink-droplet stream. A strobe light system was used to photograph the in-flight droplets, as shown in Figure 7-2. Portions of the train of droplets are deflected by a time-varying electric potential on the two large plates and proceed through the hole to the paper. The undeflected droplets, then, are collected on the curved collector and returned to the ink reservoir. Given the needs for a non-particulate fluorescent ink and a complete stream cut-off valve, it was a difficult research problem to get the nozzle and ink-impulsing system to form uniform droplets while at the same time using ink that would dry quickly without smearing. The system produced the required droplet rate of 48,000 per second and was successfully built and licensed to several companies, including REI the sponsor, A.B.

Dick, and 3M Corporation.[E] This same encoding process was later used to encode information on the backs of bank checks, credit card invoices, and, in a Post Office project, to encode ZIP-addresses on envelopes so that in subsequent handling they could be more easily and reliably read by inexpensive readers/sorters (see Chapter 3). That SRI project with the Post Office produced their first experimental inkjet printer for zip code printing.

Figure 7-3. Nonimpact, stenciled printing on the yolk and white of an uncooked egg.

SRI also developed some stencil systems that, in about 1965, could even print on surfaces as delicate as the egg-yolk shown in Figure 7-3. This technique involved the flow of toner through a stencil, first by applying a potential between the toner cartridge and the opposite side of the target and later through the use of implanted charge on the target object itself.

Nonimpact inkjet printing would have a host of other applications such as printing labels on the plastic insulation of wires for the Boeing Company and, for A.B. Dick, the now commonplace printing on bottles, cans, and a variety of manufactured products. In this last case, A.B. Dick had developed a "Sweet-type" printer and SRI's Sam Graff and Dean Parkinson developed its ink. Significantly, this new ink had to dry fast, be very durable, and do both on nonabsorbing surfaces.

While SRI had very early roles in inkjet printing, to be clear, it did not participate in the development of the "drop-on-demand" inkjet printers so popular today as computer peripherals. As we will mention later, however, SRI did make innovative changes to their inks.

A New Fax Machine

The facsimile machines of the late 1960s were expensive, slow, and much larger than the desktop sizes common today. To those who believed in the information revolution, this was an opportunity. So, on November 24, 1970, representatives of Savin, CBS Television Services, and a new company called Dacom sat down at SRI to explore a new, more rapid, and more affordable facsimile machine. Within a month of that meeting, SRI had a contract for $239,000 to build just that. SRI's role was to design the printing component and do the overall design and integration effort. CBS's participation was largely financial. Dacom was a Bay Area company formed by two Lockheed engineers, one of whom had developed a compression technique that seemed attractive for facsimile.[5] Arthur D. Little had also been

targeted as having a promising optical scanning technique that would be useful.

The goal of a new product was evident early, and the pace was rapid. Earle Jones, the SRI project leader, and representatives of Dacom and A.D. Little were off to Japan within the first two months of the project. There they looked over Ricoh as a potential manufacturer and surveyed the status of Matsushita and NEC, the dominant players in the Japanese fax market. As the project progressed, several sources of a digital modem were examined and that of a subsidiary of Rockwell was chosen.[6] With the optical scanner and modem sources in hand and using SRI printer and signal processing skills, the development proceeded rapidly.[7] The prototype, called the Z-60, resulted in a facsimile machine that, though initially bulky, could scan, compress, and transmit data at 4800 bps—fast enough to give it a clear market advantage over existing fax machines.[8]

By October 1971, Ricoh would invest in the project as Savin created a specific subsidiary called Rapifax to continue its development. By March 1973, Ricoh acquired the technology and formed a subsidiary, Rapifax Corporation, in the United States to market and distribute the new machine. Ricoh would, over time, also engineer the digital machine to more modest dimensions and a lower manufacturing cost. According to the Ricoh web site, the first commercial realization of this machine, the RIFAX 600S, became the world's first digital fax machine. A later version, the Rapifax 100, and its derivatives would soon become one of the most important factors in leading the world to the high speed, affordable fax machines used everywhere today. Although Ricoh takes credit for inventing the digital fax machine, SRI and its partners as listed above provided the first prototype.[F]

Savin Office Copiers

The SRI-Savin connection actually had started with an SRI project for Sun Chemical to explore building an office copier that didn't infringe on

---

[5] Dacom was founded in Sunnyvale, CA, by Lockheed engineer Dan Hochman, exploiting a run-length encoding technique designed by colleague Don Weber. Savin and CBS had their eyes on Dacom. According to the *Wall Street Journal* of January 4, 1971, Savin and CBS would partner to purchase 60% of Dacom with options to buy the rest. SRI's facsimile work would eventually be funded through Dacom.

[6] The subsidiary was American Data Systems.
[7] Seven prepatent disclosures were collected on the project, but no applications were filed.
[8] The machines of the day were typified by Western Electric's "Teledeltos," 3M's "Thermafax," and Xerox's "Phonocopy." All these required about six minutes per page regardless of the density of information on the page.

the rich and unfolding Xerox patent portfolio. It wasn't an easy pathway, but many were probing it, including Sun and consequently SRI. A person at Sun Chemical had come to SRI with an idea for a non-Xerox copier and from that visit came a research project to explore it.

The Sun researcher's approach used a difficult process of moving a cloud of liquid toner through holes in a mask. SRI helped replace that process with one that projected light through a negative to a photo-electric surface. While SRI's process was feasible, the ultimate need for special dielectric rather than plain paper ended the project. During this work, however, the Sun researcher introduced to SRI a very energetic and entrepreneurial person by the name of Paul Charlap. As a ranking officer of Savin, Charlap had been trooping the world looking for new technologies that had relevance to office products such as those that copied or handled information. He must have first arrived at SRI about 1970.

Charlap's global technology search focused on ideas for non-Xerox-like copiers that still used plain paper. He had formed a working relationship with the Japanese office product company, Ricoh (which, by the way, means "copy" in Japanese), and was trying to find some additional technology that Ricoh could license. Charlap was already getting some royalties from them, but more important for SRI, he began to use SRI as the source of technical improvements of the Ricoh copier development so that he could harvest even more royalties. Hence, SRI had a significant input to the design of a machine that by 1976 was the world's largest selling copier. Principal areas where SRI helped in the development of the copier were an automatic plate bias system that kept the drum clean, an automatic document feeder, and its variety of toners. For several years, the copier was widely sold in the United States as a product of the Savin Corporation. By 1995 Ricoh would acquire all of Savin.[G]

Inks, Toners, and Paper

SRI's first in-depth interest in toners arose between 1976 and 1978 as part of its substantial work for Savin. That work led to a liquid-toner approach to copiers, and it became an important alternative to dry toner because it provided a higher resolution, given a much smaller particle size. The approach also

included a lower-powered fusing operation that enabled (1) the use of normal power outlets rather than the special high-amperage circuits then needed for the high fusing energy to melt dry toners and (2) a more rapid fusing process because of a shorter warm-up time. This last advantage also avoided the occasional fires that occurred when paper became stuck in the fusing apparatus of dry toner machines.

The SRI formula for black liquid toner and the associated Ricoh- and SRI-designed copier helped take Savin quickly from a minor player to a dominant player in the office copier marketplace. In spite of early success, this particular liquid toner had a problem: it released a hydrocarbon gas as it dried. Unfortunately, enough people were allergic to this gas that the Canadian government effectively embargoed liquid-toner Savin copiers. Savin then dropped its use.

Some ten years later, however, interest again arose at SRI in the use of liquid toner—this time for color. Kodak and Xerox had been putting a lot of research into color liquid toners. SRI research staff had also been looking at these toners for use in the higher quality industrial copying systems and where the air pollution problems mentioned above might be more easily mitigated. At the same time, the people at SRI's exclusive venture capital investment broker, CommTech, also caught interest in these toners. To CommTech, it was the convenience copier market that had the big market potential. After surveying the major printer manufacturers, CommTech picked Hewlett-Packard (HP) for further negotiations. In this relationship, HP gave CommTech about $1 million to explore how SRI's color liquid toners might lead to a new, nontoxic product. Unfortunately for SRI, HP too was targeting the convenience copier market and toward that pursuit, its business plan required a two-cubic-foot copier—a size constraint that SRI's more industrial process could not meet.[H]

Water-Fast Inks and Paper

SRI's work in water-fast inks had its roots in the drying properties of the inks in the earlier continuous flow inkjet printers. For these inks to dry quickly, given the very high speed of the paper they printed on, their base contained volatile organic compounds, which were unfortunately toxic. Inks based on water rather than volatile organic compounds would be nontoxic, but because they were water-based, they were likely to run or smear on contact with water.

In 1995, using about $50,000 of internal investment money, SRI chemist Dr. Asutosh Nigam conducted a feasibility study in which he developed a proprietary approach to black water-soluble, water-fast, polymer-based, nontoxic ink. According to SRI commercialization specialist Dan Morris, this was a surprising accomplishment in the field. The new ink used easily available monomers and polymers, was resistant to water and solvents, and could be stored in solution without changing its characteristics. The U.S. Postal Service laboratory made a wide range of chemical and physical attacks on the ink, and it passed them all to become the best available indelible color ink available.[I]

SRI licensed Nigam's new ink to Domino Ltd. for just Post Office use, retaining all other rights. After a number of years of failing to license the technology, Domino dropped the license. This became yet another good technology that didn't sell. But there would be continued intellectual resilience and still more disappointment.

From the first introduction of today's common $50-$500 inkjet printers, they have used inks that water will smear even after the ink has dried.[9] Given that problem, there would seem to have been an enormous market for cheap, water-fast inks usable in the cartridges sold by the likes of Canon, Epson, and HP. So, during the 1996 internal investment year, Nigam continued development of the same water-based, water-fast inks, both black and color—this time for inkjet printers. His search was on and, if successful, it seemed commercialization would be a veritable slam-dunk. It wasn't. While admitting the SRI inks were better, none of the major players in the printer/ink cartridge business would change their lucrative in-place processes. Another factor was that Nigam's black inks were either nearly black and water-fast or they were very black and not as water-fast as the colors. Though close, there was no cigar. The water-fast issue was evidently not an important enough marketplace differentiator at the time to warrant a completed product.[J]

The resourceful Dr. Nigam returned to another opening that had surfaced in the 1995 feasibility study—the paper itself. SRI understood the chemistry very well, and if the ink manufacturers wouldn't support him, perhaps the paper manufacturers would. Once you knew the reactions needed, you also knew that it didn't make any difference how the water-based ink, the water-soluble polymer fixing-agent, and the paper came together. Applying a polymer coating on the surface of the paper during manufacture was actually simpler than the more precise approach of mixing it directly into the ink. That this new polymer-treated paper was no longer "plain" should not be seen as inconvenient to the end user because photo-quality ink-jet paper is already special and clearly not inexpensive. SRI tried unsuccessfully to commercialize this technology through a newly formed spin-off called Cyance.

The coating Nigam developed actually renders the chroma and hue of the existing inks much better than uncoated paper. I remember my introduction to these new inks when I walked into Nigam's lab and saw a faucet running in a sink, on the bottom of which were several brightly colored prints. Each of these had been made on normal inkjet printers of various brands using normal ink cartridges and yet the water was having no influence on their clarity and brilliance!

Besides the plain and coated paper options in this technology, SRI also developed two other print media. One was a type of metallic coating that would accept color inks and the other was an ability to color-imprint cloth. These two print media have been licensed. As yet, the coated plain-paper option has not, and SRI is still trying to work through the reasons.

One lesson in the above story illustrates the difficulties of commercializing even excellent technology. Because the inks of the various major printer manufacturers were an enormous source of profit, the manufacturers were uniformly reluctant to experiment with new inks. And because they each had a lot of chemists working this problem, they weren't willing to disturb their present market position or pay royalties. The circumstance was similar when SRI offered its set of color liquid toners to HP for its new color laser printers. That offer came very close to happening but in the end also failed in spite of producing superior images when HP, although seriously behind the

---

[9] Epson has very recently added some water-fast capability to their inks.

This is a good place to draw attention to the diverse skill base of a flexible research institution like SRI. Designing and building the office machines described above required a broad range of in-depth knowledge and talent, including electronics and mechanical design, the chemistry and physics of the optics and charge-retention surfaces common to copiers, the intricate chemistry of dry and liquid toners and the paper to which they would adhere. However, all these are a normal part of the working life of skilled researchers at SRI. Getting these results did not require hiring specific talent, and it is that characteristic of SRI that best defines the technical grounding of its research staff. Add to that expertise the need for meeting the cost design of a particular product or project and the ability to replicate such work over a wide range of applications and you have an idea of the talent level that has defined SRI from its outset.

Not all SRI research projects succeed, of course, including those in printing. In 1961, a company wanted SRI to devise a paper and ink system that would make a document self-destruct in a specific number of years, so that an outdated drawing or classified report would crumble to dust. After a brief investigation the staff could not conceive of a paper and ink system that would destroy itself after a particular time and yet remain stable and usable until then.

learning curve, chose to develop its own toners in-house. According to SRI's Ron Swidler (May 2002), part of the HP decision was also related to the return that the SRI venture capital associate, CommTech, was seeking. It was more than ten times what HP was willing to accept.

Rapid differentiation in a highly competitive, commodity market would seem to be highly desirable. In fact, it was not. Color images have not yet seriously made it into the business world. Until the cost of color copies comes down substantially and their reproduction speed is increased, the business community will be content with black and white images whenever large printing jobs are needed.

Development of the First Optical Videodisc

Optical discs, in the form of Videodiscs, CDs, CD-ROMs, and DVDs, are now everywhere. Cheap and accurate lasers, perhaps more than any other technology, created this revolution in recording media. And the revolution is far from over. Future advances in blue lasers will permit even more compaction of information than we see today.

But, even before the availability of lasers that could modulate the material of today's optical records, videodiscs had been built at SRI. In fact, SRI developed the first optical disc for recording video signals. In March 1961, 3M Corporation asked SRI for help in determining the feasibility of recording a full-bandwidth television signal on a disc similar to those used in phonograph records. 3M had been experimenting with extending that approach to video to create an inexpensive home video system but had encountered difficulty in resolving the micrometer size "bits" needed for video bandwidths.[10] 3M then began pursuing an electron beam technology that was expected to yield 10 to 15 minutes of playing time on each side of a disc for monochrome video. By the end of the first monthly reporting period, however, SRI had ruled out 3M's method in favor of optical recording and playback, using a high-resolution photographic plate. Such an approach looked much more promising, but it still needed to be tested.

The method for testing whether the optical approach would work was clever and resembled what one might do if a digital recording were to be made.[K] An array of 1-micrometer latex spheres, suspended in distilled water, was spread over a glass microscope slide and the water was evaporated. A thin but opaque film of aluminum was then deposited over the top of the slide. The latex balls were then broken off, leaving small 1-micrometer holes. These holes were used to determine if the signal-to-noise ratio of a photodetector receiving a light signal through the hole was adequate for commercial use. It was. Given the adequacy of the static test, detection at a 4-MHz rate was then verified, as was the ability to make a contact print of the pattern of holes.

Although the presence or absence of a transparent hole lent itself to digital signals,

_____

[10] A micrometer is one-millionth of a meter.

digitizing the video caused a large increase in bandwidth, so SRI decided to record the analog signal. This approach required some type of graded surface emulsion, and by February 1962, a small photographic glass plate containing an image was pasted on a disc and read optically to produce the image shown in Figure 7-4, a single video frame. The SRI researchers then knew that an optical, photographic disc would work.

One problem with the photographic plates of the day, however, was the time and energy it took to expose the emulsion. Because this work was before lasers, high-pressure mercury or xenon lamps had to be used and a special (Kerr) cell was designed and built to modulate their output. An overall recording and playback system was then built that laid down a spiral track in the disc's photographic emulsion, with radial lines on the disc forming the horizontal and vertical synchronization pulses. One line of a video frame was entered between each set of horizontal synch pulses at each track of the spiral. By October 1962, SRI had successfully recorded and played back black and white video at 24 frames per second. By the time SRI's role in the project ended in June 1963, several 16mm movies had been recorded on these photographic discs. The disc format created in this work was used for later analog video recordings. Although approaches were explored, SRI never placed an audio channel or color information on its disc. 3M carried the SRI

Figure 7-4. SRI optical recorder with insets showing an analog disc where each 180-degree annular trace created one frame, a reproduced image, and the final lab prototype of a playback unit.

technology into the laboratory prototype shown in Figure 7-4.[L]

The period from 1965 to 1975 was a time of intense movement in the technology of recording materials. Lasers were introduced and many types of disc materials were examined. In the meantime, and in parallel, 3M had developed an electron beam recording disc of very high resolution. This was an unwieldy system and difficult to commercialize. Being more a materials company, 3M concentrated more on the problem of finding optical disc material appropriate to the mass market. By 1981, 3M was providing optical recording discs to Thomson-CSF and Philips and never went into the disc playback business.

SRI continued to explore videodisc technology. In late 1975, through an enterprising individual named Lee Sowicki, SRI entered into a project to build a digital read/write optical storage system.[11] The notion was to write once and read many times. Using a tellurium coating on a plastic substrate, SRI achieved disc storage densities of about 100 million bytes per square inch with seek times of about 1 second. SRI was issued a patent on this storage technique.[12] Gas lasers were used for both reading and writing. The prototype was intended only for the scanning and storage of text documents. The approach was eventually sold to Toshiba, which produced a file storage system that was ultimately brought to the marketplace. It was billed as the world's first optical document storage and retrieval system.[M] The Laserfile prototype, as it was called by the SRI sponsor, is shown in Figure 7-5 along with most of those responsible for developing it.

Figure 7-5. One of the first read/write optical filing systems, called Laserfile. Toshiba ultimately made a product starting with this laboratory model. Staff who worked on the unit are (from the left) Termpoon Kovatona, Lou Schaefer, Hugh Frohbach, Phil Rice, Jim Young, John Nelson, and Gerry Pierce (June 1979).

---

[11] From Hugh Frohbach on September 20, 2002.
[12] Patent 4,189,783 was granted to SRI with inventors Ivor Brodie and John Kelly. *New York Times*, February 23, 1980.

Vacuum Microelectronics

Imagine a flat panel display for your computer or television set that is perhaps a quarter of an inch thick, exudes very bright colors, changes faster than video rates, has no viewing angle restrictions, and draws very little power. Such is the promise of an emerging technology known as field-emission displays (FEDs). These displays are a consequence of the field of vacuum microelectronics, a technology born at SRI in the late 1950s. In spite of its potential, this technology still has not appeared in the commercial marketplace, with perhaps one or two exceptions, after 40 years. We review here the origins of this work, what promise it holds, and the trouble it has seen in becoming accepted.

For much of its early years, SRI had a place for those whose thought patterns poked strongly at the edges of known technology, trying to break new ground. The condition for that freedom has always been, however, that someone with equal imagination could be found that had the funds and the fortitude to sponsor such privilege. During the very late 1950s, one such expansive thinker plied the frontiers of vacuum microelectronics at SRI. His name was Ken Shoulders, and though he didn't come equipped academically (only a high school education), his curiosity and innovative capacity seemed boundless. He loved to enter a new world from the laboratory side, acquiring theoretical underpinnings as they would help point the way to his vision. In this case and from the vantage point of 1960, he could see the future of electronics as the massive integration of extremely small components. He saw machines able to consist of 10^{11} parts and yet have overall dimensions of but 1 or 2 inches. This was at a time when integrated circuits were just being conceived in the laboratories of Silicon Valley, so Shoulders' components were to exist and operate entirely within a vacuum!

Shoulders' vision of micro-devices is documented in a lengthy article in the second volume of *Advances in Computers*, 1961.[N] That it appears in an account of the progress in computing is befitting of his concepts, even though semiconductors rather than vacuum devices would rapidly become the technology of choice for computing. His article describes triodes, tetrodes, and other active devices of micron size, both as standalones and as part of more integrated devices that could offer the functionality he knew computing needed. Figure 7-6 gives the schematics of one of these original devices, a triode. Shoulders saw such devices being "built layer by layer on two-dimensional surfaces." From such elementary components could come low-power memory and optical sensors.

Along with his description of devices are plenty of acknowledgments about the critical care that had to be given their design and manufacture and of the materials used. Mainly because of their miniature nature, the electron sources of Shoulders' devices were of the field emission type; that is, they required no heating.[O] Though not the first use projected, the notion of a flat display using field emission soon arose and became the subject of a patent issued in 1970, developed at SRI, and assigned to the sponsor, the U.S. Army.[13]

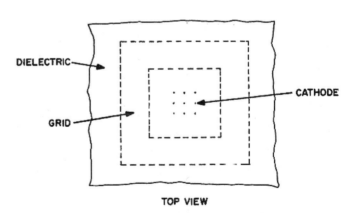

TOP VIEW

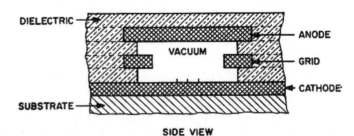

SIDE VIEW

Figure 7-6. An early microscale triode depiction by SRI's Ken Shoulders.

---

[13] SRI, too, was putting its own money into getting the technology started. One indication was over $12,000 awarded in 1966 to explore the applications of these micron-sized devices.

Figure 7-7. Charles "Capp" Spindt, inventor of the cathode that carries his name.

work in a practical vacuum.

The SRI group also learned how to remove much of the contamination in the critical cathode tip region that was a by-product of the fabrication process. This purification and ultimately the introduction of resistive material in the cathodes helped stabilize the current across an array. With these insights and the onslaught of integrated circuit fabrication tools, the SRI approach was to become ever more powerful.

The configuration of today's field emission device looks something like those shown in Figure 7-8. The base plate is monolithically grown and the individual cathodes look very much like they did when Spindt first designed and built them in 1966. (The first regular two-dimensional array was created at SRI in 1973.) The individual cathodes appearing as black dots in Figure 7-9 are incredibly small, as can be seen in comparison to a human hair overlaid for perspective. The basic structure of part of an FED display is shown in Figure 7-10.[Q]

With an improved method in hand for making the small cathodes, SRI addressed other applications. Perhaps the first was as an electron source for a storage tube, a cathode-ray tube that would hold an image as long as desired. The field-emission array was capable of delivering high brightness to such a display. In another application in 1968, SRI performed some of the first electron-beam lithography to pattern a uniform, orthogonal array of these cathodes. Now, over 30 years later, these same

In the beginning, however, the fabrication of the field emission devices was both inconsistent and without some of the desirable cathode characteristics such as high current density and long lifetimes. Forming the cathodes was also imprecise and slow, and sponsorship began to wane. It was at this point that Charles "Capp" Spindt (Figure 7-7), an early member of the same SRI group, developed a way to grow field-emission cathodes uniformly and monolithically.[P] This opened the way for the manufacture of cathode-grid base plates that achieved high currents, were controllable with modest operating voltages, and would

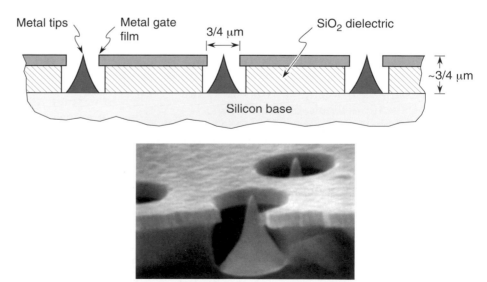

Figure 7-8. Configuration of individual field emission cathodes. (upper) cross-section of a Spindt cathode base, (lower) electron micrograph of a single cathode.

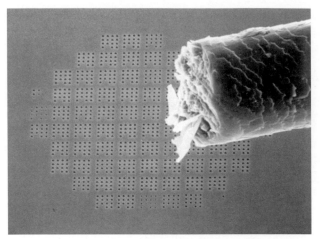

Figure 7-9. Overlay of human hair on an FED substrate

spectrometers. Of note is that a Spindt cathode array was used as an ionizer for a mass spectrometer on a Russian spacecraft that flew through the tail of Halley's comet in 1985 to analyze its gases. Over the years, SRI became the prolific source of the technology and sold hundreds of small field-emission packages for a wide variety of applications all over the world.

The ultimate promise for this technology, however, is still flat-panel displays. After the NASA satellite project had run its course in 1983, SRI began a relationship with a venture capital organization by the name of CommTech International (CI).[14] Under the arrangement, CI was to have a first-right-of-refusal on SRI's intellectual property. One of the properties they

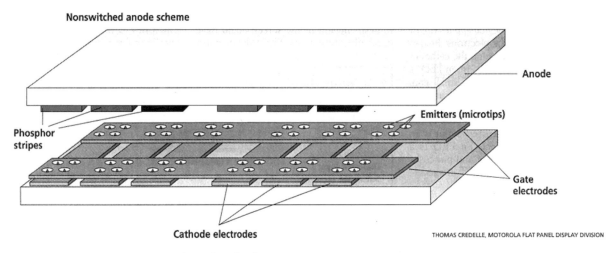

Figure 7-10. Diagram of a section of a color display

cathodes are being explored as sources for such lithography. They also offer advantages as electron sources for electron microscopes.

Satellites offered other potential uses for field emission devices. Because of their power efficiencies, the use of field-emission cathodes in microwave tubes would be ideal for space applications. To develop that use, NASA sponsored work on field-emission devices for about 13 years. Another, more recent space application was satellite space charge neutralization. Even in the vacuum of space, photo-ionization and solar wind particles can cause charge to accumulate on satellites that, if not limited, can discharge internally and disrupt sensitive electronics on board. The SRI cathode arrays are a power-efficient means to generate large neutralization currents. SRI also did a lot of work on adapting these high current arrays to other devices such as mass

singled out to help raise their funding pool was field emission technology. SRI had a good patent position in field emission and so under this new agreement SRI granted CI worldwide exclusive rights to its FED technology. This happened in early 1986, and within a year CI agreed to fund 18 months of continued development work. That effort was supplemented by a contract SRI had won with Boeing for the development of new, bright displays for the aircraft cockpit. As a show of good faith, SRI transferred the management of the contract to CI, but by about 1988 Boeing decided to withdraw its plans for an FED and CI, though still believing the technology promising, discontinued its direct support. In January 1990, CI formed Coloray Display Corporation (CDC) and transferred its SRI FED

---

[14] See Appendix D.

license to them. Over several years, CDC tried to get a sponsor to finish the development and manufacture FEDs. Alas, CDC repeatedly failed in its attempts at FED commercialization and because SRI had not included adequate due diligence conditions in the original license, SRI in effect became locked out of the development of FED technology. Some development of the general field-emission technology continued at SRI but in other, non-display uses. This SRI curtailment continued for over 10 years, during which time the world began to discover the promise of FEDs but also, on the critical competitive side, the continued manufacturing refinements of liquid crystal displays.

Figure 7-11. A prototype of a 14-inch field emission display made by Candescent of San Jose, CA (image received May 2000).

Seeing the inherent potential of FEDs, in the early 1990s the Defense Advanced Research Projects Agency (DARPA) began investing millions of dollars in a local FED start-up competitor called Silicon Video (see box on Candescent Technologies below). At SRI, after years of acrimonious discussions with a series of CI's failed and bankrupt licensees, SRI finally was freed enough to propose to DARPA for support in helping further FED technology. A 3-year contract was awarded in 1996 but SRI, at least to this point, has never reentered the commercialization field for FEDs. This inability to profit directly from innovation is one of the poignant downsides of intellectual property licensing.

In spite of this untimely curtailment, the SRI technology continued to have important effects on the field. Of the dozen or so manufacturers that have built some type of FED in the 1990s and later, only one has used a different cathode configuration and only two have used a different cathode material than the molybdenum of SRI's original units. The promise of this FED technology still remains.

Liquid crystal, electroluminescent, and plasma panels don't have the combination of brightness, low power, viewing angle, operating temperature, and response time of FEDs—but they do have the market (see the box for why). The omnipresent liquid-crystal displays have continued to improve and with plasma are capturing the burgeoning flat television and computer monitor market.

SRI is not the only casualty in attempts to commercialize FEDs. Other organizations that have left the field are LETI of France, the first to build a monochrome display and whose commercial interests were transferred to PixTech, which in turn also acquired Micron's FED technology and business. In Asia, Futaba and Canon have abandoned the technology along with FED Corporation and Motorola in the United States. Only Silicon Video, now Candescent Technologies, maintained a continuous presence and, as of December 2002, that too seemed over (see box). But to show the progress Candescent made, note their May 2000 prototype of a 14-inch display shown in Figure 7-11. Sony now owns the Candescent technology and has yet to decide its fate. Both Sony and Samsung are exploring FEDs in the area of large, flat, HDTV-type displays with Sony having built a 20 in. version.[R] In spite of

By the late 1990s Candescent Technologies (originally Silicon Video) had emerged as the most promising supplier of field-emission displays. Founded in 1991, it raised over $600 million through initial Government (DARPA) sponsorship, participation by the venture capital community, and the development of well-chosen strong industrial partners such as HP, Sony, and Compaq. Much of this money went for building a pilot plant for large, 14-inch displays, but there have been ample challenges on the road to manufacture. The crucial weakness of many FED approaches was trying to maintain low (~100 V) anode voltage. This track required the very expensive and eventually dead-end development of low-voltage phosphors. Candescent opted for kilovolt anode voltages and was then able to use existing phosphors. But the spacers that held the glass plates apart under vacuum proved to be the next challenge. The spacers had to be invisible to the viewer and have minimal impact on the electron optics. Once that problem was solved, prototype 14-inch displays were made in small numbers. Curiously, the cathodes are still made of molybdenum just as those at SRI were 40 years ago.

The display has these advantages over back-lit LCDs: it is markedly brighter, has wider and more variable contrast levels, richer color saturation, the vastly better viewing angles of a regular CRT, superior video rates, a substantially wider range of operating temperature, draws about 25% less power at comparable brightness, and has the same or greater XVGA resolution. But the physical flexibility of LCDs is an important criterion for use in laptop computers, from the outset one of the large potential uses for FEDs. Sony now holds much of the intellectual property rights of Candescent, which has now ceased operation. So, only Sony and perhaps Samsung are perhaps still weighing the role of FEDs. After nearly three decades of development, a promising technology is languishing. Whether it will ever find a place in the burgeoning large flat television screen market remains uncertain.

A very similar technology is in the offing from a combine of Canon and Toshiba. That technology is called surface-conduction electron-emitter display (SED). Their production of flat-panel displays is scheduled for July 2007. Colors are said to be rich and vibrant, with no angle restrictions.

its superior characteristics,[15] FED technology, particularly in the laptop application, has suffered from the mass production of LCD displays and its future remains cloudy indeed. In a related front, Canon and Toshiba have recently announced their intention to build flat-panel television screens using a similar technology they call SED for surface-conduction electron-emitter display.[5]

One additional recognition of SRI's important contributions to FED technology came with the upsurge of interest in the mid- to late-1980s: the start of an annual worldwide conference on the field in 1988. It was called the International Vacuum Microelectronics Conference and, because of Spindt's role in the creation of the technology, he has had leadership roles in this gathering from the beginning. The conference still continues in 2004.[16]

---

[15] In addition to the characteristics above and those mentioned in the box, field-emission technology can offer currents of 2000 A/cm2 and even 100 μA for a single cathode, all while operating at temperatures from 4 to 1100 Kelvin. This makes them usable in tough environmental situations (such as in automobiles where LCDs have temperature problems) and for the brightest of displays such as large format, stadium displays, or just plain light sources.

---

[16] Major SRI players in the development of field-emission devices are Ken Shoulders, Capp Spindt, Chris Holland, Ivor Brodie, Paul Schwoebel, Bob Stowell, and Arne Rosengren.

Reliable Color Prints for the Movie Industry

It was a solid, well-engineered system and it resulted in an important award for SRI. In 1959 the Motion Picture Academy of Arts and Sciences awarded SRI and its sponsor, the Technicolor Motion Picture Corporation, their Scientific and Technical Award for solving a huge problem in the production of color film prints; that is, film that was distributed to the theaters around the world.

As happened more frequently in the early days of SRI than now, Technicolor came to SRI with a major problem: how could film negatives, taken by different cameras and exposed under wildly varying conditions by different cameramen in the making of a movie, be brought together to form one consistent, aesthetically pleasing print? It was early 1952, and achieving the consistency and quality of the distribution print was an intensely manual process. Highly skilled technicians would make repeated attempts to get an acceptable film print, controlling both the exposure and the chemical development process. It was called "timing the negatives" and it was critical to an acceptable product. This uncertain approach required several iterations and invoked unpredictable and therefore costly delays. Technicolor's technical director, Waddy Pohl, had the notion that a very carefully controlled television system, acting as an "analog computer" to mimic their photographic process, might work. However, Technicolor was unsure if the existing technology was adequate. Could SRI look at this problem and help them shorten the time to when a movie was generating income?

This was in the early days of color television and SRI had some perspective on this rapidly changing technology. Bill Evans, head of SRI's Television Laboratory, and Paul Bohlke, head of the Vacuum Tube Laboratory, believed that such a system could be built and that television-based equipment to measure the negative's color was, in fact, a good place to start. So, these labs created a high-quality closed-circuit television system that could accurately measure the color of the input camera negatives.[17] Then, converting the assembled camera negatives to the desired print required an accurate color transfer function that could be expressed in terms of the controlling variables: exposure time and the chemical development.

Getting that transfer right required being able to view a positive image on a cathode ray tube of high color fidelity. However, because such tubes were not available and because they needed to get each color component right, SRI actually broke out the component colors at the negative and retained that separation in three different primary color tubes (made in SRI's Tube Lab) that showed the corresponding color positive. The finished print had to be tailored for each segment of the negative film so that the final print would be consistent and reflect the feeling it was to portray.

By February 1953, about 10 months and $70,000 dollars later, Bill Evans, Werner Hopf, Bill Lynch, and Dick King had built a prototype print-producing system so accurate that it frequently produced an acceptable print the very first time. When the system was demonstrated to Messrs. Pohl and Howse of Technicolor, it worked so well that it was immediately put to use in producing films. This system gave Technicolor a big advantage because the number of color films was increasing. Two of the early films produced by the new timer were "The Naked Forest" and "Border River."

The industry so benefited from SRI's innovation that it received, along with its funding partner, Technicolor, the 1959 award shown in Figure 7-12.

---

[17] The color film technology was moving so fast during the project that, in the beginning, the Technicolor cameras produced three separate black and white negatives, one for each primary color. During the project, color negative film was introduced and the SRI negative timer system had to be changed accordingly.

Figure 7-12. Bill Evans, with his wife, Fleda, receiving the Academy's award for scientific and technical achievement from SRI President Finley Carter.

Encoding Color onto a Monochrome Video Camera

Producing a color image accurately requires an independent, accurately registered image in each of a set of three primary colors. In the early days of video cameras, and even today in the best of them, this requirement meant splitting the incoming image into three identical images, each to pass through its own color filter to a light-sensitive detector. Such cameras were, and still are, very expensive. Since each of the separate color detectors can then have the highest manufacturable resolution, the overall system has the highest possible resolution. Such systems suffer, however, from having to keep the registration between the three detectors near perfect. Needed, then, was a single tube color camera and, moreover, just *one detector* that would be

used for all colors. This single detector would provide two important advantages: inherent registration of the three separate color images and a much lower cost to manufacture.

In 1960 Al Macovski came to SRI and to Bill Evans's Television Laboratory.[18] Macovski had been at RCA Laboratories and had become one of the most prolific inventors there in the development of color television. Sometime after arriving at SRI, Macovski became interested in how to encode color images on black and white

---

[18] As a measure of the stature of these men in their field, Macovski and Evans, with SRI's Phil Rice, would come to be awarded the IEEE Valdimir Zworykin Prize for contribution to television.

film using three spatially oriented gratings in a camera. While the techniques he developed with Phil Rice and Hugh Frobach worked, they didn't work well enough, given the limitations on the image projectors of the day. But his approach would eventually work as Macovski came to apply it to building a revolutionary single-tube, single-gun television camera.[19]

By the spring of 1966, Macovski was ready to embark on a project for RCA to simplify the color video camera. RCA's cameras at that time were multitube or multiple-sensor and cost about $60,000. RCA was looking for a new market enabled by a cheaper camera.[T] The project was client private and was expected to run for about 10 months at a cost of about $140,000. It actually wound up lasting more than 3 years.[U]

The single-gun technology SRI developed was based largely on the fact that the human vision system is dominated by luminance, the essentially gray-scale detail of an image. Because of the color sensitivities of the eye, separated color information requires much less transmission bandwidth than luminance.[20] Luminance, however, can be computed from the contributions of three primary colors at the same pinpoint location. The eye's varying sensitivity to different colors is also evidenced in the working definition of luminance:[21]

Luminance =
0.51 Red + 1.0 Green + 0.19 Blue

So, Macovski was looking for a way to exploit that particular aspect of how we perceive color. Needed were ways to eliminate not only a camera's multiple color tubes, with their associated individual power and registration problems, but even multiple electron guns and scanned detector arrays within a complex single tube. Could one design a single-tube, single-array system, resembling closely a monochrome camera, that would record a full color image?

Happily, the answer was yes and Macovski chose the following path: to place between the input lenses and the lone two-dimensional detector array[22] a spatial color filter or grating that would produce in the output scan of the detector array information appropriate to each independent color. Because color represents a fraction of the total video bandwidth needed, two orthogonal channels of color, in this case the two less-sensitive red and blue, were chosen to be separated from the unfiltered signal. Each of the red and blue gratings was rotated from the vertical a number of degrees that left the two color-modulated signals outside the passband of the luminance signal and also prevented them from interfering significantly with each other. Also, since each of the gratings consisted of lines alternately transparent and opaque to the color being sensed, they each saw a 50% loss in amplitude. However, these gratings, appropriately oriented, approximated the above luminance equation.[23]

Filtered Luminance =
0.5 Red + 1.0 Green + 0.5 Blue

The spatial frequency of the gratings, defined by the spacing of the grating lines, was made nearly as high as the camera lens could resolve. That choice, together with the grating lines being angled away from the vertical, had the effect of amplitude modulating the reds and blues on frequency subcarriers of a composite signal. The two subcarriers, after some further processing, plus the luminance signal were then sent to the receiver where the image was reconstructed. This separation of signals used, in principle, the same approach followed when black-and-white-compatible color television was first developed.

The SRI approach led to several patents that became valuable in later litigation with a Japanese company that, Macovski noted, was infringing on them. There was an out-of-court settlement, and eventually the know-how was assigned to RCA. The insight and the intellectual property gave RCA a commanding market position using the single-tube color camera. The cost of the new camera turned out to be less than a tenth of the earlier camera.

---

[19] SRI's Earle Jones says that during 1964-1965, concepts in building a single-gun color camera were explored at SRI using Institute funds. I didn't find any in IR&D reports around that time. The only film work in 1965 was by Phil Rice with no mention of collaborators.
[20] This characteristic was also used to build earlier black-and-white-compatible color television.
[21] These ratios of primary colors are those that best deliver a white image when a white image is scanned by a three-color camera.

---

[22] Then an electron-beam scanned the plane on which a charge distribution faithful to the image existed.
[23] The differences could be easily removed in later signal processing.

Although the single-gun color camera was innovative, it did not survive the progress in semiconductor electronics. Solid state, light-sensitive devices called CCDs, and more recently, CMOS arrays have replaced the electron beam tube cameras in almost all but studio settings. CCD-based cameras may have one or three detector arrays, depending on intended use. In single CCD cameras, the color filters are built directly into the individual elements of the CCD. There are a few different spatial arrangements of the red, green, and blue light sensitive cells, again with the green outnumbering the other two. Each set of colored cells is then scanned individually to form the output for that specific color. Now even that technology is being threatened by tri-color silicon detectors capable of resolving each color within the same pixel. In any case, before these advances were introduced, the single-tube color camera was a breakthrough for RCA, and RCA became one of the world's largest suppliers of television cameras.

Endnotes

[A] Earle Jones, personal communication, November 12, 1999. The technology SRI proposed for nonimpact electronic duplication would ultimately require special dielectric-coated paper and was thus discontinued. The approach was made jointly by the tube lab under Phil Rice and the television lab led by Bill Evans to A.B. Dick's VP of R&D, Allen Roshkind.

[B] See the Videojet Technologies, Inc., web page at www.videojet.com/pro_history.html.

[C] Conversation with Earle Jones on July 30, 1999.

[D] Richard G. Sweet, *High-Frequency Oscillography with Electrostatically Deflected Inkjets*, Stanford Electronics Laboratories, SEL-64-004, March 1964. A patent was submitted in 1963 and awarded in 1971.

[E] Conversation with Laboratory Director Fred Kamphoefner in the spring of 1999.

[F] From an interview of Jim Ivy, President of Ricoh (USA) Products Group, on September 5, 2000, by the *Digital Times*. "Ricoh...created the first digital fax machine, which was a Ricoh invention."

[G] Interview of Jim Ivy, President of Ricoh (USA) Products Group on September 5, 2000, by the *Digital Times*.

[H] Telephone conversation with SRI's Ron Swidler, May 2002.

[I] Email from Dan Morris, the SRI person then responsible for commercializing the intellectual property defining the inks, July 25, 2002.

[J] Email from Dan Morris, July 25, 2002.

[K] Phillip Rice and Richard F. Dubbe, Development of the First Optical Videodisc, *Journal of SMPTE*, 91(3), 277-284, March 1982.

[L] Philip Rice, Albert Macovski, Earle D. Jones, Hugh Frohbach, R. Wayne Crews, and A. W. Noon, An Experimental Television Recording and Playback System Using Photographic Discs, *Journal of the SMPTE*, 79(11), 997-1002, November 1970.

[M] *Asahi Evening News* (newspaper), Tokyo, October 16, 1979

[N] K. R. Shoulders, Microelectronics using electron beam activated machining techniques, *Advances in Computing*, F. L. Alt, Ed., 2, 135-293, 1961.

[O] Ibid.

[P] A retrospective view of the field and of Spindt's role in it is given in a review article: John A. Nation et al., Advances in Cold Cathode Physics and Technology, *Proceedings of the IEEE*, 87(5), 865-889, May 1999.

[Q] From the *IEEE Spectrum*, April 1998.

[R] Capp Spindt, personal communications, June 24, 2004.

[S] Canon and Toshiba Go Their Own Way in Flat Panels, *IEEE Spectrum*, page 24, November 2004.

[T] *SRI Intercom*, No. 164, August 11, 1971.

[U] Albert Macovski, *Encoded Color Systems*, SRI Final Report on Project 5941 for RCA Laboratories, October 1969.

Chapter 8
National Security Systems Research and Close Support

The pronounced tendency in the United States to fund a significant part of its research through its national security agencies means that a similarly significant portion of SRI research contracts come out of that part of our government. While much of the work described elsewhere in this book had such sponsorship, its applications were not just for the military. In this section we will cover some of those research areas whose applications are unambiguously important to the DoD mission or to civil defense. Because the DoD sector's share of SRI revenue has at times approached 60 percent, there are, of course, many such tales to tell. Given the obvious constraints, we will treat only ten or so here.

SRI's Early Antenna and Communications Efforts

Electromagnetic wave propagation and radio communications systems played an important part in the early development of SRI. The motivation came from an increased need, in both military and commercial aviation, for continuous in-flight communications and navigation. A critical part of that capability was greater attention to the design and measurement of aircraft antennas. For example, increasing flight speeds in the 1950s meant that the aerodynamic drag imposed by existing antennas was reaching the equivalent of 90 horsepower at 300 mph and would go to over 700 horsepower at 600 mph.[A] Something needed to be done. Also unfolding was the very large increase in air traffic in the United States. The number of airplanes flying had increased from 23,000 to 127,000 in the 12 years ending in 1953, a change possible only through better aviation electronics. For example, such electronics had enabled 330,000 instrumented landings in 1952, yet the cost of electronics for a large jet bomber could run over $300,000. Radio and navigation systems aboard both commercial and military aircraft were coming to represent a very significant fraction of the cost of the plane.[B]

SRI became engulfed in the problem. In the area of antenna design, two solutions emerged: (1) conformal or surface-fitting antennas to reduce drag and (2) antenna multi-couplers and tuners that, by permitting more than one transmitter/receiver per antenna, would reduce the number of antennas required. The considerable need for this work led early to the establishment of an aircraft antenna laboratory at SRI called the Aircraft Radio Systems Laboratory. By 1950 SRI had built an antenna range high atop one of its flat-topped Menlo Park buildings to measure the radiation pattern of aircraft antennas to be used on high-performance aircraft. SRI conducted virtually all of these investigations using scale models. The models were accurate enough that the distribution of currents over the body frame could also be measured to help understand their impact on the total radiation field from the aircraft. By 1954 SRI had seven model ranges in operation both in Menlo Park and at its Mount Lee site in Los Angeles.

Figure 8-1 shows a part of one antenna range on which the radiation pattern of an antenna-fuselage combination could easily be measured. This pattern gives the true indication of the utility of an antenna design because it depicts the far or long-distance field of the aircraft's radiation distribution. The other part of Fig. 8-1 shows the use of a probe to assess the distribution of radio-frequency electrical currents on the metal fuselage itself. SRI's conformal antenna design plus the associated electronics worked so well that it came to be used on 26 different types of aircraft.[C]

The new technology behind the multi-coupler was largely centered in the electrical matching circuits that lay between the transmitter and receiver and the antenna. SRI's innovation consisted of an automatic tuning of the antenna to the characteristics of the selected transmitter or receiver, regardless of the antenna's immediate properties, which meant that conditions such as icing could be

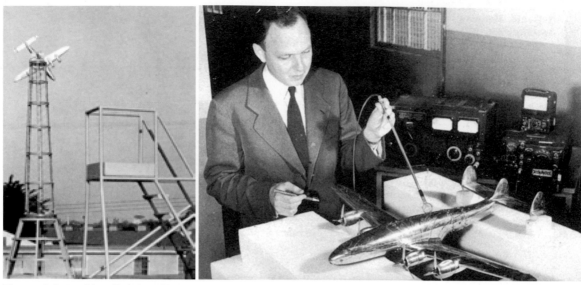

Figure 8-1. Lockheed Constellation on the antenna range and John Granger, Antenna Lab Director, measuring skin currents in the laboratory.

accommodated. As planes began to be built from more plastic and composite, nonmetallic materials, the antenna's electrical isolation from the aircraft skin would also change, often requiring new designs.

One important contribution to radio design at SRI was the introduction of so-called single-sideband (SSB) transmitters to aviation. While SSB in general was not new, a revolutionary design created by Dr. Oswald "Mike" Villard at Stanford University gave higher efficiency and greater simplicity than any earlier method. Created for the U.S. Army starting in 1949, it was one of SRI's earliest projects and the first from its engineering group.[D] Using Villard's later patented approach, SRI's Jack Honey, Don Scheuch, and Oliver Whitby built a 500-W transmitter for the 1.5-30 MHz range, so critical to aircraft in the presatellite era.

SSB was a remarkable improvement in avionics. All other things involving the quality of the signal received being equal, the voltage required at the antenna was but one-third that of conventional amplitude modulation. Thus, SRI was able to increase the efficiency of airborne transmitters and decrease the weight and power requirements in the airplane. The advantages were obvious. For example, the electronic equipment aboard a B-377 Stratocruiser of the day weighed about 800 lb, each pound of which displaced about $5 per year in cargo revenue (about $30,000 per year per plane in today's dollars). Beyond such efficiencies, the new modulation also doubled the number of simultaneous users of the equivalent radio spectrum. This advancement, then, was soon accepted widely in the aviation industry.

National Security Policy and Military Operations

Though not exactly by design, the U.S. defense establishment has been SRI's single most prominent client sector. While much of the funding for that sector goes toward research topics of quite general use, an important component has been in close, direct support of the U.S. national security effort. Here we will briefly discuss just a few of those programs. The first of these programs addresses the nation's civil defense response to the growing Soviet intercontinental ballistic missile (ICBM) threat of the 1950s. Second is SRI's important role in

the design of tactical training systems for both air and ground operations. Next, we will relate how SRI contributed close technical and experimental support to the Services, and finally, we will touch on SRI's role in national security policy.

SRI's Role in the Policy and Practice of U.S. Civil Defense Programs[E]

As the number of nuclear weapons of the Soviet Union and the United States increased rapidly during the 1950s, both nations realized that a program of civil defense was an essential part of any national defense program. A United States policy implemented at that time declared nonmilitary defense programs to be an important component of our ability to deter a nuclear attack. This policy stemmed from a recognition that the United States' announced policy of nuclear retaliation in response to major aggression by the Soviet Union would not be very convincing if the United States were not capable of withstanding such an attack. From this reasoning, the U.S. government established a formal Civil Defense program following World War II.

In the early 1950s SRI became engaged in civil defense research for a variety of government agencies. As the nuclear threat from the Soviet Union became more intense and ICBMs entered the equation, SRI was given an increasingly larger role in assisting U.S. government agencies in analyzing and preparing for that threat. Here we recount some of the research SRI conducted to address what might be termed the passive defense measures the United States could reasonably take.

SRI's role in this area ranged widely, from the development of damage assessment systems to the analysis of post-attack problems of survival and recovery. By 1959, SRI had published more than 60 separate reports in civil defense analysis and planning. The following list illustrates some of the tasks that SRI undertook:

- Based on intelligence of Soviet capabilities, analyze the threats to the United States of possible Soviet attacks. Analyses of threats were essential for effective damage assessment and planning efforts.

- Analyze the cost and effectiveness of a variety of shelter programs.

- Study ways to save lives by evacuation from potential target areas or from heavy fallout fields.

- Assess potential post-attack food and water supplies for a survival and recovery period and identify possible problems in production and distribution.

- Analyze the potential damage, recovery, and post-attack capacity over time of the petroleum and fuel industry in the United States.

- Examine the problems and possibilities of predicting the recovery of the medical products industry following a nuclear attack.

- Analyze the damage to transportation systems from a variety of possible nuclear attacks and estimate the post-attack system capability. Between 1959 and 1969 SRI conducted several studies for rail, truck, air, and water transportation systems.

- Study and make recommendation on decontamination and reclamation, facilities restoration, procedures and systems for realistic damage assessment, and command and control issues for operations in a post-attack environment.

These research issues allowed SRI to build up a substantial expertise in U.S. civil defense matters. Its contribution to knowledge in this field led to a meeting held at SRI on May 15, 1959 by the Program Advisory Committee of the Office of Civil Defense and Mobilization (OCDM). The outcome of the meeting was that the government gave SRI a contract to manage a significant portion, at least a third, of the U.S. Civil Defense research budget.

An example of the esteem with which the federal government viewed SRI's civil defense work concerned SRI's manager of Industry and Civil Defense, Rogers Cannell. Following John Kennedy's election in 1960, Cannell was on the "short list" of candidates for appointment as head of OCDM. Although someone else was appointed, the appointee set up an office for Cannell adjacent to his office so that he could use him as a special advisor. Another example was an SRI report by Harvey Dixon and his colleagues suggesting an entirely new approach to analyzing the hazards to people who must operate in an environment of radioactive fallout.[F] Guidelines in existing OCDM manuals for operation in fallout environments were much too conservative in estimating the time that must elapse following a nuclear attack before operations essential to survival and recovery could begin. The quality of Dixon's analysis was such that OCDM completely revised their tables for planning for operations in a fallout environment. A few years later, the National Research Council adopted the same guidelines proposed in the SRI study.

For perhaps two decades SRI made major contributions to the overall civil defense posture of the United States. Research was conducted for three different administrative levels within OCDM and its predecessor agency, the Federal Civil Defense Agency. SRI contributed to the nation's civil defense program by developing research tools and data for government technical staff, conducting systems analyses and operations research for administrators responsible for operations and planning, and helping policy makers develop and tune government policy.

The Development of Modern Air Combat Training Ranges[G]

In the early stages of the Vietnam air war, Navy fighter pilots were experiencing frustration in some of their air combat maneuvers. For example, a squadron operations officer debriefing a Navy fighter pilot upon return from a combat mission might have heard something like this: "Commander, I can't understand it; I'm sure I had that bogey in my sights a long time, yet when I got my shot off, the missile missed wide to the right. I can't figure out what went wrong."

As it turns out, the reason for the miss could have been one of many, including (1) not all of the pilot's cockpit switches were set properly, (2) the pilot was a little inside or outside missile range or slightly outside the maximum aspect angle, (3) the plane was at the wrong attitude, or (4) the missile guidance system failed. Unfortunately, none of these could be known conclusively after the fact. This frustrating ambiguity in the review of actual combat missions prompted the Navy to conduct an "Air-to-Air Systems Capability Review," completed in 1968, that evaluated actual combat operations. The study concluded that there was a critical need to better train Navy pilots in the use of the extremely capable weapons systems that were becoming operational. It also became clear that new concepts were needed to support the air combat training exercises where pilots gained their combat proficiencies. Furthermore, it would be necessary to bring more realism into such exercises so that pilots would come to "train like they fight." Thus, the focus turned to enhancements needed at the Navy's air combat training ranges.

SRI had been advising the Navy for several years on technical improvements to its range instrumentation and so it was natural that SRI would be selected in 1969 to evaluate the available technologies for a brand new in-flight pilot training system. The new system would be revolutionary in that it had to provide a training environment where pilots engage in actual air-to-air combat against other aircraft using all available weapons systems, yet fire no live rounds. The weapon firings and trajectories would be represented by accurate computer simulations, with capability to score results in near real time, and data would be collected to document all the activity so that the entire training mission could be replayed and reviewed from every aspect after the aircrews returned to base. To be sure that SRI fully understood the complexity of the training requirements, SRI project leader John McHenry qualified to fly air-to-air combat training missions in the back seat of an F-4 Phantom, fully participating in actual air-to-air combat exercises and operating the aircraft radar (see Figure 8-2). SRI completed its analyses and recommended a specific technical approach that was adopted. It then developed the system performance specifications, helped the Navy conduct a competitive procurement and select a contractor, and then acted as the Navy's agent in the building and installation of the first system in late 1972 at the Navy's range near Yuma, AZ. The new capability was designated the Air Combat Maneuvering Range, or ACMR.

Shortly after the Navy's first system became operational, the Air Force contracted for several similar systems, which they named Air Combat Maneuvering Instrumentation, or ACMI. Training on these ACMR/I systems proved so successful that they quickly gained acceptance among U.S. fighter pilots as the "gold standard" for realistic air combat training. The total number of ranges continued to grow so that all U.S. fighter pilots (Navy, Air Force, and Marines) not only would be trained on a stateside ACMR/I but would have systems installed overseas to assure that they could maintain their proficiency while deployed. In addition, several of our allies also obtained ACMR/I systems for training their combat aircrews. The SRI design had defined the state of the art. Although actual combat missions were infrequent, pilots who engaged in such missions (e.g., the Libyan incursion in 1981) verified how similar their encounters were to the realistic combat environment now provided in training.

To understand how the ACMR/I systems work, consider that each participating aircraft is equipped with a pod containing range instrumentation including a transponder that is interrogated from a set of ground stations to determine an aircraft's exact situation.

Figure 8-2. SRI's John McHenry entering a Navy F4 (circa 1970).

range systems by enabling more simultaneously participating aircraft, instrumenting larger areas, achieving greater accuracy, and adapting to new digital avionics systems. Major innovations, such as the ability to include electronic warfare and air-to-ground weapons, were also added. As the training functions of the system grew well beyond air-to-air "dogfight" training, the Navy updated the name of the system to Tactical Air Combat Training System (TACTS).

SRI has also supported new uses of the TACTS/ACMI ranges for research and development applications. For example, range exercises were used to evaluate how much combat advantage could be expected from proposed changes in missile performance by using modified weapons simulations that include the improved performance parameters. Another example was the use of the inertial data collected during training exercises to develop in-flight databases for evaluation of aircraft loading and fatigue. In spite of the fact that SRI was engaged with both the Navy and Air Force in the evolution of each system, they grew separate and distinct through emphases that each Service believed important.

A transponder probe of the pod reveals the aircraft's position, but the pod also contains gyros and accelerometers to measure aircraft attitude, acceleration, and rates. The newest systems also incorporate a Global Positioning System (GPS) receiver. Because the pod attaches the same way a missile would, it also obtains power, weapon system status, and cockpit switch settings. All of these data are sent to the ground via the system data link for reconstruction in near real time by the ground computers. When the pilot triggers a missile during an exercise, the computer flies a simulated missile at the selected target and calculates, based on the initial firing parameters as well as the maneuvers of the target, whether or not a hit would have occurred. This information is made available in near real time to the pilots in the cockpits and is stored for post-flight reconstruction and display. Scenes in the popular movie "Top Gun" showed fighter pilots flying in these kinds of air combat training exercises and participating in postflight debriefings at the Air Force ACMI in Nevada.

During the first 2 years of operational use, SRI conducted an evaluation of each observed system deficiency, ultimately achieving a ten-fold improvement in system reliability. This scrutiny continued to improve the training utility of each range. At the same time, SRI made incremental design improvements to the

The training also enables the testing of various levels of pilot proficiency. Newly available data varied from continuous feedback to both the attacking and target aircraft to only the kill/no-kill outcome. Also, to reinforce and analyze the experience gained during the live training mission, the TACTS/ACMI systems can replay the entire exercise using high-resolution graphics displays and simultaneous numerical display of important parameters for each aircraft. One of the most useful features of the system is its ability to show the progress of the action from several perspectives, including the view from the cockpit of each airplane involved. With this capability, a pilot can reenact any part of an exercise from his own point of view, or he can see what the action looked like from his target's perspective. This near-real-time, post-flight reconstruction has been a valuable and efficient approach to making American pilots the best in the world. SRI's role in these joint programs has continued for over 30 years, and SRI is now engaged in the next-generation range systems that will have greater accuracy and be able to operate anywhere in the world, independent of fixed ground facilities, by incorporating advanced applications of GPS positioning technology.

GPS Systems and the Training of Armored Ground Forces

One of the most effective innovations for defense systems has been the advent of GPS. Able to provide accurate position information almost anywhere in the world, free from fixed ground facilities, this satellite system has offered new capabilities for both operational and training systems. SRI has contributed significantly to both.

Before relating the SRI contribution to ground force training systems based on precision GPS systems, it is important to understand how SRI got to a point of expertise in that field. Earl Blackwell of SRI had been interested in the use of high-accuracy, differential GPS (DGPS) since the mid-1980s. Such systems use a ground-based reference receiver, whose location becomes precisely known, in conjunction with current satellite transmissions in the proximity of the reference point to compensate for a few of a set of component errors intrinsic to GPS-based systems. The use of DGPS enables sub-meter position accuracy that can provide, for example, the basis for systems such as the automatic landing of aircraft. Under DARPA sponsorship, Blackwell and his SRI colleagues developed in the mid-1990s a DGPS capability for use on precision-guided munitions. The resulting system reduced the navigation component of the overall munitions error to less than 1 m and, in some cases, very much less. Blackwell's team's innovation came in developing a so-called wide-area DGPS approach that used an array of widely spaced reference receivers, thousands of nautical miles apart, to be able to create a virtual reference receiver in the vicinity of the GPS receiver in use.[1] These concepts are now part of a

high-precision, all-weather guidance system that does not have to rely on active sensor measurements for guidance in the proximity of the target. Although the SRI wide-area precision technology has been available for years, as of this writing it is just being introduced through Boeing into the Air Force and joint-Services use of GPS-guided munitions.

This ability of DGPS to sense very small changes in the position of a sensor formed the basis for a new and innovative technology for *ground-force* tactical training exercises. As with the Vietnam War instance cited above, Desert Storm illustrated that many of its participating armor units arrived on site with an average of only 39 days of training each year.[H] Some of these were National Guard units whose available training days are clearly limited. They well illustrate the need for a training support system that leaves as much time as possible for actual training maneuvers. Earlier systems for non-fire training maneuvers were based on lasers that required time-consuming calibration and, more importantly, suffered from a lack of visibility through the dust and smoke common to such exercises. Enter SRI and its expertise in DGPS.

SRI's opportunity to bring a new GPS solution to the problem began with a 1994 program at DARPA. It was called Project SIMITAR, and it was intended to provide advanced technology to create realistic, cost-effective ways to build the proficiency of the United States' increasingly called-upon National Guard units. Remarkably, in just 15 months SRI developed an inexpensive, easily deployed instrumentation system called DFIRST™, for Deployable Force-on-Force Instrumented Range System. It was first demonstrated in October 1995 at the Idaho Guard's training area and deployed operationally there the following year. Let's see how it works by stepping into a real, live training situation:

> Over the next two hours, the crew of the 70-ton Abrams tank designated "Charlie 12" will seek out and engage an opposing force hidden amid the rolling hills of the 138,000-acre Orchard Training Area southwest of Boise, Idaho. When an enemy is sighted, the tank turret swings around and the gunner

---

[1] The conventional separation from a reference receiver for DGPS was less than 300 nm. The SRI wide-area system, with baselines of over a thousand nautical miles, still produced positional errors of less than 1 m. See "A Global DoD-Optimized DGPS for Precision-Strike" by Earl

Blackwell, Mark Moeglein, and David Nakayama, presented at the 8th International Technical Meeting of the Institute of Navigation in Palm Springs CA, 12-15 September 1995.

locks onto the target with his 120-mm main gun. The gunner squeezes the trigger. Within milliseconds, processing software in Charlie 12's DFIRST™ instrumentation package verifies that the enemy tank has been correctly targeted and is within range of the gun. An electronic "hit" signal notifies the instrumentation package on the targeted tank that a hit is imminent. The targeted tank's instrumentation package then calculates the virtual damage the "impact" has imposed. When the damage is evaluated as "fatal", the victim tank is stopped in its tracks and all of its weapons systems are disabled. Charlie 12's simulated round was on-target and has given the Blue Force its first success in this battlefield training exercise.

This vignette has a strong resemblance to the air-combat system mentioned above. But in this case the entire DFIRST™ instrumentation suite, including all hardware and software, was not only designed and developed, but also built by project teams at SRI under the leadership of Chris Terndrup. A DFIRST™ unit can be installed on a participant vehicle in less then 30 min. The instrumentation package contains a single-board computer, two GPS receivers, a high-speed radio transceiver and antennas, and a programmable interface controller that connects to the vehicle's electronics system. This interface enables status reports to be broadcast over the vehicle intercom, creates a smoke signature when the gun is fired, and employs a strobe light when the tank has been damaged by enemy fire during an exercise.

The two important measurements for this simulation overlay are the precise location of the vehicle, in this case a tank, and the even more precise knowledge of where its gun is pointing when it is "fired." To learn this latter fact, SRI developed a 1-m-long jig with a GPS antenna attached to each end. The jig can be clamped tightly and accurately to the gun barrel and does not require time-consuming optical boresighting alignment procedures typical of previous laser gun-tracking instrumentation (see Figure 8-3). GPS carrier-phase interferometry software developed by SRI uses the signals received from the two GPS antennas to calculate the gun pointing angles (azimuth and elevation) with an

accuracy of less then 0.2 degrees![2] The tank's position is defined using DGPS. Interestingly, the instrumentation package in each vehicle can be made to represent the capability and vulnerability of *any* friendly or enemy equipment. This adds great flexibility to the scenarios the exercises can portray. Even more flexibility and threat types come from simulated or virtual artillery batteries and minefields, the existence of which are briefed up front and which can be "exercised" during a maneuver. As of late 2002, the ability to integrate live and virtual or simulated conditions regarding enemy orientation and actions was being installed for the California National Guard. There, through computer networking, a command post in south Los Angeles can send orders to a tank unit at Camp Roberts near Paso Robles, while another Guard Unit in San Luis Obispo dispatches simulated soldiers to a virtual, interactive battlefield that is shared by all participants! With these options and the freedom to maneuver anywhere, the composite experience becomes realistic indeed.

As in the case of the TACTS/ACMI air combat range systems, all the firing, positioning, and communications events in the practice exercise are recorded for detailed review after the fact. A trailer, designed as an exercise control center, is also the setting for the visual depiction and study of each completed exercise.

As a final comment on the resilience of the SRI system and it designers, the Guard decided they wanted to use live rounds in some instances. The GPS jig on the barrel was modified so that just its computing module was hid behind the turret to protect it from the recoil and blast. DFIRST™ chief engineer Gerald "Jerry" Lucha and other SRI staff did this all in the field, and at the same time gave the exercise safety officers the ability to monitor gun-pointing directions to ensure that rounds would land in safe areas. The "live fire" modification was later incorporated into the design.

Since the initial DFIRST™ deployment, another half dozen systems are on tap for use at other Guard locations around the United States,

---

[2] While this accuracy from GPS is good, it is only good enough to indicate which target is struck and not how badly the target is damaged. For that, the exercise support system rolls the dice and indicates to the target its degree of incapacity. Also, the algorithm computing the ballistic trajectory of the shell does not yet allow for intervening terrain. In other words, no digital terrain map is involved, as there eventually should be.

Figure 8-3. SRI's attitude-measuring jig mounted on the barrel of an Abrams tank.

organization whose functions were closer to continuous broad technical support. This work tended to deal mostly with the introduction or evaluation of new technology or systems. Two such SRI groups were prominent: the Combat Development Experimentation Center (CDEC), which ran from 1958 to 1966 for the Army's Combat Development Command, and the Naval Warfare Research Center (NWRC), which began in 1957 under the aegis of the Chief of Naval Operations and later shifted to the joint purview of the Office of Naval Operations and the Marine Corps.

Combat Development Experimentation Center (CDEC)

In the spring of 1958, Brig. General Fred Gibb landed his helicopter in the SRI parking lot for a meeting with SRI's president, E. Finley Carter. The Army wanted SRI's help, and Gibb's message was that it was SRI's "patriotic duty" to submit a sole-source proposal to the existing CDEC unit at Fort Ord, CA. It was an opportunity that SRI had earlier decided to pass up. After Gibb left and a few internal meetings had taken place, Tom Morrin, director of Engineering at SRI, decided to submit a proposal for nearly $1 million. To everyone's surprise the Army accepted it, and Dr. Manning Hermes became the first on-site director.

CDEC, as the name implies, was intended to explore new concepts and doctrine for the field Army through mainly observational and analytical means. New ideas were considered and discussed, then tried in the field in an attempt to learn their efficacy, often through direct, quantitative measurements. The topics addressed came mostly from the Army and this was definitely hands-on work. While the group itself was located at Ft. Ord near Monterey, CA, the "laboratory" for most of the fieldwork was located at the vast Camps of Hunter-Liggett and

and it has become a standard ground instrumentation system for a series of annual joint-Services exercises conducted to evaluate tactical combat identification systems and procedures. Thus, this system, together with TACTS/ACMI, helps explain why the U.S. forces are the best trained in the world.

Close Support in the Doctrine and Technology Enabling New Military Operations[3]

While it is true that separate, individual projects made up most of SRI's work for the DoD, there were important efforts that began instead with an organizational relationship. Somewhat resembling the RAND Corporation or other institutions such as MIT and Johns Hopkins, SRI had a few instances when, at the request of a particular military service, it established an

---

[3] This section and the one following on SRI's Strategic Studies Center were prepared with input from Larry Low, Lloyd Peters, and Maury Deatrich.

Roberts located farther south.[4] To carry out this mission, CDEC was assigned 3000 officers and men and a full complement of military equipment.

The CDEC's investigations were eminently practical. The first was to explore the vulnerability that ground fire presented to slow, low-flying aircraft and helicopters. In this project, fiberglass helicopter mockups were towed over "hostile" terrain, where they were shot at by various types of ground fire. Actual quantitative damage assessments were then made. The SRI analysis, when presented to the Commander of the Army Aviation School in the spring of 1965, led to a redesign of such tactical aircraft maneuvers. Another recommendation, relating to a new, more mobile Army, precipitated the procurement and integration of armored personnel carriers at the normal infantry company level. Many other experiments were run, including ones that addressed the basic individual arms carried by the soldier and a large one concerning the design of the Army's so-called Forward Area Air Defense system. The latter addressed the topography of Germany, where wargaming was carried out in anticipation of a breach of the border by Soviet troops and armament. SRI's involvement in CDEC continued for 8 years, ending in September 1966. As one might expect, not all concepts that were explored, like the five-platoon infantry company, were successful, and many of those that were, never saw implementation.

The Naval Warfare Research Center (NWRC)

As with most of SRI's dealings with the DoD, the origins of NWRC were rooted in exploring the potential roles of new technologies, in this case for future Navy operations. Because of Dr. Fred Terman at Stanford and Tom Morrin at SRI, the Navy hierarchy thought of the Stanford community as they pondered their need for another outside research center where analysts, unencumbered by day-to-day operational turmoil, could reason about longer-term (10-15 years) developments. Because of this longer-term perspective, NWRC became aligned with the Office of Naval Research and, somewhat because of an existing void in the Navy's consideration of amphibious operations, the Headquarters of the Marine Corps.[5] The NWRC enlisted specialists not only from SRI but also from Stanford, other universities, and industry.[6] An advisory committee consisted of senior officers and civilians of the Navy, the director of SRI, and Stanford's provost, Fred Terman. It began operation in 1957 under the direction of Harry Bridgeman and ran until the summer of 1979.[7]

By 1962, the Navy would narrow NWRC's mission to examining new technologies and systems that could enhance naval tactical warfare, again in the long term. With such evaluations there came the attendant need to develop better analytical models and evaluation methods with which to determine whether such changes, in fact, constituted progress. Of the many concepts explored by NWRC, and there were more than 250, only a few of the most important ones will be mentioned here.

Fleet Air Defense. The development of advanced air- and ship-borne radar systems opened the way for a more comprehensive approach to the air defense of an entire carrier task force or battle group. Under the initiative of Larry Low, later to lead the NWRC for over a decade, and Fred Forsyth, SRI analysts created over a period of 8 years a method to determine the effectiveness of a carrier-group air-defense system. Its evaluation included the individual contributions of components like early warning and shipborne radars, air-to-air and surface-to-air guided missile systems, electronic countermeasure systems, and the command and control systems that managed all of them.

---

[4] The early SRI CDEC team included Manning Hermes, who led the overall project; Frank Harris, who led military plans and programs; Phil Sorensen, who led operations; Vincent Fend, who led data analysis; and Henry Alberts, who led instrumentation. Maury Deatrick was the project scientist. Oversight responsibility was first given to an SRI committee and then to Gordon Wiley.

[5] Placing such a *research* center away from the bustle and demands of the Washington, D.C., area was initially considered a virtue; hence a location on the West Coast such as SRI. Still, it did compete with very long-standing institutions such as the Navy's own Naval Studies Center at the Naval War College and the Federally Funded Research and Development Center located in the D.C. area called the Center for Naval Analyses, begun in 1942. The proximity of this latter organization to Navy headquarters lent itself to the rapid turnaround and "short string" control characteristic of *operational* support groups. The inherent competition between the three centers initially led to a partitioning of work that left the NWRC aligned only with the Office of Naval Research in the role of exploring the long-term operational impact of new technologies. NWRC's role with the Marine Corps remained more general.

[6] The NWRC was started somewhat at the expense of an aging relationship the Navy had with MIT.

[7] Subsequent directors were: A.E.D. Rist, Larry Low, and Al Bien.

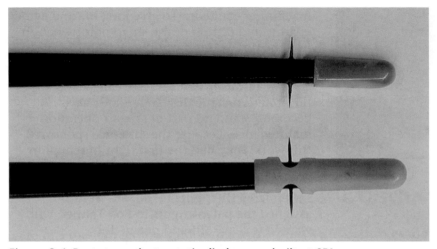

Figure 8-6. Prototype electrostatic dischargers built at SRI.

particles, one of the important producers of charge buildup in subsonic aircraft, continued to increase charge with speed, but at speeds approaching Mach 3 the ice actually began to melt on impact, leaving water droplets, which have a much reduced charging ability. In other words, the results didn't indicate that a separate solution for supersonic speeds was needed.

Matters of Stealth

Dr. Oswald G. Villard (Figure 8-7) had a distinguished career of technical achievement. Known throughout the radioscience community as "Mike," he was a professor at Stanford for most of his life, held many awards, and was a long-term, high-level advisor to the Navy, the Air Force, and other government agencies. Villard also had a relationship with SRI almost from its inception. The first interaction came in 1948 when he chose to explore cooperatively with SRI a new idea he had for the power-efficient (single-sideband) modulation mentioned earlier.[N] A second collaboration came when SRI and Stanford University co-developed and built the radioscience facilities on the hills behind the Stanford campus, when Villard was director of the Radioscience Laboratory at Stanford. The third interaction happened after a couple of Stanford Labs were relocated to SRI in 1969 after the student uprisings concerning the Vietnam War. This last affiliation became the most complete and most notable, for though retaining a few responsibilities at the University, Villard joined SRI and remained on its staff until his retirement in 1996.

Of all the projects that Mike Villard contributed to at SRI—and there were many—none were to have as much impact as those dealing with the general subject of controlling the returns of radar and sonar signals, an area now widely known as "stealth." In particular, his contributions involved "active stealth," called that because it required real-time measurement of the incoming enemy radar or sonar signal and a related

retransmission back toward the radar from the object being illuminated. Here we will recount his early exploration of stealth at SRI, both in the electromagnetic and acoustic realms. Both resulted in a very long series of excellent scientific investigations at SRI and correspondingly long periods of sponsored R&D. Both had a significant impact on SRI and the U.S. military posture. Let's look first at the radar or electromagnetic side.

Active Electromagnetic Stealth—Radar Signature Control

In the electromagnetic realm, there are three ways to diminish the returned signal that a

Figure 8-7. Dr. Oswald G. "Mike" Villard

radar uses for detection. One is to absorb the incoming and outgoing (reflected) wave so that it falls below the threshold of the radar receiver. The second is to deflect or scatter the signal in directions other than toward the receiving radar. The third is to radiate a signal in the direction of the radar that adequately represents the composite reflection from the target in the radar's direction, but is of opposite phase to the normal reflection. This results in sufficient cancellation of the total radar return to draw it below the radar's threshold. This last technique is called active cross-section control, and one of its earliest realizations took place at SRI in the early 1970s. In fact, at the time of the SRI investigations, the term "stealth" was not yet coined for this technique. These first experiments were truly "proof of principle" and were conducted in the same manner as all of the work Villard and his team performed: doing fundamental work, keeping good records, and either publishing the results or taking them to research sponsors to get the resources to develop them further.[22]

Active stealth was associated mainly with low-frequency radars where the wavelength was of the order of the plane's largest dimensions. In the mid- to late 1960s, these radars were being developed for the long-range detection of airplanes, often beyond the horizon. These two facts dictated the use of frequencies of the order of 10 MHz so Villard began his investigations at about 8 MHz. The question was simply put: Could an airplane that was being illuminated by a low-frequency radar transmit a signal back in the direction from which the radar signal came that would cancel the one being reflected by the skin of the airplane? Being able to do this required some knowledge of how the airplane appeared as a reflective source from all the angles from which it might be illuminated—a complex concept that could prove difficult to solve. As it turned out, understanding the concept was manageable, but let's turn to the experiments that confirmed its utility.

The setting was the Palo Alto airport, a small community airport serving the civil aviation needs of the local communities. As just mentioned, testing the concept of active radar signal cancellation required a radar, a way to

detect the radar and its direction of arrival in the target plane, and a means to generate there a canceling signal in the exact reverse direction. Figure 8-8 shows the makeshift setup at the Palo Alto airport on May 23, 1972. On the table is a laboratory "radar" with its corresponding antenna some distance away. First, the airplane's polar radiation pattern, that directional scattering of signal when the plane is illuminated from various directions, was examined while the plane was on the ground. Over the range of frequencies of interest, the pattern was well behaved, at least as compared to microwave frequencies. Its pattern was not unlike that of a simple half-wave dipole. If so, then, the placement at the center of this dipole of a signal of equal and opposite phase would reduce the reradiated signal, including in the direction from whence illumination came.

This concept was tried first in the laboratory and then repeated in the air aboard a rented AeroCommander 500. Flying in the distance, the plane was equipped with a dipole stretched along its wings, and inside, the secret weapon: a well-informed, highly dexterous SRI team member, Jim Lomasney. His job, amid no small amount of turbulence, was to gauge the characteristics of the incoming radar signal and then adjust the characteristics of the one to be radiated so as to just cancel the current at the center of the dipole. This meant he was simultaneously juggling both the amplitude and phase of the outgoing signal. Switching this signal on and off gave clear evidence at the radar receiver that the returned signal could be made to disappear. Villard, Wanner, Lomasney, and the others had clearly shown that active cancellation worked…at least at these low frequencies!

All of this exploration was done on SRI's own internal research money. With these results they were able to get DARPA funding and, with the additional involvement of SRI's Phil Fialer, Larry Sweeney, and others, SRI refined the approach even further and applied it to other, larger airplanes. The time frame was 1973-4.

Within a year or so, and after the technique was refined, they took their system to Florida where a high-frequency (3-30 MHz) surface wave (low angle) radar was being developed and tested. The SRI technique worked so well that the first look the radar operators got of the airplane was when it was directly overhead. Ralph Wanner remembered that SRI's

---

[22] The SRI radar cross-section reduction team consisted of Villard, Jim Lomasney, Clair Powell, Ken Johansen, Robert Lloyd, and the person from whom came much of this account, Ralph Wanner. Ernest Aho would help in the acoustic wave analog to follow.

Figure 8-8. At the Palo Alto Airport, site of the first active stealth experiments. Shown are laboratory radar equipment and dipole antennas (May 23, 1972).

Villard and others on the SRI radar cross-section (RCS) reduction team created over a hundred memoranda, and this library of knowledge formed the basis to seek long-term research sponsorship. SRI was able to get a considerable number of research contracts over the approximately two decades that this important technology evolved. While there were several sponsors for the work, the foremost of these was DARPA and their Military Service affiliate, the Office of Naval Research. SRI built an anechoic chamber, introduced complex models of military aircraft, and performed finite-element modeling of their complex structures to learn just how reradiation had to be tailored. The capabilities became so useful that very early on they were drawn under the cloak of secrecy. Thus, stemming from the freedom to explore a relatively simple but powerful concept, Mike Villard and his SRI program team made extraordinary contributions to the U.S. military capability.

Active Underwater Acoustic Stealth

technique eventually caused the cancellation of the development program for that radar!

While in retrospect this may all seem straightforward, this test, or proof of concept, was the culmination of months of preparatory work that began as early as the mid-1960s. It was first necessary to learn about the basic nature of the reflected signal. What were the magnitude and variations of its amplitude and phase? Was the rate of variation too fast to usably assess or compensate for? Would the incident radar signal arrive via multiple paths that would produce untraceable fading? First, non-cooperating airplanes were used in gathering such data. Later, a single target, the SRI AeroCommander mentioned above, was moved to varying distances on the ground and then flown with no electronics on board. After the successful 1972 demonstration, it was necessary to introduce the means to automatically perform the tasks that the well-coordinated Lomasney did manually. The team was expanded to include those SRI staff familiar with digital algorithms and microprocessors.

Among Dr. Villard's various roles in the early 1970s was membership on the Navy's Research Advisory Committee. Therefore, it was natural that Villard's fertile mind would extend his notions about active RCS control to the underwater world of acoustics. But although one could make guesses about the parallels between electromagnetic and acoustic wave cancellation, Villard was not one to bring speculations before such a knowledgeable group if he didn't have to. So, before he proposed it, he first wanted to see if the same success he had with radar at the Palo Alto Airport could be replicated for sonar. Thus, SRI's second area of stealth had to do with water and acoustics. The analogy with the radar case seemed valid, and

Figure 8-9. At Searsville Lake near Stanford University, location of SRI's active sonar experiments. Shown are acoustic equipment, hydrophones, with Jim Lomasney and Ernest Aho of the SRI "Navy"(about 1972).

the U.S. submarine fleet, and to some extent its surface fleet, clearly had need to cloak themselves to enemy sonar systems.

The question, then, was: Can ships or submarines radiate acoustic energy whose direction and phase is such that it would cancel a sonar reflection in that same direction? Near Stanford University was a small placid lake whose bottom contained a lot of soft mud, which would be ideal for an acoustic experiment because it would help absorb unwanted signals (see Figure 8-9). This meant that the main signals would be those direct pathways between the sonar transmitter and its targets and their reflections, much as in deep ocean water. The team found some good hydrophones that SRI happened to be working on for the Navy and, within about 6 months following the radar experiments, they were in the waters of nearby Searsville Lake. Here, hydrophones replaced the radar and its antennas and a boat replaced the airplane, but otherwise the basic setup was very similar to that at the Palo Alto airport. With these sonar experiments, SRI obtained cancellation results similar to those it had achieved with radar.

The consequences for SRI of Villard's stealth-related innovations have been

incalculable. Both investigations caused a flurry of activity by the military community and their important contractors to develop the underlying science and apply its consequent military benefits. SRI continued to pursue the acoustic and radar opportunities. The radar work at SRI lasted about 20 years and involved scores of talented researchers. Their collective outputs were, of course, classified, but their impact on both SRI and U.S. military capabilities was enormous.

Enabling a Warm Voice in a Cold War

Churchill's Iron Curtain analogy was as much a barricade against ideas and awareness as it was against ideologies and commerce. As the Cold War developed, the West decided it was useful to broadcast a more complete story of world events, and the Voice of America (VOA), created during WWII, was reenergized in 1950. The Eastern Bloc governments would endeavor to jam these transmissions to prevent contrary views or factual news from reaching their people. Because most of the VOA transmissions were shortwave, and because Mike Villard had enormous expertise in this area, he became a long-term technical advisor to the VOA. Through this relationship he became aware of

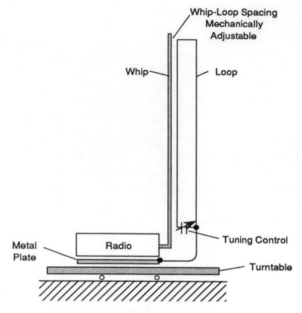

Source: SRI International

Figure 8-10. Schematic of a small directional shortwave Villard antenna capable of nulling a distant jammer.

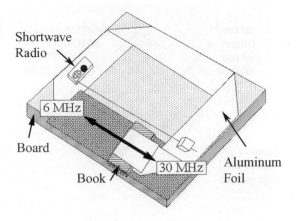

Figure 8-11. Very inexpensive, disposable shortwave Villard antenna capable of suppressing a local jammer.

how desperately the Soviet Bloc people had to struggle to listen to the many VOA radio channels. So, he decided to do something about it.

His idea was to build a *small* shortwave receiving antenna that would help reduce the influence of a jammer. This meant that the antenna needed directionality, which at these frequencies usually implied large dimensions—of the order of tens of feet—and thus outdoor installations. That, in turn, would reveal a listening capability to the local militia. Hence, it was important to make such equipment small, easily camouflaged, and, it was hoped, accommodated indoors.

First, under VOA sponsorship and then using SRI internal funds, Villard and a small SRI team developed such small antennas. One rough schematic, shown in Fig. 8-10, was intended mainly for sky waves—those shortwave signals reflected from the ionosphere.[O] If a radio jammer or other noise source was more local, such that its waves arrived along the ground, a horizontally polarized antenna was needed to reduce its effect. For this Villard designed an extremely simple, easily disposable, yet tunable antenna made of aluminum foil (see Figure 8-11).[P] Villard and colleague George Hagn continued the development of these very portable directional antennas until the anti-jamming purpose for which they were originally intended had ended.[Q,R] This end was defined by the winding down of the Cold War in the late 1980s.

Endnotes

[A] SRI's *Research for Industry,* 2(6), March 1950.

[B] SRI's *Research for Industry,* 6(6), July 1954.

[C] Ibid, plus in Joseph Stocker, "The Miracle Makers of Menlo Park," True Magazine, 1956.

[D] A note on *Communication and Ionospheric Research at SRI* by John Lomax, received December 1996, also indicates that for Bob Kulini of the U.S. Army Signal Corps, this contract began a two-decade relationship. His goal was to "establish an independent radio engineering research center" at Stanford/SRI. Also referenced in SRI's *Research for Industry,* 3(6), September 1951.

[E] This account was compiled by Harvey L. Dixon in a personal communication entitled "Civil Defense Research at SRI," dated November 25, 2003.

[F] Harvey Dixon, et al., *Comparison of Effective Biological Doses for Three Alternative Recovery Rates,* SRI Project No. 2690 for the Office of Civil Defense and Mobilization, 1959.

[G] The material and insight about SRI work in air-combat ranges was provided by two important principals in the work, John McHenry and Elliott Hinely.

[H] Major Jeff Grant, "War Games: Troops Train with GPS-Enabled Battlefield Simulation," GPS World, November 1977.

[I] "A Study of Command Control Communications," SRI Project 2841, sponsored by the U.S. Army Signal Corps, started April 23, 1959, for $116,400. Bell Laboratories was a subcontractor to the study.

[J] Conversation on January 11, 2002 with William T. Lee, who was present at the McNamara meeting.

[K] Some of this account came from a conversation with Leon Sloss (January 11, 2002), who was then a member of the SSC and present at the meeting. He later headed SRI's Washington, D.C. office.

[L] Some of the insight of this section came from a discussion with Joe Nanevicz on June 14, 2001.

[M] SRI's *Research for Industry,* 7(8), 2, September 1955.

[N] SRI's *Research for Industry,* 3(6), 4, September 1951.

[O] Villard, O.G., Jr., K.J. Harker, G.H. Hagn. *Interference-Reducing Receiving Antennas for Shortwave Broadcasts,* Final Report, Contract IA 22082-83, SRI Project 1255, SRI International, Menlo Park, CA, January 1987. Ms Cheryl Hagn also participated in this project.

[P] From http://users.erols.com/k3mt/hla/hla.htm and the hand of Michael Toia, who was Villard's technical contracting representative at the Voice of America.

[Q] Villard, O.G., Jr., *Miniature Directional Antennas for Improved Radio Reception,* SRI Business Intelligence Program Report D89-1347, SRI International, May 1989.

[R] Villard, O.G., Jr., G.H. Hagn, and J.M. Lomasney, "Converting a Small Standard Receiver into a Hand-Held Narrow-Aperture HF Direction Finder," *IEEE Antennas and Propagation Magazine,* 36(5), 25–29, October 1994.

Chapter 9
The Science and Systems of the Atmosphere

Ionospheric Research for Radar Systems

Figure 9-1. The landmark SRI "Dish" located above the Stanford campus.

Starting 40 to 50 miles above the Earth is a region of free ionized particles that extends to the uppermost reaches of the atmosphere. During the early decades of this century, research into understanding the propagation of shortwave radio signals led to the discovery of this ionized region, which, naturally, came to be called the ionosphere. Continued research resulted in a deeper appreciation of how the composition, structure, motion, and distribution of the ionosphere are related to solar and terrestrial conditions such as sunspot activity, the aurora borealis, and the day-night and seasonal cycles of its constituents. The density of ionization there is such that at oblique incidence it can reflect radio frequencies below about 30 MHz and thus provide, through multiple earth-ionosphere reflections, worldwide communications channels. For about a half century SRI has contributed both theoretically and experimentally to the knowledge of the ionosphere: its makeup and behavior, the ways it can alter radio and radar signals passing through it, and the opportunities it provides for long-distance, shortwave communications. Before communications satellites were introduced in the mid-1960s, these types of radio channels constituted all long-distance radio communications and were of critical importance to the U.S. government and its diplomatic and military agencies.

Radar and Ionospheric Studies

Most of SRI's work on the impact of the ionosphere on radar is centered either at high latitudes or in the environment produced by high-altitude nuclear explosions. Some investigations have also been made at equatorial latitudes. SRI's contributions have significantly increased our understanding of:

- The effects of the aurora on radar systems trying to detect hostile aircraft and missiles coming over the polar regions
- The impact on radars of a nuclear attack with high-altitude detonations
- The effects of trans-ionospheric propagation on signals for radar detection and satellite communications.

From these applied efforts and from very directed and fundamental investigations that are ongoing, SRI continues its 50-year contribution to the science of the ionosphere.

SRI's interest in radars and the ionosphere began with Dr. Allen Peterson (see Fig. 9-2). On the faculty at Stanford and an early staff member of SRI (1954), he had written his thesis on how a shortwave signal, when bouncing between the ionosphere and the ground, would scatter back to the transmitting source some energy from each ground reflection point. He was also interested in using meteor trails as a radio reflection mechanism and in studying how the upper atmosphere impacted radar. More importantly, he knew the implications that the ionosphere might have on pending military defense radars and how to turn that knowledge into research sponsorship. Accordingly, he brought Ray Leadabrand (see Fig. 9-2),[1] a student of his, to SRI to pursue research on the impact of the high-latitude

---

[1] Leadabrand would eventually lead SRI into national prominence in the ionospheric radar field and become one of the important leaders of SRI's Engineering Group.

Figure 9-2. Dr. Allen M. Peterson and Ray L. Leadabrand.

BMEWS[2] radar systems were being designed to detect ballistic missiles in flight, and such questions had to be answered. BMEWS was scheduled for implementation in 1960 to 1962.

Consequently, in 1956 SRI began a long-term program to help understand the impact of the aurora on such radars. Auroral reflection characteristics such as aspect-sensitivity, frequency and location of occurrence, and radar cross section became important information in the siting and signal interpretation of defense radars operating in that region. The program was sponsored by the Air Force and was generically referred to as Auroral Clutter. To examine these effects, SRI began exploratory work with radars it had built and operated here at Stanford. Quite incidentally, it was one of these that made the first radar detection of an artificial satellite, Sputnik I, on October 10, 1957.[A] In that same year, SRI placed another 61-ft auroral-diagnostic radar near Fairbanks, Alaska, the first of a series of radars to be operated in that area over the next 22 years. The Alaska radar, shown in Figure 9-3, was the first to examine the aurora at higher frequencies—from 400 to 1200 MHz. These frequencies, in combination with the 61-ft parabolic radar antenna, produced sufficiently narrow beamwidths that, with radar ranging, they could pinpoint the location of the auroral ionization.[B, 3] It provided data for the first International Geophysical Year in 1958.

ionosphere on radars, particularly that of the aurora borealis. In a new world that held the threat of ballistic missiles and nuclear warheads, an imperative question was whether they could be detected among the influx of naturally occurring charged particles from space; specifically, would they blind U.S. defensive radars to Soviet missiles approaching the United States from the north? The huge

Soon after these Alaskan studies began, however, it became clear that, because of the tilt of the magnetic pole toward the American continent, a European BMEWS site would "see" a somewhat different auroral geometry. To address these differences, SRI proposed to the

Figure 9-3. SRI's 60-ft. auroral radar located just outside Fairbanks AK (visual aurora in the background).

---

[2] The Ballistic Missile Early Warning Systems were very large ground-based radars located in the far north.

[3] This directivity was also calculated to help investigate the potential for auroral interference by means of the side lobes of the much larger and more directive BMEWS radars. Through the efforts of Walter Jaye and others, the SRI Alaskan radars were also used to explore the effects of ionization from meteor trails. (Personal communication, Ray Leadabrand, May 31, 2004.)

Air Force Rome Development Center that another investigative radar be located in Scotland. The proposal was accepted and the radar began operation in 1960 to look at the naturally occurring auroral events in that hemisphere. This radar was designed and built by SRI and operated just outside Fraserburgh, Scotland, in collaboration with the British Royal Radar Establishment. It was similar to the one at Stanford shown in Figure 9-1 and four others around the world, two of which were built by SRI. In this manner, SRI obtained from both Alaska and Scotland important information on the nature of auroral clutter for the BMEWS program and for depicting the upper atmosphere in general.[C, 4]

Before proceeding further, it is worth noting that from this ionospheric work there grew probably the closest working relationship SRI had with Stanford. Development of both equipment capability and research staff was often a joint affair. SRI owns the big 150-ft dish and an associated 400-MHz transmitter located atop a hill above Stanford and visible throughout the campus, while a 400-KW 50-MHz transmitter located nearby belongs to the University. In the early 1960s the two institutions created the Center for Radar Astronomy, with balanced leadership from Von Eshleman of Stanford, Leadabrand of SRI, and Peterson of both institutions.

The U.S. High-Altitude Nuclear Tests of 1958

But while this work on the natural ionosphere was proceeding, SRI became engulfed in an experiment resulting from a decision by the U.S. government in 1958 to hold its first high-altitude nuclear test series. The original plan was to hold the tests in the Pacific at Bikini Atoll, where earlier surface bursts had been conducted. But the risk of eye damage to people in that part of the Pacific caused the tests to be moved to Johnston Island, a very

isolated coral atoll a thousand miles southwest of Honolulu. The two detonations were called Teak and Orange, and their initial inception and planning revealed no concern for or curiosity about their potential impact on electromagnetic systems such as radar and communications.

But as the test date approached, things would change quickly. A few Air Force people began, just 90 days before the shots, to wonder about the potential effect of such detonations on anti-ballistic missile (ABM) defense systems. These people knew researchers at both SRI and Stanford, and so Peterson became aware of the concern and brought the problem to SRI. The Bikini Atoll location had strongly suggested the need for a sea-mobile radar platform. A proposal was quickly written and carried to Washington to the funding agent who, through attending Stanford himself, was also aware of SRI. After some negotiations, it was accepted and a contract was written within a few days. Design work was begun, the sea-going yacht M/V Acania purchased, the equipment installed and checked out, and the entire package sailed to Wotho Atoll, 100 miles southwest of Bikini, in time for the tests, and all in less than three months! Moreover, through the foresight of a floating radar platform, the relocation of the tests to Johnston Island was handled with ease. *That incredible ability in radioscience to respond quickly, with competent concepts and equipment, to virtually any problem anywhere in the world, has always set SRI apart from its contract research competitors.*

The nation's first high-altitude detonations occurred in early August 1958, and the six radars on the Acania, ranging in frequency from 11 MHz to 780 MHz, were the first to see how totally reflective such high-altitude plasma was. This result meant that for this scenario (the combination of radar frequency, detonation altitude, and location), radars would be effectively blacked out. Although the implications for ABM systems were profound, the United States continued, incredulously, to develop nuclear-tipped interceptors!

In addition to this scene in the mid-Pacific, SRI was, at the same time, busily engaged in another nuclear experiment half a world away in the South Atlantic. The roots of this episode began in early 1958 when Peterson was asked by Herbert York, the first director of DoD's Advanced Research Projects Agency (ARPA), to convene a high-level theoretical group, as part

---

[4] From received signals that showed wavelength dependence (the inverse seventh power) and aspect (angular) sensitivity (10 dB per degree off perpendicular at 400 and 800 MHz), there were implied elongated, rod-like forms in the ionization with transverse dimensions of 0.7 m and lengths of from 45 to 120 m. Another important event occurred at the Fraserburgh radar when Ray Leadabrand sent Murray Baron there to search for the existence of the then newly postulated radar echoes from individual electrons, called incoherent scatter. Baron recorded them in December 1960, and they became the first such returns ever detected at high latitude.

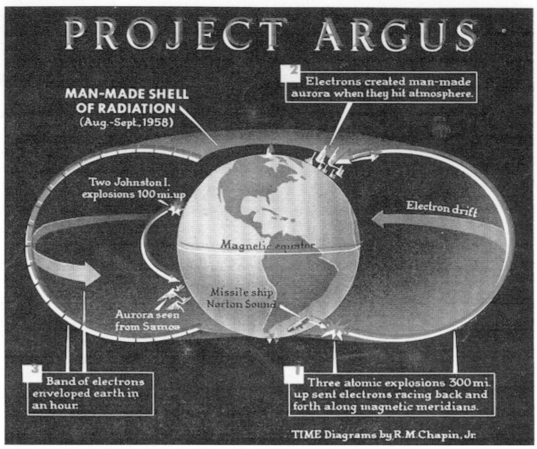

Figure 9-4. A schematic diagram of Project ARGUS (From *TIME Magazine*, March 30, 1959, page 71).

of an anti-ballistic missile defense program, to consider the possibility of a particle beam weapon. During those discussions, N. C. Christofilos, a brilliant, self-taught physicist from the University of California's Lawrence Radiation Labs, raised an ancillary proposition he had been thinking about for a year or more: Could a nuclear device, detonated in the ionosphere, produce a temporary radiation belt over the earth that might be inimical to incoming warheads?

The naturally produced Van Allen belts, just becoming evident from radiation counters aboard the Explorer satellite, had confirmed Christofilos' notion about the existence of such radiation belts, but whether man could induce one or not was unknown. So, after internal review, ARPA decided to sponsor a classified experiment, to be conducted in the South Atlantic, that was intended, by exploding a very small nuclear weapon at high altitude, to inject ionization into the Earth's magnetic field to become trapped there and precess around the world (see Figure 9-4). The location of injection was about 1100 miles southwest of Capetown,

near the Falkland Islands. Of the numerous atmospheric tests the United States would conduct, this was the only one that was not announced beforehand.

It was August and September of 1958, and the project was called ARGUS. SRI was asked to make several measurements that would indicate whether electrons had been injected. The principal SRI sites were in the Azores; at a U.S. Air Force Base in Torrejon, Spain; and with radar equipment on the launching ship, the Norton Sound, in the South Atlantic. One measurement was to look for synchrotron radiation emitted by electrons trapped in the earth's magnetic field that would indicate whether injection occurred. That measurement was at Torrejon and did not reveal any effect. A second measurement, the monitoring of very low frequency radio stations (60-300 kHz) in the Azores, saw a pronounced absorption effect indicating an impact on the lower ionosphere. The third measurement was of radar reflections made in the vicinity of the shot and at the northern conjugate point.[5] Although only one of three missiles reached the planned 300-km injection altitude, some trapped radiation was seen. SRI's 27-MHz radar data revealed high-energy particles impinging on the atmosphere in both hemispheres for two of the three shots and were the most dramatic of the SRI measurements. Visible aurorae were also seen north of the Azores.[D]

The principal indication of the amount and energy of trapped radiation, however, was made with an existing satellite (Explorer IV) and measurement rockets in the United States. Although the effect could be measured for days after the burst, the

Figure 9-5. An SRI shelter destined for ARGUS. Top row (l to r): Jim Hodges and George Hagn; middle row: Allen Peterson, two non-SRI people; bottom row: Rolf Dyce, Ray Leadabrand, and Ray Vincent. (Missing is Bob Light who ran the field site in the Azores.)

ability of the new radiation belt to act as a protective shield was not confirmed. ARGUS, noted in the *New York Times*[6] as the "Greatest Experiment," was probably the first scientific experiment to explore physics on such a grand, earth-space scale. Having little military significance, the considerable information gathered, much of it giving unique insights into the Earth's magnetic environment, was soon declassified and submitted as part of the 1958 International Geophysical Year. Some of the SRI people involved in ARGUS are shown in Figure 9-5.

As this first high-altitude testing program wound down, President Eisenhower invoked a unilateral moratorium on nuclear testing on October 31, 1958 and invited the Russians to do

the same. They did, at least for a while. Through its participation in these tests, SRI became the preeminent organization in the United States to deal with the effects of the ionosphere on electromagnetic systems both under nuclear and natural conditions. And the M/V Acania would become one of the most widely used SRI facilities for over a decade (see Figure 9-6[7]). It would be used in the Caribbean for examining the radar reflections associated with both the launch and reentry of ballistic missiles from Florida; for following solar eclipses to determine chemical recombination rates in the ionosphere; and, when the Soviets broke their test ban moratorium in September of 1961 and the United States decided to resume its own testing, it was sailed to the South Pacific for ionospheric measurements at the magnetic conjugate of Johnston Island.

---

[5] The term "conjugate" refers to a point in the hemisphere opposite from where the detonation occurs. It is determined by tracing the magnetic field lines passing through the burst area, across the geomagnetic equator, to an altitude of about 110K in the opposite hemisphere. There, particles from the hemisphere of the burst collide with and ionize particles in the normal atmosphere.

[6] Front-page headline, New York Times, March 1959. Also headlined in the Washington Post, same day.

---

[7] The Acania was said to have been built in France for actress Constance Bennett. Converting it to a radar platform and overseeing its use for over a decade was the responsibility of SRI's Roy Long.

Figure 9-6. The SRI M/V Acania in calm sea 300 miles off Samoa (1962) (photo courtesy of Boyd Fair).

Before turning to a second nuclear test series in the Pacific, a word more about the role of the SRI Acania in the Caribbean is warranted. Over time, the radar-equipped Acania was given the task of examining the ionospheric effects made by both the boosters as they powered through the ionosphere on their way up and by the reentry vehicles on their way down. Both signatures were important to remote

detection—in the first instance to recognize that a launch had taken place, and in the second to be able to analyze and target incoming warheads. The ascending, powered missile became much more detectable as it transited the ionosphere, but the very long-range examinations of that transit were not at all precise. So, the Acania was brought close in to make direct examinations that helped understand the phenomenology and improve the detection potential of long-range radars located beyond the horizon. On the other end, the reentry work helped the U.S. ability to distinguish between decoys and the real warhead.

President Eisenhower's unilateral testing moratorium from 1958 to 1961 was an uneasy one, and the United States continued to look at its preparedness. Accordingly, and in anticipation of one day returning to nuclear testing at Johnston Island, SRI made an unusual proposal to the government around 1961. To explore our ability to use ABM radars in a nuclear environment, where they must assuredly work, measurements were needed of ray paths that transited a nuclear-disturbed region of the ionosphere. SRI suggested using the moon as a reflector to direct energy to a remote nuclear test site such that the radar beam would intersect the affected region. Satellites were not yet available for this purpose, so a proposal was written and accepted. The radar built for this purpose was none other than the landmark above Stanford, the parabolic "Big Dish" shown in Figure 9-1. It was patterned after its predecessor in Scotland, which had been built for auroral studies, but has a slightly larger (150 ft) diameter. SRI engineer George Durfey (Figure 9-7) led the building of the Dish.[8]

But the nuclear tests in the Pacific arrived before the Dish was completed in 1963, so it did not ever see use for its original design purpose. Nevertheless, the antenna has been used for radio astronomy measurements at Stanford, communicating with NASA Pioneer satellites, exploratory incoherent scatter experiments of the ionosphere, testing nuclear-weapon detectors aboard GPS satellites,

Figure 9-7. SRI engineer George Durfey in a whimsical pose atop one of the trunnions that now support the Stanford Field Site Dish.

---

[8] Durfey was principally involved in the design construction of the Dish but Dr. Mike Cousins has, for many years been responsible for its operation and maintenance.

and a host of other purposes. I recall taking a Palo Alto teacher's elementary-grade class to the Dish, perhaps in the early 1970s. There we learned that on the previous day the Dish had transmitted to a Pioneer spacecraft that was just emerging from behind the sun—that is, clear across the earth's solar orbit, or 186 million miles away! (See box on Pioneer satellites.)

When the Russians resumed atmospheric testing in September of 1961, SRI went to the field again. The Soviets were to make their first high-altitude nuclear tests in October at their Kapustin Yar missile range—tests that also explored the electron injection mechanism mentioned above in the U.S. ARGUS tests. Like the U.S. weapons, these missiles were small. A few days later, though, the Soviets released from an airplane over their Novaya Zemlya arctic testing site the largest explosion ever seen, some 50 megatons. To determine whether there were any impacts at the magnetic conjugate of these bursts, SRI took instrumentation to the South Indian Ocean aboard two ships. On the way to the conjugate area from western Australia, one of the ships passed through a hurricane that produced 60-ft peak-to-trough waves that flowed over the ship. Nevertheless, the ship reached the spot in time for passive noise measuring devices called riometers, and all-sky cameras were used to try to detect the presence of high-altitude plasma or trapped radiation.

The advent of the ballistic missile threat brought another campaign, first at ONR and then at ARPA, that would explore the use of high-frequency (HF) transmissions, using both ground-backscatter radars and normal forward propagation circuits, to remotely detect missile launches and nuclear explosions. A suggestion by Peterson and Oswald "Mike" Villard at Stanford had pointed to the potential of HF systems to do this. But SRI was naturally not among those seeking to build an operational system. Being free of such an advocacy position, though, SRI was asked by ARPA to become the "objective" collector and reviewer of data from this entire effort. For over a decade, SRI ran ARPA's Detection Data Center for the collection and presentation of data and information on over-the-horizon missile detection. Unexpectedly, this had the unfortunate side effect of denying SRI even experimental roles in that same program. Eventually, this detection capability became attractive enough that both the Air Force and the Navy built operational radars to carry out

this mission. SRI's Ed Lyon was the Air Force's chief consultant on such systems for decades.

The U.S. High-Altitude Nuclear Tests of 1962

Now let us turn to the 1962 nuclear test series in the Pacific. As mentioned, the Soviet Union broke the test ban agreement on September 1, 1961, and on October 10 President Kennedy authorized planning to begin for the resumption of U.S. testing. The test series came to be called Operation Dominic, and SRI's role in its last phase, termed Fishbowl, was pivotal. SRI would again demonstrate its responsiveness, fielding a family of radars, including one 84 ft in diameter, on Johnston Island within the allotted 3 months. This SRI work was funded by the Defense Nuclear Agency (DNA).[9]

Although SRI was required to be in the field by April of 1962, there were then a number of launch failures, including one that blew up the launch pad. But five test missiles were launched between July and November. Similar to the 1958 experience, the SRI radar data proved that the detection of ballistic missile reentry in or above the ionosphere, following a high-altitude offensive or defensive detonation, could not be relied upon using ground-based equipment. The radars were either blacked out (no radar returns) for short periods or, more significantly, flooded with spurious signals from bright reflections from ionization structurally aligned in the earth's magnetic field. SRI drew these conclusions from the data gathered by the SRI Johnston Island radars, plus several airborne radars that SRI operated aboard RC-121 aircraft flying in the vicinity.

As precarious as it would seem, the results showed that a much lower ABM intercept altitude than originally conceived would be needed. The important implication of this is the significantly reduced time available to defend ABM systems. Although billions have since been spent on high-altitude sensors and interceptor weapons (e.g., the Strategic Defense Initiative), to date no real ABM system has been built by the United States for intercept at any altitude. One unexpectedly beneficial by-product of SRI's presence on Johnston Island were the photographs taken by SRI's Walter Chesnut. Taken in support of the radar work, they have become one of the most important

---

[9] Up until November 1971, DNA was called the Defense Atomic Support Agency or DASA but we will use DNA here.

IVORY ON THE CORAL

From the center of the flat, elongated coral slab that was Johnston Island (JI), one could walk north or south no more than a few hundred yards before encountering the ocean, and from there the closest land was at least a thousand miles away. With nary a tree or source of potable water, Johnston Island would make a regrettable shipwreck isle. On the other hand, this austerity meant that the bustle of the mission there didn't have to contend with any serious distractions; there simply were none. Usually, and insofar as possible, the U.S. military tries to bring a sense of home to their troops, but this operation was temporary and a bit austere. Requests for needed technical equipment were honored quickly; niceties were something else. If diversions were to be found, they had to be created. Well, SRI also cares about its people abroad.

The postponements and delays of the operation were getting to the SRI crew. Range safety officers were destroying missiles in flight, and then one blew up on the launch pad, destroying the pad. Experimenters, including SRI, would use these delays to maintain and upgrade their equipment so as to be ready when the real time came. But there is only so much of that one can do. With a concern for those isolated on Johnston Island, Ray Leadabrand and his assistant, Barbara Bunker, who were in Hawaii at the time, got creative.

Like other shipments, the huge wooden crate was delivered outside the SRI radar van on JI and laid there on the coral sand. On the crate, per airlift convention, was stenciled its contents: *VARIABLE-FREQUENCY IMPULSE-ACTIVATED TONE GENERATOR.* Puzzled, the SRI crew broke it open to find a small spinet piano. They quickly placed the piano, appropriately, inside the instrumentation van. Murray Baron, in charge of the SRI radars on the Island and who (Ray knew) played the piano, then positioned himself at the instrument's keyboard and belted out something like ragtime. Joplin could have not sounded better to the assembled bunch. The piano, as it turned out, was riddled with termites, but it served its purpose well. Murray and Jose De Leon wrote the *Johnston Island Blues,* and the instrument was later given to the Island's NCO Club.

---

sets of information available to understand the complex interactions of the various nuclear energy products with the Earth's atmosphere and its magnetic field. These data are still being studied almost 40 years later!

Following the tests in the Pacific, the government initiated what was commonly known as the Readiness Program. This name reflected the desire on the part of the United States to be ready should another violation by the Soviets enable or force a continuation of our own tests. Given the now proven uncertainty of radar performance in nuclear environments, there was plenty to be learned. Many projects at SRI fell under this umbrella: the examination of field-aligned radar echoes in the aurora as a surrogate to nuclear-produced clutter, the development of a series of satellites to measure the coherent bandwidth of the ionosphere, the development of an incoherent scatter facility in Alaska to study the background ionosphere, and the non-cooperative participation in the French atomic tests in Mururoa in 1971-1974. The latter work was to learn about the impact on radar of low altitude detonations. It came to SRI because of our deep familiarity with assessing the nuclear impacts on future ABM designs.

Regarding the limits imposed by the ionosphere on the bandwidth of radars, it is important to be able to resolve individual incoming missiles while they are still at very high altitudes. To accomplish this, anti-ballistic missile radars, of necessity, use very wide bandwidths. It was important then, to assess just how much the ionosphere might limit the resolution such bandwidth afforded. SRI, under DNA sponsorship, came up with a creative technique to measure the coherence bandwidth of the ionosphere. (See box on satellites.)

Back to More Benign Research Settings

As is often the case in the United States, equipment built for a military research purpose finds good use in basic science. Under sponsorship of the Defense Nuclear Agency, SRI built the incoherent scatter radar mentioned earlier that could look in detail at electron density, temperature, and plasma motion as a function of spatial position, including altitude. This facility was built and checked out at Stanford and then relocated in 1972 to Chatanika, Alaska, to make detailed measurements of the aurora and its more quiescent background. The operation of that radar produced perhaps thirty PhD theses and countless papers about auroral arcs and the electrical behavior of our upper atmosphere.

SRI SATELLITE WORK

It is not commonly known, but in the 1960s SRI designed and built a series of satellite packages for Stanford University that was used in studies of interplanetary space. These experiments flew on four of the Pioneer Series and on Mariner V after the Pioneer series was interrupted. The Pioneer satellites were legendary in their durability, and were the first satellites to orbit the sun. SRI's "Big Dish" at Stanford was used for both command and telemetry, and was one of the sites that transmitted the dual frequencies used to measure interplanetary electron densities. The package flown on Mariner V was used in the first Venus occultation experiment. As the satellite passed behind Venus, the changes in the characteristics of the signal that was passed from the Earth to the satellite revealed characteristics of the Venusian atmosphere. Four OGO (orbiting geophysical observatory) satellites had SRI-built VLF receivers aboard that were tuned to ground-based transmitters. These and three-axis magnetic field sensors helped in the discovery of the asymmetry of the earth's magnetosphere. According to SRI's Bud Rorden, designer of the OGO series, most of these early satellites were built from scratch using hand-selected parts. Finally, SRI designed and operated a series of innovative wideband satellites that measured the coherent bandwidth of the ionosphere in equatorial, auroral, and the more quiescent mid-latitude regions.

Pioneer 6, 7, 8, and 9 were the first solar orbiting satellites and were used to measure interplanetary features. They measured the dynamics of the solar wind and discovered its spiral nature. The SRI two-frequency package used on Pioneer was also flown later on Mariner V. As of 1996, Pioneer 6 was the oldest working satellite, having been in orbit for over 30 years.

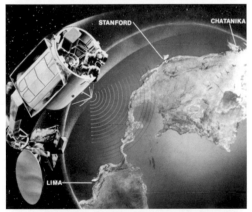

One of three SRI satellites launched in the early 1970s to measure the coherent bandwidth of the ionosphere using a set of phase-coherent spectral lines near 400 and 2300 MHz.

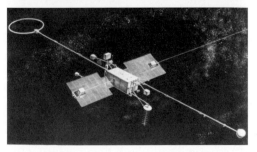

One of four OGO (2 equatorial and 2 polar) satellites. SRI also had experiments aboard Explorer 6 and the VELA (nuclear detection) satellites.

Figure 9-8. The SRI site in Greenland showing the auroral radar, a lidar beam, and auroral curtains.

After these studies of the auroral zone had gone on for almost a decade, a similar but newer and more powerful auroral radar was built in Norway. (SRI's Dr. Murray Baron became the second leader of this facility, called EISCAT.) This new radar motivated the SRI leaders to suggest moving its radar to a higher magnetic latitude and there to examine daytime auroral conditions. By this time the Defense Department's interests in readiness had declined, and ownership of the incoherent scatter facility was transferred to the National Science Foundation (NSF). In response to SRI's suggestion, NSF authorized the radar's relocation to Sondrestrom Fjord, Greenland, where it also could explore the effects of the so-called ionospheric cusp—the locations where the earth's magnetic field lines open into outer space. SRI also brought other instruments there to measure airglow and a laser radar (lidar) to look for specific constituents (see Figure 9-8).

As important as SRI's own research using the facility has been, at least as important was SRI's decision to open up the facility to all qualified scientists from around the world. That open policy, started at Chatanika, has made the Sondrestrom facility by far the most prolific source of ionospheric knowledge among the four such sites that NSF funds, and one of the best in the world. The site is efficiently run by

just four SRI staff members, and its data are available over the Internet. Some specific knowledge that has come from Chatanika and Sondrestrom includes:

• The first observations of the high-latitude convection pattern; that is, the distribution and movement of the ionic "fluid" in the polar region and the behavior of ionospheric storms caused by the variable impact of particles ejected from the sun's corona.

• Electrodynamic models of the high-latitude ionosphere, also involving neutral components, across high and low ion density regions.

• The constituents of the high-latitude ionosphere, including the presence of heavy ions and their chemical balance.

The Sondrestrom site employs more than 22 different instruments and is used by hundreds of the world's upper atmosphere scientists from 38 different institutions. Information from the Chatanika and Sondrestrom facilities have, between 1973 and 2002, given rise to more than 490 papers in the various research journals of geophysics and more than 45 Ph.D. theses.

The most recent affirmation of the SRI strength in this field was a 4-year, $44 million, 2003 award from NSF to build the world's first modular and mobile incoherent scatter system. The idea was born at a meeting of scientists at SRI some 15 years ago. John Kelly, a leader in SRI's Center for GeoSpace Studies recalls discussing the need for advanced instrumentation to address critical questions in ionospheric research such as dynamics. Current radar systems were, and still are, limited in where they can be and how fast they can be pointed. The new radar will be electronically steered and have three separate panels that can operate independently at the same or separate sites. The first site is in Poker Flat, Alaska, to be

Figure 9-9. The SRI 1.4 mile long Wide Aperture Receiving Facility near Los Banos, CA.

followed soon by two at Resolute Bay in Canada. Though remote, its operation will be accessible from anywhere on the Internet.[10]

SRI operates other unique ionospheric facilities. One is a remote laboratory on Resolute Bay for scientific probing of the ionospheric "polar cap," that region within the annular auroral zone. It is sponsored by the NSF and, like Sondrestrom, available to all scientists. Another is the Wide Aperture Research Facility (WARF), a testbed for the technology important to over-the-horizon (OTH) radars; that is, those that use reflection from the ionosphere to operate beyond line of sight. It uses a combination of transmitting and receiving arrays located approximately 100 miles apart in the Central Valley of California. There are two transmitting and two receiving arrays, each pair having different azimuthal orientations. The receiving arrays, one of which is depicted in Figure 9-9, are about 7,500 ft (1.42 mi) long and consist of about 256 vertical, twin-element receiving pairs. This array makes possible azimuthal beamwidths of the order of a half degree. The transmit arrays consist of 16 vertical-element log-periodic antennas

capable of transmitting from 6 to 28 MHz. One of the arrays was developed in the mid-1960s. The total coverage area of its associated radar is 1.3 million sq mi that can be swept using an illuminated region of approximately 15,000 sq mi. In the setting of OTH radars, the WARF pioneered the automatic detection and tracking of aircraft and surface ships, ionospheric propagation management, advanced display and signal processing techniques, and remote ocean wave-height measurements. Its design was used to develop the specification for the U.S. Navy's Relocatable Over-the-Horizon Radar (ROTHR) in Virginia, the Air Force's two installations in Maine and Northern California, and the Australian government's Jindalee experimental OTHR. Over the decade of the 1990s the WARF was upgraded to a real-time detection and tracking facility to conduct research and development for wide-area counter-drug surveillance. Coverage can extend from the southern border of Mexico to our own southern states and laterally from Baja California to the Gulf of Mexico. Even small, general aviation aircraft can be followed. The WARF is operated by a crew of six engineers and technicians who continue to improve its performance through capabilities like impulsive noise excision (lightning) and improved tracking and ground positioning techniques. Over its existence the WARF activities have been sponsored by perhaps 10 different governmental agencies.

The above discussion has been but a sampling of SRI's continuous contributions to our understanding of the upper atmosphere, both fundamentally and how it can interact with systems we find necessary to use. The time diagram of Figure 9-10 more completely encapsulates SRI's involvement in ionospheric research. Not only has it continued for over 40 years, it is still going strong today.

---

[10] While SRI is the leader of this innovative facility other collaborating institutions include MIT Millstone Hill, Stanford University, the University of Alaska and the University of Western Ontario.

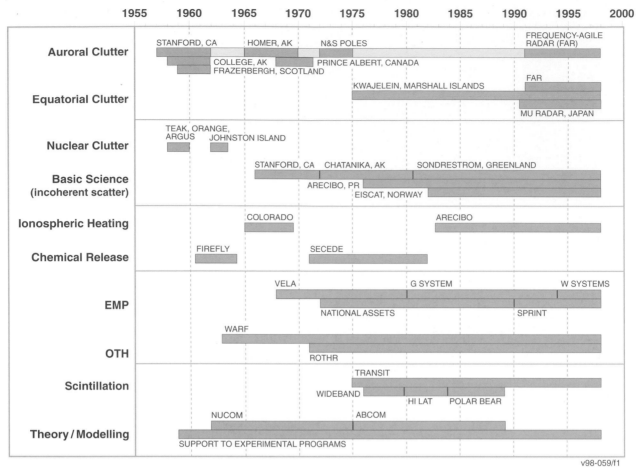

Figure 9-10. A comprehensive listing of major SRI participation in ionospheric research, only a few of which have been touched on here.

Research in Ionospheric Communications

SRI's work in ionosphere-dependent communications[11] dates back to 1951, when SRI was just 3 years old.[E] Work on several innovative approaches to single-sideband modulation techniques began earlier in 1948, but work that directly involved the understanding and use of the ionosphere came with a request from the U.S. Army Signal Corps in June 1951. Over a 2-year period SRI built a simulator that depicted the multiple simultaneous radio paths characteristic of ionospheric, high-frequency (HF) or shortwave communications. The simulator was used to test various modulation techniques. We will return to HF communications after a brief story about SRI's exploration into the use of meteor trails for communications.

Communications Via Meteor Trails

As mentioned at the outset, Peterson, and later his associate Ray Vincent, were interested in the potential of very small micrometeorites for communications. SRI and Stanford were both investigating their effects, and SRI had built a meteor-burst system for the Air Force as early as 1955 (see Figures 9-11 and 9-12). Radio reflections from these trails could extend line-of-site communications beyond the horizon to perhaps a thousand miles. Because the altitude where friction spelled the end of the meteorite was also one of fairly rapid recombination, the ionization in each trail was

---

[11] Ionospheric communication relies on the existence of a reflecting layer for radio waves that lies from about 80 to 400 km above the Earth. The propagation of radio energy in the HF or shortwave band is made possible by entrapment between two annular shells, the conducting ground and the ionosphere. Using this corridor is generally limited to frequencies below 30 MHz. The so-called medium and shortwave bands constituted the only long-range communications before the advent of satellites, and are still in use in many parts of the world.

The reception of radio signals transmitted over distances in excess of one thousand miles by the forward scattering of signals reflected by ionized meteor trails has been achieved by SRI electrical engineers. These ionized columns, about sixty miles from the earth's surface, are utilized by means of a specially designed antenna. Billions of meteors pass through the ionosphere in the course of an average day. The continuous signal provided by the meteor reflections is weak and subject to rapid fluctuations, but is reliable and not subject to interruptions by magnetic disturbances

Figure 9-11. The antenna for SRI's experimental meteor burst system (SRI's *Research for Industry*, 8, 1, 10, November 1955).

short-lived. To make the channel useful, therefore, it was necessary to store or buffer the flow of information until a new trail of the correct geometry arrived. The stored data was then burst quickly to the receiver. Usable trails could come from grain-sized meteors whose occurrence was frequent enough to sustain effective communications bandwidths of the order of 10 kHz. SRI explored meteor communications for perhaps a decade, both in system design and construction and in modeling the radio reflection characteristics of the meteor trails themselves.

One study determined the locus of trail positions that would be advantageous for a given transmitter-receiver geometry. Geometry was important because normally good signal strength depended on finding a meteor trail whose location provided a specular or equal-angle reflection. Although SRI's work was pioneering and interesting, only a few meteor trail systems were built and used. One need for which meteor-burst communications was ideal was the collection of meteorological (no pun

intended) information from remote areas. To gather snow and water level information, the Department of Agriculture's Natural Resource Conservation Service still operates a very large network in the West using such a system, called SNOTEL. Systems are still made and sold, and the Air Force reopened its interest in the medium, sponsoring research in the geographic distribution of reflection sites from a single transmitter. For the most part, however, satellites began displacing meteor burst systems in the late 1960s, and their employment today is only in very specialized situations.

High-Frequency Ionospheric Communications

Concurrent with this first meteor-burst work, the critical nature of HF communications to the U.S. military enabled SRI to continue its ionospheric communications work. It would last for another 30 years or more. The complexity of the ionospheric medium, including its global, weather-like diurnal and seasonal variations made it very difficult to predict whether communications would be available. Furthermore, because of its long propagating range, the universal (global) demand for HF and its very limited range of usable frequencies meant a very crowded radio spectrum. Because of these complexities, the advent of computers offered a natural approach to harnessing our knowledge of the ionosphere and building computational models of it. In 1956 SRI was awarded a contract from the U.S. Army Signal Corps to look at the use of computers to do just that. SRI built some of the earliest computer models of this type of communications. Subsequently, the National Bureau of Standards in Boulder, CO, began building an improved model of the global and temporal ionosphere using a worldwide distribution of ionospheric data collection stations. These data, together with more accurate propagation models, meant improved frequency allocation and selection for the far-flung HF radio systems of the U.S. government.

Figure 9-12. Meteor burst equipment designer Russ Wolfram with lab director Ray Vincent (inset).

Neither SRI nor others had made any directed communications measurements, and the test ban treaty that followed the 1958 tests preempted any further exploration of such effects. That situation remained until September 1961 when the Soviets broke that treaty with the huge detonations at Novaya Zemlya. The United States immediately responded with a number of its own tests in the Pacific. This was the same Operation Dominic mentioned before, with its concluding high-altitude tests known as Fishbowl.

Somewhat fortuitously, the modeling work that SRI had been doing for the Army included some planning for possible atomic tests. Among other things this

But, though the models improved, the ionosphere, having weather-like behavior, has never been totally predictable, nor the models totally accurate. At best, models deal with average daily and seasonal conditions, yet its wide variability often leaves the mean unmeaningful. Regions like the auroral zone, the polar cap, and the equator were often too dynamic to model, particularly across their vast expanse. But the concern over such unpredictability was taken to unprecedented heights when, in 1958, we saw the ionospheric complexities introduced by the aforementioned high-altitude nuclear detonations over Johnston Island. These explosions brought far more dynamics to the ionosphere than do natural phenomena, at least for a time, and that uncertainty caused an open concern about our ability to communicate at all if the Russians were to launch a thermonuclear war. The substantial degradation of communications circuits transiting the Pacific near the 1958 nuclear tests was appreciated only after the fact.

Figure 9-13. SRI's Operation Fishbowl's Communications Leader, John Lomax

involved the testing of a new HF communications tool with the arcane name of "sweep-frequency oblique-incidence ionospheric sounder." From that kind of pre-positioning, and a working relationship with the Defense Atomic Support Agency on the radar side of the house, SRI was in a very good position to design and participate in any upcoming nuclear communications experiments. Given its background, SRI could, within the limitations of the tests, determine just how inimical high-altitude nuclear explosions were to long-distance communications. So when the decision was made by President Kennedy to resume testing, our earlier planning on communications tests could be carried out in a hurry. As mentioned earlier, SRI excels in being able to competently and quickly design and carry out field experiments. But the scope of this experiment would far exceed anything SRI had ever done. Directly testing the impact on long-distance communications of a series of high-altitude nuclear tests in the Pacific required a grid of HF communications trunks that spanned the

Pacific and crisscrossed the detonation area at Johnston Island. With SRI engineer John Lomax (see Figure 9-13) leading the effort, SRI rose magnificently to the task.

As with the radar program already mentioned, President Kennedy authorized test planning to begin on 10 October 1961, and by the following April, SRI had designed and fielded a comprehensive set of communications circuits across the Pacific: From Rarotonga in the South Pacific to Fairbanks in the north, and from Okinawa in the west to Palo Alto, CA, in the east, 13 different sites yielded 27 different circuits having a range of distances from the Johnston Island bursts and their magnetic conjugates. The geographical layout is shown in Figure 9-14. As the vast breadth of locations suggests, just visiting the potential sites and negotiating their lease was a big task. The project actually got under way in January of 1962 with an incredible goal of being in the field by April! The type and means of data collection had to be decided, the communications equipment had to be built and

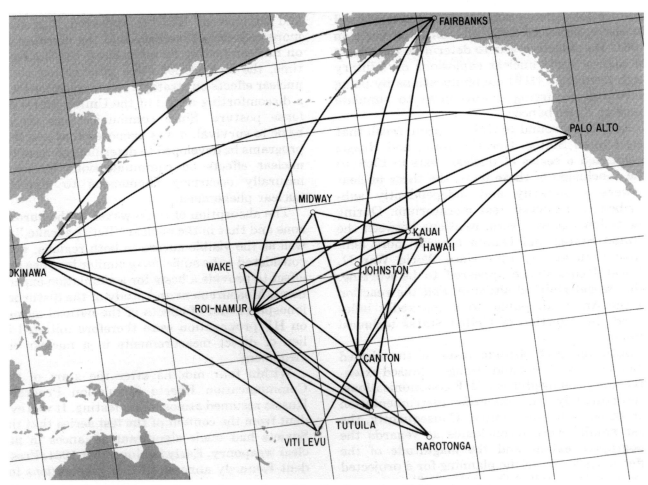

Figure 9-14. The communications paths monitored for the Operation Fishbowl nuclear tests.

Equipment preparation at SRI

Sounder van arrival in Samoa

The SRI field site in Samoa (Tutuila)

Figure 9 15. Outfitting and deploying the SRI communications equipment for fishbowl.

delivered, and all the provisions for operation in austere environments needed to be assembled. As depicted in Figure 9-15, all this materiel for all of the sites was rapidly assembled at SRI, loaded aboard C-124 aircraft, and flown to the Pacific sites. Amazingly, and a genuine tribute to SRI, all sites were ready by

15 April 1962, an impossibly short 3 months after the order to proceed!

Rather than using normal fixed-frequency transmitters and receivers, SRI drew on its recent instrumentation experience and proposed the use of newly available sounding equipment built by Granger Associates, a company that had earlier arisen out of SRI. This equipment permitted not only flexible, synchronized connections between multiple sites, but also scanned the radio spectrum on each circuit from 4-64 MHz in a matter of seconds. This equipment was operated for the five different high-altitude bursts in the Fishbowl Series that took place from July to November of 1962.

Information derived from this network of sounders gave the United States the ability to calibrate emerging models of communications in a nuclear environment and, in the cases of newly observed phenomena, build supplemental models that, when incorporated, let us estimate whether we could communicate or not. For example, it was the network of oblique- and vertical-incidence ionospheric sounders that recognized the existence of acoustic-gravity waves that propagated out from the burst and had great influence, positive and negative, on the ionosphere. Another was the recognition of new high-altitude, mostly field-aligned, ionization from the burst that could be used for communications under certain circumstances.

Beyond the collection of the relevant HF and higher frequency data in the field, SRI was asked to analyze that data and later build the computer models that would describe the effects seen. These models were embodied in a set of DNA handbooks and used by the United States for over 25 years to predict our ability to communicate at HF under various attack scenarios. Some of the same computer codes were also found to better portray the natural ionosphere and thus found use there. The last test of the Dominic Series in November 1962 was the last U.S. atmospheric test. The subsequent readiness program that was designed to improve the instrumentation for radar also enabled a somewhat smaller continuing development in communications. As in the radar case, the auroral region was taken as a surrogate for nuclear conditions, and these same sounders explored communications at those latitudes, albeit on a much reduced scale.

Soon another benefit from the Pacific sounder network emerged. Those same, hard-to-predict ionospheric dynamics, that now plagued us in both the natural and nuclear conditions, suggested another approach in how to use the HF part of the radio spectrum. The rapidly scanning electronic sounders had shown an ability to assess the available HF channels in near real time and thus, through better operating frequency selection, aid in maintaining the continuity of HF circuits. SRI received a contract from the Defense Communications Agency to explore that use. Properly automated and shared across multiple paths, the sounders could largely remove the guesswork from managing HF circuits. SRI supervised the implementation of this automation in a number of trial sites from about 1964 to 1967, and improvement clearly followed. But communications satellites were becoming increasingly capable and that meant, except in a few special circumstances, that HF was no longer the preferred long-distance communications choice. Therefore, the resulting frequency management system saw but limited operational use.

One other communications aspect of SRI's participation in the Fishbowl operation was a set of measurements at very low frequencies (VLF). Existing worldwide VLF transmitters in this 3-30 kHz range were monitored at various field sites during the tests. VLF is important for communicating with submerged submarines, and few serious effects were observed.

Some Comments on SRI's Ability in the Field

The SRI contributions to our understanding of the ionosphere and its radio-based systems have been truly legion and, accordingly, this account has been embarrassingly inadequate. Moreover, research and new insights continue to this day.

SRI is active in studying the dynamics of the equatorial ionosphere, operating the high-latitude Sondrestrom Fjord incoherent scatter facility for the NSF and analyzing its measurements, operating the world's widest aperture (narrowest beam) HF facility in California's Central Valley, and other ionosphere-related work. Our ability to have such pivotal roles is attributable to those SRI staff who, through their brilliance and accessibility to critical government decision-makers, gave us both insight and influence. Competent researchers could then carry out what was needed in proposals and contracts to give SRI a preeminent national R&D position in ionospheric matters for over 40 years.

Just a final story about those who went to the field. During the early attempts to launch the Thor rockets at Johnston Island in 1962, nearly all of the military personnel were evacuated to carriers lying offshore. During the first few months of the tests, when the safety officers began blowing up errant or failing launch vehicles, pieces would rain down and in at least one case puncture the SRI radar antenna. This led to building bunkers on the Island for the "critical personnel." But throughout the tests, the SRI people were not in those bunkers but instead in their flimsy "shelters," ready to capture the information they came to get. And get it they did. The vans were later shown to be incapable of sheltering those inside from even a modest-sized piece of falling metal. It was not that the SRI personnel necessarily felt safer in them; that was simply where they needed to be.

SRI's Murray Baron recalled one instance where the commanding general on the Island wanted to tell President Kennedy of a successful detonation and requested that the SRI radars be turned off because he mistakenly believed they

One other humorous anecdote occurred on the southernmost site, SRI's communications field site on Rarotonga. The island was, of course, famous for its tropical allure, but getting in and out of the island was not easy. There were no docking facilities for large ships, and the only landing strip was also the golf course! Approval had been given to land the very large C-124 Globemasters like those that brought in the SRI sounder van. But in the early phase of the Pacific tests, things got a bit out of hand. As with any field experiment, sometimes parts were needed, and needed soon. Planes would be dispatched out of Honolulu to the many outlying sites. The problem was that those planes themselves would break down all too frequently and almost exclusively in Rarotonga. The consequence...the golf course was fillitng up with large U.S. military airplanes! A military solution presented itself: Upon specific order from the commanding general, there would be no more aircraft breakdowns on Rarotonga. The problem magically cleared up.

were causing interference to his communication system. Baron knew they weren't but, more important, there were still plenty of radar effects showing. So he kept stalling as the phone calls escalated. By the time a full colonel personally visited him at the radar van, the observed effects were gone and Baron obligingly turned off the radar.

Many other stories came from around the Pacific about how the SRI staff managed their sites—ashore, afloat, and in the air. Support and supplies came via daily sessions on a short-wave net operated out of a picturesque beach house near Diamond Head on Oahu. All sites ran complex electronic equipment for the better part of a year, many under primitive conditions and saddled with finicky diesel generators. Dedicated and competent, the SRI staff helped define SRI's splendid reputation in this field.

Atmospheric Pollutants and Ozone— Flagging the Troubles of Man's Creation

Ozone, that variant of an oxygen molecule with three atomic oxygen atoms bound together, is both friend and foe. Just as whether a plant in your garden is a flower or a weed depends not only on what it looks like but where it is growing, ozone is either a benefactor or a pollutant depending on where it is found. In that part of our atmosphere near the earth, an overabundance of ozone is toxic to both animals and plants. Yet 20 miles above us, in the stratosphere, ozone becomes not only beneficial, but a lifesaver. In the stratosphere it is a shield against harmful ultraviolet (UV) rays from the sun that can damage the DNA of living things, including important components of the food chain such as the ocean's plankton. In humans, UV light can cause such problems as skin cancer and cataracts. Here we look briefly at these two roles for ozone, the first investigation coming in the late 1940s as SRI itself was just emerging.

Low-Altitude Ozone and the Causes of Smog

SRI was not quite seven months old when it undertook its first work on a peculiarity of the atmosphere over Los Angeles that the world now knows as smog. That the term was still in its infancy is indicated in brief writings about 18 months after the work began, in which the term "smog" was still introduced in quotation marks. The impetus for the study was the problems of poor visibility and eye irritation that were characteristic of the Los Angeles Basin. Curiously, these characteristics appeared much more severe there than in the more industrialized cities of the eastern United States, and there was a clamor to find out why. The Western Oil and Gas Association[12] sponsored the first work at SRI in May of 1947, and because of the complexity of both the problem and its mitigation, the work lasted for the better part of a decade. During that early effort, SRI contributed monumentally to the understanding of just what the airborne pollutants were and from whence they came. We will see how SRI effectively led the early investigation that would give the local governments in that area the information they needed to attack the problem.

In the beginning it was "not entirely clear" what gave the Los Angeles area its unusual scourge of bad air. Old timers in the area definitely said it was not new, with recollections of its presence as far back as 1912.[F] On the other hand, air problems, particularly eye irritation, had increased in frequency and severity in recent years. From weather records, the SRI investigators had learned that the number of sunshine days, dating back to 1896, had not significantly changed. Measurements showed a decrease in visibility during the World War II years, but the confusion with fog and natural, long-term weather changes made this diagnostic unreliable. Thus, at the outset, the team was left with only qualitative accounts.

The big components were obviously the weather, the topography, and the presence of man...but how did they play together to precipitate the problem? What was the mechanism? So the SRI investigators, led by Dr. Paul Magill of the SRI-Pasadena office,

---

[12] This association was formed by the petroleum industries operating in the Los Angeles area. Interestingly, it had a committee on smoke and fumes that was the specific SRI client. The initial contract was SRI's third and was for $505,649 over a period of 30 months.

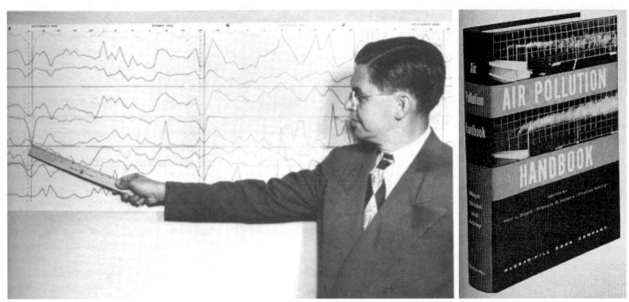

Figure 9-16. Dr. Paul Magill pointing to a smog index line and the sharp dip on Black Friday, September 13, 1946 (one of the worst smog days in Los Angeles history). Also shown is a 1956 McGraw-Hill handbook, edited and contributed to by the SRI staff involved in early pollution work, that is still referred to today (Magill, Paul L., Francis R. Holden, and Charles E. Ackley, eds, *Air Pollution Handbook*, McGraw-Hill, 1956).

started with a model of the normal convective atmosphere over Los Angeles (see Figure 9-16). The climate was subtropical, and the presence of barrier mountains on three sides had an impact not only on the ability of the air to mix vertically, but also on the formation of all-important temperature inversions—when upper atmospheric temperatures are higher than those on the ground. Those inversions were also amplified by the presence of coastal water that was cool near the surface. The common high-pressure regions and weak seasonal winds common to the California coast were also factored in. To the extent that such conditions were understood and were influential in forming smog, its occurrence could at least be predicted using meteorological information.

Of course, the formation of smog also depended on some set of noxious constituents. Measurements, many made by SRI over a period of several years, were clearly needed to catalog the type and amount of compounds and particulate matter present in the Los Angeles atmosphere. Early measurements indicated that there were not one or two culprits, but more than fifty, spewed out by a wide, diverse, and increasing range of human activities. The question was, how many of these contributed to the pungent, eye-burning degradation of the atmosphere? Suspected early by the SRI researchers were so-called aldehydes, formed of

carbon, hydrogen, and oxygen, and of which formaldehyde is an example. These were known to cause eye irritation. Also suspected were sulfur dioxide and trioxide, the latter having known fog-forming properties. The January 1948 report[G] to the client mentions some of the early suspected culprits such as "burning rubbish (estimated at about 300 tons per day), industrial operations, and the operation of motor vehicles." Nothing, however, had been singled out as the major offender.

SRI built a special test chamber to make controlled, quantitative measurements on individual contaminants and to determine whether they induced one of the most obvious impacts of smog: eye irritation. To gain direct evidence, human volunteers were asked to occupy the chamber and indicate when eye or throat irritation was noticeable. Some of these volunteers were SRI employees. The questions were intended to give approximate, subjective answers only, to rule out those contaminants with no detectable effects; that is, no discernable eye irritation at levels above those known to exist in the atmosphere. From these early screening tests the SRI scientists were able to rule out some of the previously suspected agents. Part of the problem at this early stage was an inaccurate knowledge of the agent levels that did exist in the atmosphere. Improved measurement techniques later showed, for example, 5 to 10 times higher levels of aldehydes, a product of incomplete combustion, than had been estimated in the earliest samplings.

Later, in the Pasadena Lab, SRI built a 40-ft-long cylindrical chamber called a transmissometer in which a concentrated light beam could pass repeatedly through a specifically composed atmosphere of known types and amounts of constituents at controlled humidity and temperature. For the first time they could quantitatively tell how much some of the concentrations they had observed from samples were contributing to what the population experienced.

As this initial work was going on, the world was becoming aware of smog. An indication of SRI's prominent role in this new environmental concern was evidenced when SRI hosted in Los Angeles on 10-11 November 1949 the first National Symposium on Air Pollution. The meeting had a scientific bent and was attended by both academic and industrial researchers from all over the U.S. SRI would again lead the second such conference in 1952.[13] The work continued.

A status report written in 1951 showed a few new conclusions being drawn.[H] From improved gathering and analysis techniques, the focus had narrowed to: oxidants, liquid droplets, crystals, aldehydes, and sulfuric acid. Of these, the category that seemed most correlated with eye irritation was the oxidants, one of which was ozone. But the correlation with eye irritation was still complex. To try to understand better what specifically caused eye burning, SRI returned to "smog chamber" tests. Volunteers were again exposed to potential eye irritants, this time to various combinations of nitric acid vapor, sulfur dioxide and trioxide, diesel and crankcase oils, lampblack, sodium chloride, and ozonized gasoline. As it turned out, the removal of any one of the constituents didn't statistically change the amount of eye irritation. As to attribution, the origin of the candidate pollutants was believed to come from incomplete combustion in its various forms. Of the total combustion and evaporation products released into the Los Angeles air daily, about 60 percent were judged to come from the

general public (driving of automobiles, trucks, and buses; heating of homes and businesses; and burning of trash), 25 percent from the petroleum industry, and 15 percent from other sources. Exhaust fumes from the then 2 million vehicles each day, driving an average of 50 miles, contribute over 350 tons of organic substances into the air, not counting 30 and 40 tons of aldehydes and nitrogen oxides, respectively. As with the Pogo imperative, it was becoming clear as to who the enemy was.

The last of SRI's almost eight years of analytical and experimental work on smog in the Los Angeles basin came in a summary report entitled, *The Smog Problem in Los Angeles County*, issued in August of 1954. The 134-page report brought together both SRI's and other scientific work in the area. The following is an extract from an SRI article about the report:[I]

> "The research indicates that substances responsible for smog are always present in the Los Angeles atmosphere and require conditions of strong sunlight, stagnant air, and temperature inversion for smog to develop. The sun is apparently the 'motor element' which drives the chemical reaction, producing an atmosphere with unusual chemical activity.
>
> Ozone—a highly reactive molecule consisting of 3 atoms of oxygen—is one of the best indications of smog intensity and Los Angeles has the highest known concentration of ozone on the earth's surface."

SRI chemists isolated in the lab the active wavelength, between 3,600 and 4,000 angstroms, that forms ozone. From field measurements its concentration in the Los Angeles area was well correlated with commute traffic. Significantly, SRI measurements also showed that, although values of smog intensity may differ with location across the LA basin, its formation on a typically smoggy day begins everywhere at first sunrise. SRI determined the critical constituents of smog, estimated the vast amounts that were being released daily into the Los Angeles atmosphere, and concluded that automobile exhaust was the largest single source of pollutants. It contained hydrocarbons, oxides of nitrogen, aldehydes, and particulate material that, collectively, represent about 7 to 9 percent by weight of the gasoline fed into the automobile motor!

---

[13] Dr. P.A. Leighton, one of SRI's founders and a chemistry professor at Stanford, was instrumental in the conferences and, significantly, influential in getting SRI into this field. A session chairman in both conferences was A.O. Beckman, who during that time founded Beckman Instruments and later became a member of the SRI Board.

Although some of the major culprits had been identified, SRI continued its measurements and analytical work, and the SRI Pasadena lab became noted for its collection of the best smog analyzing tools in the world.[14] The lab used instrumentation ranging from huge (500 ft^3) mixing chambers with artificial sunlight to new mass spectrometers. SRI also continued very controlled human testing of the irritation qualities of various exhaust gas components and worked to find ways to reduce the automobile exhaust components in smog.[J] As the constituents themselves, the role of the sun, and the important diurnal and meteorological inversion characteristics of the Basin became well understood by the late 1950s, SRI's studies on the constituents of smog came to an end. However, investigations on the effect of smog on agricultural plants, including citrus, continued in the Pasadena or Menlo Park laboratories until at least 1961. Then SRI's long, continuous, and clearly beneficial effort, nearly all sponsored by the petroleum industry, finally ended.

Stratospheric Ozone

The Earth's ecological balances are often finely tuned. Over the past 20 years, the public has become increasingly aware of one of those balances: the presence of ozone in the stratosphere (between about 15 and 35 km altitude) and the amount of UV radiation that reaches the Earth's surface. That particular balance is precarious because a high exposure to UV rays can be harmful to both plants and humans. Amazingly, the UV shield offered by upper atmospheric ozone occurs with the presence of only a very small amount of ozone, typically a few parts per million of normal stratospheric constituents.[15] The alarm that has raised the collective attention of chemists and governments worldwide is the decreasing amount of stratospheric ozone.

The culprits in this saga are now confirmed to be some of the by-products of man; namely, chlorine, bromine, and a few related elements. They exist in many of the compounds man has created for refrigeration, inert pressure gases, cleaning chemicals, and manufacturing. A certain class of these compounds and those inimical to our atmosphere are called chlorofluorocarbons (CFCs). Over eighty percent of those observed in the stratosphere are manmade. Hence, protocols have been written and laws established to drastically reduce their production.

What was SRI's role in this first scientific, then governmental, awareness? The basic realization of the role of CFCs in ozone depletion came from University of California, Irvine, chemists Sherwood Roland and Mario Molina, for which they shared the Nobel Prize. Postulating the presence of highly reacting forms of chlorine in the stratosphere, they showed that such molecules could directly deplete ozone. The question remained: How did they get there? Many CFCs are very stable and do not react well with near-Earth gases. Although they are heavier than the normal constituents of our air, through turbulent air mixing they can reach high into the atmosphere unchanged because of their stability. That stability continues until they reach the stratosphere, where sunlight wavelengths that normally don't reach the Earth can decompose these compounds into active forms of chlorine or related gases. SRI's contribution involved showing that one of these CFCs, chlorine nitrate, reacted with some of the naturally occurring constituents to yield more reacting chlorine forms: chlorine alone and hypochlorous acid. These were verified in laboratory tests that simulated stratospheric conditions. A resulting paper, by Margaret Tolbert, Michel Rossi, Ripudaman Malhotra, and David Golden, won the prestigious Newcombe-Claybourne Award as the best paper in *Science* for 1987 (see Figure 9-17). But more importantly, it helped solidify our understanding of a balance in nature critical to us all.

[14] The San Gabriel Valley newspaper, STAR-NEWS, of September 10, 1956, carries the following statement by a participating scientist: "No other place in the world is studying natural and artificial smog under controlled conditions with anything like the battery of precision instruments we have assembled here." Some of these instruments were on loan from other groups participating in the research. They included UCLA, Cal Tech, UC Riverside, The Franklin Institute, and the American Petroleum Institute. (Courtesy of Betty Neitzel, an SRI staff member in Pasadena.)

[15] On the average, ozone concentrations are about 300 molecules per billion of all air constituents. At its peak concentration in the stratosphere it is but a few parts per million, and if one integrates through the entire atmosphere, the total amount of ozone available for UV protection would be no more than 2-3 mm thick at the standard temperature and pressure at the Earth's surface.

Moreover, even small reductions in ozone levels can have large effects on the level of UV. Indeed, the shield is a very "thin" and sensitive one.

Figure 9-17. In SRI's ozone modeling laboratory are Michel Rossi, Margaret Tolbert, and Dave Golden.

Center conducted measurements of all types of air pollution for many years, employing, among other things, the lidar system developed in the meteorological group at SRI (see later in this chapter).

The decision by the U.S. government to name NASA the U.S. agency with responsibility for dealing with the ozone depletion problem stemmed from the early belief that rocket fuels may have promoted the presence of chlorine. However, the chlorine compounds generated by rocket fuels turned out to be present only in the troposphere and did not have much influence on ozone. SRI's Dave Golden has been on NASA's committee to keep track of the chemistry and the models since their role began. Dave is also on a similar National Academy of Sciences committee. In a continuation of the search for other influences on ozone depletion, the effect of jet airplanes is also now being studied and SRI has two related grants. With new capital equipment resources, three different SRI groups are contributing to the study of the aircraft problem.

As a footnote to this discussion, it should be mentioned that SRI has worked in atmospheric sciences throughout almost its entire history. Beginning in about 1967, the increasing worldwide interest in environmental impacts led to the formation of an Environmental Research Department under Elmer Robinson. Here the studies were wide-ranging, even containing some projects that tried to model both natural and manmade forms of air pollution, both sources and sinks, on a global scale.[K] Later the SRI Atmospheric Sciences

Lidar—A Light-Based Radar

In the middle of a very long hall of one of the old World War II hospital buildings in which SRI was housed, morning and afternoon coffee breaks took place every day. It was in the very early 1960s, and in retrospect such gatherings now seem a luxury. In a discipline-centered place like SRI, these interludes took people away from the intensity of their own investigations and by doing so sometimes fostered cross-discipline discussions and innovations. One such case occurred when the leader of the Aerophysics Group, Dr. Myron "Herb" Ligda, approached one of the laser specialists, Dr. Dick Honey of the Electromagnetic Techniques Lab. He raised the question as to whether SRI could build a laser that would work like his meteorological radars. "Why of course," was the reply, and so quite easily the notion of a

meteorological lidar first arose at SRI. Lidar is an acronym that mimics the term radar and stands for light detection and ranging; in other words, a light-based radar. The term lidar was actually coined much earlier in the 1950s by those working on another meteorological application, the incoherent pulsed light measurements of cloud levels. While at this time lidars employing coherent light or lasers were being used for other radar-like applications at Hughes[L] and MIT, but along with NYU and MIT, SRI was among the first to apply laser lidars to meteorology.[M,N,O,P]

Pulsed-light sources, built from electric sparks, had been used as early as 1938 to probe the cloud heights above France and were perhaps the first radar-like system used in atmospheric observations. Such systems were still in use in the early 1960s but, with the development of radar over the postwar years, microwave radar had by then become a principal meteorological probe. But the advent of the laser suggested to Ligda, Honey, Ron Collis, and others at SRI that this new mechanism offered much greater sensitivity to the detection of atmospheric constituents by providing a powerful, monochromatic, coherent light. Consequently, starting with internal funds first allocated in 1962, SRI designed, built, and tested the first of what would become dozens of different types of lidars to emerge from SRI over the next 40 years.[16]

That first lidar's capabilities were indeed modest. SRI researchers placed a donated laser from Trion Instruments, a photocell, and some government surplus optics on a gun mount, and the result is the instrument shown in Figure 9-18.[Q] The lidar used a pulsed ruby laser of a very modest 5-mW output, emitting just one 30-ns pulse per minute, and its 4-in. optics gave a 0.5-degree beamwidth. The pulse and its return were observed on a new, fast oscilloscope. The whole system was placed on the roof of Bldg. 404, and the time of its first operation was remembered well: it was Ron Collis's birthday, July 22, 1963.

Just what were the expected meteorological uses of lidar? Like any radar, the lidar depends on the amount of signal scattered or reflected back to the receiver as a function of range. The directivities of the source and the receiver, along with range, locate in space where the specific scattering occurs. Hence, some of the lidar's first meteorological uses were analogous to that of microwave radars: looking at the location and movement of clouds and precipitation. Only now one could, under certain conditions, probe the cross-sections of clouds and the exact nature of their turbulence, roughness, and flow patterns.[17] Even more remarkably, lidars could "see" constituents that are part of what would be considered visually a

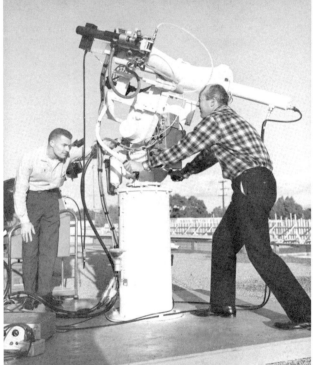

Figure 9-18. The SRI Mark I Lidar atop SRI Bldg 404 and (top) Myron "Herb" Ligda (bottom), Lloyd Alterton and Earl Scribner.

clear sky.[R] A good case for its utility was made on its very first night of operation. Ligda found that he could detect "things" in the upper atmosphere as high as 30 miles up, where there was presumably very little to reflect a light beam.[S]

By February of 1964, lidar data were revealing horizontal structure in the lower atmosphere that was being missed by more conventional sources such as radars and balloon-born radiosondes.[T] By 1965, through continued improvement in the power, sensitivity, and wavelength of SRI lidars, vast

---

[16] The 1962 expenditure was $9,197 but by the end of 1965, SRI internal funding of laser and lidars was almost $75,000. Other money of the order of $10,000 to $20,000 was spent on their meteorological uses. This early team consisted of the above-mentioned players plus Earl Scribner, Lloyd Alterton, Robert Pierce, Bill Evans, C.A. Northend, Paul Perich, George Davis, and Bernard Belt.

[17] Because of the high scattering and absorption of water vapor, lidar has a hard time working *through* heavy precipitation. However, depending on the moisture content of a cloud, the lidar can probe clouds to see their internal dynamics.

new areas opened up. In September of that year SRI meteorologists were tracking individual layers of dust in the altitude range of about 20-40 km.[U] A four-color instrument, using two lasers and some frequency-doubling devices, was also developed that year. Its frequencies ranged from the infrared to the ultraviolet, and made possible the identification of cloud constituents, precipitant formations, and atmospheric pollutants. This ability to detect and track particles, particularly pollutants, opened up an entirely new field of environmental sensing.[18]

But it is a lidar's ability to detect and track specific species of atmospheric constituents that really sets it apart. The ability to tune the laser

Figure 9-19. An SRI lidar in the field being used to detect effluents from smoke stacks in western Pennsylvania in 1968.

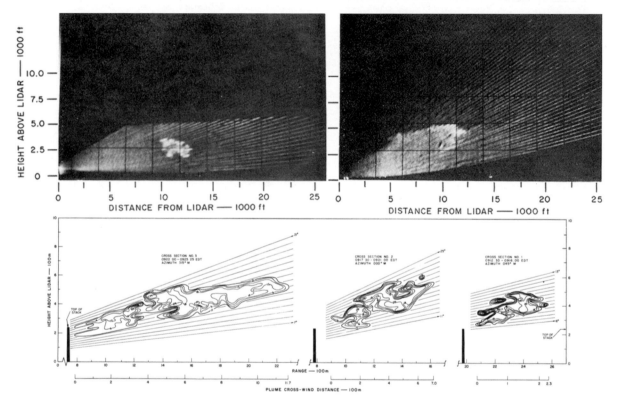

Figure 9-20. Plume of effluents from a Pennsylvania power plant. Measured flowing through a vertical plane located (top left) 1 km and (top right) 4 km away. The plume was invisible to the eye, yet showed appreciable particulate concentration and, on the left, a turbid layer with ceiling at about 5,000 ft (May 1970). These plots also conveyed concentration levels at another location (bottom). (From *SRI Journal*, No. 27, December 13–14, 1969) Some of the participants in this phase of lidar work at SRI were Warren Johnson, Ed Uthe, Jim Hawley, and Bill Grant.

wavelength of the lidar allows the detection and tracking of specific aerosols and particulate matter. Remarkably, lidar can also determine whether particulates are being synthesized in the air from different effluents entering it.

Computer analysis of the received data can show the observations made in a single horizontal or vertical plane. Working with the National Air Pollution Control Administration, SRI lidars, such as the one shown in Figure 9-19, were used through the 1960s and 1970s to study airborne pollution. Figure 9-20 shows an

---

[18] Sponsors of the new lidars were the Office of Naval Research and the Lear Siegler Corporation.

example of effluent data taken downwind from the Keystone power plant in western Pennsylvania in 1968. The plume was not visible to the eye. Lidars have come into extremely wide use as a means to monitor our atmospheric environment.

Figure 9-21. SRI lidar van used in the detection of trace levels of atmospherically transported chemical agents.

Finally, starting in the mid-1980s, SRI made a series of sophisticated improvements to its lidars that have given them an ability to detect trace amounts of chemical warfare agents in the atmosphere. The risk of these agents to both soldiers and civilians lends great importance to such investigations. Detecting such agents requires an ability to finely tune the wavelength of the lidar and to greatly increase its sensitivity over the earlier meteorological lidars. One of the principal innovations in this direction was differential absorption lidar, or DIAL.[19] To detect specific agents, DIAL uses two or more wavelengths to help calibrate out the intervening atmosphere and obtain range-resolved returns from concentrations of various gas species along an extended path. Ranges may extend to several kilometers. These tunable lidars operate in the visible, ultraviolet, and infrared spectral regions. Figure 9-21 shows one of the larger, van-mounted instruments. In contrast with the first lidar, units like this may have 12 megawatts of peak power that can operate at ten pulses per second over a wide range of wavelengths.[V] Their light sources, though, are large gas lasers. Much smaller, portable units that use infrared diode lasers have also been designed and built at SRI, along with countless other types of lidars and remote sensing instruments, including airborne ones.

This aspect of the SRI lidar program has been very successful. SRI received an Army Services Commendation Award for a variety of test results that included specific vapor detection at long range (5-8 km) in the presence of fog, rain, dust, and infrared smoke, as well as detection of two vapors simultaneously. The award also recognized the ability to detect vapor deposits on soil and concrete surfaces. SRI also showed its quick reaction capability when it was called upon to create specific sensors for the Gulf War. When it became clear that a chemical warfare threat existed there, SRI staff worked continuous 15- to 20-hr. days to design and fabricate point sensors that could detect the presence of certain agents believed to be in the Iraqi weapon inventory. Even after the Gulf War, SRI participated as part of the inspection teams searching for caches or stockpiles of chemical and biological agents.

SRI has conducted remote and point sensor work not only for the DoD, but also for utility companies and their research consortia, such as the Electric Power Research Institute. Over the nearly 40 continuous years of the above efforts, including both ground- and aircraft-based lidars, SRI has become a leading innovator in the sensing of environmentally harmful substances in a variety of settings as well as in the modeling of atmospheric properties and its constituents. As evidence, SRI received the American Meteorological Society's 1985 award for outstanding services to meteorology for the "creative development of laser-oriented remote sensing systems which have produced new levels of information on atmospheric transport of gases and fine particles."[W]

---

[19] The term DIAL was coined by SRI, but the first differential absorption lidar, built using temperature-adjusted ruby lasers, was made by a colleague of Ligda's, Dr. Richard Schotland, now emeritus professor at the University of Arizona.

Upconverting Phosphors for the Detection of Undesirable Agents

The technology of upconverting phosphors (UCPs) seems ripe with opportunity. The basic mechanism makes use of the property of certain phosphors to absorb radiation, in this case in the infrared portion of the spectrum, and radiate at different wavelengths (colors) in the visible region. Since this type of conversion does not take place in nature, the background for this detection process is very quiet, giving it great sensitivity. Different phosphors with characteristic color reradiation can then be linked to tailored sensors that are designed to reveal the presence of very specific harmful agents. As such they can be used to create diagnostic sensors for clinical health care, food supply screening, and military and civil defense needs.

Right now, the growing threat of biological agents and the difficulty in knowing when they are present and where they came from seems the most important first use of UCPs. The concern comes from possible terrorist use of such weapons or the unintended migration of deadly viruses such as ebola to more populated areas. But regardless of their origin, deadly agents released in large and mobile populations possess great potential for confusion and hysteria, particularly when the location and extent of the pathogens are unknown. DARPA, the DoD's prominent R&D body, is exceptionally aware of this threat and is acting to deal with it by sponsoring a set of inexpensive, UCP-based sensors that can cover a family of chemical and biological agents. The relevant scenarios show critical needs in both military and civil defense settings and in worldwide healthcare.

Point Detection of Biological Agents

As mentioned earlier, lidar is one of the only means for the remote detection of specific chemical agents. It can stand kilometers back from a threat and thus provide needed warning time. But while lidar has been shown at SRI and elsewhere to detect the presence of biologic-bearing aerosols, its ability to identify specific constituents is extremely limited.[20]

Such identification is, of course, critical. So, practically speaking, the detection of biological agents is now the province of point sensors which, when handheld, would most likely give warning too late. But point sensors can be valuable if there is a means to deploy them remotely and then assure that they communicate their findings reliably to a safe distance. Such remote sensors must ideally be small and consume little power. Over the last several years SRI has developed a family of new, small detectors that can detect a wide range of very specific biological agents. The goal was to build a detector with greater sensitivity, more discrimination or specificity, and faster detection time.

The detection technique SRI has developed is very general, but its characteristics are quite remarkable.[21] In simple terms, the sensor consists of three parts: a probe designed to interact strongly and uniquely with the target biological agent, a reporter that signals the existence of the agent, and a detector that is sensitive to the reporter. The process is shown schematically in Figure 9-22. A surface is built with "docking" configurations that are very specific to each expected agent, using a technique called polyclonal antibodies. Molecules of the target agent are then introduced and come to reside on the prepared surface. To test for the presence of the specific biological agents, small reporter-probes are introduced. These are small spherical particles of very special phosphors that are chemically linked to even smaller probe units that have the

[20] Back in the 1970s, SRI showed that bacteria fluoresce in the long-wavelength part of the UV spectrum when excited by a shorter UV wavelength. But this sensing technique tells

almost nothing about the kind of pathogen present. Even indications that a particular biologic-containing aerosol cloud might be dangerous has to be inferred from other factors. Simply, the remote lidar sensing of *biological* agents is not yet practical.

[21] The SRI Independent Research and Development (IR&D) report for 1994-5 shows a proposal for $20K to "prepare and conjugate phosphor particles to the detection antibodies and perform assays at various serial dilutions" to determine system sensitivity in detecting a specific toxin. Early work on upconverting phosphor technology came in part from SRI's subsidiary, David Sarnoff Laboratory. Building such an instrument has been truly interdisciplinary. Some of the important contributors beyond the leadership of Drs. David Cooper and John Carrico have been Greg Faris, Yihong Chen, Naheed Mufti, Luke Schneider, Gary Rundle, Jan van der Laan, Karen Nashold, Angel Sanjurjo, and James Kane of Sarnoff.

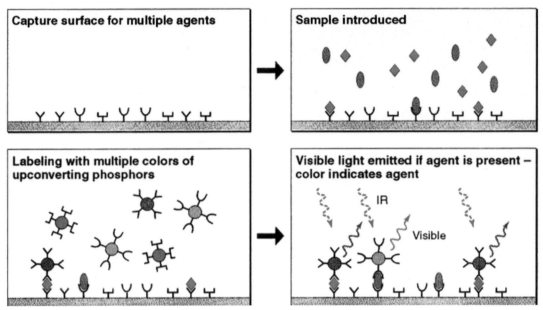

Figure 9-22. The SRI phosphor-based detection process.

same "docking" properties as those on the surface. Each different agent has a unique phosphor. Once the reporter-probes are docked, the surface is scanned with infrared light and the individual phosphors reradiate visible light whose color is unique to each agent-phosphor combination. Those specific emissions are then monitored using very small versions of photomultipliers, each of which incorporate the very narrow filters appropriate to the agent-phosphor combinations. These narrow filters reject extraneous noise and also contribute to making the whole system very sensitive.

This approach to biological agent detection permits sensitivities of the order of 10-100 picograms per milliliter of small antigens (virus or toxin) in 5-15 min with a 1-ml sample volume. The 5-15 min wait is because at the moment the process takes place in a liquid bath. For spores and bacteria, the estimated goal is sensitivity below 1000 cells per milliliter. Importantly, the device can be battery operated and is small enough to be handheld. But its most logical use is to be stationed remotely or made airborne on remotely piloted aircraft to grant both safety and early detection.

A Healthcare Diagnostic

In the area of clinical healthcare there is a test administered to those suspected of a heart attack called CKMB (creatine kinase – MB). In healthy people certain enzymes found in the blood are associated with origins in different parts of the body. Skeletal muscle produces creatine-MM, the brain, creatine-BB, and the heart, creatine-MB. In the presence of an acute myocardial infarction (heart attack), cell deaths produce an elevated level of CKMB four to six hours after the onset of chest pain and peak at 12 to 24 hours. Coronary surgery can also cause elevated levels, but they don't have the characteristic time history exhibited by infarctions. The procedure for the administration of CKMB tests requires that the patient not be released until the results are known, several hours later. UCP technology can make the results of such a test known immediately with greater accuracy and less cost than present methods.

Commercialization of UCP Technology

To illustrate the utility of the UCP technology, SRI, under the sponsorship of DARPA and other, more operational governmental agencies, has built a prototype system. The sensing unit is small enough to be handheld and battery operated. A version of the prototype is shown in Figure 9-23 along with an image of a test strip and, in the background, the fluorescence of phosphor reporters.

To help bring such technology into existence, SRI licensed it in 1998 to a diagnostic company called STC Technologies. In September 2000, STC merged with another company in HIV diagnostics and became OraSure Technologies. The license is exclusive for the measurement of biological agents but

Figure 9-23. An early SRI prototype sensor and a notional view of a test strip multiplexed for four agents. The background is a photomicrograph of a suspension of different upconverting phosphor particles of different colors that would be scanned for quantitative measurement.)

the company is directing the technology strictly toward the healthcare industry, specifically to detect minute quantities of antigens, proteins, and even DNA. Their name for the process is called UP*link*™, and the portable, benchtop processing unit produces a very sensitive, multiple-analyte assay in less than 10 minutes. The results can also be read out digitally. Although DARPA has given some support to OraSure, use of the technology against the threats of the battlefield or terrorist action has remained the interest of SRI.

Endnotes

A Mentioned in the SRI Annual Report of Operations, 1957, and reported in *Proceedings of the IRE*, 45(11), November 1957. (See Appendix H for a more complete story.)

B A.M. Peterson, The Northern Lights and Northern Communications, *SRI Journal*, No. 2, pp. 46–51, 1958.

C Leadabrand, R.L., J.C. Schlobohm, and M.J. Baron, "Simultaneous Very High Frequency and Ultra High Frequency Observation of the Aurora at Fraserburgh, Scotland," *J. of Geophysical Research*, 70(17), September 1, 1965.

D Conversation with Robert H. Light, the SRI person running the field site in the Azores. Also in *Journal of Geophysical Research*, Vol. 64, No. 8, August 1959.

E *Communication and Ionospheric Research at SRI*, a compilation by John Lomax, received December 1996.

F Paul L. Magill, *Smog – What Is It and Where Does It Come From?*, SRI Report, Project 105, January 9, 1948.

G Magill, op. cit.

H SRI's *Research for Industry*, 3(4), 6–8, May 1951.

I SRI's *Research for Industry*, 6(7), 6–7, September 1954.

J SRI's *Research for Industry*, 9(2), 8–9, January 1957.

K Elmer Robinson and Robert C. Robbins, Where Does It All Go?, *SRI Journal*, No. 23, 4–8, December 1968.

L M.L. Stitch, E.J. Woodbury, and J.H. Morse, Optical Ranging System Using Laser Transmitter, *Electronics*, pp. 51–53, April 21, 1961.

M R.T.H. Collis, Lidar, *Applied Optics*, 9, pp. 1782–1788, August 1970.

N R. Collis and W. Johnson, *Brief on Lidar in Air Pollution Studies*, SRI paper, June 1970.

O R.T.H. Collis, Lidar: a new atmospheric probe, *Quarterly Journal Royal Meteorological Society*, 92, pp. 220–230, 1966.

P Edward E. Uthe, *Lidar Environmental Observations*, paper at Optical Sensing Environmental Monitoring International Symposium, October 11–14, 1993.

Q From "My Days at SRI" by Earl J. Scribner dated December 13, 2000.

[R] R.T.H. Collis, F.G Fernald, and M.G.H. Ligda, Laser Radar Echoes from the Clear Atmosphere, *Nature*, 203(4944), 508, August 1, 1964.

[S] SRI's *Research for Industry*, 16(1), 8–10, January to February 1964.

[T] *SRI Journal*, No. 2, 7-10, 1964.

[U] *SRI Journal*, No. 9, page 13, January 1966.

[V] Clinton B. Carlisle, Jan E. van der Laan, Lewis W. Carr, Philippe Adam, and Jean-Pierre Chaironi, CO_2 laser-based differential absorption lidar system for range-resolved and long-range detection of chemical vapor plumes, *Applied Optics*, 34(27), September 20, 1995.

[W] *SRI Journal*, Vol. 5, No. 2, p. 8, April 1985.

Chapter 10
Drugs and Healthcare

Drug Discovery and Development

SRI has had an extended, almost 50-year, history in the exploration of new drugs and a bit of that history is related here. But before proceeding, it is helpful to understand drug development and testing at SRI and the process shown in Figure 10-1, which shows the phases needed to bring a drug into use. This process is long, expensive, and sometimes tortuous, littered with opportunities to fail.[1] As a research institute, and a player lying outside the normal pharmaceutical industry, SRI has characteristically worked in the earliest phases of drug discovery. Here the research content and the risks are high, but the costs are—relatively speaking—low, and the special facilities and personnel qualifications found in a clinical setting are not required. SRI has also engaged in some preclinical testing, and this somewhat broader charter has prompted some initiatives that may alter its more limited discovery role.

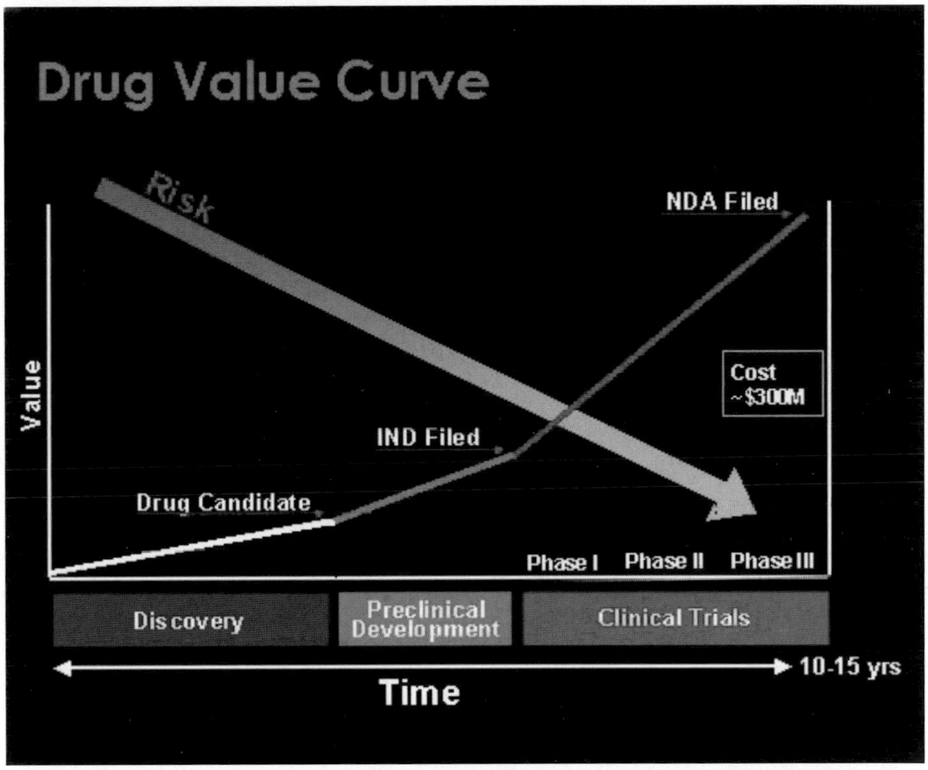

Although drug discovery is just the first part of drug development, the discovery process itself is complex, time-consuming, and exceedingly dependent upon the competency and imagination of the research staff. Figure 10-2 shows the major steps involved in discovery itself and, like the overall drug development process, each step can be a showstopper.

With over 40 years in the field of drug discovery, SRI is now trying to broaden its role in drug development. Doing so is very consistent with its new orientation toward a greater participation in the commercialization of its intellectual property. The reasoning goes something like this. Over time and in a somewhat piecemeal fashion, SRI has acquired the competency and the facilities for conducting many preclinical tests. Both government regulatory and research agencies and drug companies have sponsored these

Figure 10-1. Notional model of drug development and testing showing the phases and the exponentially increasing costs.

---

[1] According to a recent article in *Science*, the average cost of developing, testing, and gaining approval for a new medicine is a staggering $897 million. This cost includes the 99.9% of compounds that wash out in the development pipeline! But of even those drugs that enter human testing, only 1 in 5 get approved for sale. Obviously, the earlier in the development process an unmarketable drug is eliminated, the better. (Robert F. Service, "Surviving the Blockbuster Syndrome," *Science*, 303, 1796–1799, March 19, 2004)

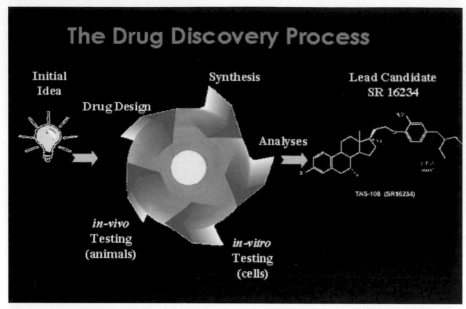

Figure 10-2. Steps in the drug discovery process. The wheel depicts it as an iterative exploration.

whether those houses are established biopharmaceutical companies or simply financial frameworks for drug exploration and development. A vice president of a local biotech company told the *San Francisco Business Times*, "We've looked into the matter of doing it ourselves versus getting it outside. There's just no way you can compete with an established firm that already has its facility in place and established procedures and staff."[A] Time will reveal the value of this initiative.

activities. There arises the notion, then, of offering a more comprehensive drug development service. SRI already has experience in screening drug candidates and in testing for stability, manufacturability, and toxicity. Because of this established capability, SRI claims that it can now perform preclinical work faster and cheaper than pharmaceutical houses,

With that background, we now review some of the specifics in SRI's drug discovery and development history. Work in testing the toxicology of drugs and some environmental pollutants will also be covered as well as SRI's work in the healthcare sciences.

Antimalaria Drugs

Although malaria was once considered a controllable disease, its effect on the world is not only staggering but is rapidly rising. About 40% percent of the world's population is at risk in about 90 countries. Estimates from the World Health Organization and other interested groups place the number of new clinical cases each year at several hundred million with the annual death toll over 1 million.[2] As bad as that seems, it is actually a lower rate than existed, say in the 1920s, when most cases were in Asia (see Figure 10-3).

Today, malaria is largely controlled in Asia, relatively speaking, but is actually a growing threat in Africa where over 90% of those one million malarial deaths now occur. That rise in Africa began in the 1950s and 1960s. When the major inroads on malaria were made starting in the 1930s, it was mostly because of better

control of the vector, the mosquito, and because of introduction of drugs like quinine (or more important, chloroquine), which were hostile to the responsible blood parasite. The parasite associated with malaria invades the red blood cells and causes them to stick to the linings of capillaries and small blood vessels. This blockage effectively shuts off the supply of glucose and oxygen to the body's cells by decreasing the number of viable red blood cells present.

The *Plasmodium* parasite responsible for malaria has several types. One of the more prevalent is called *Plasmodium vivax*, which results in a recurrent infection that attacks only a certain age of red blood cells (about 5% of the total) and is therefore usually not fatal. Another form, *Plasmodium falciparum*, attacks all red blood cells regardless of their age and is lethal, responsible for about 95% of malarial deaths. This most deadly strain has been reason alone to seek new and more powerful drugs.

---

[2] The Canada-based International Development Research Center places the annual death rate at between 1.5 to 2.7 million. Other sources, such as the presentation from WHO in Figure 10-3, are closer to 1 million.

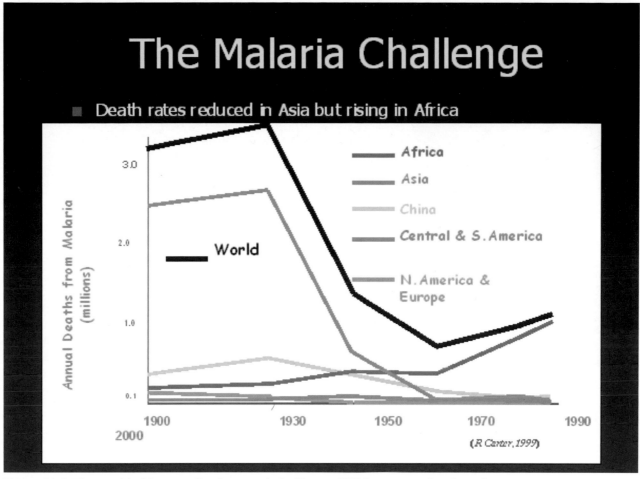

Figure 10-3. The worldwide mortality from malaria (from a WHO presentation found at www.who.int/rbm/presentations/us-canada/uscong/sld006.html).

But something else began to raise concern in the post World War II era. New malarial strains were becoming resistant to chloroquine, the 1940s drug that had gained such wide use because of its effectiveness and its reduced side effects relative to quinine. By the 1960s, this resistance was also beginning to surface in *falciparum*.[B] Later, it was observed that a newer antimalarial drug, mefloquine, synthesized to help chloroquine resistance, was itself losing some of its effectiveness. The bugs are relentlessly and frustratingly adaptable.

SRI's Halofantrine

Malaria has long been a particular concern to members of the armed forces, who may be called on to serve in the regions of the world where malaria is still prevalent. So, in about 1964 the Walter Reed Army Institute of Research (WRAIR) entertained a proposal from SRI to look into drugs that could address the more lethal malarial forms. A contract was awarded in 1965 that began a decade-long search at SRI for a new and effective antimalarial drug, particularly for the deadly *falciparum* form of the *Plasmodium* parasite.

The opportunity came to an SRI medicinal chemist, Dr. William Colwell (see Figure 10-4), and to the leader of the Bio-Organic Chemistry Program, Dr. David Henry, who had developed a considerable background in anti-parasitic chemotherapy. Before them lay this always present, fine line between a compound that was powerful enough to kill the parasite and specific enough to avoid damaging side effects. Most of the antimalarial drugs, such as quinine, have terrible side effects and often unreasonably difficult regimens. SRI examined a wide variety of compounds that had displayed antimalarial behavior but suffered from clinical ineffectiveness.

In the fall of 1970, Colwell investigated the "docking" of some compounds to a likely active site on a yard-long ball-and-stick model of a generic segment of DNA. He began to understand how he might improve the efficacy

Figure 10-4. SRI organic chemist, Dr. Bill Colwell.

of a class of compounds, called arylamino alcohols. These were already known to have some activity against the *falciparum* parasite. Although the exact mechanism is even today a matter of conjecture, Colwell's radioisotope studies showed a high absorption of the compound into the unicellular parasite and, in particular, a concentration around its nucleus. So, Colwell and his colleagues were convinced that they could find something in that family that was more effective than the existing set of malarial drugs.

Having synthesized a series of new variants from this arylamino family, they submitted them to a clinically predictive mouse assay developed for WRAIR by the University of Miami. The arylamino propanols they had focused on using their model predictions proved four to six-fold more effective than the predecessor (aminoethanols). Preclinical toxicity (side-effects) was at least comparable. The researchers published the drug series and its bioassay results in the technical literature in 1972.[C] The first compound selected was named halofantrine by WRAIR, and it and four promising relatives were assigned to the sponsor for further action.

Halofantrine entered into several trials; perhaps the earliest was done using U.S. volunteers in 1974. Later, trials were conducted in many African, Southeast Asian, and Middle East countries. The license to produce the drug was awarded by the Army to Smith Kline & French in 1984. Halofantrine became authorized for use in France in 1988 and in the United States in 1992. It was not marketed in the United States until 1998, presumably due to the small market. Under the arrangements of the day, the drug became the property of the U.S. Army and SRI has never received any commercialization income from it. Regrettably, except for a few well-known medical indices, SRI has also been left unrecognized as the inventor of halofantrine.

As to its impact, halofantrine has successfully treated the strain of malaria for which it was designed and has been used worldwide for the successful treatment of millions of people. It is an important member of the group of antimalarial drugs recommended by the WHO and is used in all regions where malaria is present. Colwell's original choice, the mono-butyl form of halofantrine, now called desbutylhalofantrine, with perhaps even fewer side effects, was placed on Phase I trials by the Army in 1998. Specifically, this form of halofantrine has a much-reduced tendency to decrease heart rate through a prolongation of the heart's electrical cycle.[D]

As with earlier malaria drugs, there remains the crucial question of whether halofantrine will remain effective in this critical battle with the *falciparum* parasite. Will it develop any cross-resistant characteristics with other antimalarial drugs; will malaria parasites such as *falciparum* that have developed a resistance to, say mefloquine, also lose their susceptibility to halofantrine? We still don't know. In the meantime, halofantrine is likely to become a primary pharmaceutical for preventing malaria for travelers from western countries in addition to its continued role for the treatment of critical infection in the host countries. Reasons also exist to be cautious of halofantrine. One is that, taken in combination with mefloquine, another antimalarial drug, halofantrine can cause serious changes to heart rhythms. Halofantrine is also much more expensive than the first line drugs such as chloroquine and mefloquine.

Two additional compounds from the SRI program were among the total of five, including halofantrine, selected for clinical trial by WRAIR. These two compounds successfully passed Phase II and III investigation and have been reserved for future use in case of resistance development to the current drugs.

Artemisinin

Although antimalarial drugs have a broad range, they are up against a formidable and highly adaptive enemy, so new counter-measures are being sought. Today, there is a groundswell of interest in developing an understanding of the genetics of how both the *falciparum* parasite and its mosquito vector reproduce and adapt. Such solutions still have their controversy, however, and their promises are a long way off.[E] In the meantime new drugs are needed, and one that has shown promise in Asia is a class called artemisinins.[F] In the mid-1980s SRI chemist Mitchel Avery heard of the possible efficacy of this drug from visitors to a Chinese folklore medicine institute in Shanghai.[G] The drug was made from the sweet wormwood (*Artemisia annua*) or ginghaosu weed and was reported to be effective against *falciparum*.

Over a period of 3 three years, Avery, with colleagues Wesley Chong and Clive Jennings-White, made 55 different analogs of artemisinin. These were sent for testing in whole blood at the Walter Reed Army Hospital in Washington DC. Though there have been considerable reported successes of the drug, the WHO and the U.S. AID have been cautious in its approval partly because of the drug's expense and the dangers of its dosage.[H] To those working in the field, however, artemisinin in combination with more conventional but increasingly ineffective drugs like chloroquine, is the next best hope. SRI is no longer involved in the synthesis of artemisinin.

So, this SRI research into antimalarial drugs is over, yet the death rate from malaria is still enormous, with some 2,000-3,000 African children dying from it each day.[I] Much of the research battlefield has now switched to studies of genomics, including the parasite and the mosquito carrier, and to those humans who have a natural high resistance to the disease.

Anticancer Drugs

Before describing SRI's contributions in cancer drugs, we explain briefly some of the concepts and terminology that will appear.[J] Much of the approach to chemotherapy involves the basic cell processes enabled by the protein-building template that is DNA. While we think of DNA in the production of normal cells, it is necessary for the replication of all living cells, including those of cancer. So, understanding the cell replication process in general may help identify the vulnerabilities of rapid-growing cancer.

DNA, or deoxyribonucleic acid, is the heredity-defining molecule in living cells. It is a polymer consisting of two very long, interconnected helical strands, each of which is made up of structural subunits called nucleotides. These nucleotides are the building blocks or monomers of each strand of the helix. Removal of a monomer-linking phosphate group from a nucleotide leaves a nucleoside of which, with almost no exception, there are but four types in all of DNA.[3] It is the order of these

four nucleosides in their extensive repetition along the DNA molecule that gives rise to the genetic code. The two strands are complementary in structure and are reversibly bound in a double helical coil. For DNA to replicate, its components, including the above building blocks and their constituents, must be available. This means individual elements such as phosphorus, carbon, nitrogen, and oxygen must also be present and available in some form or the replication process ceases and cells and their host die.

It was toward inhibiting the formation of the DNA-building components that SRI targeted its early anticancer investigations. This included denying the availability of some of the components of the nucleotides. Since the replication of normal cells must also go on, interrupting that process without discrimination produces undesirable side effects. SRI's early anticancer drug research focused importantly on the synthetic chemistry of nucleosides, with an objective of altering nucleoside structures so that their chemical incorporation into the DNA replication process would effectively terminate it. Because cancer

---

[3] A nucleoside is a structural subunit of nucleic acids, which control the hereditary properties of all living cells. It consists of a sugar molecule and one of four attached nitrogen bases: two purines (adenine and guanine) and two pyrimidines (cytosine and thymine). With the addition of a phosphate group, nucleosides form nucleotides, which are the repetitive basic building blocks of the DNA molecule.

The sugar molecules can be of two types: deoxyribose and ribose. The former is in DNA and the latter in RNA.

Figure 10-5. Organic chemists, Drs. Bernard R. Baker, Bruce Graham, and Leon Goodman.

cells are characteristically fast growing, a drug lacking tissue-specific attributes would still cause greater cell termination in cancer than in normal cells.

SRI's Entry into Anticancer Drug Discovery

SRI's work in cancer chemotherapy began in the mid-1950s with the arrival of Dr. Bernard R. Baker from Southern Research Institute (see Figure 10-5). His prior accomplishments had included the early synthesis of a nucleoside, puromycin, which had anticancer properties. His purpose in coming to SRI was to start a group in the search of new anticancer agents. This opportunity came in response to an initiative from the Cancer Chemotherapy National Service Center (CCNSC), a part of the National Cancer Institute (NCI).[4] Baker was a brilliant chemist who had a close relationship with that Center. He actually left a Center-sponsored project at Southern Research to come to SRI to establish yet another. To give the new SRI laboratory a sense of completeness, he organized it into a synthesis group, which could produce testable quantities of both final drugs and their intermediates, and an analytical group with capabilities in infrared and magnetic resonance spectroscopy. To round out this mix, there was an existing SRI group that

was already doing drug screening in mice for the same NCI. This ability to perform locally the efficacy testing of new drugs on mice would provide rapid feedback.

The synthesis group consisted of 15 chemists whose objective was to synthesize gram quantities of target drugs as well as larger quantities, sometimes in the hundreds of grams, of chemical intermediates. These efforts were divided between the syntheses of analogs of known anticancer compounds and creating new compounds of interest, based on postulated biochemical mechanisms. The analytical group supplied analytical and spectral data to check the identity and purity of the various chemical agents. The major emphasis of the CCNSC was to increase the general awareness of new drugs and their effects by placing all results in the open literature. This stipulation had long-term consequences for SRI. Although SRI was to gain national prominence from its work in chemotherapy and nucleosides, SRI did not create any patent position on the corresponding work at that time.

An early success of the program was the first synthesis anywhere of a natural purine deoxynucleoside (called 2'-deoxyadenosine), one of the four building blocks of DNA.[5] From this work also came a drug called adenine B-D-arabinofuranoside, a compound intended to be a tumor inhibitor with minimal side effects. Unfortunately, it was too easily deactivated for that role by other body

---

[4] A leader in this emerging part of SRI was Dr. Bruce Graham (see Figure 10-5). He had received a phone call from the San Francisco airport from a staff member of the NCI, informing him of new programs they were promoting and that he thought SRI might be interested. Graham drove up to meet him and learned about the programs and also that there was someone the NCI thought would be qualified to lead an anticancer effort should SRI be interested; namely, Bernard Baker. Since this was a good opportunity to participate in a large NCI activity, Graham followed up.

[5] See Footnote 3.

enzymes, but the drug turned out to have good anti-herpes attributes.[6]

In 1957 Baker began examining certain biochemical targets in the DNA replication process. The approach was to inhibit the metabolism of folic acid, which had a critical role as a "carrier" for the carbon atoms needed in the DNA replication process. These antifolates effectively shut down the production of the nitrogen bases needed for the biosynthesis of the nucleosides that make up DNA and RNA. The problem was how to make such an inhibitor selective for only cancer cells. The early antifolate inhibitors, unfortunately, were also toxic to normal mammalian cells, so that kind of work slid briefly into the background at SRI.

In about 1959, Baker initiated another program at SRI in specific enzyme inhibitors. This was a search for certain compounds that he liked to call "fraudulent nucleosides" that took advantage of an existing concept of agent intervention called a "lock and key mechanism." Here the target enzyme represents the lock and the synthesized chemical agent the key, which, in this case, had the property to seek out the lock. Once the key enters the lock, the other end of the active molecule would bind to another reactive site on the enzyme in a process called alkylation. If this latter bond were strong enough, the binding would be irreversible and could block the enzyme from further biological functioning.[K] This approach gained broad use in the anticancer community and Baker later wrote a book about it.

With the departure of Baker in 1961 and under the new leadership of Dr. Leon Goodman (see Figure 10-5), SRI's chemotherapy work brought a new emphasis in the exploration of two areas: a family of drugs called nitrogen mustards and a revisit of ways to inhibit the metabolism of folic acid and its analogs. The nitrogen mustards, a type of alkylating agent,[7] were among the first anticancer drugs used anywhere (e.g., chlorambucil and cyclophosphamide for various forms of lymphomas). These substances interfere with

the DNA/RNA replication process. In that process, however, they also affect normal cells and thus produce serious side effects. This family also happens to have antibiotic as well as anticancer properties and two members of this family received special emphasis at SRI.

The analytical chemistry group that Baker started also needs to be mentioned. Under the direction of Dr. Peter Lim, it was able to win its own NCI support as early as 1956. Remarkably, that analytical chemistry project has continued for nearly 50 years, making it SRI's longest continuous project.

The Antibiotic Called Adriamycin

By the 1970s Adriamycin (doxorubicin) and Daunomycin (daunorubicin) were two antibiotics that had come to be very popular as chemotherapy drugs. As with many pursuits in drug discovery, the work begins with efficacious drugs and looks for closely related analogs that have higher success rates, lower side effects, or both. That was what Dr. Ed Acton and others at SRI undertook in the 1970s (see Figure 10-6). Both drugs had shown reversible binding to DNA and an interference with DNA/RNA synthesis. Adriamycin was then called the most active compound against cancer because of its broad range of activity—notably against major tumors that did not respond to other drugs. In many cases, however, the efficacy rate was too low—perhaps in only 1 in 3 patients. Further, toxic side effects limited both the dose level and the duration of treatment. Hence improved analogs of these new drugs were widely sought, and soon the drug development community had created some 2,000 active analogs of adriamycin.[L]

This large number of analogs illustrates a recurring problem in drug discovery: how to choose for further study from among analogs that are active in a primary screen and thus displaying some clinical potential. To assist in dealing with this at SRI, Dr. Dave Henry set up one laboratory in conjunction with the synthesis group to do simple *in vitro* screens for inhibition of DNA and RNA synthesis, supplemented by data from the NCI's own mouse screens. From this filtering, the SRI group came up with at least two new analogs that received wide attention in the cancer drug development field. One was 5-iminodaunorubicin, which was significantly less cardiotoxic, and the other was cyanomorpholinodoxorubicin (CMDR), which

---

[6] SRI's virologist, Dr. Gus Freeman, suggested that adenine B-D-arabinofuranoside's characteristics might make it a good antiviral agent, but NCI nixed that investigation. A few years later, Parke-Davis isolated the same drug from other natural sources and applied it to antiherpes use. Parke-Davis gave it the trade name Virazole and it is still in use today.

[7] An agent that can transfer a chemical alkyl group onto DNA. Widely used in chemotherapy.

Figure 10-6. Organic chemists, Drs. Ed Acton, Bill Lee, and Joe DeGraw.

need of an independent research house like SRI to have drug development partners. No matter the merit of the SRI work and the promise of the drug, a hand-off in the development cycle must occur. Because of the high cost of proceeding and the in-house competition from potential drug-development partners, the transition is difficult.

Antifolates

A revived attention given to antifolates also produced important results at SRI. As just mentioned, most drug development efforts require both a chemist and a clinician. In this case, the medical partner was Sloan Kettering in New York City. The principal SRI organic chemist was Dr. Joe DeGraw, working with colleague Dr. William Colwell. DeGraw and Colwell were familiar with the folate process and its inhibitors. In particular, they focused on an enzyme that helped stage the acquisition of carbon by folic acid. That enzyme, called a reductase, was a target for chemists as early as 1950. The existing inhibitor for that enzyme, called methotrexate, was effective only in limited forms of leukemia or lymphomas. It also had serious side effects, particularly on fetuses, and was essentially ineffective against solid tumors. Therefore, SRI undertook a search for related forms that would gain a greater concentration in tumor cells than in normal ones.

The first major discovery in this search was a modification of methotrexate that would still be a powerful enzyme inhibitor but would be more easily absorbed through the walls of tumor cells than through normal ones. Two forms of the drug were synthesized: one called 10-deazaaminopterin (or 10-DA) and one called 10-ethyl-10-deazaaminopterin (10-ET). SRI developed an efficient synthesis method that could produce enough of these two drugs for clinical trials, and by early 1985 Sloan Kettering began Phase I testing.

was 600 times more potent, in terms of the required dose amount, than adriamycin, and its binding to DNA was irreversible.

A significant academic achievement by SRI in this family was the first synthesis of daunosamine, the sugar component within each of these more effective drugs followed by a formal total synthesis of adriamycin in 1983.[M] Adriamycin is still used worldwide in the treatment of a variety of cancers and is of great clinical importance in chemotherapy.

During the late 1970s and early 1980s, two important policy changes occurred in drug development that affected SRI. First, in 1977 the NCI stopped awarding contracts for drug synthesis. After some 20 years of sponsorship by the CCNSC, SRI's efforts in cancer drugs now rested not on an Institute relationship with a major client but on the much smaller grant petitions from individual researchers. Second, SRI changed its policy on owning and holding patents.[8] As a result, SRI came to have good patent coverage on these and related drug candidates. A license for the CMDR was awarded to a drug company, but despite widespread interest and attention at the preclinical level, neither the 5-imino nor the CMDR was entered into clinical trial. This failure is not uncommon in drug development for a variety of reasons, but it does illustrate the

---

[8] This change in policy is keyed to the 1984 passing of the Bayh-Dole act that allowed nonprofit organizations to take ownership of intellectual property developed under Government sponsorship. See Appendix B.

As a result of the trials, 10-ET was shown to be more effective that either 10-DA or methotrexate and its side effects were less pronounced. 10-ET was then selected for Phase II trials both alone and in conjunction with existing drugs. The results were excellent in breast and lung cancer. Early reports from Sloan-Kettering stated that its use in a new chemotherapy regimen yielded 59% tumor regression and major relief of symptoms for lung cancer. It was also "far more effective" in the most common form of unresponsive lung cancer, non-small-cell carcinoma.[N]

With that kind of encouragement, the drug was licensed to Ciba-Geigy for Phase III clinical trials. Here the testing leaves the high scrutiny and familiarity with which the creators administer the drug and enters the real world where new risks are faced. Is the drug reliably taken and in the correct amounts? Do the side effects alter the physician's approach to the protocol? Although the drug, now called edatrexate, passed Phase III trials, there arose enough toxicity issues (primarily mucositis[9]) that physician compliance with dosage stipulations could not be guaranteed.[10] Such real-world conditions are important and legitimate experiences for the Phase III trials, but they represent one of the many potholes along the road to commercial use. There are others.

In the mid-1980s, when Ciba-Geigy took edatrexate into the regulatory process, getting a new drug approved by the FDA was very difficult. Clinical trials had to prove not just that the drug was effective but that it was clearly more effective than, in this case, methotrexate, already in use. That was harder to prove significantly. Because of this hurdle, the Phase III results described above, and some internal difficulties at Ciba-Geigy, such as being bought out by Roche, Ciba-Geigy gave the rights to edatrexate back to SRI and its co-owner, Sloan Kettering. Edatrexate was then licensed to a small start-up company in California, SciClone Pharmaceuticals, which, after three years, also failed to commercialize the drug.

So, in spite of its efficacy in early testing at Sloan Kettering and some successes in its Phase III trials,[11] edatrexate is no longer on the path for production. Interestingly, Ciba-Geigy produced so much of the drug it is still being studied and applied within the medical research community. Although its use is still being explored, its patent has only a year or so to run and edatrexate's future, at least for SRI, is about over.

But the last word on SRI's work on antifolates has not been written. SRI is still pursuing an analog of edatrexate for lung cancer that SRI was the first to synthesize. This analog is called 10-propargyl-10-deazaaminopterin, or PDX, and it is working its way, with partnerships, through clinical trials.[12]

Radiosensitizers

Most cancer patients who have localized tumors receive radiation therapy either by itself or in combination with other treatments. The ability of such radiation to kill cancer cells is in part determined by the amount of oxygen the cells contain. Cancer cells need some amount of oxygen to live, but there is a class of such cells that are oxygen-poor, or hypoxic. Simply put, hypoxia develops when the oxygen demand of a growing tumor exceeds its oxygen supply (see Figure 10-7). Hypoxic cells are less sensitive to radiation and can enter a resting state from which they can later multiply. There is evidence that significant portions of tumor cells are hypoxic, and the types of drugs that can help attack them are called radiosensitizers. Other types of drugs, which attack hypoxic cells directly, have the logical and rhythmic name of hypoxic cytotoxins.

To be successful in killing a cancer cell, radiation must ultimately modify, either directly or indirectly, the DNA of the cell,

---

[9] Inflammation of the lining of the gastrointestinal tract.
[10] This kind of outcome was at odds with earlier experience according to the inventor Joe DeGraw. When combined with mitomycin and vinblastine (together called EMV), the side effects were so small that it could be administered on an outpatient basis and quadrupled life expectancy. (Ref. *SRI Journal*, 10(1), 1990)

[11] According to medical science bulletins (http://pharminfo.com/pubs/msb/edatrexate.html and htm), edatrexate has been successful in treating non-small-cell lung cancer, mesothelioma (a cancer of the lining of the lung and abdomen generally from asbestos exposure), metastatic breast cancer, colon cancer, non-Hodgkin's lymphoma, and other forms of cancer.
[12] It is called PDX and it is a propargyl derivative of edatrexate, targeted specifically for smoking-induced lung cancer. SRI, with collaborators Sloan-Kettering and Southern Research Institute, has licensed PDX to Allos Therapeutics and it is now in Phase II trials by Sloan-Kettering (personal communication from Mas Tanabe and from the Sloan-Kettering web site, January 17, 2003).

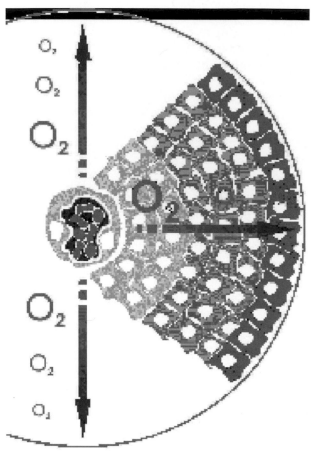

Figure 10-7. Diagram showing how oxygen consumption near a feeding blood vessel (center blotch) creates oxygen gradients within a few cell diameters. (Thus, unlike normal tissues, tumors contain zones of oxygenated, hypoxic, and dying/necrotic cells.)

making it nonreplicating. This means adding lesions to or, preferably, breaking either one or both DNA strands. The process is generally one of oxidizing DNA. Since normal cells are rich in oxygen, the question becomes one of how to raise the oxidizing vulnerability of those cells with little oxygen while avoiding a compounding effect on normal cells.[13]

In the late 1970s, SRI began exploring the field of radiosensitizing agents in collaboration with the Stanford Medical Center and under the sponsorship of the National Cancer Institute. The analytical and synthesizing work for the search was done under the leadership of SRI

biochemist Dr. William W. Lee.[14] He knew that, as with most all anticancer drugs, a successful radiosensitizer must

- Selectively sensitize hypoxic cells and have insignificant effects on normal cells
- Be nontoxic at clinically acceptable dose levels
- Diffuse to and through the tumor tissues efficiently
- Be metabolized slowly enough that radiosensitizing concentrations can be achieved
- Be effective against hypoxic cells at all stages of the cell cycle.

So the search began for a compound that would mimic the effects of oxygen. The two major ways oxygen interacts chemically are through free radicals and oxidation. Compounds having these properties had been under investigation for some 20 years. Free radicals had the problem of instability and being so reactive that they might not have time to migrate to the target site. So the SRI search first concentrated on agents that had oxidation-like potential, that is, those that had an affinity for electrons.

One problem presented by the radiosensitizing agents already in existence was that they dangerously attacked the nervous system. That toxicity posed another design constraint to SRI chemist Lee. Here Lee and Stanford colleague Martin Brown reasoned that a nitro group in the structure of these drugs might be the cause. Eliminating that group, together with eliminating the entire drug as rapidly as possible following radiation, should reduce the toxicity. Following this reasoning, Lee synthesized one of SRI's early offerings showing reduced neurotoxicity. It was called etanidazole. In mice, it showed three times the radiosensitizing effect of existing drugs at doses inducing no observable nerve damage.

---

[13] While one might suggest simply adding oxygen to the blood before irradiation, the vulnerability of hypoxic cells is more complex than such a simple notion implies. There are both chronic (long lasting) and acute (temporary) cellular hypoxia. Blood oxygenation addresses only the chronic type. (See Footnote 14.)

[14] The principal investigator at Stanford was biologist Dr. J. Martin Brown. Brown won the 1999 Cain Award of the American Association for Cancer Research for his work on hypotoxicity, including radiosensitizers. In his acceptance speech, he showed a picture of SRI's Bill Lee and acknowledged that he owed his award to Lee's drug synthesis work. (J. Martin Brown, The Hypoxic Cell: A Target for Selective Cancer Therapy, Eighteenth Bruce F. Cain Memorial Award Lecture, *Cancer Research*, 59, 5863-5870, December 1, 1999.)

But as etanidazole was introduced into some Phase III trials, it surprisingly failed to show a significant overall benefit. The answer lay, apparently, in the increasingly complex picture that hypoxia was presenting. Etanidazole, as it turned out, was effective mainly against the most oxygen-starved cells and was less effective against those with oxygen in intermediate amounts. Moreover, the dosage of this radiosensitizer that would make the cell vulnerable increased exponentially with the amount of cellular oxygen present. On the surface this sounds good because a dose

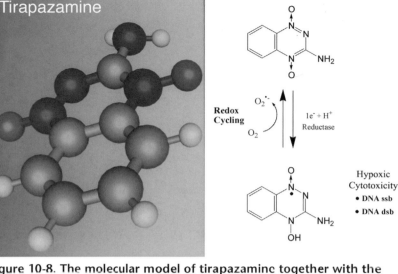

Figure 10-8. The molecular model of tirapazamine together with the hypoxic versus aerobic reaction it produces.

adequate to kill hypoxic cells might leave the more normal, oxygen-rich cells unaffected. Alas, tolerable dosages left too many intermediate level cells untouched.[15] Could the team find a drug that could kill hypoxic cells directly so that, when used in combination with radiation therapy, the overall result would have greater efficacy than either used alone?

In the mid-1980s Lee and Brown were still searching for better radiosensitizers that didn't cause nerve damage. With some serendipity, when testing one class of their trial compounds, they noticed that the compound's lethality to the hypoxic cells was about the same whether they were irradiated or not![16] This class not only didn't damage nerve cells but, using much lower concentrations, it killed as many hypoxic cells as the best radiosensitizers. More good news: their differential toxicity to hypoxic versus non-hypoxic cells was greater than any other known drug.

They called the lead compound TPZ or tirapazamine, and in rough terms its mechanism is as follows. In the intercellular structure, the drug undergoes a reaction that transforms it into a highly reactive radical. In the absence of oxygen, this negatively charged radical is capable of drawing a hydrogen atom from a nucleotide segment of one or both strands of a DNA molecule, thus killing it. However, when oxygen is present, that radical either never forms or is quickly neutralized, effectively returning the drug to its parent form.

That exchange is shown in Figure 10-8. Tirapazamine was thus attractive enough to enter into clinical trials.

Known as SR 4233, tirapazamine's record in clinical trials has been good. Phase I studies at Stanford, Harvard, and Glasgow Universities set the acceptable dosage level on the basis of side-effects. Phase II trials showed the drug to be effective against a wide range of cancers, and it is now in Phase III trials, particularly exploring its use in combination with other drugs for non-small-cell lung cancer (NSCLC). This is an important area because lung cancer is by far the leading cause of cancer mortality in the United States and 75% - 80% of lung cancer is NSCLC. During these trials, it was noted that tirapazamine was useful not only in conjunction with radiation therapy but also as an adjunct in chemotherapy. Tirapazamine has also entered Phase I trials at Stanford using oral delivery.

But, what of the drug's commercial side? In spite of its apparent potential, the licensing of tirapazamine has been checkered at best. In the beginning, SRI and Stanford became interested in a newly developing arm of Eastman Kodak as it decided to enter the pharmaceutical business. However, Kodak later abandoned that initiative and sold the new division to a somewhat old and staid drug company, Sterling Winthrop, which would later be bought out by the French pharmaceutical company, Sanofi (now Sanofi Winthrop Pharmaceuticals in the United States). Each of these corporate shuffles required a reexamination of the kind of drug business SRI was in and which of those companies were

---

[15] Ibid.
[16] These compounds were benzotriazine di-N-oxides.

to be SRI's heroes. The fate of tirapazamine is still before us.

An Hypoxia Probe

One of the limitations on the use of radiosensitizers, of course, is knowing whether hypoxic regions of a solid tumor exist and, if so, exactly where they are located. The nature of those regions and their vascular characteristics are described in the next section, but it is enough to say that hypoxia arises because of the disorganized nature of blood delivery systems in rapidly growing tumors. The need to identify such locations and the need to monitor the properties of a growing tumor motivated development of a drug now known as SR 4554, which is now in the first phase of clinical trials. Its role is that of a diagnostic probe rather than a therapeutic agent.

The roots of SR 4554 are a bit unusual.[O] The work on radiosensitizers described above was, as Lee approached retirement, being continued by Dr. Mike Tracy. As a consequence, Tracy was continuing to ponder that area of drug development as he attended a meeting at the University of Oxford in December of 1987. On that occasion he renewed an acquaintance with a long-time colleague, Dr. Paul Workman of the University of Glasgow. The venue was a local pub and the conversation centered on the nature of a molecule that would help identify the presence of hypoxia in solid tumors. The molecule should be as benign as possible and cause high illumination under magnetic resonance examinations. As Workman rattled off the molecule's needed characteristics, Tracy was jotting on a napkin how the molecule could be realized. Tracy returned to SRI, and within about a month, including the holidays, he had made the first synthesis of the molecule.[P]

The resulting drug is known as a fluorinated 2-nitroimidazole and it began with three design goals. It was to have

- A nitro group that would have an oxygen reduction potential to act selectively on just hypoxic tumor cells
- An affinity for water and hydrogen bonding that would limit its penetration to nerve tissue, thus giving it low neurotoxicity
- Fluorine components that would make whatever they were bound to more visible under magnetic resonance imaging and spectroscopy.

These design goals were met *in vitro* with hypoxic tumor cells showing a greater affinity for the drug than, say, normal brain or other cells. Its working levels were low enough that it was also nontoxic. Preclinical trials were slowed because of its nontherapeutic nature, but over almost a decade it proceeded toward clinical trials.

All syntheses of the drug have taken place at SRI, including those necessary for clinical trials. Phase I trials began in late 2000 and are still under way in England. These are sponsored by what was called the Cancer Research Campaign, now known simply as Cancer Research U.K. Again, because the probe is diagnostic and does not offer immediate relief to a tumor patient, its somewhat limited volunteers are acting solely for the advancement of science. The Phase I tests are continuing.

Fighting Blood Vessel Growth in Tumors

There is one more vulnerability in a tumor's blood supply that SRI is addressing. As mentioned, for a tumor to keep growing, it must develop and maintain an adequate blood supply. Interestingly, tumors begin this process while still 1-2 mm in size and do so by inducing new and sometimes rapid blood vessel growth; a process called angiogenesis. Biochemically, tumors may induce angiogenesis by tripping the "angiogenic switch," which is a dynamic balance of angiogenic inducers and angiogenic inhibitors, to favor the effect of the inducers.

These growing tumor vessels are an attractive target for anticancer therapy not only because they are accessible but because they are composed of normal cells, called endothelial cells, which make up the blood vessels in all tissues. Unlike cancer cells, endothelial cells are genetically stable and therefore unlikely to develop resistance to anticancer drugs, currently a major problem in the treatment of tumors by chemotherapy. The tumor blood vessels are also abnormal in ways beyond the oxygen starvation or hypoxia mentioned earlier. Because of the excessive demand for blood, tumor-feeding blood vessels also have important structural and functional differences, the former of which is illustrated in Figure 10-9. Functional differences offer another avenue of attack.

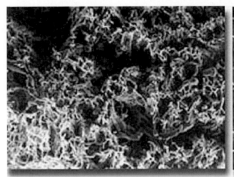

Figure 10-9. Normal and cancer-induced blood vessels. An image of normal blood vessels in mouse muscle is shown on the left while the one on the right shows the aberrant blood vessels in a mouse tumor. Notice the tumor vessels have chaotic structures in both size and placement and there are areas with no blood supply at all.

Note that this tendency for blood vessel growth is not common in adult humans, occurring only in situations like menstruation, pregnancy, and wound healing. So, assuming some stability in the life of normal human blood vessels, drugs selective to angiogenesis will target mainly those vessels contributing to cancer growth. Scientists at SRI investigating this new area in cancer therapy have come up with several trial drugs, but none more important that those steroidal ones dealing with breast cancer, as discussed below.

Steroid Hormones and Breast Cancer

In the world's war on cancer there are many fronts, but few get more attention than the hormone-sensitive cancers of the breast and prostate. Important in combating these cancers are steroid hormones, compounds discovered in the 1920s that help define us as male or female. These steroids have been the center of work for SRI's Dr. Mas Tanabe and his colleagues for over 40 years (see Figure 10-10).[17] They consist of such well-known drugs as cortisone, estrogen, and testosterone plus those from the oral contraceptive field. While not extensive, cortisone work at SRI has explored its impact on such diverse topics as mitigating

stress in Air Force pilots and the treatment of rheumatoid arthritis.

In the mid-1960s, however, funding for such work on steroid hormones began to dry up, at least for the treatment of cancer. This was largely because their broad activity produced too many side effects. In contrast, however, and as an indication of the exceptional competence at SRI, the NIH and drug companies like Schering Plough and Taiho have sponsored work on steroid hormones here continuously for over 30 years. The contract with Schering Plough began in July 1957 and was still going strong in 1983! By that point, SRI had granted Schering eight patents and more than 30 journal articles in the area of new anti-inflammatory steroids.[Q] Now a resurgence of interest has occurred because of their ability to be selective and to activate or repress genes.

Although the field of steroid hormones has again become "hot," there is a shortage of the chemists needed to build the compounds for the biologists to test. The big goal at the moment and a focus of the SRI work is to try to build modifications of the natural hormones that are very tissue-selective. To illustrate one

Figure 10-10. Dr. Masato Tanabe about 1960.

---

[17] Dr. Tanabe is, in the opinion of many of his SRI associates, one of the most dedicated and brilliant chemists to have worked at SRI. Stories are told about his not only dragging technical papers on what few vacations he took, but actually studying them. His probing mind never seems at rest. In the days when traveling to conferences meant sharing hotel rooms with colleagues, one roommate remembered being awakened in the night when Tanabe rose up in bed and shouted, "But we should try the acetate!"

CHRONOLOGY OF TWO SRI ANTI-ESTROGEN DRUGS	
July 1996	Synthesis search began
December 1998	Discovery phase ended for SR 16234 and 16287
April 1999	Preclinical testing of absorption, toxicity, etc.
December 1999	Synthesized 1.4 kg in tablet form Began investigational new drug (IND) testing
August 2000	IND application submitted to Food and Drug Administration
September 2000	Phase I trials began
March 2002	Phase I trials ended

avenue, consider the currently popular drug for breast cancer treatment—tamoxifen.

The natural hormone estrogen is required for the growth of cancer cells in about two-thirds of breast cancer cases. Tamoxifen is a purely synthetic compound that acts like natural estrogen in that it is accepted by the estrogen receptors of breast cancer cells but, once attached, normally does not permit the cell to replicate. Hence, tamoxifen is called an anti-estrogen. At the moment, tamoxifen is the most widely used drug for breast cancer therapy, but it is not perfect because it does have some estrogen activity. That is, it appears to some tumor cells as natural estrogen and thus enables their growth. Approximately half of the patients using tamoxifen will not be helped. So tamoxifen resistance has become an unmet medical need. In addition, tamoxifen increases the risk for endometrial (uterus-lining) cancer.

The goal for SRI was to create a very tissue-selective estrogen that would act like an anti-estrogen in the breast and uterus but would appear as normal estrogen to bones and other responsive tissue such as cardiovascular tissue. The possibility of this duality first arose from a lead compound found under an SRI contract from NIH.[R] That idea, then, was proposed to Japan's largest anticancer pharmaceutical house, Taiho Pharmaceuticals, in July 1996. Taiho's acceptance of the proposal began a six-year attempt to find, develop, and test such a compound. The above table shows the incredibly short time frame over which the development took place.

The SRI team was able to design and synthesize these drugs so quickly because of

their many years of work dedicated to steroids. In a comparatively short time and a discovery phase cost of less than $3 million, SRI invented two new anti-estrogen agents that are much more tissue-specific than tamoxifen. Their code names are SR16234 and SR16287 and they were to be directed at those patients who had experienced tamoxifen failure. In an important step, SRI also designed the compounds so that the drug could be taken orally, thus substantially lowering the cost of administration.

Amazingly, the SRI drugs had other important advantages beyond just estrogen-blocking. The two SRI drugs are members of a general class of compounds capable of tissue differentiation called selective estrogen receptor modulators or SERMs. Tamoxifen is a member of that family but has the above-mentioned limitations. During the discovery phase of SR 16234, chemist Richard Peters and biochemist Wan-Ru Chao discovered that the "234" compound not only inhibited blood vessel growth (angiogenesis), it accelerated the programmed death of cancer cells (apoptosis). As mentioned earlier, cancer tumors need blood vessel growth to deliver nutrients, but because the human body grows blood vessels only during pregnancy, menstruation, and wound healing, inhibiting angiogenesis outside those times might make it an effective anticancer mechanism, as in postmenopausal women. So, SR 16234 has several ways to fight cancer and its trials are encouraging.

As the SRI team continued the refinement of SR 16234, the drug showed six important benefits. It:

- Inhibited tumor cell growth through estrogen-blocking (SERM)
- Inhibited blood vessel growth (anti-angiogenesis)
- Somewhat accelerated cancer cell death (apoptosis)
- Is safe for estrogen-responsive, normal tissue
- Showed no toxicity for other normal cells
- Could be administered orally.

The combination of SERM and anti-angiogenesis means that the drug can potentially be used for breast cancer, even after metastasis. SRI also pursued and secured its intellectual property on SR 16234, obtaining a worldwide patent position including a general formulation process for the drugs.

With this attractive outlook, Taiho Pharmaceuticals bought a worldwide license to the two compounds in the spring of 1999, targeting them as replacements for tamoxifen. Taiho also agreed to conduct preclinical testing at SRI, and with favorable outcome, carry it through Phase I trials. Those trials have now been successfully completed.[18] They will also continue to explore acceptable manufacturing costs as the testing explores its value against tamoxifen-resistant strains of cancer.

SRI researchers believe that their new agent may even have a potential for *preventing* breast cancer and a useful role in hormone-replacement therapy, where estrogen has proved to have significant risk. Many researchers were involved with Tanabe in this work[19] and, as of this writing, SR 16234 is about to enter Phase II clinical trials. Because of excellent Phase I results, Taiho will continue to carry the large financial burden of the Phase II clinical trials.

Other Tanabe contributions also deserve mention. The first is his pioneering use of stable isotopes to do fundamental studies of metabolism. More specifically, he showed how to insert the traceable isotope C_{13} into antibiotics to show how a microbe could actually assemble a particular antibiotic to defend itself. Before this technique was developed, people had to break down the antibiotic and guess how it may have been constructed. Tanabe tagged small, elementary, one- and two-carbon chains and placed them in the presence of the microbe. He then took the resulting antibiotic and analyzed it using magnetic resonance spectroscopy to reveal the presence of the imposed C_{13} and thus the manner by which antibiotic material was formed.

On March 27, 2001, Tanabe was awarded the Japanese Pharmaceutical Society's Distinguished Service Award for a long history of helping Japanese academic scientists and companies in the chemical and pharmaceutical fields. In particular, the award recognized his dedication to the scientific exchange represented by the 45 scientists who have come to SRI to study under him. He is the first person outside of Japan to win this honor.

---

[18] Richard Peters mentioned that in one situation with 16 nearly terminal patients, 40% were stabilized. Metabolic absorption has been very good, particularly when taken after food, and from CancerEDGE.com comes a report that SR 16234 is doing well against similar anti-estrogen drugs such as tamoxifen, raloxifene, and Faslodex (March 20, 2002).

[19] Besides Richard Peters and Wan-Ru Chao are Andrew Kelson, Ling Jong, Robin Van Lengen, John Johansson, Cris Olsen, Jyanwei Liu, and Barbara Sato. Chao and Sato are biochemists while the rest of the team are organic chemists.

Chemical Hazards in Our Environment

Pollution, Pesticides, and Pests[5]

It was exactly on the third anniversary of SRI's very first project when in December of 1949 SRI agreed to help Alcoa assess the biological effects of an effluent from its fertilizer plants. The effluent, airborne fluorides, was affecting the plants and animals downwind of its reduction factories in several western states. The chemical was part of the phosphate ore rather than one introduced into the reduction cycle. Alcoa went outside its corporation for the study not only because Alcoa didn't have the capability internally, but because doing so no doubt gave the work some useful objectivity. The specific quest was to assess the effects of fluoride on cattle, and to Alcoa's credit, the work was to be done openly and the results published in the open literature.

So, SRI's 259th project started what would become a six-year investigation into the measured effects of fluoride on milk production as well as the teeth and bones of cows. The most obvious effects from the ingestion of plants laden with the chemical were the softening of the cows' teeth and some changes in the structure of their leg bones, making it difficult for the cows to walk. These effects were known in general terms, but the important question was how much fluoride it took to cause noticeable damage.

To help measure and evaluate the effects on individual cows, SRI enlisted a veterinarian from Modesto, CA, and the cooperative use of his dairy farm. By measuring the daily amounts of sodium fluoride fed to the cattle, photographing the incisor teeth of each animal at regular intervals throughout the multi-year experiment, recording daily milk production and documenting the condition of the autopsied cattle that had undergone various levels of exposure, SRI was able to quantify the levels of impact. These were used to resolve several litigations and settlements concerned with safe ingestion levels of fluorides. Later, scientists from SRI's Los Angeles Laboratory also investigated for Alcoa the damage of fluorides on fruits and vegetables. The main effect in this case was a pockmarked appearance on the skin that could ruin the marketability of the product.

In a related vein, SRI undertook work for Shell Development as Shell decided to go into the agricultural product line of insecticides and pesticides. Beginning in 1953 and continuing for about 20 years, this work lasted long enough to look into the safety and toxicity of Shell's agricultural products on certain animals and their offspring.

The same expertise in insecticides enabled SRI to evaluate the efficacy and safety of flea collars. Shell was a pioneer in this area. SRI was able to show that when flea collars were applied too tightly, skin lesions occurred, in either dogs or cats, but with a looser application, the collar was effective in killing fleas and yet not harm the pet.

In another pet-related project for the California Fish Canners Association, SRI identified the reason red meat tuna was causing a disease called steatitis (yellow fat disease) in cats. Red meat tuna had little vitamin E and because of lax processing conditions, the unsaturated fats were allowed to oxidize, thus producing a toxic product. Thus, there was a need to keep the tuna's fatty acids from oxidizing. Vitamin E had been added by the processors to improve the health of the cats and to preserve the tuna. However, the form of vitamin E they had chosen simply wasn't biologically available to the animals. So a change in the chemical structure of the antioxidant, vitamin E, and improvement in the sanitation conditions during processing, cured the problem. Beyond pets, the effect of toxins on fish, upland game birds, and other animals were also examined for several clients. As we will now see, humans can also be victims of airborne toxins.

Animal Models in the Pursuit of Preventing Chronic Lung Disease

Today's attention given to the discharge of chemicals into our atmosphere obviously came from our heightened awareness of their effects on humans and other living things. In the 1940s and 1950s, pollutants had some fairly direct and lethal effects in the "killer fogs" of London and similar but more modest effects in the eastern United States. The effects of less severe concentrations, however, weren't so measurable or clear. Because many of the effects of such exposure in humans do not manifest

10–16

themselves until middle age or beyond, our awareness would have come much slower if we had relied only on the measurable air pollution for its ultimate effects on humans.

In the early 1960s, SRI, in the person of Dr. Gus Freeman, began an inquiry into the environmental causes of two respiratory diseases. One is termed chronic obstructive pulmonary disease (COPD) and the other is emphysema. COPD is a loss of elasticity in the air sacs (alveoli) of the lungs, whereas emphysema is the loss of their surface area. Both are overwhelmingly associated with smoking but also have ties to the quality of urban air. The number of cases of emphysema is growing; it currently affects about 2 million Americans.

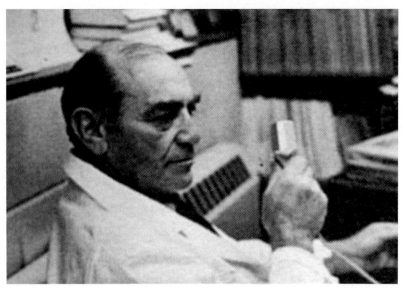

Figure 10-11. Respiratory disease researcher, Gustave Freeman, M.D.

One of the first invitations for SRI to investigate what was becoming an increasing health problem came from the California Department of Health. Recognizing the growing problem in the Los Angeles Basin, they sought some insight into the causative mechanisms. The representative calling on SRI claimed the only person who could effectively examine the toxic effect of the oxides of nitrogen was SRI's Freeman, who had looked into the subject while in the Army and who had just come to SRI from the NIH's National Cancer Institute by way of Cal Tech (see Figure 10-11).[T] Freeman saw the problem more as a regulatory issue, but his interest in the cause and pathogenesis of respiratory diseases persuaded him to undertake the study. Because of its general importance, the work also came to be supported over the 1960s and 1970s by NIH's National Institute of Environmental Health Sciences and the Environmental Protection Agency.

Because of the slow development of emphysema in humans and particularly the difficulty in obtaining human tissue during its early stages, it became necessary to look for an analog in animals. Earlier attempts at this approach had failed, mainly because of a lack of adequate consideration of the importance of the slow onset of the disease. Recognizing this, Freeman's SRI team worked for over 10 years to develop a representative model in rats. The approach came to consist of their exposure to nitrogen dioxide, an important constituent in tobacco smoke and present in automobile exhaust and other urban smog pollutants including power plants. Various levels of nitrogen oxide (NO_2) and ozone (O_3) were introduced.

Some lower levels produced no clinically observed discomfort in rats but, over a period of months, did cause morphological changes to their lungs. Such changes were observed to depend on the concentration and the duration of exposure. Consistent exposure levels of 10-15 parts per million over several months were enough to cause life-threatening COPD. Because it was important to watch the development of COPD over the *normal* life span of the rat (2 to 3 years), exposures were also made intermittently and at varying concentrations. "Smog" level concentrations of 0.8-2.0 ppm, offered consistently, showed cellular changes characteristic of the more heavily exposed rats but still permitting a more normal life span, perhaps suffering a reduced lung capacity.

Using this model in rats, SRI was able to show that there were important thresholds in the levels of NO_2 and O_3 and its consequential effects. Levels in the vicinity of 1-2 ppm caused cellular damage, some of which could be recovered from, and were not life threatening. Levels 10-15 ppm, however, were fatal under long exposure and caused permanent damage at lesser exposure.

To better approximate the condition in humans, Freeman began what turned out to be an 11-year study of the effects on primates.

Exposure during these tests was a nearly constant levels of 9 ppm of NO_2 and 4 ppm of ozone. The results were evaluated with the help of the University of California, Davis, School of Veterinary Medicine. Ozone proved to be over ten times as toxic to the rat population as nitrogen oxide. Emphysema was present in 1 in 6 of the primates. While admittedly a simplistic model, these thresholds of NO_2 became an important guide to regulatory groups interested in the health aspects of air pollution. The results of the NO_2 work were presented at conferences of the World Health Organization in 1977-1978. The EPA limit on the amount of allowed NO_2 is in continuing flux but is now less that 0.1 ppm.

So, for over 15 years Freeman and his colleagues such as Glen Haydon, Bob Stephens, and Mike Evans revealed the toxic effects of airborne oxidants on the bronchial lining and the alveolary surfaces of the lungs. They also examined the ability of the body to heal itself from such damage. Freeman's passion was understanding enough of the pathogenesis of the respiratory system so that meaningful preventive measures could be taken. All this helped set the limits on the environmental concentrations of the atmospheric pollutants, the nitrogen oxides, and ozone.[U]

Comparative Metabolism and the Role of Human Tissue

Over the last 40 or 50 years, the number of chemicals in the world has increased dramatically. Some find use in the industrial world, some in farming and other food production, and many in new forms of drugs for curing what ails us. Surprisingly, the consequences on humankind for many of these chemicals are still largely unknown. Whether a new chemical or drug is hostile to our health should be a question answered *before* it goes to production, both to protect us and to avoid the high capital investments needed for its production or remediation.

Although there is little such screening of industrial chemicals until after there is a perceived problem, drugs are directed, under government regulation, through well-defined procedures from which both their danger and their efficacy are measured. However, these trials are expensive and in some cases risky to the human subjects participating. Needed is a way to determine, in a very complete sense, just how dangerous a specific drug is. Can its side effects be gauged well enough to decide whether its harmful effects outweigh its potential benefit *before* it is even taken to Phase I trials where its incidental risks are evaluated? Is there a way to predict the effects of potentially toxic substances on humans before some subpopulation actually has to experience their risk?

In 1977 Dr. Charlie Tyson, a chemist working at the University of Wisconsin, came to SRI and began looking into the promotion of some projects that interested him (see Figure 10-12). A try at one with a colleague at UCLA didn't pan out. Then Bill Skinner,

Tyson's boss, approached him with some overhead funds and, in one of those seemingly prescient moments, asked him to look into new assay methods in toxicology. Tyson, who had some background in toxicology, soon recognized that, since the point of such evaluative experiments was to determine the effect on humans, why not expose human tissue rather than animal tissue to a toxin of interest. In particular, since many foreign things we ingest encounter first the liver, its tissue would be a good starting point for the detection of toxicity. This concept led to SRI's liver cell toxicology assay system.

Figure 10-12. Sr. scientist Dr. Charles Tyson and toxicologist Dr. Carol Green.

Because the concept rested on the presence of living human liver cells *in vitro*, building the liver cell assay system first meant finding enough post-mortem human donors and then determining how to separate their liver tissue into enough functional cells, called hepatocytes,[20] to reliably measure effects. This separation process is called isolation. Tyson examined several isolation methods around the world and concluded that one developed at the University of California, Davis, was the best. It had high tissue yield; that is, a small number of cells would retain all the properties of the liver for that cell type. Gaining access to that process was very important to the SRI work, but one of its best consequences was that UC Davis graduate student, Dr. Carol Green, would come to SRI as a postdoctoral associate (see Figure 10-12).

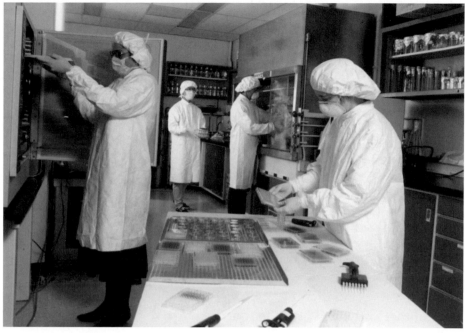

Figure 10-13. SRI's liver cell toxicology facility. Though not easily recognized, they are, from left to right, Kathy Allen, Toyomitsu Sato, Jack Dabbs, and Carol Green.

The liver cell facility was completed in 1983, making it the first such facility in the world operated as a normal service (see Figure 10-13). Now the real purpose of Tyson's idea could be tested: Would the exposure of human hepatocytes *in vitro* to a specific exogenous agent adequately predict the effect of that same agent to human exposure; that is, *in vivo*?

This approach would require analysis of the *in vitro* data and construction of models to predict *in vivo* response. This had not been done before. The model building would also benefit from those special cases where considerable human testing had already been done, as in drug trials already completed. The team included Tyson, Green, Sue LeValley, Jack Dabbs, Shirley Gee, and Katherine Hawk-Prather from the Toxicology Laboratory and other SRI people including Ron Spanggord, Bob Stephens, and Dave Thomas. The SRI team began a variety of experiments and together

wrote a series of papers that put all these new ideas on firmer ground. This new approach brought SRI a reputation that has continued to the present as one of the foremost laboratories in the development of *in-vitro* human and animal tissue model systems. From its beginnings in the early 1980s, to the construction of the facility, to a number of supporting papers in the mid-1980s, SRI's work became widely known.

Beginning in 1983, certain progress was evident. The isolation techniques had been perfected from both animal and human sources. The resulting hepatocytes were characterized in terms of their metabolic capability and their response to both toxic and nontoxic agents. These results were then compared with known *in vivo* responses to the same agents. Agents included standard liver toxins such as carbon tetrachloride and some traditional antidotes for cyanide poisoning. But it was a 1986 paper in the *Journal of Pharmacology and Experimental Therapeutics* that gave the team and their approach wide validation and recognition.[V] The authors were able to show that the *in vitro* responses to the chemical amphetamine by tissue from the livers of rats, dogs, squirrel monkeys, and humans retained the same metabolic distinctions or differences that they displayed *in vivo*. This similarity extended to the production of certain

---

[20] Literally, liver cells.

metabolic products unique to the different species examined. Comparative metabolism across these species was possible; that is, the *in vitro* process was indeed a legitimate surrogate for human and animal responses.

These results, probably more than anything else, led to Green getting a contract from the National Institute for Diabetes and Digestive and Kidney Diseases (NIDDK) for establishing a liver tissue bank. This was a service type of contract, but it led to the formation of the SRI liver tissue facility, which is still used in metabolism studies. In a related vein, Tyson has now been placed on the Board of Directors of the National Disease Research Interchange, a leading group that acquires human tissues from tissue banks and distributes them to where they are needed.

Another fairly obvious benefit of the use of human cells in testing is the decreased emphasis on animal testing. Almost from his original concept, Tyson recognized this advantage. Other work outside SRI had shown that, for many chemicals, you didn't need to use animals to gauge the potency needed to kill humans. Because the SRI work has been primarily in human tissues, Tyson was asked to co-chair a workshop in October 2000 on how to do away with animal tests for acute lethality. Other leadership roles in the alternatives to animal testing have followed.

Up until now, the *in vitro* systems and their models have been simple ones—simple in the method of isolation or the fact that only one cell type was involved. But the real world is much more complex and so, as most people would anticipate retirement, Tyson is beginning, as he says, the most exciting part of his career. To continue and improve on SRI's liver work, it is necessary to look at more than one of the 3 to 5 liver cell types. With some well-qualified colleagues in the field of human tissue toxicology, Tyson will be trying to move the field forward so that we can make reliable predictions about the effect of a drug on humans when no human has ever been in contact with it. Over the next few years, they will be looking beyond the liver to other organs, such as the heart, lungs, kidneys, and even the brain. They are already looking at bone marrow. There would be a different assay for each of these. Tyson says, "We may have to look in detail at how proteins, or parts of proteins, behave to understand and predict an outcome." (Tragically, Charlie Tyson died unexpectedly as this book was going to press.)

SRI's contribution to the ability to anticipate in the laboratory human responses to toxic agents has now taken the form of supplying the method as opposed to the testing itself. Through the literature, consultation, and the liver tissue bank, SRI has had global influence. Today, the FDA and the drug companies themselves are increasingly requiring this kind of testing against human tissue before drugs proceed very far in the development cycle. It is cost effective and safe. As a validation of its approach and reputation, SRI was recently awarded a $2 million NIH grant to further its work. The goal of this project will be to look for more quantitative, predictive models of the toxicologic impacts on human tissue.

Health Sciences

In addition to its contributions in medical technology and drug research, for many years SRI has also performed important work in selected areas of health science. The precursor of this work began in the early 1970s with a focus on the monitoring of the alcoholism programs of the NIH.[21] This work continued for years and involved the difficult subject of surveying that segment of the population affected by alcoholism in order to provide needed feedback on the efficacy of the sponsored activities. Thus, the SRI emphasis at that time was on health *services* and would remain so over the course of a decade.

Also during that time, separate areas arose within the group that began to examine the interplay of health and the environment. With that additional perspective, the group became known as the Behavioral Medicine Program, and it proceeded to gain a good reputation in the study of cardiovascular disease, including associated risk factors such as stress. But it was the extended experience with the monitoring of alcoholism that would eventually lead, around the early 1980s, toward trying to understand the effects and reasons for addiction to alcohol and tobacco. In each of these, the emphasis

---

[21] Specifically, the National Institute on Alcohol Abuse and Alcoholism.

Figure 10-14. Health researchers Drs. Dorit Carmelli and Gary Swan.

became more one of *science*, as opposed to service. In about 1986, under the leadership of Dr. Gary Swan (Figure 10-14), the program began a decade-long growth that resulted in its becoming laboratory size. With this new prominence, it became known as the SRI Center for Health Sciences, but two of its research emphases would remain the causes and treatments of our common addictions, such as alcohol and tobacco.

Another aspect of the Center's growth came in 1995 with the arrival of Dr. Adolf Pfefferbaum and his field of brain imaging. That work has led to examining the impacts of aging and other factors, such as alcoholism, on the brain, its composition, and its performance. By 2000, expertise in behavioral pharmacology was introduced; in 2001, the study of human sleep; and by 2002, molecular genetics. Throughout this steady expansion, the Center has maintained its high quality of work, as evidenced by its prolific publishing record. Over the past 3 years, working on individual grants and through collaboration with medical schools such as Stanford, UCLA, UCSF, UC Davis, Indiana University, Emory University, the University of Texas, and others, more than 200 published papers or symposium presentations have been produced by the researchers in the Center.

As another recognition and to aid in its important work on medical imaging, SRI has partnered with GE Medical Systems, which has elected to base the western part of its Advanced Systems Laboratory on the SRI campus. This facility comprises two research magnet systems and houses several of GE's prominent developers and researchers in the field who actively collaborate with SRI Drs. Pfefferbaum and Ian Colrain. The center has also established a state-of-the-art, four-bed human sleep facility. This is being used to support several NIH-funded projects on human sleep and daytime electrophysiology. A few examples will relate a sense of the work done in the Center and its value.[W]

Human Addiction— The Role of Nicotine

Though smoking has developed enough of a stigma in our society that laws restricting it in many public places have been passed, there are still approximately 50 million Americans, or one in five, who smoke. While a few special interests continue to minimize the overall impact of smoking, the social and healthcare costs of this addiction are, by all accounts, staggering. Smoking leads to approximately 415,000 premature deaths each year, and the consequences for U.S. society in medical costs and lost productivity total about $157 billion during 2004.[X] Worldwide, the problem is enormously greater, with about a billion smokers and approximately 3 million people per year dying of tobacco-related illness. It is the leading cause of preventable death in the United States, and in spite of the omnipresent warnings, the success rate for smoking cessation is a dismal 20%. I remember my own father often jokingly repeating that old adage, "Quitting is easy. I've done it a hundred times!" The addictive nature of nicotine is clearly a problem worthy of study, and the Center continues to seek the answer to a number of questions: What causes nicotine to become habit-forming? Why is it much more difficult for some to quit than for others? What are effective treatments for those who want to quit?

In this work, and at the base of much of the SRI work in addiction, is the question of what drives addiction: genetics or the environment —i.e., nature or nurture? To address this question, the staff has made extensive use of twin registries, including those of the National Academy of Sciences, the NIH's National Heart, Lung, and Blood Institute, and SRI's own Northern California Twin Registry. Exploring the susceptibility and impact imposed by one's genes, they use the similarities and differences between identical and nonidentical (fraternal) twins. These databases are now large enough to give meaningful statistical bounds when the hypotheses are well drawn.

One of the Center's most important contributions has been to affirm the role of genetics in nicotine dependence. The first paper from SRI to receive widespread recognition from the field appeared in 1992. Before that time, the scientific community was uncertain, perhaps even skeptical, about a genetic contribution to smoking or, if so, its real significance. To examine that point, the SRI staff determined, using more than 20,000 returned questionnaires from the National Academy of Sciences/National Research Council World War II Twin Registry, that an important part, perhaps 50%, of the susceptibility to nicotine dependence is genetic.[Y] Further work showed that the weight gain incurred by many as they try to stop smoking also has a large genetic component. Even in the strong, cross-population correlation between cigarettes, alcohol, and coffee consumption, genetics plays a role. The attribution of the controlling factors is too complex to relate here, but SRI has published articles detailing them, and the results have been corroborated by others, some using molecular genetic strategies.

Another facet of the nicotine addiction question is the problem of quitting, including the efficacy of different approaches. For example, the transdermal approach, the so-called nicotine patch, was examined as a function of cigarette consumption, motivation to quit, sex, body mass index, and age. Expectedly, motivation was an important factor; but unexpectedly, women relapsed sooner than men, and those with high body mass indices sooner than those with low indices.[Z] The effectiveness of certain cessation drugs, such as bupropion, was also examined.

The SRI work in nicotine and alcohol addiction is of high quality and widely respected. Perhaps the best evidence of that reputation is NIH's creation in 2000 of a multidisciplinary team of SRI experts to constitute the Nicotine Addiction Research Center. In this context, nicotine addiction research at SRI continues to be addressed in terms of genetics, environmental factors, and their interactions. Further, the work explores the determinants of smoking onset in youth, the factors that help in smoking cessation, and the basis for addiction through genotyping, gene expression, and proteomics. In addition to SRI staff, this Center has a worldwide core of collaborators representing a broad range of research practices and disciplines.

Cardiovascular Risk Factors and the Brain

Because of the importance of cardiovascular disease in the U.S. population, there have been continuing and obvious reasons to explore its root causes. One of those pursuits has to do with stress and behavior patterns. This area of research came to SRI through the extended tenure of Dr. Ray H. Rosenman, the co-author of the concept of Type A behavior. Although he created that notion before coming to SRI, he continued to examine and refine the relationships between behavior patterns, stress, and cardiovascular risk over the dozen or so years he researched here. With Drs. Margaret Chesney, Marcia Ward, Michael Hecker, and others, he looked into the medical consequences of Type A behavior in the work setting and also into new interview methods to determine the presence of Type A behavior. Furthermore, he refined the most important components that comprise it. The findings included the now-confirmed cardiovascular consequence of chronic hostility.

Other factors in cardiovascular risk continued after Dr. Rosenman's departure in 1990; in particular, the hereditary question arose in the mind of Dr. Dorit Carmelli (Figure 10-14).[AA] How much of cardiovascular disease is genetic, and are there important environmental factors? Carmelli and Swan again explored this question by including an examination of twin registries. In a 1999 paper they showed that, independent of shared genetic or familial influences, midlife cardiovascular risk factors such as high blood pressure, lower levels of high-density lipoprotein cholesterol, and high 1-hour blood glucose levels were predictive of structural differences in the brain at old age. High alcohol consumption and low physical activity also contribute to poor brain morphology. Structurally, lower volumes of gray matter and degrees of brain interconnectivity (white matter) were evident in such cases, and both have influences on cognitive and physical functioning. In other words, the same activities that lead to increased cardiovascular risk are also inimical to brain function in old age. Other work on the detailed connectivity, gray-matter volume, and other physical composition of the aging brain continues.

Magnetic Resonance Imaging (MRI)

One of the most important and creative aspects of the Center's work addresses the ability to actually look at the structure of the brain by using high-resolution imaging and doing so at a time of one's choosing. Using such methods means being able to watch the progression of changes in response to a variation in pathologies, medicines, or aspects of lifestyles such as alcohol abuse. This capability is far better than examining the cumulative effects one sees at autopsy. Using high-resolution MRI, SRI's Dolf Pfefferbaum has become widely known for his insight and innovative computational techniques to image brain features over time, such as the changes in brain connectivity or the shrinking of gray matter.[22] One remarkable contribution has been to document the ability of the brain to restore itself following the removal of a particular brain-impinging factor. This reversibility can be studied in animals as well as humans. The two GE MRI units now at SRI are part of a collaborative effort between the two organizations to further both the science underlying brain morphology and the instrumentation with which to better understand it. A major ambition of the Center is to use such imaging as a basis for identifying interventions that can limit damage and improve function. Can brain changes, identified early, help prevent downstream problems or, perhaps, illuminate possible windows in brain development when certain brain-enhancing opportunities exist? At the moment, such imaging is directed mostly at the recognition of certain brain pathologies and whether they respond to specific medicines or lifestyles.

Representative New Areas of Study

Lately, the Center has been investigating the reasons why various identified risk factors contribute to cardiovascular, brain, and other pathologies. As just one example, the Center has done a longitudinal study on the genetic causes of obesity, finding that, with aging, certain genes begin to contribute to both the distribution and amount of body fat.

We end this section with a word on the increasing insight we are gathering on the role of genetics in important diseases. The Center is assessing how that knowledge can be used in ways that are beneficial to early intervention and how its use can be made consistent with our social and ethical practices. It is a new frontier with some risk for such problems as unwarranted discrimination in employment or the availability of health and life insurance, yet with vast potential for improving the health and well-being of us all.

---

[22] Using high-resolution MRI, new cutting-edge imaging techniques have been created by SRI's Pfefferbaum in collaboration with colleagues from Stanford University, including Dr. Edie Sullivan and Dr. Elfar Adalsteinsson. One MRI technique shows the sophistication of these new analytic tools. The team uses something called "echo planar diffusion tensor imaging" to define the orientation and coherence of the microstructure of white matter. The health of this tissue is related to how the cerebral fluid diffuses either along or across the aligned microstructure, with cross-structure or isotropic flows indicating an aging or deteriorating condition in that part of the brain.

Chapter 11
Physical Chemistry and Materials

Background

Given the thousands of materials or chemical processes that SRI has explored over its lifetime, selecting just a few as representative becomes an impossible task. Nevertheless, this fairly eclectic chapter examines a few new materials, several processes and their modeling, and an SRI service that for years was the largest information source in the world on the availability of a wide range of materials. But first, to help represent the wide range of this type of SRI work, I will briefly mention a few materials research projects here. They are indicative of many that should have been mentioned had there been enough time and space.

During the late 1950s, SRI had a metallurgy group headed by Dr. Rudy Thielemann. One of his specialties was superalloys, materials with superior strength that were capable of operating in high-temperature environments (>2000°F) without appreciable oxidation or corrosive effects. One use for such materials was in jet engines. In work for the Tungsten Institute and for the American-Marietta Corporation, Thielemann and his group invented a series of new alloys of steel that employed tungsten, cobalt, nickel, and a host of more minor elements. These alloys made their way into the manufacture of jet turbines. Names like WI 52, SM-200, and SM-302 were among the alloys that either originated or were significantly improved at SRI. After leaving SRI in 1961, Thielemann continued in this field, and in 1980 an international quadrennial conference on superalloys was dedicated to him and his contributions.

A second example relates to something every housewife or cook understands: the difficulty in cleaning an oven. But because of an opportunity from the Whirlpool Corporation and some technical insights at SRI, that chore has been eased significantly. In the early 1990s SRI performed a very detailed study on why pyrolized food (i.e.,

food that has been chemically decomposed by heat) adhered to different surfaces through mechanical, chemical, and even ionic bonding. The research not only sought to find low-adherence, cleanable surfaces but also considered their cost of manufacture. More than 30 potential oven materials were tested for their ease of cleaning plus susceptibility to abrasion. The answer came in recommended changes to the porcelain enamel surface used in ovens and how it is applied. The recommended process improved surface smoothness, added material with low ionic content, treated the surface to enhance the presence of chemically inert nitrides, and added a basic film that turns fat and fatty acids into water-soluble esters. These SRI improvements have made their way into most of today's consumer ovens.[A]

Finally, there is a more current illustration involving the burgeoning world of portable power sources: the ubiquitous battery or its equivalent. Over the past decade and under the leadership of Dr. Subhash Narang, SRI has been researching more capable and useful energy sources. One of the first was removal of the flammable gel in lithium-ion batteries that made them dangerous to use. The solution was a polymer electrolyte that SRI announced in 1998. Building on that experience, SRI began to explore new and more flexible forms of the lithium-polymer battery. This work has led to batteries of arbitrary shape, and even to the potential of a battery fiber that will allow clothing to act as a power source. Batteries that can assume other roles in portable devices will afford a considerable reduction in both size and weight. More recently, SRI began research into miniature hydrogen-based fuel cells whose energy density exceeds present battery technology. SRI has created laboratory fuel cells that operate more efficiently and have lower manufacturing costs. These new technologies are still emerging but seem promising enough that SRI has launched a new company called PolyFuel. PolyFuel has announced a new membrane material, a critical component of hydrogen fuel cells, that is more power efficient and significantly lowers the now prohibitive cost of fuel cells for their biggest market, the automobile.

One of the most unusual alternatives to consumable power sources such as batteries is SRI's innovative use of a material called electroactive polymer. This elastomer material, sandwiched between compliant electrodes, can create a voltage source when deformed, or, inversely, it will deform itself when a voltage is applied. This technology has enormous applications, from flat acoustic speakers to battery replacement. The DARPA

is sponsoring research to place such material in the heel of a soldier's boot. The expected result: every 8 hours of walking using a 2-watt boot generator (4 watts for both boots) saves approximately 200 grams of battery weight while adding no additional carried weight. SRI researchers, such as Dr. Ron Pelrine, Joe Eckerle, and Roy Kornbluh, are on the threshold of several products, and, consequently, SRI has just formed a new company called Artificial Muscle to commercialize their efforts.

Before proceeding with more detailed project accounts, however, I would like to mention an important, multifaceted person in the early growth and character of SRI.

Dr. Thomas C. Poulter (1897–1978)

While this book is primarily about SRI's research and innovations and not individual people, one person of the SRI Sciences Group deserves special mention—Dr. Thomas C. Poulter, known as "Doc." Doc Poulter was already a prominent scientist and explorer when he came to SRI, along with Dr. Jesse H. Hobson, about 2 years after its founding. Both were leaders at Chicago's Armour Research Foundation, and both would be instrumental in the early growth of SRI.[1] As SRI's second director, Hobson was a strong leader who brought SRI through its first period of significant growth. As associate director, Poulter helped SRI bring in its first funding for seismic and geologic research. Over the next 30 years, Poulter would become one of the most highly respected leaders at the Institute.

Poulter had been second in command in Admiral Richard Byrd's 1933 expedition to Antarctica and became the leader of the mission that would rescue Byrd when he was dying alone of carbon monoxide poisoning in a small shack near the South Pole. Following that first trip to Antarctica, Poulter became scientific director of Armour. He also made a second trip to Antarctica with Byrd in 1939.[2] During World

War II, Poulter was a consultant to the Secretary of the Navy, helping to develop the use of sonar on submarines. After the War he returned to Armour, and in March 1948, joined SRI as its associate director.[3]

Poulter's life at SRI was one of both leadership and the pursuit of his own investigations. The eclectic Dr. Poulter did research into the phenomena of explosions, examined seismic wave probing in everything from glaciers to potential oil reserves, and investigated the design and effects of explosive charges. After stepping down from management, he spent 14 years trying to understand the aural and sonic capabilities of undersea mammals and, ultimately, how to implant a new, bionic cochlea that would allow the deaf to hear.

An outgrowth of Doc Poulter's interest in the engineering use of explosives was a legacy called the Poulter Seismic Method.[B] This

---

[1] Armour Research Foundation became Illinois Institute of Technology Research Institute in 1963.

[2] A popular story about Doc Poulter needs retelling here from a write-up by Steve Miller who worked for Poulter in his early days at SRI. During Byrd's second expedition to Antarctica, a seismic scientist reporting to Poulter brought, as part of his equipment and supplies, fifty cases of whiskey. Poulter learned of this after the ship had left Antarctica, so he arranged with the US Navy to fly an airplane, a Ford Tri-

motor, into Little America for the first time ever. The plane brought in the needed seismic supplies that had been displaced by the liquor and left with the hapless scientist aboard. Poulter then personally poured all fifty cases through a hole in the ice, knowing that anyone with a high alcohol blood content could die in the extreme cold. Now, missing a seismic scientist, Poulter himself worked out how to launch plane seismic waves into the ice and earth. This seismic approach has come to carry his name.

[3] Poulter, while traveling in California, heard that the new SRI was looking for a leader. He returned to Armour Research Foundation where he was working and mentioned this to its director and his boss, Dr. Jesse H. Hobson. They both were disenchanted with Armour and came to SRI on March 1, 1948 (see Appendix B).

approach used an array of explosives placed atop a line of poles to approximate a plane wave acoustic signal that was better able to probe the earth or things resting on it, like glaciers. SRI used this method in the early 1950s on glaciers in Alaska and Greenland and to look for oil reserves in the Edwards Plateau in Texas.

In 1953, to continue to exploit this technology, Poulter formed a group called the Extreme Pressure and Explosives Laboratory with an initial staff of about six people. This was the beginning of 50 years of research conducted around the theme of explosives, their effects, and related phenomenology. The group grew rapidly, and in March 1954 in formal recognition of Poulter's contributions, the SRI Board voted to change the lab's name to Poulter Laboratories. That name was later changed to its present one, Poulter Laboratory.

Figure 11-1. Dr. Tom Poulter with an Año Nuevo Pup.

In 1961, Poulter visited an uninhabited island, Año Nuevo, off the California coast about 12 miles north of Santa Cruz. He was looking for a place to do atmospheric probing with sensors housed aboard missiles. But the island was full of seals and sea lions and he became so captivated by them (see Figure 11-1) that he soon abandoned his interest in upper atmospheric weather and became engaged in learning about these creatures. Though he would later come to investigate the role their sounds had in both communications and biological sonar, he first moved to protect this island so important to their breeding.

By May of 1962, Poulter had applied for and received a permit from the California Division of Parks and Recreation to study the marine inhabitants of Año Nuevo. Shortly after receiving the permit, Poulter applied to the National Science Foundation (NSF) for a grant to rehabitate the island and convert it to a marine biological research facility that would study the six marine mammals that frequented the island. Although his proposal was unsuccessful, he and colleagues from the

California Academy of Sciences and the University of California at Santa Cruz continued the work, reporting it in papers dated from 1965 through 1967. They then recommended that the State set Año Nuevo aside as a reserve to protect its unique marine life. Their recommendation was accepted, and on June 29, 1967, the island was closed to the public. Their research continues today under the management and guidance of marine biologists at UC Santa Cruz.[C]

As a more formal means to pursue these interests, Poulter started the SRI Biological Sonar Laboratory in about 1964 to investigate the remarkable ability of sea mammals such as seals and sea lions to detect and discriminate between objects under water. With other colleagues like Ronald Schusterman, Richard Hubbard, Danny Del Carlo, and Richard Jennings, he developed the first laboratory in North America devoted primarily to the study of the behavior and physiology of sea mammals.[D] Creating an underwater acoustic laboratory in an abandoned Nike antimissile site just off the shore of San Francisco Bay, Poulter would be among the first to assert that these mammals could use echolocation—that is, active sonar—to locate food. In thousands of trials in light and total darkness, California seals would be fed fish in acoustically anechoic chambers equipped with hydraphones. These tests showed for the first time a seal's ability to use underwater clicking sounds to quickly locate live or dead fish.[E] While some have questioned this sonar-like ability, most researchers now accept it.[F]

In 1967 Poulter turned to whale recordings by visiting the calving grounds of the gray whale off Baja California. Here he carefully sorted out the whales' variety of emissions from those of other creatures and from background noise coming from within and out of the water. He was able to isolate several gray-whale vocalizations including one that sounded like a loud rasp followed by a Chinese gong. It seemed to be an alert signal emitted when a helicopter or plane would pass at a low level. This signal caused the immediate cessation of all other whale sounds. The silence would then be ended with a series of echolocation clicks.[G]

In his pursuit of understanding sea mammals, Poulter was to record and analyze about 600 miles of magnetic tape of such sounds from seals, sea lions, and whales. He made 15 trips to the Arctic and 3 to the Antarctic pursuing the various species and their habitats.

One account of Poulter's insight in biological acoustics comes from Ted Griffin, who in 1962 became the first person to extensively interact with and train a killer whale, one he called Namu, for the British Columbia town near where it was captured. Griffin had been observing the whale for some time and had shown that it was not dangerous to humans. His dealings with Namu had gained media interest, and one day a film producer came to Seattle and suggested that, if Griffin could swim with Namu and show some conviviality, he could make a documentary about it. To explore this possibility, Griffin's brother jumped in the water first, some filming was done, and he emerged unscathed. Then, as Griffin started to swim with Namu, he was wondering how far the interaction could go. Would the whale come when he called? Would the whale call him? Would the whale indicate whether it was hungry?

Over the first few days in the water, the whale—no matter where he was—would come to Griffin, even in the dead of night. Not knowing exactly where Namu was, Griffin could sense its presence and would reach out, find his nose, and then caress Namu across its body. They became friends. Further, he would squeak to the whale and it would squeak back. So that he might learn more about communicating with Namu, Griffin asked Poulter to come and take some recordings and lend his insight. After several days of observations Poulter surprised Griffin by concluding that he, Griffin, was not sounding like the whale, but the whale was altering its normal vocalization to sound like Griffin's whale imitations! Griffin was astounded. The whale was consciously trying to reach out to him. Thereafter, their communication was enriched, as the whale would do its best to imitate Griffin even when he was doing tasks underwater not related to Namu directly. This little episode underscores Poulter's insight into the vocalization of undersea mammals.[H]

Doc Poulter died in 1978 at the age of 81 while working in his laboratory. One of his associates, George Duvall, who had come to lead Poulter Laboratory for a time, summarized his respect for this genuinely caring, imaginative, and energetic man with the three principles Poulter lived by:

- Never look back; that is, don't waste time regretting your mistakes. Learn what you can from them and go forward.

- Do not let your visions be bounded by the limitations imposed by your present knowledge and skills. If you want to do something worthwhile that requires knowledge or skills outside your present limits, learn what is needed if you can, get others to help where you can't, and forge ahead.

- Let your enthusiasm flow out and engulf others. It will inspire them and let your work go faster; it will be reflected and will also regenerate your own.[I]

He was one of SRI's best-loved people.

Radiation Chemistry

Very early in its history, SRI undertook several research contracts with the Atomic Energy Commission (AEC). Some of these were from the AEC's reactor division, which was searching for industrial uses for its radioactive waste. From these explorations came a working relationship with the AEC that would lend SRI some privileged positions in exploring the uses of radiation chemistry. One of these positions occurred in August 1954 when SRI became one of only three sites in the United States—and the only one in the West—to receive a very large public depository of unclassified AEC reports of interest to industry. This library was appropriate to SRI because of its ongoing interest in the industrial application of radiation. But it was a bit earlier, in late 1952, that SRI received from AEC-Brookhaven the largest radioactive source then outside the government. It was a 4,500-curie cobalt 60 gamma-ray source that SRI housed in an elaborate facility appropriate to its safe and effective use.[4, 5, J] Figuratively, part of that housing was the formation of a new laboratory in radiation engineering (see Figure 11-2).

The potential uses of radiation in industry were many, involving areas of biology, chemistry, and related engineering disciplines such as electronics. Some of the early research directions at SRI were

- Nondestructive testing of metal casings
- Nonthermal sterilization of foods and drugs whose composition precluded heating
- Prevention of sprouting in onions and potatoes
- Triggering of commercially important chemical reactions
- The structural effect of radiation on some plastics.

While only its earliest insights arose at SRI, this last area would come to have great influence on the local economy and would become the basis for a very large industrial company.

The person who was to head the SRI Radiation Engineering Laboratory was MIT

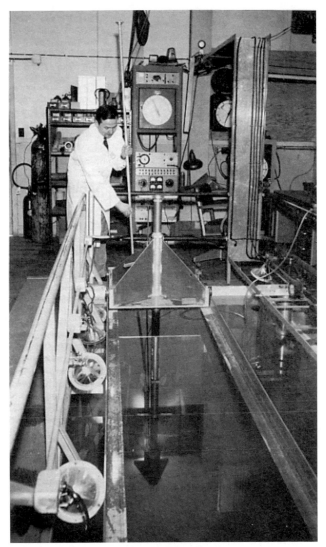

Figure 11-2. SRI's cobalt radiation "swimming pool" (Dr. Ed Kinderman with the pole).

chemical engineering graduate Paul Cook. Arriving in 1948, Cook became instrumental in the growth of radiation chemistry at SRI and saw in some of its results important commercial potential. As it would turn out, starting companies was simply a natural inclination for Cook. Before coming to SRI he had founded a wire company with his brother, and in 1951, while still affiliated with SRI, he started another company to provide lighter weight wire to the aircraft industry. Cook's new company, called Sequoia Process Corporation, was located in nearby Redwood City. As time progressed, and building on insights he was gaining from some of his SRI work on the radiation of plastics, Cook introduced that technology at Sequoia. The relevant latent product from the SRI experience had to do with polymer-based wire insulation, in particular, polyethylene.

---

[4] This cobalt source was powerful enough to be lethal if fully exposed to a human for 7 seconds. Therefore, part of the physical housing was a 720-cu-ft concrete underground storage chamber holding 5,400 gal of water. This was the cobalt storage area and adjacent to it, also underground, was an instrumentation room in which experiments could be run remotely. Joining the two rooms was an aluminum "window" to which both the source and the target could be moved for precisely controlled radiation exposure. (SRI's *Research for Industry*, 5(2), 1-9, January 1953).

[5] According to Ed Kinderman, a researcher in the same group (phone conversation, January 28, 2003), the cobalt source arrived not quite "as advertised." The neutron bombardment of the cobalt at Brookhaven was incomplete and thus developed only about half of its labeled output. Sam Taimuty of SRI got them to rebuild it and in turn helped set up the instrumentation to do the dosimetry for the whole chamber.

Polyethylene was light, cheap, and had good electrical insulation properties. It was a polymer in that it consisted of very long molecules that formed tiny, quite independent polymer crystals. The plastic didn't, however, hold up well under high temperature, and it didn't have much flow above the melting point of the crystals. Based on observations that dated back to the Manhattan Project and early 1950s work at General Electric, Cook and others began to explore how the properties of polyethylene were changed under radiation.[K] For example, how could the temperature-tolerant properties and the structural strength of such a plastic increase dramatically as a result of gamma radiation?

The main structural effect from radiation was called cross-linking, which would have two consequences for the polymer. One was greater stability at high temperatures, and the other was something called structural memory. As cross-linking implies, it is the forming of bonds between individual polymer molecules. Under radiation, hydrogen atoms were knocked off the polymers, permitting a cross-molecule bond to form. This connection essentially transformed the plastic from a two-dimensional structure to a three-dimensional structure, increasing its stability under high temperature. Irradiation also improved another weakness of polyethylene, stress cracking. Removing that weakness improved its electrical insulation property.

These and other innovations, including improving polyethylene's oxidation properties, grew in part out of a joint effort between SRI and Sequoia that began in early 1955 and involved four projects totaling about $60,000 in just over 2 years. From these efforts came the formulation for a new wire insulation product at Sequoia called Hyrad that could withstand continuous temperatures in the vicinity of 300°F (see Figure 11-3). Remarkably, the close working relationship helped the concept move from the laboratory to an online production state in less than one year.[L] While running Sequoia, Cook continued to participate at SRI until the spring of 1953.

However, within a few years an SRI board member, who had funded Sequoia to the extent of holding a controlling share, took over operation of the company. At this point, in 1957, Cook mortgaged his house and founded a second company to exploit this use of radiation chemistry. He called it Raychem and immediately began selling a flame retardant polyethylene coated wire, reaching profitability within seven months.[M]

At Raychem, the resourceful Cook also returned to the second important property of irradiated polyethylene—structural memory. This property was recognized during the time irradiation work was going on at SRI.[N,O,P] To realize this other attribute of cross-linking, the polyethylene mix, as augmented by the work mentioned above, is extruded at the desired

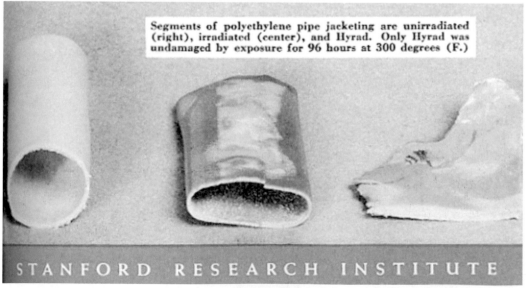

Segments of polyethylene pipe jacketing are unirradiated (right), irradiated (center), and Hyrad. Only Hyrad was undamaged by exposure for 96 hours at 300 degrees (F.)

STANFORD RESEARCH INSTITUTE

Figure 11-3. Temperature Consequences of unradiated versus irradiated polyethylene (SRI's *Research for Industry*, 8(4), 1-2, May 1956).

final diameter and irradiated. Then the tube is heated to soften it enough to expand it to a level that stretches but does not break the cross-link structure. Allowed to cool, it remains stable at this expanded diameter. This constitutes the packaged product. When the tubing is used, and on being reheated to about 125°-150°C, the tube returns to its original and smaller diameter, where it again stabilizes. This memory property enabled a brand new product line called heat-shrink tubing. With this and a continuing stream of useful products, Raychem grew to become a Fortune 500 company with revenues of $2 billion.

After many years of growing the company, Paul Cook rekindled his penchant, the founding of start-ups. After his tenure at Raychem was over, he also returned to the chairmanship of SRI and while here left this same entrepreneurial imprint on his alma mater (see Appendix B). Today, the indefatigable entrepreneur is again immersed in starting companies not necessarily related to SRI work but here on its campus.

Rod Polymers

Here, from the Internet is a description of a new type of sailcloth called Zylon, manufactured by Toyobo in Japan:[Q]

> For 1996, a new ultralight mainsail made from Dimension Polyant's PBO/Zylon cloth, a new 0.6 oz. nylon runner, and a heavy # 1 genoa were added to the inventory. PBO is a new cloth available from Dimension that exhibits 40% less stretch than traditional Kevlar. Even more impressive is its breaking strength. PBO has more than twice the tenacity of Kevlar. This allowed us to produce by far the lightest main possible. The 12,000-denier cloth used (normally 18,000- denier is used) is lighter than the material that would usually be used in a J-29 main. Built using Ultra Bond construction, the sail weighed only 28 lbs! It has performed extremely well due to its construction and minor changes in last year's design. Constant improvements in our spinnaker designs continue to make Banks spinnakers the fastest available.

From the *Denver Post* of September 27, 1999, the following describes the use of Zylon to protect fans at auto racing events:

> "Today's spectators can expect warm weather. And thanks to the IRL's 2-race-old tethering system, spectator injury or death because of on-track Indy-car accident debris might be tragedies of the past.

> The Suspension & Wheel Management System (SWEMS) is required on every car competing in the Radisson 200. IRL officials, along with car constructors Dallara, G Force and Riley & Scott, have worked vigorously to minimize the possibilities of wheel assemblies becoming detached during high-speed accidents. The SWEMS principle utilizes multiple restraints attached to a car's chassis and suspension. The

Figure 11-4. A Zylon spool and sails made from it (from the Toyobo web site, www.toyobo.co.jp).

restraints are made of FIA-approved Zylon, which has a breaking strength of 5 tons."

We are surrounded by and, to no small extent, composed of polymers. Some are natural such as silk, natural rubber, cellulose, and proteins. Others are synthetic such as plastics, nylon, and synthetic rubber. Polymers are extremely large molecules composed of many structural subunits, called monomers, which are linked repetitively into long chains. A polymer molecule may contain from 1,000 to more than 250,000 atoms and have a molecular weight as high as several million. By contrast, a molecule of methane, CH_4, has a weight of 16. Polymers have a lot of forms and display an enormous variety of useful properties such as films, membranes in the body, wool, violin strings, and solid fuel rockets. The repeating units of a polymer, composed primarily of carbon and hydrogen, can also be linked together in a linear fashion to give the extremely long molecules useful in fibers. Those necessary for cloth and fiber-like forms are called rod polymers and are the root of an important SRI contribution known as the PBZ family.

In the early 1970s, Dr. Jim Wolfe was a polymer chemist at the Air Force's Wright Laboratories in Dayton, Ohio. He had been working on rod polymers there in search of an ultra-light, ultra-strong material for military aircraft. He came to SRI in early 1977 with ideas on how to continue that research and sought sponsorship from the Air Force Office of Scientific Research and his former lab.

The SRI team built a new class of polymers whose properties were sufficiently novel that

several patents were issued on their composition and synthesis. The family is called PBZ— for poly(2,6-benzothiazole)—and its synthesis is difficult. It involves selected monomers that interact in a phosphoric acid bath to form the so-called doping polymers that are then used in another solution and drawing process to form the final fiber. The PBZ axial ratios may be very high—that is, very long and very thin—and, in this case, provide the basis for building a very strong fiber (see Figure 11-5).

The polymerization process carries some risk. Bock Loo, a former engineering assistant in the lab at SRI where this process was invented, mentions that the monomers were not only difficult to make but were somewhat toxic.

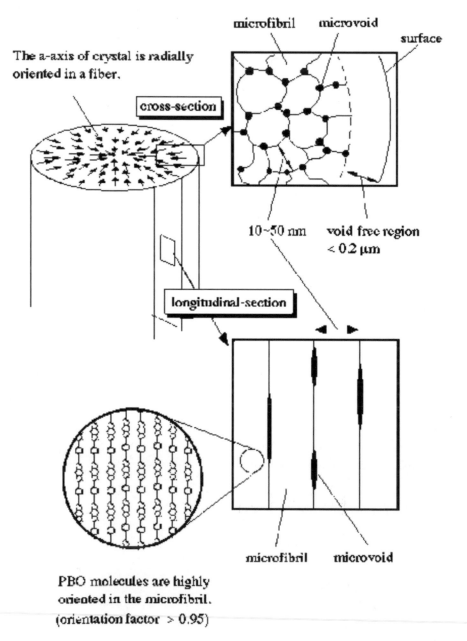

Figure 11-5. A depiction of the polymer molecules within the fiber.

Masks were required because the mere presence of the yellow material made everyone sneeze; getting any of it on ones clothes meant an immediate trip to a sink to wash it off. Thus, most of the work was done under exhaust hoods. As the properties improved, the batch sizes grew from grams to as much as 30 pounds.[R]

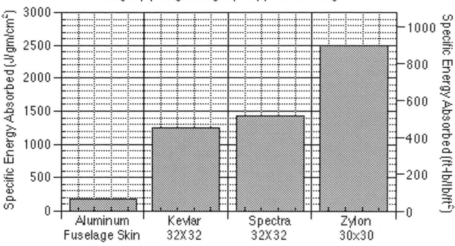

Figure 11-6. Comparison of kinetic energy absorption by various barriers.

Early fibers from the PBZ family displayed encouraging properties: light weight, stretch resistance, very high strength, heat resistance, and nonabsorption of water. To help converge on the best combination of product and process, Wolfe's group tested each fiber created and recorded the process and the end results. These were then subjected to computer analysis and the process was repeated. SRI received several patents in this area with awards from 1980 to 1988. The specific one for the PBZ family was applied for in 1982 and issued in August of 1985.[S]

In the late 1980s, SRI licensed the manufacturing process for its rod polymer to Dow Chemical. After investing about $1 million to reach a manufacturing capability, Dow gave up and licensed it in turn to the Japanese textile company, Toyobo.[6] By 1998 Toyobo had placed Zylon, its product name for the SRI polymer, on the market. Zylon is now appearing in a wide range of applications where strength and lightness are critical. As one might expect, Zylon's main competitor is Kevlar™, but as will be shown in the few applications to follow, Zylon's attributes surpass Kevlar and other alternatives.

One of the important uses of Zylon is now being explored at NASA and SRI: the protection of airline passengers from the lethal release of turbine blades from engine failure. Normal insulation-filled aluminum airplane skins are not very effective against such failures. Zylon sheets, however, are so strong that adhering them to the outside of the interior airplane walls can be an effective aid in increasing passenger protection. In SRI gas gun tests, 25-gram projectiles, simulating turbine fragments, were accelerated to 80 meters per second against aluminum and several fabrics made of high-strength polymer yarns. These tests demonstrated that aramids (Kevlar™), polyethylenes (Spectra), and polybenzoxazole (Zylon) absorbed over 5 times more kinetic energy than aluminum fuselage skin on an area density basis. The specific energy absorption (SEA), which we define as the energy absorbed per unit area density, of one particular Zylon weave was 15 times that of 2024-T3 aluminum, as shown in Figure 11-6. Results of experiments to investigate the effect of weave tightness and multiple fabric plies suggest that SEA increases linearly with a real density, independent of weave tightness and number of plies.

Similar advantages over Kevlar can be seen from the ballistic tests at NASA's Glenn Research Center shown in Figure 11-7. Here 1.9 lb titanium discs were fired at 1,600 feet per second at the inside of a cylindrical aluminum structure simulating a section of a jet engine fan enclosure. The wall consisted of a thin aluminum skin, five layers of either Zylon or Kevlar™, and on the outside, a 1-inch-thick

---

[6] This technology was one pursued by SRI's exclusive commercialization agent at the time, CommTech International. When Dow was ready to abandon the manufacture of rod polymers, it was CommTech who solicited Toyobo's interest and facilitated the relicensing. This license had produced considerable royalties for SRI since about 1998 and Toyobo is still trying to enter Zylon's perhaps most lucrative market, bullet-proof clothing. (Conversation with Bonnar Cox, May 20, 2004.)

layer of honeycomb aluminum. The tests again show the superiority of Zylon.

Other, more fundamental properties of Zylon are those shown in Figure 11-8 from the Toyobo web site.

A very recent and interesting application for Zylon is in golf clubs. Though it may seem a natural for golf club shaft design, and it is, that's not the unusual aspect of its use. Instead, it's in the club head design itself. Today's large-faced metal "woods" are made of very strong lightweight materials such as titanium. But the hollow or lightly filled volume of these heads undergoes a distortion at impact that represents an energy loss. The tension on steel reinforcing rods in concrete construction gave David Boone, club designer for Zevo Golf, the idea of putting the club head permanently under tension. In a very innovative step for golf club design, he tied the top and base of the head together through a stretched membrane of Zylon. Zylon's lightness and high tensile strength have made this new driver a novel addition to golf.[T]

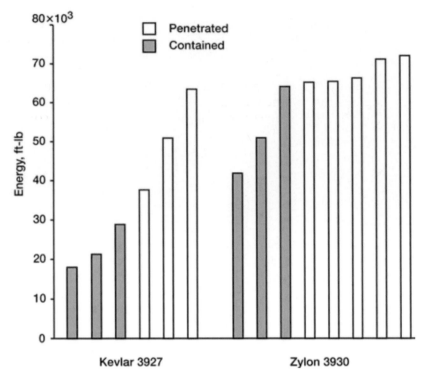

Figure 11-7. Projectile tests at NASA comparing Kevlar™ with Zylon.

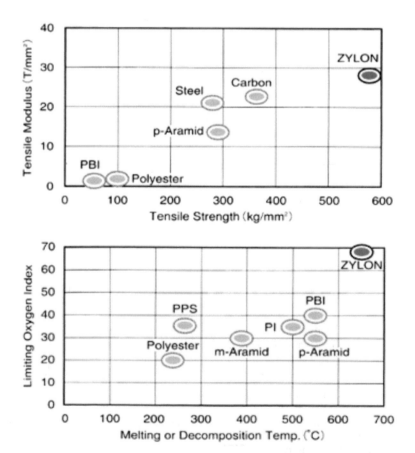

Figure 11-8. Comparative tensile and melting characteristics of Zylon (from the Toyobo web site).

11–10

Modeling Chemical Processes

As with many aspects of present day science and engineering, mathematical models and available computing power are combining to play a huge role in the design of chemical processes.[U] Often there are a variety of ways to manufacture a substance, so it is important to discover the most efficient means, the process with the least environmental impact, or the one that yields the purest product. Today, a lot of this exploration uses a computer code developed by Stanford professor W.C. Reynolds, called STANJAN. The main objective of the code is to calculate the chemical species composition that result when a given elemental input composition has been brought to thermal equilibrium at temperatures and pressures of interest. Using that code, however, requires a set of thermodynamic input parameters associated with every elemental or molecular species involved in the chemistry of the system.[7] It is in this later area of measuring or evaluating the needed parameters that SRI's Materials Research Lab has contributed for over three decades. Here are a few examples.

Much of the SRI work surrounds high-temperature reactions such as those used in combustion or refining processes. One long-term client, the Gas Research Institute, has a continuing interest in catalysts that will not only produce the most efficient flame but will not be consumed prematurely in the combustion process. SRI has modeled the behavior of a range of metallic catalysts, showing which will or won't have commercially acceptable lifetimes.

There is another, more pervasive combustion process in the engine of your car. In the early 1920s, the Ethyl Corporation introduced tetraethyl and tetramethyl lead to effectively increase the octane or anti-knock performance of gasoline. Those additives, along with MTBE, have serious environmental impacts and have been generally outlawed. Another, somewhat less toxic additive, called MMT, contains manganese and has been used in limited amounts overseas, in Canada, and to a lesser extent in the U.S. (under a waiver granted by the U.S. Environmental Protection Agency or EPA). But the emission of elemental manganese in the exhaust gases could be a problem, and SRI has worked for Ethyl to clarify this issue by modeling the combustion process when MMT is present. The SRI work indicates that manganese can be captured prior to emission as a solid, manganese phosphate. But the complex four-way interchange between the suppliers of additives, the automobile industry, environmental groups, and the EPA concerning MMT is ongoing.

In the meantime, another SRI effort reflecting environmental concern is that for the government's National Renewable Energy Lab. This work involves the complex chemical processes in the energy conversion of biomass. Here SRI has developed a STANJAN thermodynamic database for the 20 or so constituent elements that occur in various biomass compositions for NREL to use in modeling the various combustion and gasification processes.

The last two efforts to be mentioned here are the production of titanium metal and the white pigment in paint, titanium dioxide. The importance of titanium and its alloys to our national defense prompted DARPA to investigate more cost-effective processes for its production. In this case SRI has developed a new fluidized-bed chemical vaporization process for the deposition of pure titanium or its alloys using intermediate compounds (precursors) like titanium tetrachloride. SRI's chemical modeling of the vapor deposition process was key to the development of that fluidized-bed process. Curiously, another process in which titanium tetrachloride is an important intermediate is the production of the all-important ingredient in paint, titanium dioxide. This oxide is the principal whitener in all paints and because it is a very important product of Du Pont, they asked SRI to help refine both the chlorination and oxidation steps of that production process. Not only did SRI successfully complete that modeling

---

[7] Needed for each atomic or molecular species are the various energy absorption and production parameters, such as enthalpy and entropy, important when heat, pressure, and temperature are varied. These thermodynamic parameters are often determined experimentally at SRI using mass spectrometry in specially designed chambers called Knudsen cells. While the species to be examined are chosen by clients, the results are often placed in the large international database for such information called the JANAF tables.

investigation, but in doing so found previously unknown chemical species that helped more accurately model the chemistry of Du Pont's manufacturing process.

These few examples, out of hundreds, depict a range of important contributions SRI is making to the chemical process industry and the mitigation of such processes on the environment.

Oxidation Chemistry

There is no more important element to us than oxygen. By weight, it comprises about half of our bodies and, curiously, half the planet itself. Through the dynamic processes that oxygen enables, it is essential to all living things. When we inhale, oxygen forms the basis for our energy absorption and the temperature stabilization of our anatomy. But as much as anything, oxygen is associated with what we normally think of as aging, the decomposition of almost all materials into oxides. Our adapting and modulating those processes for different purposes, from near-benign environmental protection to explosive energy release, has been the focus of the SRI's chemistry laboratories for several decades. We will mention here just a few of those lab's notable accomplishments.[V]

High Energy Materials

In the core of the solid propellant rockets that put the space shuttle into orbit there is an oxidation process of extremely high energy. Given a certain rocket size, that process effectively determines the allowable payload of the shuttle. Today that reaction consists mainly of a fuel made up of powdered aluminum and hydrocarbons, an oxidizer of ammonium perchlorate (AP), and a binder to hold them evenly dispersed. The energy potential and efficiency of such a fuel mixture can be viewed in terms of the velocity of the exhaust gas. For obvious reasons, this fuel-oxidizer combination also needs to be as stable as possible prior to ignition.

Around 1990, the SRI Chemistry Lab was working for the Office of Naval Research (ONR) on a program to develop new explosives, specifically by exploring those oxidizers that had high energy but didn't involve the caustic and other negative properties of chlorine. They had been concentrating on a particular type of organic structure called cubanes, from the cubic form in which eight carbon atoms were arranged. Because of the inherent high bonding strain of this structure, the ONR community believed it would have very high energy potential. The particular form of the cubanes ONR had targeted involved compounds of nitrogen called N,N-dinitramines. But no one in that community, including SRI, had been able to synthesize them.

SRI senior chemist Dr. Jeffrey Bottaro had an insight. He believed that the dinitramide salts themselves, without the difficult covalently attached cubane configuration, would be more easily synthesized, have the needed stability, and provide the energy performance sought over the chlorine-based oxidizers in use. He synthesized a new compound called ADN, or ammonium dinitramide with the formula $NH_4N(NO_2)_2$. When ADN was put in propellant form, this new oxidizer would demonstrate both an increased stability and a predictable increase in lift capacity over current propellant formulations. Dr. Rob Schmitt, Bottaro's colleague and supervisor, calculated that ADN would provide an 8% percent increase in the shuttle's payload. Even better, the avoidance of chlorine in the formulation meant that it would be more environmentally friendly, produce none of the chlorine-based compounds inimical to the upper atmosphere, and have fewer "contrail" signatures than the present oxidizer used in the shuttle. The lack of an exhaust trail signature would also be a strategic advantage for rocket-based weapons.

SRI received four patents on the material and its manufacturing processes. When this new propellant will be introduced is uncertain, but the Army and Navy are exploring the use of ADN for both environmental and efficiency reasons.[W] The Navy also believes ADN will reduce the weight of rocket motors by 40% and so is trying to reduce the manufacturing cost of ADN to about $100 per pound.[X] Morton Thiokol is currently working with the Navy to increase the specific impulse (effectively the exhaust velocity) by about 20% over the AP oxidizers through the addition of aluminum hydride as a fuel.[Y]

An interesting aspect of this story flows from the competitive intricacies of the Cold War.[Z] Bottaro and his SRI colleagues were attending a 1993 meeting of the American Institute of Aeronautics & Astronautics (AIAA) when they heard a group of Russians giving a paper on the same ADN-based propellants that they had built. As it turned out, the Russians had been secretly using such propellants in the missiles of the former Soviet Union since the 1970s and the Russian delegation was in this country ultimately hoping to market them. Their presentation was a solid affirmation of the SRI approach, but their history of secrecy, of course, meant there was to be no challenge to the SRI patent position. Schmidt and Bottaro later tried, unsuccessfully, to bring these Russian scientists to SRI to continue work on ADN along with SRI researchers.

The future prospects for ADN are emerging and amazingly varied. The European auto supplier Autoliv developed the salt guanylurea dinitramide as a state-of-the-art airbag propellant devoid of any physical or toxicological hazards, only to have TRW patent the same material, precluding worldwide marketing of guanylurea-based airbags by Autoliv. In the military area, the British are exploring ADN as a potential propellant for air-to-air missiles, and ADN offers unparalleled performance prospects as a major ingredient in torpedo warheads.

There are even medicinal applications for this broadly useful compound. In the spectrum of psychoactive drugs, most are nitrogenous and in the physiology of the brain have a negative (base) pH. They are also in the form of positive ions that have difficulty in transitioning the barriers between the blood and the brain. Usually, complex indigenous proteins aid this transition, but they have a very narrow range of drugs with which they can work. Dinitramide salts, however, have the unique ability to transport a wide range of organic ions across such biological membranes. Thus, ADN shows promise as an agent for delivering pharmaceuticals to the brain in situations not previously enabled. SRI is now obtaining a patent on this pharmacological use of ADN. So, the technological possibilities for this simple material are substantial.

Oxidation in Environmental Chemistry—Organic Compounds

When considering ways to clean up or prevent harm to the earth's environment, at least two questions about the oxidizing transformation of organic materials are important to answer:

- What are the chemical processes that can occur?
- What are the rate constants of such reactions?

The answer to the first question identifies what products lie in the chain of decomposition, including which of those are toxic. The answer to the second question defines how long these products will be around. Simply put, but extraordinarily complex, the net rate of change in concentration of a given chemical is the sum of all the equilibrium and kinetic processes that affect it in a specific environment. (See box for a partial list.[AA])

Unfortunately, observations and measurements intended to extrapolate or generalize are not all that useful. For example, measuring the depletion rate of most chemicals is not very helpful because isolating the entangled processes and adequately defining what is often a complex environment make extrapolation to another site almost impossible. The relative contribution of different processes can change with location and season. This difficulty leaves only the option of trying to identify the few, most important processes involved with a given chemical in either water or air and then trying to understand and quantify them in the laboratory.

Although we think easily of oxygen's attraction to metals, as in the rusting of iron, oxygen actually has a much greater affinity for organic compounds. Given that the world now produces a billion tons of organic chemicals each year, some of it will be inadvertently introduced into the streams, rivers, and coastal waters around industrial cities or areas of concentrated use. Once such material is introduced into ground or surface water, there is ample opportunity for the hydrolysis of such compounds (their reaction with the H^+ and OH^- ions of water) with unknown consequences. Because of the implied threat to our environment, SRI has been exploring the hydrolysis of organic chemicals for at least two decades.[BB]

ECOLOGICAL RISK ASSESSMENT

Process	Parameters
Atmosphere	
Photolysis	Light Intensity
Oxidation	Oxidant concentrations
Rain out	Precipitation rate, sticking coefficient
Transport	Wind velocity
Surface Waters	
Volatilization	Preference of substance for air or water, surface roughness
Sorption/bio-uptake	Organic/lipid content of sediments, organisms
Hydrolysis	pH, temperature
Photolysis	Light intensity
Biotransformations	Organism population, nutrients, temperature, and pH

Because the transformation of many organic chemicals under hydrolysis can either reduce or increase their potential toxic effects on biological communities, the government agencies responsible for water quality, such as the Environmental Protection Agency (EPA), are very interested in such processes. And because some of the inimical products can have half-lives ranging from seconds to centuries, we need to fully understand these processes in both fresh and marine waters. Let's look at some examples of the EPA's long relationship with SRI in this area.

SRI has contributed to EPA regulations both by developing the general methods and protocols for testing the presence of questionable material as well as by determining the properties of certain individual, potentially harmful chemicals as they are created and transformed in the earth's environment. For the past 20 years SRI's chemistry labs have helped EPA and its overseas counterpart, the Organization for Economic Cooperation and Development (OECD), define test methods for hydrolysis, photochemical reactions, and sorption in soil[8] as well as vapor pressure and volatilization models for dispersion in air. These SRI methods were incorporated into EPA testing procedures starting in 1982 and have continued to the present. Also, the 2002 OECD methods for photochemical protocol were developed at SRI.

One example of the pursuit of individual chemicals is the case of a specific member of the family of dioxins. Certain important toxins in our modern environment come from a family called polychlorinated dioxins. Among other sources, these are the byproduct of pesticides or the incineration of chlorinated wastes. One such highly toxic member of that family is called tetrachlorodibenzodioxin or TCDD. It was one of the many toxic chemicals that oozed to the surface in New York's Love Canal episode in the late 1970s. Several years later, at the request of the EPA, SRI set out to learn more about how this hazardous chemical behaved in the natural environment. If it indeed were a present threat, how long would it remain so? Two relevant properties were examined: (1) how easily would TCDD evaporate, that is, what was its volatility in both water and air and, (2) what were its persistence properties under photolysis or exposure to sunlight?[cc]

To gauge the former, Tom Podoll, Helen Jaber, and Ted Mill measured the vapor pressure, solubility, and diffusion properties of TCDD under a variety of conditions. From these measurements they could estimate that TCDD in water would have half-lives of about 32 days

[8] Soil sorption is the integration of a chemical into soil either by absorption or by adherence to its surface.

in lakes and ponds and about 16 days in rivers. Given some assumptions, its persistence in air and soil were also estimated. The results of this work became part of the EPA's assessment of TCDD and other dioxins that, among other things, led to the EPA's emissions standards for flue gas in 1993.

The Experimentation, Science, and Utility of Explosions

When you first learn that something as violent, rapid, and turbulent as an explosion has very predictable and often precise utility, even at large scale sizes, it seems counterintuitive. The shocks from such events are literally over in a flash and the effects on materials are varied and complex. Nevertheless, for the past 50 years SRI's Poulter Laboratory has followed and contributed to the experimental and theoretical science of explosion-produced shock waves and their effects on all kinds of materials and structures. SRI's investigations have covered the control and influence of a very wide range of sizes and types of explosions as well as their use in simulating very high-energy events that could not be housed in an affordable experimental setting.[DD]

This research capability began with what are called terminal observations, a repetition of similar explosions or shots in an attempt to characterize what happened. This method used optical instruments to image effects observable on the outside surfaces of materials. Then came the ability to directly measure some of the parameters of the explosion itself and the response of materials to it. Finally, with the advent of computer modeling, each shot can incur greater experimental design, much more sophisticated and multidimensional monitoring, as well as more detailed post-experiment analysis.

The evolution of techniques for studying explosive effects at SRI began in the mid-1950s and continues today. One of the early uses of explosives in Poulter Lab was to simulate the effect of nuclear radiation on ballistic missile nose cones. SRI undertook years of investigation for the

DoD to determine the resilience of missiles to a variety of explosions under real and simulated conditions. To conduct the simulations, SRI built an experiment site in the foothills east of San Francisco Bay. There, explosive charges could be fired safely with minimal disturbance. As urban development drew closer, the site was moved eastward to a new 480-acre location near Livermore, CA.

As the modeling and understanding of explosive effects grew, so did the range of problems Poulter Lab could address. From the idealized nose cone environments of the outer atmosphere that enabled the simulation of shock loading from x-rays, the work moved to the more complex interactions near ground level. Here, the Lab's increased modeling and experimental capabilities were extended to address damage to structures, vehicles, and military systems from the airblast produced by nuclear weapons. Figure 11-9 shows Poulter Lab's 8-foot-diameter, 250-foot shock tube, driven by explosive charges, to simulate nuclear airblast conditions on specific targets. Obviously, this work helped us better understand how different materials and

Figure 11-9. SRI's Corral Hollow test site near Livermore, CA, showing the eight-foot shock tube in use.

structures could survive a nuclear attack.

Not all of SRI's nuclear test experimentation would be simulated. As the United States continued its nuclear testing program after World War II, SRI became involved in assessing directly the blast and shock effects of a nuclear explosion. SRI's involvement started with high-explosive preparatory tests at Dugway Proving Ground in Utah very early in the 1950s, later moving to the Mercury Nevada Test Site north of Las Vegas, and to a lesser extent in the Pacific Proving Ground where much larger weapons were tested. SRI would be one of the few laboratories outside the government to make measurements on such tests, which would eventually include atmospheric, near-ground, and under-ground locations.[9] The relevant SRI groups were Poulter Laboratory and the Physics Division. After the moratorium on above-ground tests in the 1960s, Poulter Laboratory continued measurements on underground tests and in the process developed new measurement techniques sensors, and gauges that would find a wide range of uses.

With this brief background, then, in what way did these laboratories make their greatest contributions? Very conservatively, one could easily recognize three: instrumentation, overpressure load simulation, and modeling material failure. We will cover them briefly in that order.

Instrumentation

The first instrumentation problems were associated with measuring the shock wave effects in the air and ground surrounding a detonation. It was 1951 when SRI first tried using commercial equipment to instrument and record a nuclear test. It quickly became clear that the commercial sensors and instruments of that day could not cope with the range or magnitude of the variations witnessed. So, SRI immediately began a program of gauge design, construction, and use that would continue for over two decades. At first, the engineers were delighted when even one gauge survived the nuclear blast long enough to record even one millisecond of data. SRI went on to build gauges that would accurately measure the displacement and velocity of the ground movement and the important pressure

dynamics induced by the primary damage mechanism, airblast.

Next, given the multiplicity of such sensors needed across the test site, SRI designed a clever and cost-saving data acquisition system. These arrangements multiplexed data retrieval onto the power leads to the remote sensors and then to the instrumentation vans where data recording took place. The system had variable bandwidths, high dynamic range, and its multiplexing design saved enormously in instrumentation costs. The system remained in use until about 1982.

Even with ground and airblast results now in hand, the complexity of extending them into exactly what would happen inside the affected materials was difficult. Thus came the second area of SRI contribution to instrumentation, the amount of stress and strain in the affected materials.

To learn something about how much strength was needed in a material for it to survive some specific blast, it was necessary to become quantitative about that material under shock-wave impact. Keep in mind two things about instrumenting material in this environment. One is the extremely high pressure involved and, just as important, the range of pressures that must be accurately recorded. These meant that the instrument not only had to survive but had to accurately and dynamically measure a pressure span of as much as 4 or 5 orders of magnitude. The SRI-built material-impact sensors were novel indeed. They were small and thin enough to be attached to or even easily embedded inside a material. For the first time, then, the effect of shock waves could be measured *within* the material being examined rather than from visual inferences of its outside surfaces. Today, the manganin and ytterbium piezoresistive transducers that SRI invented are the standard by which all other sensors used in dynamic pressure measurement are judged.[10, EE] Next, then, comes the question of simulation.

---

[9] Other SRI participation was in the areas of radar and communication effects. These involved the high altitude nuclear tests of 1958 and, after the Soviet moratorium violations, those of 1962. See Chapter 9.

[10] SRI's Dr. Douglas Keogh and his colleagues designed many of these novel sensors. One of the most notable was a gauge that would linearly sense an overpressure of over one megabar (a bar being ~14.5 psi), perhaps a thousand times what existing gauges could do. It used the piezoresistive characteristics of a copper-manganese-nickel alloy called manganin and under that name it remains the principal choice for any strong overpressure measurement.

Overpressure Simulation

Computer modeling and simulation helped build and make practical a theoretical basis for shock waves and their predictable impact on materials and structures. This development lent a greater value to experimental design and a basis on which to explain results. For example, Poulter Lab pioneered the development of above-ground conventional explosive techniques to simulate nuclear airblast and ground shock effects. Similarly, sheet explosives could simulate x-ray loading on specific materials and structures. To represent the effect of slower-moving shock waves, the large shock tube in Figure 11-9 was built and instrumented. Other shock wave simulations were successfully applied underwater in large pools added to the SRI test sites. These pools were used to study the effect of underwater shocks on submarine models, underwater mines, and obstacles in surf zones and on beaches.

Another dimension to simulation is the use of scale models and how to interpret their behavior in terms of the structure they represent. Poulter Lab became a world leader in understanding the advantages and limitations in this field, and that work is continuing. Some examples include the modeling of missile silos subjected to nuclear attack, underground tunnels being attacked by conventional weapons, nuclear reactors undergoing core disruption, trains in derailment accidents, and the safety of automobiles under various crash scenarios.

Modeling Material Failure

Finally, there is the damage to material itself. Members of Poulter Laboratory developed a class of material models that describe how materials fail. This class, called nucleation and growth and fragmentation (NAG-FRAG) began with physical observations of microcracks and voids that occur naturally in materials and that grow and coalesce under shock wave loading. The models were originally developed to describe the nucleation and growth flaws in space heatshield materials but were then extended to cover several materials, even rocks. This SRI work has made a lasting theoretical and practical contribution and is described at greater length in a later section.

Shockwave-Produced Diamonds

A more modest use of explosions occurs in a laboratory or factory setting where they can create the very high temperatures and pressures used in metallurgy. It was 1959 and SRI metallurgist Paul De Carli was trying to make high-pressure versions of some minerals by using explosions to shock-load them.[FF] One of the minerals he chose was graphite. In the post-shock residue, Paul noticed some particles that were hard enough to scratch sapphire, had a density higher than fully dense graphite, and revealed faint lines of the x-ray diffraction pattern of diamond superposed on the pattern for graphite. This was an exciting discovery but since De Carli's technical director, George Duval, had just read a classified report that said that diamond could not be synthesized by shock methods, it took two years before the result could be published.[GG] Concurrent with the submission of the paper for publication, and in one of its early excursions into trying to profit from its intellectual property, SRI applied for a patent in July 1961. The diamonds produced by the SRI process had no relevance to gem production but were appropriate for the coating of abrasion tools whose value industry was just beginning to discover.[11]

A vice-president of Allied Chemical saw the paper and contacted SRI. By mid-1962, this led to a $250,000 research contract, complete with a royalty clause. Allied became so eager that it started pilot plant production of shock-synthesized diamonds before the scientific basis of the process was fully understood.[12] As that understanding grew, and after exploring a British patent on shock synthesis, a continuation-in-part was filed on the patent. U.S. Patent 3,328,019 was issued to SRI on March 1,1966.

But Du Pont was also working on the shock synthesis of diamonds. Their Patent 3, 401,919 was granted in 1968, and it appeared to infringe on SRI's. To restrict entrance to a budding market, Du Pont had also bought up the rights to the earlier British patent and, rather than

[11] In 1955 researchers at the GE Laboratory developed a very high pressure and temperature process (about 1 million psi and 3,000 degrees F) to create synthetic diamonds. That is the leading industrial diamond production process today, with only a small fraction of that being produced using shock techniques.

[12] According to an online reference (www.mrw.interscience.wiley.com, September 4, 2004) shock-produced diamonds were first manufactured in 1961, making the Allied effort perhaps the first.

sorting out their respective rights, Allied and Du Pont decided to sign mutual cross-licensing agreements. Unfortunately for SRI, Allied then decided that the market was still too small to support both large companies and Allied dropped out. As it has turned out, the market has grown considerably since.

Du Pont treated shock synthesis like a small business and spun off a quasi-independent small division to commercially produce industrial diamonds. With the expiration of the patents, Japanese and Chinese companies have also been making shock-synthesized diamond. In the end SRI had secured a very early patent on an increasingly important process but, in retrospect, its license agreement simply failed to protect its interest.

Other Applications

SRI's measurement insight and experimental innovations became a springboard for many other types of practical research applications. Explosives and propellants have been used to develop a technique for simulating the ground motions produced in earthquakes. To characterize the hazards associated with a pipeline rupture and subsequent ignition, Poulter Lab conducted the world's largest natural gas fire test in an isolated section of the Canadian pipeline. In anticipation of the growing interest in hydrogen as a fuel, SRI has performed extensive studies of hydrogen explosions.

Other studies include ways to neutralize terrorist bombs and to harden structures against their use. One such application relies on special methods for strengthening existing windows so that glass fragments do not fly inside the building from a bomb outside the building. Another is the lining of airplane fuselage and baggage containers with another SRI invention, the rod polymer called Zylon (see a previous section on rod polymers). Innovations and experiments such as these have kept SRI's Poulter Laboratory vital for nearly the entire history of SRI.

The Modeling of Fractures—FRASTA

To most of us, a crack is just a crack, perfectly random, and the only story it tells is that whatever broke wasn't strong enough. But to Don Shockey and Takao Kobayashi of SRI's Center for Fracture Physics, a crack is a special kind of fracture with an intriguing story to tell.[HH] When an aircraft engine turbine disc fractures or a bridge or building collapses or a refinery vessel fails, considerable damage or loss of life can occur. Whenever the collective costs are high, it becomes critical to determine why a failure happened. For this field of fracture analysis, SRI has built one of the world's best tools for probing fractures and for using their characteristics to find not only what weakness caused the fracture but also the time history of the event itself. The name of this tool is FRASTA, which stands for Fracture-Surface Topography Analysis.

To easily see the utility of such an analytical tool, take the case of a crack opening on just one side of the wall of a 22-year-old boiler tube in a fossil fuel power plant. Using FRASTA, SRI was able to tell when the failure process began, the rates and growth history of the crack, and the effects on such growth of any chemical cleanings and hot starts. All this information helped define the future operating conditions and maintenance procedures needed to prolong the life of the plant.[13,II]

The foundation for developing the FRASTA system began over 30 years ago in work SRI was doing for the Department of Defense. Part of one study on whether an antiballistic missile defense system was feasible was the question of the kill mechanisms for incoming warheads. To the extent that another nuclear device was to provide that mechanism, it was necessary to understand how the heat from the x-rays of a nearby explosion would affect the material of the incoming warhead. The likely effect would be a heat-induced shock wave in the impacted material. But would the material be destroyed?

In 1967, SRI staff members Dick Crewdson, Lynn Seaman, and Troy Barbee began working on simulation experiments using a gas gun to generate shock waves whose features could be specified. They tested various target specimens and then tried to give consistent, quantitative characterizations to the fractures and other damage they saw. It was metallurgist Barbee who drew the relationship between the

---

[13] More recently, FRASTA was used in settling several lawsuits, where it helped pinpoint the source of very costly failures.

observed fractures and the well-studied field of metallurgical phase evolution—equations that described how fractures grew under tensile stress. Would they apply in the case of temperature-induced stress? The answer was yes, and the team developed a mathematical basis for the nucleation[14] and fracturing of several materials under different impact intensities. Although Crewdson and Barbee left SRI in 1969 and 1971, respectively, Don Curran and Don Shockey joined the effort and succeeded in developing crack nucleation and growth (NAG) rate models. The models were verified for

Figure 11-10. Dr. Takao Kobayashi and a FRASTAscope.

simple metals whose fractures arose from x-ray bombardment in underground nuclear tests. But, when used successfully to predict failures in nonmetallic objects such as phenolics, on various size scales, in purely kinetic impacts as well as static loading, the model's greater generality became appreciated. NAG became the basis for crack propagation predictions by focusing on the small microstructure failures occurring at the tip of a macrocrack. The technique would be applied to a wide range of failure problems for the next 20 years.

At the time, most failure analysts routinely examined and interpreted fracture surface features to ascertain the fracture origin, the propagation direction, and the general type of loading. But these evaluations were heavily qualitative. Being able to suggest improvements in structural design that would deny future failures required more quantitative information about the loading conditions and the nucleation and growth history of the crack.

That information just wasn't decipherable at the time. Additionally, most fractures involve three dimensions and any comprehensive model needed to reflect those dimensions.

In 1982, Takao Kobayashi came to SRI having the notion that three-dimensional, quantitative modeling of fractures was possible (see Figure 11-10). With the help of his SRI coworkers Don Shockey, Yvonne Wu, and Jim Kempf, he was able to offer a major advance in fracture mechanics. He understood that the three-dimensional roughness of fracture surfaces held the needed information about the loads that caused the failure as well as the kinetics of the fracture event itself. More significantly, he thought the information could be extracted. As a material is loaded, it first deforms elastically. Upon further loading, certain sites of defect or points of geometric load concentration begin to deform inelastically. Still more loading produces microcracks around the inelastic zones. At points where small separations arise, the material becomes stress-free and—very important—the material captures in its topography the preseparation deformation. This process proceeds in the direction of crack formation, leaving a trail of inelastic

---

[14] Nucleation in fractures is the process whereby specific points in a material, where the material becomes inelastic, become the sites of fracture initiation. It has to do with the microcomposition and structure of the material, the type and configuration of stress it is under, and even the loading that produced the damage.

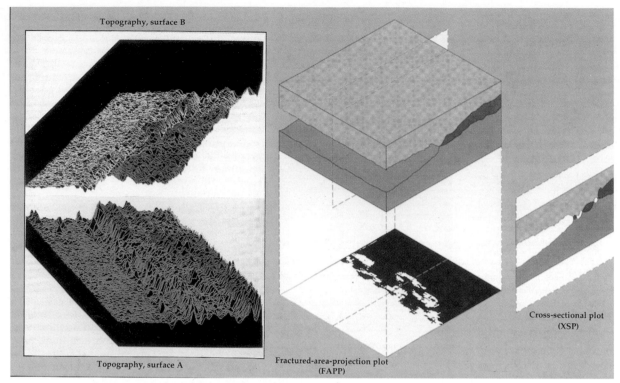

Figure 11-11. FRASTA images depicting the analysis of a fracture.

deformations that vary with distance from the nucleation point. That variation encodes the crack history.

With this understanding, the question became one of illuminating those traces. After trying several approaches, Kobayashi arrived at the notion of using a scanning laser microscope to map topographically the fracture surfaces. The group first developed three-dimensional tools to reassemble (mate) the conjugate surfaces. Then they created small, variable offsets between the pair and the ability to examine them in projected and isometric views. These views, it turned out, permitted the fracture event to be reconstructed. This approach was a major advance in fracture analysis and gave SRI the ability to extract from topographic fractures a quantitative picture of what had happened.

This set of imaging and analytical tools became FRASTA. Figure 11-11 gives an example of a specific analysis, starting with a three-

dimensional scan of the two "halves" (conjugates) of the fractured specimen. This is done using the scanning laser microscope called a FRASTAscope. When the two halves are "reassembled" virtually, this assemblage reveals, by means of projections like those shown, the microcrack initiation sites and several other characteristics of the fracture. The time history of the fracture is a sequence of the individual projections, only one pair of which is shown in the figure.

The technology of FRASTA has come to the attention of the fracture analysis community around the world. As with many SRI innovations, the government provided most of the development money. However, both commercial and government organizations are now using FRASTA or asking SRI to use it for analyzing their failure problems. As of March 2004, four FRASTAscopes have been sold and the team is exploring whether the techniques could be made to work when only one of the two surfaces is available.

SRI's Chemical Economics Handbook

This story is not about the science of materials but their supply and demand on a global scale.[JJ] From the Institute's earliest days, it has provided a service that has illuminated the

production and use of a very wide range of industrial chemical and related materials. The service was spawned in the Institute's economics environment but has benefited over

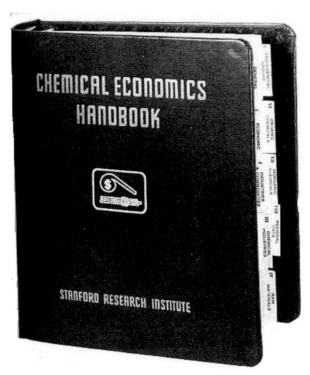

Figure 11-12. First issue of the *Chemical Economics Handbook* (1950).

the years from the technical insights of the chemists and materials scientists in sister SRI organizations. The centerpiece of this service is the SRI *Chemical Economics Handbook* (CEH). Started in 1950, the *Handbook* has become the standard global source on the production, use, and economic aspects of virtually all chemicals of commercial importance. For over a half century, the SRI program producing the CEH has been supported by 200 to 300 organizations in more than 25 countries. Throughout the world, SRI's "Chem Handbook" has come to be recognized as the bible of the industry. Given such a presence, how did this unique resource begin at SRI?

The CEH was the brainchild of Dr. Raymond Ewell.[15] Before joining SRI in March 1950, Dr. Ewell worked in an area of Shell Chemical that performed economic evaluations on materials important to Shell's industry. Inside Shell, the group's chemical market assessments were highly regarded as rigorous and Ewell brought that discipline to SRI. By 1950, advances in technology and the lure of

---

[15] After launching the handbook, Dr. Ewell went to India for SRI to help establish a small business presence with Dr. Gene Staley (see Chapter 15). He left SRI in 1957; by 1963 he was assistant director of the National Science Foundation, and by the spring of 1971 was Chancellor for Research at SUNY—Buffalo.

new products, such as plastics, which had started replacing metals, paper, glass, and other traditional materials, suggested to Ewell the need for comprehensive but simple, industry-relevant information. A better knowledge of the availability of chemicals would have an appeal to any company needing to use them. Collecting such information from open sources and removing its inconsistencies was a tedious process, easily put off by companies for less precise estimates.

In a nutshell, Ewell saw in the burgeoning chemical industry a critical need for timely, detailed, and accurate information about the production, sales, shipment, and price of its constituent materials.

Companies that were expanding their present production or contemplating new products would profit from a standardized inventory and availability of the materials they needed. He was right. Those companies soon saw the value in such a service because their decisions about the size and timing of their large capital investments, typical in the chemical industry, were crucial to profitability.

That initial CEH staff numbered five, and the annual subscription fee was a very modest $250. The service started with a 250-page volume that gave basic information on the production and price of major chemicals. There were 51 initial subscribers to the *Handbook*, and it became one of the first attempts at systematic industrial marketing research by an independent organization anywhere in the world.[KK]

However, there was an obvious problem. A little arithmetic shows that, with such pricing, the annual gross income from subscriptions of $12,750 amounted to just a bit over $2,500 for each of the five people. Clearly, this effort was not going to be profitable even in the 1950s. So why was it started? Between the beneficent words of the SRI charter and the clear need, the SRI managers had found sufficient justification at the time to proceed. The CEH was started not to make money but to serve an industry and hopefully provide a lead-in to single-client work for some of the member companies. This orientation would continue for quite a few years, abetted by an accounting system that couldn't quite address the net income of a subscription type of project.

Most of the early CEH compilations were simple tabulations or semi-log graphs of the supply side of a relatively few important chemicals and essential raw materials. The work consisted mainly of updating these from available sources, converting quantities to standard metrics and format, and periodically distributing them. Still, keeping accurately abreast of a growing industry took a lot of attention. The CEH also came to add data on the general economy, accounts of other industries important to the chemical industry, as well as the earlier statistical profiles on chemicals.

The compilation work was very rigorous. A research analyst tabulated data from available sources. These data were then verified by someone else, and then verified yet again, so that they were essentially free of compilation errors. This was a very important point: From the very start, CEH established a reputation for accuracy, reliability, and thoroughness. But these procedures also were adding cost to an already unprofitable arrangement whose price was still just $365 or so per year by 1960. If SRI was going to charge more—and it had to—some value proposition had to be made.

After several years of operation, the SRI staff became so familiar with their chemicals that a couple of things started to happen. The data and graphs became heavily footnoted with ancillary information and insights and, more important, they began to look into the consumption or demand side of the market. This new perspective, however, revealed some inconsistencies between aggregate production and consumption. The reasons for these discrepancies were aggressively pursued. It was 1957 and with this investigation in progress, Mimi Erskine joined the group and also began to explore these inconsistencies and their patterns. In analyzing both ends, so to speak, she and others were able to reconcile the differences. Her method became a check and balance for a given chemical and even further improved the overall veracity of the CEH. This new, more comprehensive representation also enabled other important changes in the CEH and its SRI operations.

While this new insight was developing in the late 1950s, the CEH still continued its unprofitable operation. About 1960, in one of SRI's belt-tightening moments, the CEH group was asked to work its way out of subsidization.[16]

John Strickland, who had taken over leadership in 1955, became an advocate for expansion and profitability. As a means of attacking the financial problem, he saw in the expanded knowledge they were compiling and, from the creative offerings of Mimi Erskine, the potential for a set of new reports to take to their subscribers. He felt it would be worth repackaging the explanatory notes about the markets for specific chemicals, the information about the industries that relied on them, the analyses of producing companies and their capacities, the supply/demand relationships, and the end-use patterns. The increasingly reliable contacts in the producing and consuming industries were also adding a lot of value.[17]

All this access and in-depth awareness were giving the individual SRI analysts their own global reputations in their chosen chemical groupings such as fertilizers or organic chemicals. This combination of information and expertise, then, was evidenced in a set of new prototype reports taken to the client community in the early 1960s to test their interest. The samples were personally shown to the project's domestic clients, and foreign clients were contacted by telephone and mail. Armed with this new value, Strickland and colleague Tom Gunn were looking for an increase in subscription price to $1,800 per year to reach break-even.

The response was almost totally positive. Even some who had not joined before were now attracted. So these expansive reports were added to the CEH in 1964 and soon comprised the single most important feature of the *Handbook*.[LL] In Tom Gunn's words, "This was really a major turning point. The program went from being a 'look-it-up' type of research resource to an interactive service. Our [staff] was contacting people in industry with all sorts of questions and those in industry were doing the same with our staff."[MM]

To help justify the cost, each client would now receive two additional sets of the CEH to distribute inside the company. Some wound up inside the research and development operations

[16] SRI's new President, Karl Folkers, noticed the unprofitability of the CEH program and actually advocated selling the operation. However, plans to make it profitable

were under way and so it remained in operation. That option would, however, be revisited.

[17] Not so incidentally, this willingness of industry people to yield private facts about their operations comes, almost certainly, from SRI's nonprofit objectivity—something the staff zealously guards.

as guides to the design of new products.[18] So by 1975 the annual fee was $4000, which covered three copies of the CEH to each subscriber. The expanded use, size, and update rate of the *Handbook* continued to be promoted by its successive directors.[19] With all this effort, the CEH continued its pattern of wide acceptance and, internally, attained consistent profitability.

As a measure of the CEH scope, by 1975 more than 130 chemicals and chemical products were covered in the expanded "Marketing Research Reports," each issued on a three-year cycle. In addition, over 550 chemicals were addressed in data sheets and smaller marketing reports. Researchers spent a considerable time reviewing findings with industry specialists to ensure quality work. The new reports also included coverage on technology and environmental issues. The CEH, now produced by 34 staff and consisting of 19 volumes containing 7000 pages, had broadened its coverage to include the following chemicals and allied products, with examples:

- Petrochemical feedstocks (ethylene, propylene)
- Organic intermediates (ethylene oxide, propylene oxide)
- Plastics (includes about 25 in all)
- Elastomers (styrene-butadiene, neoprene)
- Fibers, (including polyesters, nylons)
- Derivative products (dyes, pigments, adhesives, surface coatings)
- Agricultural chemicals (fertilizers, pesticides, animal feeds)
- Inorganic commodity chemicals (industrial gases, chloralkali products)
- Specialty chemicals (plastics additives, surface-active agents, fluorocarbons).

Industry growth was also proceeding both in the quantity of material manufactured and in its globalization. As examples of the former,

U.S. production of petroleum-derived benzene increased from about 50 million gallons in 1950, to about 1 billion in 1975, to almost 2.4 billion in 2000. Production of high-density polyethylene (HDPE), used to make milk bottles, film, pipe, and many other goods, increased from about 50 million pounds in 1950, to 2.5 billion pounds in 1975, and to 14.3 billion pounds in 2000.

Industry growth was also coming from globalization. During the 1970s, the chemical industry began to globalize. The disruptions caused by two shocks in crude oil prices and developments in less industrialized countries also changed the nature of the industry. In 1950, when the CEH started, the European and Japanese sectors of the industry were just rebuilding and the vast majority of chemical production was in the United States. Over the next 25 years, the economies of Western Europe and Japan expanded significantly, and these areas reappeared as important chemical producers. But soon globalization would also encompass lesser-known producers. For example, in 1975 the United States and Europe made about 40% of the world's HDPE, with Japan producing half that much. By 1975, about 40% of the HDPE, was made in the U.S., 40% in Western Europe, and 20% in Japan. In 2000 the U.S. share had shrunk to 28%, Europe, 23%, and Japan 6%. The displacing producers at about 5% each were the Middle East, South Korea, Canada, and China.

As a consequence of this globalization, the CEH practice expanded geographically to meet the increasing demand for information. Offices were opened in Zurich and Tokyo to provide more complete data on Western Europe and Japan. The *Directory of Chemical Producers (DCP)* was initiated by SRI in the 1960s to give clients extensive lists of U.S. producers with their locations and products; the information was cross-referenced to list the producers and locations of all products. By 1980, the DCP for Western Europe was available, and by 1990, DCP Eastern Asia made its debut.

A group of SRI chemical engineers started the *Process Economics Program (PEP)* to provide clients with the technology and economic evaluations of many chemical processes.[20] In the mid-1970s, the SRI Chemical Consulting practice started the *World Petrochemicals (WP)* program to provide extensive supply/demand

---

[18] Tom Gunn tells of an episode that reveals the utility of the CEH material. He was visiting the manager of market research of Sun Oil and in the process met a new member who had good industrial experience but was not very familiar with the CEH. When this new member said he was working on a report on ammonia, Gunn handed him a copy of a recent CEH report on ammonia by Tom Blue. After examining it for only 5 minutes, he claimed it would save him 2 months work.

[19] In 1961, Tom Gunn became editor of the *Handbook* and was followed in 1968 by Kirt McCaleb, John Dean in 1972, and Fred Chan in 1974. More recently came Betty Johnson, Tom Gunn again, then Sara Soder, and today's director, Eric Linak.

---

[20] *PEP* was started by Ken Lund with help from John Strickland and Bill Sutphen.

and producer/capacity databases on ethylene, propylene, butadiene, benzene, methanol, and all their derivatives in virtually every country of the world. In the late 1970s, the *Specialty Chemicals Update Program (SCUP)* began providing analyses of the critical factors for success, profitability, outlook, markets, and trends for 35 specialty chemical markets.

To alleviate the physical bulk of the printed CEH, evident in Figure 11-13, clients can now elect to receive all five programs via the Internet or on CD-ROMs. The DCP program now covers Canada, Mexico, South America, India, China, and the Middle East. SRI also began offering CEH-type analyses in the *China Report: Chemical Product Trends* and *Asian Report: Chemical Industry Trends*.

The SRI chemical economics practice became the largest and most respected service of its kind in the world. Approximately 100 full-time professional and support staffers continue to update CEH, DCP, WP, PEP, and SCUP reports on a regular basis. Additional offices were opened in Houston and in Beijing, China. The CEH now covers about 250 chemicals in 38 binders. Clients pay almost $30,000 per year for monthly updates of 5 to 8 reports.

A number of famous companies have subscribed to CEH for all 50 years: Dow Chemical, Du Pont, Chevron, Eastman Chemical, Procter and Gamble, Hercules Chemical, PPG, Monsanto, Union Carbide, Bayer, and General Electric. The subscriber base has changed somewhat in the last 15-20 years, as the number of chemical producers has decreased due to mergers and about a fifth of the subscribers are now financial institutions, government agencies, engineering companies, or other consultants. About half the subscriber base has headquarters outside of the United States. Also, along the way, there has been some competition to the CEH from companies like Chem Systems, Parpenelli Tecnon, and

Figure 11-13. The printed form of the SRI *Chemical Economics Handbook* (circa 2001).

Chemical Market Analysis, Inc. But none has been able to match the breadth and depth of SRI coverage, and it has become virtually impossible for a major chemical or materials company to launch a major new initiative without the substantiation of CEH numbers.

All that having been said, and in spite of this long and distinguished history, in January 2004 SRI sold its stake in the CEH and related services. The buyer was a broadly based information services company, Access Intelligence, headquartered in Maryland. This transfer ends, then, at least for now, the last vestige of the Business Group at SRI.

In concluding this piece about a successful SRI service, there is one, perhaps instructive, character issue. The success of the CEH rested on the ability of SRI staff to draw out information from its sources that would otherwise be proprietary. That trust afforded SRI by its sources is the result of deliberate and continuing attention to an obligation that all of SRI takes very seriously: objectivity and the integrity that it, in turn, demands.

The Monsanto Million Dollar Challenges

The chemical industry has more than its share of difficult production problems, particularly in managing the waste byproducts it produces. Monsanto, headquartered in St. Louis and one of the larger members of the industry, conceived of a way to address some of its bigger waste management challenges. The idea was to pose one of Monsanto's technical or

manufacturing problems and invite the worldwide technical community to help solve it by competing for a million dollar prize. The winner would receive $500,000 to use in finding a solution to the problem, and if that solution was successfully applied, a second $500,000 would be awarded.

The first such competition, initiated in late 1994, was a search for a way to remove ammonia from the wastewater of some of Monsanto's plants. Out of 180 applicants, SRI came in first, with a proposal written by Drs. Abhoyjit Bhown, Ron Smith, and Luke Schneider. SRI successfully completed the initial design phase.

The second competition took place a year or so later and involved another difficult waste management problem: finding a practical, cost-effective technology that would recover high-purity amino acids and phosphoric and phosphorous acids from a particular waste stream, leaving clean sodium chloride. Recovery of these materials could lead to recycle and reuse by the company. Again, out of 34 applicants, an SRI proposal by David Bomberger, Neeraj R. Pakala, Charles K. Hiebert, and Eugene R. Moore was evaluated highest. During the final stages of internal review, however, a Monsanto vice president refused to approve the award to SRI because it had won the previous year's award and should not get it two years running. He then asked that the award go to the second place proposal. Alas, that was also from SRI, a proposal written by Bill Asher! The vice president therefore reversed himself and made the second award to the first-ranked SRI proposal. This second award was announced at the Fifth World Conference of Chemical Engineering in July 1996.

Figure 11-14. The Monsanto trophies won by SRI.

As it turned out, neither of the plans was ever implemented, due not to their lack of efficacy, but because of the changing business patterns within Monsanto. These consistent awards, though, among worldwide competition, reflect not only SRI's considerable talents in chemistry and chemical engineering but also its excellent ability to address real-world technical challenges.

Endnotes

A As related by Dr. Angel Sanjurjo and from B.J. Wood, A. Sanjurjo, S.M. Johnson, B.R. Taylor, T. Kobayashi, and Jacques Giovanola, *Improved Coatings for Ovens*, Final Report to the Whirlpool Corporation, July 1992.

B Phyllis Flanders Dorset and Stephen Miller, *"A Finite Difference—A Short History of the SRI Physics Division,"* author-published, copyright 2003.

C From the notes of Earle Jones, a retired SRI Vice President and docent at Año Nuevo, March 1, 2001.

D Biography of Ronald Schusterman (www.pbs.org/safarchive/3_ask/archive/bio/93_schusterman_bio.html) and *SRI Intercom* 6, April 7, 1965.

E T.C. Poulter, "Whiskers and the Penguins," *SRI Journal* 26, 8-14, June 1969.

F T. C. Poulter, Marine Mammals, in *Animal Communication*, T. A. Sebeok, Ed., Indiana University Press, pp. 405-465, 1968 and T. C. Poulter, Underwater Vocalization and Behavior of Pinnipeds, in *The Behavior and Physiology of Pinnipeds*, R. J. Harrison, R. C. Hubbard, R. S. Peterson, C. E. Rice, and R. J. Schusterman, Eds., Appleton-Century-Crafts, New York, pp. 69-84, 1968.

G T.C. Poulter, "The Voice of the Gray Whale," *SRI Journal*, No. 19, 8-9, March 1968.

H Taken from www.pbs.org/wgby/pages/frontline/shows/whales/interviews/griffin.html, January 14, 2001 and *SRI Intercom*, 23, December 1, 1965.

I From *Poulter Laboratory Celebration—1954 to 1986*, held at SRI on September 5, 1986.

J Dorset and Miller, op. cit.

[K] Interview with Paul Cook on February 14, 2003.

[L] SRI's *Research for Industry*, 8(4), 1-2, May 1956.

[M] Paul Cook, op. cit.

[N] From an account of several interviews of Bruce Graham, founding director of SRI's Life Sciences Division, taken over 1997 and 1998 by Elmer Reist and Gordon Newell.

[O] James B. Meikle and Bruce Graham, Electrons Produce High-Temperature Dielectric, *Electronics*, 29(5), 146-150, May 1956.

[P] SRI's *Research for Industry*, 8(4), 1-2, May 1956

[Q] Toyobo web site, www.toyobo.co.jp.

[R] Conversation with SRI's Bock Loo, November 9, 2000.

[S] Patent No. 4,533,724, James W. Wolfe et al., Liquid Crystalline Poly (2.6-Benzothiazole) Compositions, Process, and Products, issued August 6, 1985.

[T] Wyatt Haupt, Staff Writer, *North County Times*, San Diego, CA, June 5, 2002.

[U] This description of SRI work came from an interview with SRI physical chemist Dr. Don Hildenbrand.

[V] Much of this account derives from material sent by and conversation with Drs. Ted Mill and Jeff Bottaro.

[W] www.serdp.org/research/PP/PP-1058.pdf

[X] www.ih.navy.mil/emtc2.pdf

[Y] Referenced in the Navy's 1999 Report to Congress on dual use technology (see www.dtic.mil/dust/cgr/navy00cgr.htm).

[Z] Advanced Energetic Materials Emerge for Military and Space Applications, *Chemical and Engineering News*, pp. 18-22, January 17, 1994.

[AA] Taken from Theodore Mill, Environmental Risk Assessment, Chapter 4 in *Environmental Chemistry*, Lewis Publishers, 1993.

[BB] Evidence of contribution may be found in Theodore Mill and William Mabey, *The Handbook of Environmental Chemistry*, Vol. 2, Part D, "Hydrolysis of Organic Chemicals," Springer-Verlag, 1988.

[CC] T. Podoll, H. M. Jaber, and T. Mill, Tetrachlorodibenzodioxin: Rates of Volatilization and Photolysis in the Environment, *Environmental Science and Technology*, 20(5), 1986.

[DD] This all too brief story was compiled from the writings of Poulter Lab leaders, George Abrahamson and Jim Colton, and from the informative history of SRI's Physics Division by Dorset and Miller (op. cit.)

[EE] D. Bernstein and D.D. Keough, Piezoresistivity of manganin, *J. Appl. Phys.*, 35,1471, 1964 and P.S. DeCarli, D.C. Erlich, L.B. Hall, R.G. Bly, A.L. Whitson, D.D. Keough, and D. Curran, *Stress-Gauge System for the Megabar Range*, Rpt. No. DNA 4066F, Defense Nuclear Agency, SRI International, Palo Alto CA, 1976.

[FF] Most of this section came from discussion with Paul DeCarli in September 2004.

[GG] P.S. DeCarli and J.C. Jamieson, *Science*, 133, 1821-22, 1961

[HH] Some of this section came from discussions with Dr. Don Shockey.

[II] *SRI Highlights*, page 3, January/February 2000.

[JJ] Material for this account came from a 25-year summary of CEH operations, a telephone interview and correspondence with former CEH head, Tom Gunn, an article by Bob Schwaar for the *SRI Alumni Newsletter*, and input provided by Eric Linak, the current CEH director.

[KK] Conversation with Eric Linak, current CEH director.

[LL] K. E. McCaleb, "The Biography of a Chemical Economics Handbook Report," paper presented at the National Meeting of the American Chemical Society, Los Angeles, CA, March 30, 1971.

[MM] Tom Gunn, personal communication, June 3, 2001.

Chapter 12
Research in Education

Background

Because SRI was founded by Stanford University, its charter quite naturally contains reference to the field of education. In this case, the reference was to support the educational goals of the University, and that orientation led to some of SRI's early research contracts being in the education field. As early as 1953, SRI had a dozen education-related contracts in what was then called the Behavioral Sciences Program.

Following those early efforts, SRI has essentially maintained a continuous role in educational research work. The main thrusts of this work lay in two areas: one area has been a decades-long interest in the assessment and evaluation of educational methods and programs and the other area has been a number of significant explorations in the use of technology in learning. That SRI has had impact in these fields is underscored by its role of effectively guiding the U.S. government, including Congress, in its oversight of educational and child development programs. These have included programs such as Follow Through, the role of technology in aiding the disabled, and, more recently, aid to the government in ongoing support of special education; that is, the education of children with disabilities.

Project Follow Through— Assessing the Impacts of "Head Start"

When it commenced in the summer of 1965, the U.S. government's Head Start program was intended as a "temporary" source of supplemental funds to better prepare poor, inner-city, preschool children during the summer so that they would enter school in the fall with a better chance of succeeding educationally. The purpose was to supply nutritional and health experiences, along with some social and mental health services, that were intended to break the so-called "cycle of poverty" that afflicted the inner city. The program flowed from the Economic Opportunity Act of 1964, an element of the widely heralded War on Poverty. It was housed in the Office of Economic Opportunity and later transferred to the Office of Child Development in the Department of Health, Education, and Welfare. Though intended to affect the scholastic readiness of disadvantaged children, it was not, by content, an educational program. Regardless, it quickly gained support among both the public and Congress, so much so that it still continues today. In fiscal 2001, the Head Start program was budgeted at $6.2 billion covering an estimated 916,000 children.[A] In its first 33 years it served more than 15 million children at a total cost of more than $30 billion. Remarkably, according to the U.S. General Accounting Office, this early childhood development program continued for more than three decades without any substantive validation of how well it was working.[B] That observation applies more to the noncognitive consequences of the program, for some early and extended attempts were made to understand the educational progress of Head Start children.

Head Start, of course, was intended to have an educational impact. In early measurements, it was noted that the IQ of Head Start children went up by as much as 10 percent compared with those who did not participate. But other studies showed that this and other preschool gains seemed to dissipate as the children entered school.[C] The Johnson Administration, perhaps seeking evidence of the desired benefits of Head Start, decided to explore their efficacy and staying power. In 1967, just 2 years after the initial Head Start implementation, Congress approved Public Law 90-92, creating another very large program that would "Follow Through" on Head Start. In other words, it would track Head Start-eligible students into their normal schooling and, even more, seek effective methods for teaching them. In pursuit of the latter objective, it was decided to examine a wide variety of teaching theories or methods for such children and to find out which were the most effective. The process was called "planned variation" and sponsors of different educational models were invited to implement them on a cooperative basis with selected schools. Designing and implementing a complete full-day curriculum governed by each educational model had never before been done in educational reform.[D] The scope of the research project was also unprecedented, with close to 10,000 children from 120 communities involved each year from 1969 to 1975.

SRI had several early roles in Follow Through.[E] One was to design, administer, and score the testing of Follow-Through children for both cognitive and noncognitive development across a range of 10 to 20 teaching methods.[F] Others were to determine whether a set of distinguishable teaching methods were, in fact, being used and, finally, to evaluate each teaching method in that set. Because of the sheer size of Follow Through and the nature of longitudinal studies, aspects of these roles continued for some 5 to 6 years.

Much of this methodology for evaluation was groundbreaking. First, SRI created a set of observational methods that were original, innovative, and more comprehensive than anything prior. They allowed for a spectrum of student groupings, how materials were used or not, the instruction methods used, and, of course, a wide range of childhood development outcomes: behavioral, cognitive, problem solving, attendance, and others. The SRI observational method and its analytical adjunct have been widely replicated in this country and adapted to settings in France, Spain, and China.

SRI's second important contribution was to determine whether some subset of the various teaching methods, which eventually came down to seven,[1] were actually in place and "pure" enough to have educational results

unambiguously associated with them. Considering that this involved four first-grade and four third-grade Follow-Through classrooms and one each non-Follow-Through classroom in each of 36 cities, this was a huge task. Though each educational method had been in place and practiced for 2 to 3 years, assessing the adequate presence of each teaching method was still difficult. But SRI showed that each of the seven was unambiguously present. It then became necessary to measure student outcomes over a wide range of developmental and educational characteristics. The measuring instrument included more than 600 categories that described both students and teachers. Collectively, there were more than 1,000 observation days.

Though it tried to win a wider scope in the analysis of the data, SRI participated only in that part related to classroom observation. Here are a few important results from that work as reported by SRI's project leader, Dr. Jane Stallings:[G]

- The teaching methods and classroom environment are important to student achievement, certainly by the third grade and to a large extent by the first. The finding removed the uncertainty about the relative importance of a child's aptitude upon entering school. Even in the early 1970s, some researchers thought aptitude at school entrance was dominant, but Follow Through showed, for example, that even in the first grade a child's entering ability accounts for about one-third of the child's achievements in math, while instructional procedures account for about 40%. For reading, entry ability accounts for about half the achievement.

- Each of the seven instructional methods brought selected improvement to childhood development, but no individual method was universally better or consistently worse than all others. Each had a spectrum of successes and failures. For example, and perhaps not surprisingly, superior scores in math and reading for both first and third grades could be positively correlated with the average length of time spent on them during the school day. In open classroom settings, children attributed their success to themselves and failure to others, whereas in the more structured classrooms a successful child attributed success to the teacher and

---

[1] The seven consisted of two based on positive reinforcement theory (Univs. of Kansas and Oregon), one on Piaget's cognitive development theory (High/Scope Foundation), one on open classroom (Education Development Center), and three on combinations of Dewey's science-based cognitive development and the second and third just listed (Far West Laboratory, Univ. of Arizona, and Bank Street College). That each was adequately distinctive, however, was SRI's first burden of proof.

Figure 12-1. Education researcher, Dr. Jane Stallings.

happens in school, therefore, is important to whether the child comes to school or not.

- Success in nonverbal problem-solving skills was favored by an environment where questions were more open-ended and the use of materials was extensive.

- An ability to respond well to testing is best served by so-called direct instruction. Direct instruction uses closed-ended verbal questions followed by assessment and explanation. That approach benefits from memorization.

In the opinion of SRI researchers, the best instructional method involves a blend of several of the methods isolated in Follow Through. That blend may include some direct instruction, some that favors nonverbal problem solving, and some of the more planning-intensive methods.

For better or worse, the U.S. educational system, with its highly distributed and diverse nature, is also highly resistant to change. Even though Follow Through evidenced some clear directions, little of what was learned in these evaluations has found its way into our elementary education system.[H]

failure to him/herself. Very little of the absence rate was explained by a child's outlook at entry, whereas instructional procedures accounted for almost two-thirds of the cases of inordinate absenteeism. What

Evaluating Programs in Special Education

One of the most significant and beneficent programs that SRI's education researchers have worked on is a nearly 20-year run in evaluating U.S. educational efforts for children in special education.[2]

The motivation for doing this kind of work started with a small statistical study for the Department of Education (ED) in the mid-1970s that tried to count the number of handicapped children who could attend school. Many such children were invisible to the existing census and other counting methods. Beyond the outcome itself, the project was important to SRI's future work in special education since Phil Sorensen, then head of education research, used

it in 1972 to bring to SRI Dr. Marian "Mimi" Stearns from ED's Bureau of the Educationally Handicapped, the agency that had funded the study (see Figure 12-2). She would come to have considerable impact on SRI's contributions in the field of education.

SRI's initial major opportunity in this field arose with the passage in the late 1970s of a new special education law, Public Law 94-142, intended to provide an improved education to such children.[3] Stearns received a contract in 1978 to perform the first longitudinal study to measure the effect of the Law. This was a 5-year study to watch how well 32 different school sites were meeting the mandate of P.L. 94-142; that is, to get children with disabilities out of their cloistered, institutional environments and into the schools. This included children with all kinds of disabilities and with ages from preschool to as old as 21. Each year SRI would submit to the client, ED's Office of Special Education Programs, an evaluation of how the target schools were doing. Regulations

---

[2] "Special education" is an umbrella term for a variety of programs intended to assist children with physical and/or educational disabilities that cannot be accommodated in a regular classroom.

[3] The Education for All Handicapped Children Act.

Figure 12-2. SRI vice president, Dr. Marian "Mimi" Stearns.

Figure 12-3. Dr. Mary Wagner.

stemming from the Law were redone every 2 years and the Law itself was modified every 5 years. Both regulation and legislation have been strongly influenced by the SRI observations. As perhaps one of the most regulated parts of education, the new provisions governing special education and even the law itself came to reflect what SRI had observed. With this influx of disabled children into the regular schools, an important but nebulous boundary came to exist between those in regular education and those in special education. Federal research money was made available to study that boundary and, importantly, SRI would participate in those studies.

The first evaluation study ended in 1983 and, after a 2-year hiatus, a second longitudinal study was conducted, this time to study the *children themselves*, not just the schools. It was a huge study involving 8,000 children and went on for 9 years! The study led to SRI testifying before Congress, and important changes that reflected SRI's findings were made in the reauthorization of the Individuals with Disabilities Education Act (IDEA). For example, SRI's data showed dramatically that a large fraction of emotionally disturbed children effectively fell into nonproductive and even criminal lives after they left school.[4] As a result

of this insight, a whole new research program was started to learn more about that regrettable transition. Other disability categories are still being looked at; for example, what is the etiology of mental retardation and what is the role of public education over the formative years relevant to that condition?

With the exception of an unfortunate hiatus in the 1990s, longitudinal studies have continued at SRI in a variety of child development areas, all dealing with disadvantaged children. One ongoing study looks at a nationally representative sample of infants and toddlers with disabilities, along with their families, as they transition into elementary school. The purpose is to consider the circumstances of individual children and learn what factors produce good outcomes in the early years of school. Another study relates to an older age group as its members transition into middle and high school.

The consequences of these studies and their influence on legislation have helped define the framework of special education policy, something that was new to the field of education. SRI has earned a unique position in measuring and understanding this aspect of education. When the time arrives for a

---

[4] A specific example: some of the first statistics on what was happening to emotionally disturbed kids when they reached high school showed that 75% had been arrested by the time they were 3 years out of high school. New

interventions had to be developed for such children. A new longitudinal study starting in January 2000 will look at younger emotionally disturbed kids (6-12) to see if school and other agency improvements are working. A separate study will look at babies with disabilities. With that SRI will have covered all age ranges. (Also, see *SRI Journal*, April 82.)

reauthorization of the enabling congressional legislation, the Department of Education and SRI are queried extensively about the current successes and failures of special education. Stearns, Mary Wagner (see Figure 12-3), and other SRI research leaders have made huge contributions to the guidance of the necessary legislation.

As mentioned, the original source of this work was the Bureau of the Educationally Handicapped, now known as the Office of Special Education Programs. SRI's relationship with this client has been extraordinary. For more than 25 years the principals of these two organizations have had a relationship of mutual respect and contribution. In fact, recently, they asked SRI to help them develop their long-range program for the next twenty years. As Mary Wagner points out, that's twenty years of relevant experience at SRI on which to base a twenty-year forecast. That requires a clear 20/20 vision, and SRI will be up to the task.

Technology in Learning—
The Role and Promise of Computing in the Classroom

As with most places we frequent, computers, in all their manifold embodiments, have found their way into the classroom. Unlike many situations in industry, however, that migration has been intermittent and uncertain. You can easily imagine several reasons for this: teachers who are untrained or averse to computers yet are required to use them, the unevenness in building a clear and valid context for their introduction into the classroom, and their almost scheduled obsolescence, which spells recurring capital costs that invoke the chronic shortage of money. Also, perhaps more than in other environments, the presence of computers in the classroom has not come to imply their effective use.

While computers fairly easily entered the school districts' and even teachers' offices for administrative use, placing them in the hands of students has been less straightforward. Adding to the uncertainty or confusion, over the approximately 30 years that such classroom exploration has gone on, computers have also evolved and their potential has increased dramatically. They now range from scaled-

Figure 12-4. Dr. Barbara Means (who led SRI into the realm of technology in learning).

down, but more affordable and powerful "mainframes" in the district office to those that now approach wearability in the classroom. So, what are their educational roles? What is their educational efficacy? What do they enable by way of communications and collaboration? Perhaps most importantly, how do both the teacher and the students naturally and powerfully assimilate them into the curriculum? How do you prepare children for an increasingly technological world? These probing questions have been part of SRI's research for more than two decades.

The first time that educational technology became part of the organizational taxonomy at SRI was at the beginning of 1982, when Dr. "Mimi" Stearns initiated a program under Teresa Middleton called just that, Educational Technology. The scope later broadened a bit to include the technology of training. But the genesis of studying the role of technology in classroom instruction was created in the spring of 1989 with the formation of a group in Advanced Instructional Technology under Dr. Barbara Means (see Figure 12-4). Probably more than anyone else, she has been responsible for the growth of this work at SRI.[5]

[5] Though accepting a leadership position within 3 years after arriving at SRI, Dr. Means continued to contribute to her field. One very important contribution she has made is to the pioneering use of case studies as a method to evaluate the role of technology in education reform. She has written several books on the subject of technology in education, including the ways in which the Internet and its advantages can be successfully integrated. Two volumes with colleague Dr. Geneva Haertel containing papers on educational technology are also in press.

A very common thread through all of the SRI work, in one form or another, is the Internet and the technology that is increasingly a natural extension of it.

Research in computer-aided instruction at SRI has had three major thrusts: the building of tools or programs that help teach specific subjects, creating a computer-based environment to help teachers retain and hone their skills, and the very critical question of evaluating the efficacy and value of computers in the classroom. They will be addressed in that order.

Subject-Specific Educational Software

Elementary Probability and Statistics—Major Munchy

One of SRI's important achievements in educational software has the unlikely name of "Major Munchy" (see Figure 12-5). Funded by the National Science Foundation (NSF), this is a video-based, instructional software system that teaches middle-grade students elementary probability and statistics. It takes real-world problems and brings them into the classroom setting in the context of a game. Teachers show a few minutes of the video each day, and students become involved in classroom simulations using dice, random numbers, and (optionally) a computer to promote the learning of important concepts in probability and statistics. *Making Money with Major Munchy: Explorations in Probability* is a week-long instructional set that was designed and built by Andy Zucker and Ed Esty. It has been endorsed by the National Council of Teachers of Mathematics (NCTM), and in 1994 it won the top award among some 800 entries at an International Film and Video Festival in Columbus, Ohio, and third place in a similar competition in New York. Today it, along with three similar video kits, is in use by tens of thousands of students in grades 5 to 9 and has become a commercial educational product distributed by HRM Video of New York.

Another math-oriented program began at SRI in 1998 under NSF sponsorship. It is called *Math Insight*, and it also subscribes to the NCTM standards. With the collaborative participation of Virginia public schools and the careful observation of students' experience using computer-based mathematical tools, *Math Insight* was built around a structured math

Figure 12-5. The lead-in and student use of the SRI-developed probability and statistics program called Major Munchy.

problem-solving process. It can stand alone or be used as an adjunct to normal math textbooks.

Visualizing Chemistry—ChemSense

ChemSense is another NSF project, begun at SRI in 1999, which is intended to use the visual and representational aid of a computer to help students understand and learn chemical systems and to help teachers become more aware of the progress or difficulties students encounter. SRI partners were the University of Michigan, PASCO Scientific, NCSA ChemViz, and the students and teachers of local Northern California schools.

The brainchild of Drs. Robert Kozma and Elaine Coleman, the project builds on several theoretical approaches to learning, including collaborative investigations, ability to represent chemicals and their interactions, curriculum, and a place where knowledge building can occur. Students work together, ask questions of each other, and ultimately try to conduct a chemistry experiment or investigation, complete with data representation and analysis and the presentation of a conclusion or findings. The flexibility of a computer environment provides a source of standard chemical symbols, a workspace for experimental design, the use of animation to depict chemical change, and, importantly, an opportunity for collaborative input and peer review. An image of such a workspace is given in Figure 12-6.

Five areas are addressed that help portray observable states or changes in molecular structure:

- Connectivity or the structural representation and reactivity of molecules
- Molecular geometry or shape importance, particularly in biochemical reactions
- Proximity conditions, sometimes multiple, that enable some biochemical reactions
- State of a molecule in its environment under influences such as heat and light
- Concentration of molecules in a volume and the consequences of their collisions.

These five areas form a framework for developing a chemistry curriculum, for knowledge building, and, ultimately, for gaining a new or better understanding. The participating high schools in Northern California can prepare animated representations of experiments they have conducted, and place them in the ChemSense database, from where they can be viewed anywhere across the Internet. ChemSense is also being explored for use in instructional chemistry at the undergraduate level at the University of Michigan. A number of papers on this new teaching tool have been presented or published by SRI and its partners.

Educational Software Development and Testing

As mentioned earlier, educational software for the classroom has a checkered history. Often because of expensive development, limited acceptance, or interprogram incompatibility, such software doesn't find a profitable market or enjoy much longevity. So SRI approached NSF with another idea. The result was a 1998 project that addressed the building of instructional software through the use of small,

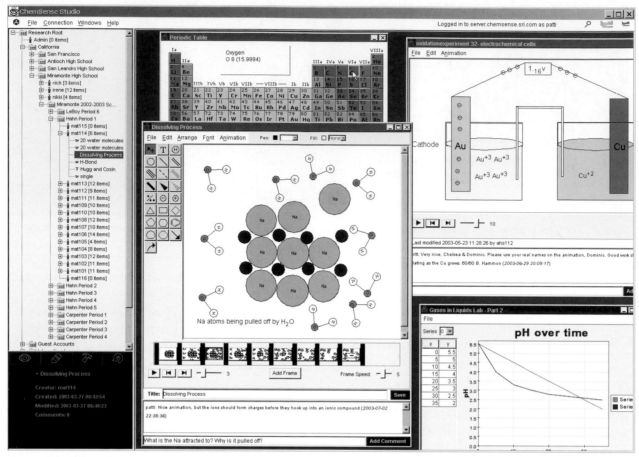

Figure 12-6. Browser window showing ChemSense.

portable software modules with enough compatibility and longevity to find use as components in larger programs. The initial specific target was reform in middle school mathematics, with a general goal of having an impact on the quality of math and science education from kindergarten to 12th grade. The project, called Educational Software Components of Tomorrow (ESCOT), uses the broad access to the Internet by both teachers and developers to build, collect, evolve, test, and use a wide variety of software components that can be applied to identified educational needs in mathematics. Teachers may draw on the ESCOT web site for components as needed. The hope is that, through this medium, valuable software components will aggregate over time, enable cheaper instructional software, and ultimately form the core of better math instruction.

Support of Teacher Development

Tapped In—An online meeting place for teacher interaction and development

An important, perhaps critical aspect of how well a given profession works is the interaction of its members. In spite of an almost total social immersion, in the context of professional interaction teaching can ironically be a lonely profession. The workday is enormously crowded with demanding schedules and continuous interaction. Afternoons and evenings are often filled with offering individual help, grading papers, and planning for the next class or subject. The opportunity to compare ideas or learn of new approaches from peers or others is limited, leaving most teaching improvements to be self-discovered. Greater teacher interaction and mutual support are simply unmet needs.

It was the occasion of the annual request for SRI internal investment funds in 1995, and Mark Schlager and Wayne Grant of SRI's Center

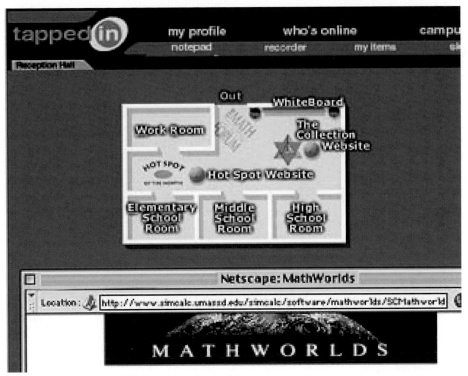

Figure 12-7. A starting page of SRI's first *Tapped In* (a virtual collaboration space for teachers).

for Technology in Learning (CTL) were applying for money to provide classroom teachers with the means to better interact with one another as they try to improve their classroom performance. Their idea was to use the emerging worldwide Internet as the basis for a very broad forum in which topics such as curriculum, teaching methods, and discipline could be explored. Since there was no time in a teacher's normal day for such potentially useful discussion, the Internet could offer after-hours interaction among interested teachers, no matter where they lived. The SRI funding was approved, and so began an important innovation in teacher development support, a virtual meeting place called *Tapped In.*[1]

Beginning with modest support from SRI and the Walter S. Johnson Foundation, CTL created the early mechanisms for *Tapped In.* Teachers were involved from the beginning and helped design the functionality needed. NSF then became involved and wisely encouraged SRI to concentrate on building an easily used, richly communicative medium and to use partnerships with the professional development community to provide the content materials and methods. Taking this approach, *Tapped In* has created an environment where teachers can improve their skills in individual disciplines such as math or biology. The materials and methods promulgated here are derived from partnerships with established organizations in teacher development.

A web interface to this virtual environment is shown in Figure 12-7. Modeled after physical space, it has meeting rooms, private rooms, a library, whiteboards, an auditorium, etc. modifiable according to the preference of the teachers. Since their access is very likely to take place after hours, teachers can sit in their pajamas, move into the math forum suite, look for resources available, or even interact with forum staff. Although initially many of the web-centered interactions across the education community were totally asynchronous, *Tapped In* developers at SRI believed that much of the learning experience required synchronous or real-time interaction. One of *Tapped In*'s notable contributions so far has been to cause others to see that need for immediacy and, as a result, both synchronous and asynchronous interactions are possible.

Tapped In includes forums that deal with both a traditional subject and the role of new technology in teaching it. While the SRI facilitators, mainly Drs. Mark Schlager and Judi Fusco, help new visitors get together,[6] the virtual venues that exist are the product and responsibility of the participating teacher community (see box). This gathering offers ordinary teachers the chance for dialogue with each other, and sometimes with the leaders in their field. Perhaps most importantly, it goes a long way toward breaking down the isolation that almost all teachers, but particularly new teachers, feel in their classroom.

---

[6] Others involved in the development and use of *Tapped In* are Alexandra Harris, Patti Shank, Melissa Koch, Larry Hamel, B.J. Berquist, Kari Holsinger, Richard Godard, Donna Hendry, Michael Hutchison, and Aaron Becker.

One very popular program that helps teachers bring the Internet and its information into the classroom is called *WebQuest*. It offers the student a means to search for and locate material relevant to a broad set of classroom subjects or assigned projects. Its popularity led Dr. Judi Fusco of SRI and a few interested teachers to open a *Tapped In* forum on how to use *WebQuest* more effectively. At their first online meeting, who should show up unannounced but Bernie Dodge, the creator of *WebQuest*! Dr. Dodge, from San Diego State University and often called "the teacher's best friend," is one of the country's most respected figures in bringing the new online technology to the classroom. The session went so well and the environment offered by *Tapped In* was so conducive to the interaction that Dr. Dodge became the forum leader and now holds monthly online meetings on the uses of *WebQuest* with teachers from all over the country.

Tapped In is also being used to offer formal educational opportunities for teachers. For example, Pepperdine University pays an annual institutional fee to use *Tapped In* for its masters and doctoral programs in education. The intent is to formally train teachers in new ways of interacting with each other. In addition, teachers who are not physically close to such a school can take advantage of such interactions.

The *Tapped In* program has been so successful that applicants to NSF for online teacher improvement regularly incorporate *Tapped In* as part of their process. In late 1999 this aspect of *Tapped In* involved about 8,000 teachers and was picked as one of the 20 most important innovations in educational technology to be presented at an educational summit for state governors. In spite of the fact that the SRI leaders have purposely let *Tapped In* become known only through word of mouth so as to not outstrip available resources, each month some 700 members and twice that many guests log in for sessions that are, on the average, 40 minutes long.

In spite of its meeting a clear need, *Tapped In* had to face a moment of truth as its extended funding from NSF was winding down. Lacking that support and with access privileges that hopefully would remain free to individual teachers, a continuation strategy was needed. How could it continue on its own and yet reach an even larger fraction of the country's 3 million teachers? The participating teachers didn't want it to become an in-your-face commercial environment, now so common to the web, and yet finding some operating model was critical. An answer came, at least for a while.

First, NSF provided SRI a supplemental grant to carry the operation through 2002. This money also served as a bridge to a new, expanded role for *Tapped In*. In early 2003 NSF,

through a new 5-year grant, asked SRI to create a new version of *Tapped In* to help foster collaboration among a family of new research centers it was creating across the country. This change presented an opportunity to revamp *Tapped In* software and its functionality, but it also meant that existing users were left without a service as the old program was retired. By the fall of 2003, the new program was capable of serving not just the NSF centers, but an improved meeting place and service for individual teachers, private virtual teaching environments for groups of K-12 students, and other private meeting areas that were income-producing. The last and important revenue part derives from the ability of separate organizations, such as universities and teacher groups, to build their own virtual private environment for which they pay a fee to *Tapped In* operations.

Rebuilding its user base from late 2003, TI2, as the new version of *Tapped In* is called, now has more than 17,000 participating teachers. This service, with worldwide reach and typical low-cost web efficiencies, has become an important and innovative framework for not only helping teachers, but also expands the notion of what a meeting place or classroom can be.

Teachscape—An SRI-assisted company offering high-quality teacher development

Just as *Tapped In* is an online resource for teacher development sponsored with grant money from NSF, SRI also had a hand in a for-profit enterprise called Teachscape that has also targeted online teacher development. The motivation for its founding arose outside of SRI through the efforts of its present CEO, Mark Atkinson, a former producer of television news programs. But very early on he enlisted the expertise of SRI and, in particular the insight

Figure 12-8. Dr. Roy Pea.

and broad educational influence of Dr. Roy Pea[7] (see Figure 12-8). As Teachscape unfolded and rooted in the technology-in-learning work SRI was doing for NSF, there came the realization that the Internet, as its communications bandwidths increased, was a perfect place to involve teachers in their quest to improve their classroom skills. Higher bandwidth is necessary because one of the important means for this development process is digital video. Video is but one component, however, of the multimedia approach of this new company.

The aim of Teachscape is to further the professional development of teachers and to do so by forming a broadly based team of educators, staff developers, multimedia producers, technologists, and researchers willing to work with educational institutions. All Teachscape resources are available in online libraries that include video-based case studies of exemplary teaching in real classrooms, teacher reflections on those videos, examples of student work in featured classrooms, and the commentary of educational specialists. Other features include study groups; facilitated discussions with experts, featured teachers, or colleagues; and self-assessment aids. Assistance is also available to help tailor the online library to the needs of a specific client.

Teachscape has an impressive list of partners. Among them are the two major teacher unions in the United States, several universities prominent in K-12 education, curriculum publishers such as McGraw-Hill, and authorities on teacher quality like the National Board for Professional Teaching Standards.

Critical to the launching of the company, this need for better education for young Americans got the favorable attention of one of the most noted venture capital firms of Silicon Valley. Two major partners at Kleiner Perkins Caufield & Byers provided the seed money for a new charity venture fund called "**new**schools."[8] From this fund and others, like education-oriented Arcadia Partners, Teachscape received an initial $20 million, followed by several more rounds of funding. Because of its important contributions, SRI has a small equity stake in Teachscape. At present, it has clients in several states, including the support of more than 13,000 teachers in California.

Assessment and Evaluation in the Classroom

On the surface of it, determining the value of computer technology in learning seems straightforward: simply measure the differences in student performance over time in two statistically similar cohorts, one with and one without computers. Well, it is certainly not straightforward, and there are a host of reasons why the introduction of computers produced a somewhat turbulent debate about their educational efficacy. Beyond those mentioned at the beginning of this section there are:

- The wide range of teaching styles, preferences, and commitments
- The even broader range of potential computer-based applications with classroom relevance and the effort needed to use them well
- The huge spectrum of student interests and capabilities
- The controversy that early introduction of computers displaces basic skills
- The care with which experimental design and evaluation must be done to assess their value in education.

Because of this complexity, drawing conclusions about how computers can be beneficially used has taken years. Perhaps this difficulty should not be so surprising, for computers are machines built primarily to aid one's mind rather than brawn. As such, their

---

[7] His collaboration in Teachscape earned him the title of co-founder, and he currently sits on its Board. (When Atkinson brought the program to SRI it was called "Minerva.") Roy, since 2001 a professor at Stanford, is a nationally recognized leader in education research who was encouraged to come to SRI by Dr. Barbara Means in 1996 to head its Center for Technology in Learning. He would later come to head the NSF-funded Center for Innovative Learning Technologies, to be covered later.

[8] The two partners were John Doerr and Brook Byers, who both have deep interest in seeing U.S. education practices improved and want to put some financial rigor into the for-profit and nonprofit organizations serving this field. (Venture Philanthropists: The New School Fund, *Time Magazine*, 24 July 2000)

utility may be as varied and individualistic, as rational or irrational, as the mind itself. As Barbara Means points out: if you really want to understand what is happening in educational technology, concentrate not on the technology itself as the innovation, but the *underlying learning experience*. That is what must be recognized and evaluated.[J]

Aside from the issues of cognitive and emotional complexity is the continuing evolution of computers themselves, not just what they can do but also how affordable they are. Computer-related functionality, including communications, is still evolving, and the importance of computers is unquestionably increasing. The breadth of their utility is also enough that they can be both helpful to student performance and detrimental, the latter coming from some important preoccupations outside the classroom. With the sheer breath and depth of their utility, then, defining the proper roles for computers in learning takes a lot of insightful and careful research. Through a long history of work for NSF and foundations with educational interests and a broad involvement with other educational researchers around the country, SRI has developed an excellent reputation in the field of evaluating technology in learning. We will now examine a few projects on which that reputation is built. [K]

GLOBE—The world as an environmental classroom

GLOBE, which is an acronym for Global Learning and Observations to Benefit the Environment, was created with the support of Senator Al Gore in 1992 as a way to aid the environment and at the same time help primary and secondary students learn science. It has broad and ongoing support within federal agencies such as NOAA, NASA, NSF, EPA, and the State Department. In also tries to teach children how to participate in real science projects and in that process to collaborate both within and beyond their own classrooms. Again, it is the Internet that provides this opportunity. The subject is the monitoring of our environment and the participants are K-12 students from around the world.

SRI's role in GLOBE has centered principally on its evaluation. It was again Means's influence and the efforts of Dr. William Penuel that secured this important work for SRI. It is a role SRI has maintained for the past 7 years and, through a recent extension, will continue

for another 4 years. To understand what this involves, we must say a bit more about the mission of GLOBE.

As mentioned, it tries to elevate K-12 students into roles they can play in helping monitor the life-critical properties of the environment, such as our water and air. Teachers and students collect local measurements on some aspect of the environment and submit the data to scientists, who in turn mentor the teachers and students in how to think analytically and apply scientific concepts to what they are doing.[9] In a 1998 survey almost two-thirds of the teachers participating in GLOBE said their students were involved in analyzing, discussing, and interpreting such data. Some of the greatest impacts are found in the students' observational and measurement skills and their ability to work technically in small groups.[L] In their locales they can study such environmental attributes as the quality of the soil, including its conductivity and acidity; the amount of ultraviolet radiation; and the level of carbon dioxide and certain particulates in the air. These data and insights speak to their local area yet are all pooled over the planet with some collaboration being specific to other schools.

SRI has made a number of contributions to the program. It has shaped the program's recruiting strategy and refined its teacher training program. SRI evaluations recognized that GLOBE was much easier to implement in a school when multiple teachers were trained together and articulating the kind of support teachers need when building an atmosphere for student-directed inquiry. SRI has also helped increase the focus in GLOBE on that same student-directed scientific inquiry.[M] Finally, it must be said that although the online database and visualizations of GLOBE are essential in gaining a larger and more significant environmental perspective, it is the ability of the teachers to create or enable the relevant activity that is crucial to its success.

Center for Innovative Learning Technologies (CILT)

It was on a napkin at Café Barrone in Menlo Park that Drs. Roy Pea, Barbara Means, and Marcia Linn (of UC Berkeley) first outlined the concepts of what they hoped would be a new

---

[9] Importantly, the students follow the collection protocols set up by scientists participating in GLOBE.

NSF center in educational technology. They then recruited colleagues from Vanderbilt and the Concord Consortium to join in. Since there are not many such centers at NSF, there is an implied sense of importance to the subjects they address. The proposal to NSF was successful, and CILT was formed in the fall of 1997. It involved the four institutions and was scheduled to run for 4 years plus an incentive-based 5th year.[10] The grant was made to stimulate the development and study of important, technology-enabled solutions to critical problems in K-14 science, mathematics, engineering, and technology learning. Both the Center's leadership and its approach were to be broadly inclusive of talents and efforts around the United States. There were a number of ways in which that broad mission would be carried out:

- Concentrate on four computer-related focus areas:
  - Visualization and modeling
  - Ubiquitous computing
  - Assessments for learning
  - Community tools.
- Hold workshops within the learning technology community.
- Fund seed grants for collaboration in critical directions for the field.
- Build a network of people and resources relevant to the field.
- Fund a postdoctoral program.
- Create an industry alliance program to encourage successful products.

The project participants worked for 4 years to exploit new technologies, explore interdisciplinary insights, and critically evaluate their own collective innovations and progress. Beyond the published progress of the project, its industry-aligned collaborations brought players such as Intel, Sun Microsystems, Pasco, and Palm into the exercise. Palm also chose to participate through SRI in a separate, broadly based competition for innovative educational software for its handheld platform. Thus began a series of Palm projects at SRI to explore the classroom utility of handheld computing devices. The tasks ranged from record keeping for the teacher to real-time sensor

measurements in the scientific disciplines for the students.

As of 2004, CILT sponsorship at NSF was ended. In the offing, however, is set of new NSF centers that will investigate the science of learning itself, including examining what in the brain enables learning to take place. Brain physiologists as well as cognitive scientists and educators will participate in these new centers and SRI, along with participants from the Stanford School of Medicine, will be subcontractors to one of the new NSF centers opening at the University of Washington.

Performance Assessment Links in Science—PALS

PALS is an online, digital library of standards-based science performance assessments for grades K-12. By accessing a web site, educators can find more than a hundred science performance tasks, complete with administrative procedures, student instructions, scoring methods, and response forms. There are also examples of student work and data on technical quality. These assessments have been aligned with the National Science Education Standards. The site also provides online professional development and assists in adapting the modules and their scoring to local situations. The development process for PALS is rigorous enough to satisfy state accountability requirements. Adding to all this is a secure area for educators to post directed responses and experiences. Through this confluence of assessment standards and experiences, NSF and SRI are helping advance the quality of K-12 science education.[11]

The Online Evaluation Resource Library—OERL

Earlier in this section it was asserted that a successful evaluation of computing technology in the multidimensional realm of education, requires very carefully planned experiments. Some of the evidence supporting SRI's splendid reputation in the field of education evaluation can be found in yet another web site (oerl.sri.com), devoted, in this case, to helping educators design, carry out, and report on evaluation projects. SRI operates the site on behalf of NSF with an eye toward enabling more consistent and valid results in the

---

[10] Stanford University became the fifth partner later when Pea joined its faculty.

[11] Dr. Edys Quellmalz is responsible for PALS.

evaluation of NSF's own projects, but its use has become truly worldwide.

OERL, led by Dr. Geneva Haertel, is a compilation of more than 70 plans and reports and more than 200 instruments that can be used directly or modified for tailored situations. Recently, a set of professional development modules on how to design surveys and evaluations has also been added to the library. Showing that the cobbler's children can have shoes, the site itself undergoes periodic evaluations by a panel of five nationally recognized evaluation experts. To perform this kind of review, data and surveys are taken on site usage. Through a 3-month period ending in March 2003, the site served more than 43,000 pages, or around 400 per day. Those requests came from more than 6,400 different IP addresses in 73 countries. The use of OERL to produce higher-quality and more defendable experiments has certainly saved effort and money, both in the United States and abroad.

A Final Observation

This section has covered a combination of (1) the development of educational software intended to support a new and valuable kind of learning or teaching experience and (2) innovative methods and measurements in the evaluation of such programs. It is the presence and excellence of both of these

capabilities that have brought such success to SRI in this field. Further, SRI's objective detachment enables a broad range of partnerships with *all players* in the education technology field, be they developers, users, or agents of change such as NSF and Congress.

To end this section on the role of technology in learning and its realization at SRI, here is a quote from the abstract of a paper by some of the SRI principals in the field.[N]

> "Research indicates...that the use of technology as an effective learning tool is more likely to take place when embedded in a broader education reform movement that includes improvements in teacher training, curriculum, student assessment, and a school's capacity for change."

The natural integration of computing power into our lives is a long-term process that should be aided in no more logical place than our schools. However, that integration may be recursive in that the full integration of computing into the fabric of education may well come only with its more complete acceptance in the noneducational world. Clearly, one would hope not, because, rationally, our schools should lead the way. But the inevitable pervasiveness of this new machine and its consequences will almost certainly take us on a long and uncharted path.

Instruction Outside the Classroom—The Standards of the PGA

It was about 2 p.m. on a Friday afternoon in September of 1990 when a phone call came to Gary Bridges at SRI (see Figure 12-9). A woman with a richly southern accent related that a golf professional from Livermore, California, had told her that SRI did work in education. She was frustrated in that they had interviewed 40 other consulting firms looking for someone to do an assessment of the PGA training program and make some recommendations for change. SRI

was the last firm they would call, and could she have a proposal by next Tuesday? A proposal was written that qualified SRI for further review (see box) and a site visit scheduled for that December. SRI's half-day presentation consisted of a lot of questions—so many, in fact, that the visitors, the education director of the PGA and staff, were beginning to doubt SRI's abilities. But during a working lunch, SRI's Ed Claassen summarized all the morning's discussion in seven bullets. This showed the PGA that not only did the SRI staff understand the situation better than their competitors, they were able to represent succinctly and powerfully the work to be done. Thus began a 10-year relationship between SRI and the PGA.

Figure 12-9. Gary Bridges and plaque from the PGA commending the SRI work.

SRI's work for the educational segment of the PGA opened with a needs assessment, the presentation of which played to a standing ovation and the acceptance of a multimillion-dollar proposal to address what had been discovered. The work after that has varied. The most urgent need was a training program for golf professionals, which evolved over several years. This defined the entrance schooling required of all who would become PGA members. SRI then developed the PGA certification program that evidences a golf professional's competence in a number of specialty areas, such as running a tournament, managing a profitable golf business, and teaching golf. This education and qualification program then needed to be maintained as new members joined and new needs arose.

To round out this story, it is useful to look at why being in the ranks of the PGA engenders so much pride. To become a member, you logically have to be good at golf. That means no more than 155 strokes over 36 holes. Candidates then face the SRI-designed, rigorous education and certification program involving people, business, and teaching skills that range from customer relations to merchandising, facility management, and golf-teaching methods. Candidates are tested four different times, using techniques such as performance simulations and a 100-step work experience test. Part of SRI's contribution was to transfer to the PGA the ability to maintain the program. As such, the PGA is now able to operate the entire system without further assistance. As an indication of the rigor of the program, there is a 40% attrition rate, leaving only the very best to graduate. SRI has partnered with the PGA to create an education and screening process that guarantees the professional reputation the organization has sought.

Endnotes

[A] HHS Fact Sheet, U.S. Department of Health and Human Services, dated February 21, 2001. That year the coverage was expanded beyond the previous 3- to 5-year-olds to include families with toddlers and even pregnant women.

[B] Nina H. Shokraii and Patrick F. Fagan, "After 33 Years and $30 Billion, Time to Find Out If Head Start Produces Results," American Heritage Foundation, July 15, 1998. Article heavily quotes the following GAO report: "Head Start: Research Provides Little Information on Impact of Current Program," GAO/HEHS-97-59, April 15, 1997.

[C] Cathy L. Watkins, "Follow Through: Why Didn't We," (California State University, Stanislaus), Effective School Practices, Vol. 15, No. 1, Winter 1995

[D] Ibid.

[E] SRI Project 7370, "Longitudinal Evaluation of the National Follow Through Program," about $900,000, June 1969 to September 1969; SRI Project 8071, "Preliminary Evaluation of Planned Variation in Head Start," $228,000, July 1969 to September 1970; and SRI Project 2980, "Follow Through Evaluation," $1.8 million, October 1973 to April 1975 to September 1970.

[F] See SRI reports Summary Report on Follow Through Testing Program, 1969–1975 by Ann R. Wright for the Office of Education, HEW, Contract OEC-0-74-0582, September 1976; and Summary of Follow Through Data by Teresa Middleton and Lawrence Durgin.

[G] Jane Stallings, "Implementation and Child Effects of Teaching Practices in Follow Through Classrooms," Monographs of the Society for Research in Child Development, Serial No. 163, Vol. 40, Nos. 7–8, December 1975.

[H] Watkins, op. cit.

[I] See http://ti2.sri.com/tappedin/. Tapped In is a play on the acronym TPD that stands for teacher professional development and "ti2" is short for the second version of Tapped In.

[J] Barbara Means, email of August 10, 2003.

[K] Some of the perspectives in what follows comes from a rather comprehensive look at the subject in "Changing How and What Children Learn in School with Computer-Based Technologies," found in Children and Computer Technology, 10(2), Fall/Winter 2000. This is from a topic-specific journal of the David and Lucile Packard Foundation about the future of children. The authors are Jeremy Roschelle, Roy Pea, Christopher Hoadley, Douglas Gordin, and Barbara Means, all of whom were at SRI at the time.

[L] Roschelle et al., op. cit.

[M] Dr. William Penuel, email on July 2, 2003.

[N] Roschelle et al., op. cit.

Chapter 13
The World of Business and Economics

Background

SRI's involvement in the business community was ordained from the beginning. The Institute was to be, according to its architects, of service to industry in the Western United States. Some Western clients were clearly important to the early Institute: the Bank of America's large and innovative automatic check processing project of the early 1950s comes to mind. But probably because the Institute wanted to grow and could do so much faster than such a limited region could enable, it soon sought and accepted project work far beyond the West. Revealingly, SRI's first project was not even from industry but from the U.S. Office of Naval Research to seek better sources of the natural rubber that had become so scarce during World War II.

If helping Western U.S. industry was an objective at SRI's creation, then economics was one of its charter disciplines. Over time SRI would use that discipline in two important ways: to help invent new and fundamental ways that businesses could plan and operate and to help grow the economies of what are now called developing countries.

But overlaid on this range of economic applications came a stipulation from Stanford that would limit SRI's role, at least in support of business clients. SRI was to be a place of research. In other words, in solving a client's problem, it was all right to gather and analyze facts and from that analysis to draw conclusions.[1, A] But recommendations were another matter, and providing what is now called management consulting was not encouraged. What now seem like fine and arbitrary distinctions influenced the kind of work that SRI did in the early days, principally in work for the business sector. While the stipulation may not of always been obeyed, it took SRI's separation from the University in 1970 to formally lay it to rest.

To understand what that restriction meant, let's look at a brief example involving a small project SRI undertook for Hewlett-Packard (HP).[2] At the very beginning of the era of handheld calculators, in 1968, Bill Hewlett had tasked his engineers to build a desktop-size computer and then, in about 1970, to make one small enough to fit in his shirt pocket. That first HP unit, which was to become the renowned HP-35, was designed to meet the needs of engineers and scientists. While HP itself chose to gauge that particular market, Bill Hewlett was curious about the reception of a similar calculator for the general business community.

Accordingly, Hewlett initiated a small project, in which SRI presented nonfunctional handheld calculator mockups to sets of focus groups in San Francisco. From these groups, SRI was to determine a price point for the business community. The result of interviewing the focus groups was that it should not exceed $100; that is, portability for the portrayed business calculator was not worth more. The outcome, reported orally to Hewlett in 1971, turned out to be about one-fourth what HP was targeting for the scientific HP-35. This finding frustrated Hewlett, but SRI was simply reporting its data and didn't, in this case, forecast the overall calculator market or make any recommendations. Hewlett ignored the business calculator price point, proceeded with the HP-35, and, as is well known, created a huge success. Perhaps expectedly, the myth grew in the halls of HP that SRI had misjudged

---

[1] The third stipulation in the SRI statement of policies: "[SRI would]...emphasize use of the 'scientific method' in all research investigations, pointing out that the Institute must be a 'fact-finding' organization, and not give advice and opinions supported only by experience and judgment."

[2] While the motivation for looking into this story came from former SRI employee Joe Fredrick, who now works for Agilent and had heard of the negative reputation SRI had concerning the HP-35, most of what follows came from project leader Joe Hornor and analyst Bill Waters. (The project must have been small (under $10,000) for it does not show up on SRI's list of individual projects.) The picture inside HP also claimed that the SRI people who worked on the project left after the study to work for HP competitor, Texas Instruments. As would be my distinct inclination, that clearly proved untrue.

the market. It was, of course, not SRI's judgment that was faulty, but simply a reflection of the limitations of narrowly focused market data unrelated to the scientific HP-35. The framework would change the following year when HP asked for a market study on a forthcoming business calculator.

That next year, 1972, HP asked SRI to take a more formal and complete look at the market for handheld *programmable* business calculators. Under a freer atmosphere and perhaps with greater public awareness of such calculators, SRI's market estimate indicated several hundred thousand units per year by 1980. Clearly, if there were residual bad feelings about SRI's market assessment abilities, this second request would never have come.

SRI Goes International

The pressure to undertake foreign work came during SRI's third year: in late 1949, the SRI Board began encouraging the Institute to grow its competence in the international field. One director emphasized, "a vast need exists throughout the Free World for greater economic and industrial development." Further, he suggested that the Institute look into economic development projects in India, Pakistan, Brazil, and other developing nations. The Board also foresaw the continued internationalization of business and encouraged SRI to accept a role in that process. By 1962, the Institute and many of its directors had created a policy that would govern SRI's expansion of work overseas. The targets were inclusive: the industrialization of Western Europe and Japan, the rapid economic development of other industrialized nations such as Canada and Australia, the expansion of U.S. and foreign countries into international activities, economic development in emerging nations, and the growing economic and political interdependence of a shrinking world.[3]

In July 1950, SRI negotiated its first international business with two contracts: a large ($159,000) economic review of the war-ravaged Italian mechanical industries for the Italian government and the U.S. Economic Cooperation Administration, followed within a couple of weeks with a smaller ($15,000) economic study of Cuba for the International Bank for Reconstruction and Development. Interestingly, one member of that first international project team was the Italian Lorenzo Franceschini, who became the first international fellow in the economics area of SRI. In 1955, after a short time in Menlo Park, he returned to Italy to open SRI's first overseas office. That office, in Milan, operated for over 40 years.

SRI's foreign work continued to increase from 1950 until it accounted for 10% to 20% of revenue. The exact fraction of the total revenue stream it represented was, unfortunately, not reliably broken out for the first 20 years. Indications around 1966 indicate that international work had grown to $10 million or about 18% of revenue. It should be noted, however, that about half of that 1966 revenue came from U.S. military agencies that had requested assistance overseas.[B] The incomplete accounting ended, perhaps not coincidently, with the separation of SRI from Stanford University in 1970. During the 25 years following 1970, the business sector's portion of SRI's revenues is as shown in Figure 13-1.[4]

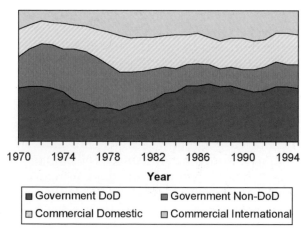

Figure 13-1. SRI revenue mix by funding sector.

[3]Weldon B. Gibson, *SRI Journal*, Feature Issue 4, 32–34 December 1966. The article goes on to say that the interest of the Board continued and that in 1963 it enthusiastically adopted a plan to increase international work and to create an entity known as SRI-International with responsibility for all international operations. This was 14 years before SRI *itself* would likewise change its name to SRI International.

[4] The four sectors of SRI's revenue, covered in Appendix D, are well enough defined to see their respective strengths over much of SRI's existence.

FOREIGN COUNTRIES IN WHICH SRI HAS PERFORMED CONTRACT WORK*

North America	Europe	Ghana	Asia
Canada	Austria	Ivory Coast	Kazakhstan
Mexico	Belgium	Kenya	Asian Subcontinent
Central America	Denmark	Liberia	Bangladesh
Costa Rica	Finland	Libya	India
Curaçao	France	Malagasy Republic	Pakistan
Haiti	Germany	Morocco	East Asia
Honduras	Greece	Nigeria	China
Jamaica	Ireland	Malawi	Hong Kong
Nicaragua	Italy	Tanzania	Japan
Panama	Netherlands	South Africa	Philippines
South America	Norway	Sudan	Republic of Korea
Argentina	Portugal	Zambia	Taiwan
Bolivia	Slovenia	Middle East	Southeast Asia
Brazil	Spain	Cyprus	Burma
Chile	Sweden	Iran	Indonesia
Colombia	Switzerland	Israel	Malaysia
Ecuador	United Kingdom	Jordan	Singapore
Guyana	Yugoslavia	Kuwait	South Vietnam
Paraguay	Africa	Lebanon	Thailand
Peru	Cameroon	Oman	Australia
Venezuela	Dahomey	Qatar	New Zealand
	Egypt	Saudi Arabia	
	Ethiopia		

* Gordon Parker, International Project History, an internal SRI document, 1986.

So, beginning in the early 1950s and continuing over the next 30 years, fueled early on by the prodigious energies of Weldon B. (Hoot) Gibson and others leaders in the Business Group, SRI would come to serve in most of the world's countries. In many cases, local, in-country project offices were temporarily created but a significant number of more permanent offices were established as well. By the early 1980s, SRI had done contract work in over 80 countries and had "permanent"[5] offices in London, Paris, Bonn, Milan, Stockholm, Lisbon, Zürich, Tokyo, and Taiwan. Because this international work was extremely varied, recounting it linearly would be impossible. In aggregate, and often with fewer "permanent" overseas offices than just listed, the number of countries in or for which SRI has done work numbers more than 110 (see the above table for a list as of March 1987).[C]

As a concluding point in this discussion of SRI's sectors of revenue, it might be useful to look at how SRI's different operating Groups

faired in the commercial field. Over most of its history the Engineering, Sciences, and Education Groups of SRI gravitated toward government research contracts whereas the Business Group concentrated on the commercial and international sectors. Though true in general, here are a few exceptions:

- The Engineering and Sciences Groups also conducted some commercial work, but it usually accounted for less than 20–25% of their revenue. That work sometimes included international projects as well.

- The Business Group did some government work but mostly for overseas governments or for U.S. foundations and the World Bank, both seeking to improve the economic situation in selected countries.

- Many multi-group projects took place, which, for the most part, were led by the Business Group and supported by the more technical side of SRI.

While the Business Group rose to international stature during the 1960s through the late 1980s, that Group, as such, no longer exists at SRI. The reasons for its demise are outlined in a brief history of SRI in Appendix B.

---

[5] Since few things are truly permanent, the use of the term here means there were either multiple, unrelated projects and/or a sales group.

Though that Group is gone in SRI Menlo Park, a very vital and ongoing counterpart to its work in economic development continues out of SRI's Washington DC Office. Some of its work will be covered in Chapter 15.

Economic Development vs. Business Development and Consulting—Definitions

As mentioned earlier, the Business Group had two major divisions of labor. The first consisted of conventional business development and consulting projects, where SRI tried in countless ways to improve the product, market, or operational positions of individual corporations. We will call this work area business development and consulting. This work was both domestic and international. As one small example of the latter, starting in 1984, SRI conducted a series of projects for the electronics and telecommunications divisions of Nokia in Finland. To cap this work off, in early 1986, Paul Beneteau, Pat Henry, and Bill Miller conducted a 4-day seminar in that country dealing with how Nokia might better address opportunities emerging in electronics and telecommunications, including cellular telephone. Though the SRI role there may have been small, Nokia has risen clearly to worldwide prominence. Chapter 14 contains other important examples of how SRI contributed to business development both in fundamental business practices with wide application such as planning, and very directed instances that benefited only individual companies.

The second economic area can be termed economic development, and it applied to the many overseas and domestic projects that SRI conducted that tried to elevate the standard of living of a target population. The work may have been sponsored by a specific in-country governmental entity or by an outside agent, but all of it was done on behalf of the general population in that country. Certainly, the results in this category were not intended to benefit a specific company or corporation directly. Most of the efforts we will cover are international because that has been SRI's major focus. But to illustrate a smaller but important segment of work in domestic economic development, a case or two of that type will also be mentioned.

As the list in the previous table shows, SRI undertook work in both industrialized and developing countries. This distinction, clearly related to the definitions just made, has other ramifications. First of all, the approach, the work to be done, and the type of SRI people to undertake it were much different in those two worlds. The work in industrialized countries was similar to the business development work done in the United States. The stability of governments, laws, and economies enabled more predictable outcomes.

Developing countries, on the other hand, almost universally posed different issues. There were the sometimes-arbitrary actions of leaders, dysfunctional governments, an absence of infrastructure, and most importantly, a lack of trained and knowledgeable people in technical, managerial, and even administrative areas. These factors made it difficult to transition ideas or practices without first training those involved. But, in a few cases, these trained people would go on to assume important roles, even becoming ministers, in the developing country's governments. In other cases, the entrenched and inflexible practices of an incapable government would swallow both SRI changes and its agents of change without a trace.

The culture of the host nation was always important. Many practices were alien to Western minds used to task schedules and assumptions about the work ethic. Since not everyone could be comfortable in this kind of altered environment, staff for the various overseas assignments was generally carefully selected. We will see some of these acculturation problems in Chapter 15.

Necessarily, then, one of the larger impacts SRI had in such countries was the education and training of the local project participants. In essence, SRI's work in most developing countries was intended to impose fundamental changes on the social and economic structure of the nation, whereas work in developed countries was much more incremental, often for the benefit of individual companies. In many cases, only a few of which are discussed, SRI made an important difference when the country was is a position to change. Also, as might be expected, that difference could be attributed to the quality of staff sent to do the work. In some cases we will cover, SRI tried to invoke changes that would enhance the economy through an increase in the economic strength of the middle class. According to SRI's Peter Duncan, by 1965 SRI had helped in the development of small industry in more than 15 countries.

But before continuing, it is critical to mention the second SRI individual singled out for brief recognition in this book. The person most responsible for the rise of SRI's reputation on the international scene is Weldon B. Gibson, known in his day throughout the world as "Hoot."

Weldon B. "Hoot" Gibson (1917–2001)

Any story about SRI's impact in the field of economic and business development must include the person who, more than any other, brought its work to international prominence. When SRI was a fledgling concern in every sense of the word, Hoot joined its small group of research entrepreneurs to help form what we have loosely called the "Business Group." Hoot's SRI ID number was 6 and, alone among the Institute pioneers, he remained longer and did more to put SRI on the global map than any other person.

Those who joined SRI in that field during the 1970s and 1980s often said that SRI's reputation was so good around the world that you could get same-day access to the vast majority of potential clients in any of the 80 or so countries in which SRI had worked. SRI's current president, Curt Carlson, was recently at in international meeting in Barcelona and while riding the bus to the conference happened to sit next to a delegate from India. Following introductions, the Indian gentlemen asked if he knew Hoot Gibson. Of course, came the reply. Well, he went on to say, my father believed that Hoot Gibson had done more for the modernization of India than any other single person![D] This is simply one piece of evidence among many about Hoot's full and productive life. He was totally dedicated to the institution he loved and served.

You will find Hoot's name mentioned in many of the series of important projects that follow, although it probably

deserves to be in many more. The Texas farm boy with the permanent drawl brought himself and SRI into the company of U.S. presidents and foreign dignitaries over about 40 very active years. He was Mr. SRI to the great industrialists of Scandinavia, to the king and ministers of Saudi Arabia, to the presidents of the Philippines and Indonesia. Seeing the growth and common interests of companies around the world, he, with Henry Luce of *Time Magazine*, in 1957 started the quadrennial conference of the "best of the best" in industry. That series, known as the International Industrial Conference (IIC) lasted 40 years and,

Figure 13-2. Dr. Weldon B. "Hoot" Gibson and the SRI achievement award that bears his name.

certainly not incidentally, helped introduce the world to SRI and vice versa. More on that later.

In addition to the IIC and with the help of SRI staff, he arranged for more than 50 regional economic development conferences in 25 countries, starting in Sydney in 1966. These gatherings became a bridge between worldwide commercial interests and the developing countries whose investment needs were critical. His regional interests also sparked the beginning in 1967 of the Pacific Basin Economic Council that continues today as a forum for 1100 companies. These activities, in which many SRI staff played important roles, not only became opportunities for SRI project work but, more importantly, enabled the industrialists of the world to come and find their own opportunities in many of the world's industrialized and developing countries. Of more direct benefit to SRI, Hoot formed its International Associates Program that at one point included dozens of the world's industrial leaders. Outside the United States, he truly became the embodiment of SRI.

To honor Hoot's contribution to SRI, an award in his name was created in 1999 that recognizes SRI staff who have made major contributions "to society, to the peace and prosperity of mankind, and to SRI's reputation around the world." These words, the intention of which can be found in the SRI charter, were indelibly written in the heart and mind of Weldon B. Gibson. A few of his specific and notable legacies will now be mentioned.

SRI's International Conferences, Confabulations, and Pacific Basin Alliances

Over the course of 30 years SRI helped form a number of organizations with common economic goals and convened some of the world's most influential conferences on economic development. Both of these initiatives lie at the nexus between business consulting and economic development (as described above). The marriage of the two was a natural act for SRI and its chief proponent in this area, Hoot Gibson. Essentially, the goal was to bring investment capital into a region with a declared need of economic assistance or development. In some instances, as in Indonesia and the case of its President Suharto, the meetings involved the highest-ranking people in the country. SRI's brokerage of investors and investment need was never formal, but it provided opportunities for the economic growth and stability that the participants found important.

Like so many of SRI's international initiatives, the building of networks of both governmental and industrial executives can be credited to Hoot Gibson. He foresaw the benefits to SRI of becoming the focal point where presidents and chief executive officers of large companies, both national and multinational, could promote their companies' growth and development. Those officials in turn saw the value in exploring new markets, developing corporate relationships and networks, collectively lobbying governments, and honing their executive skills from others'

experiences. The developing countries, for their part, needed investment capital, business acumen, manufacturing techniques, technology insertion, and other capabilities of the industrialized world to elevate their standards of living.

Over time, three important initiatives were undertaken to serve the interests of the international industrial community:

- The International Industrial Conference (IIC)
- The Pacific Basin Economic Council (PBEC)
- The Japan-California Association (JCA).

These groups, particularly the IIC, would give rise to a large number of *ad hoc* regional meetings convened by SRI to serve the economic development of a geographical region. These regional conferences would fall under the auspices of what was called the SRI International Associates Program.[6] The three

---

[6] This should not be confused with another program called the SRI Associates Plan whose main purpose was to raise money for the growth of the Institute. In that Plan corporate members would grant SRI some cash each year to help it buy needed equipment that individual projects couldn't afford and to fund public service research. It began in 1949 and added materially to SRI's early ability to grow. Carl Titus was hired to develop the membership, and he did an excellent job. By the early 1960s, the Plan had yielded over $3.6 million for SRI and by 1965 had almost 170 members. Both Stanford and SRI had been monitoring the Plan's possible encroachment on the University's own fund raising, however, and by the mid-1960s a new policy discouraging such donations spelled the end of the Plan for

business-centered convocations are discussed first.

The International Industrial Conference

Of all the SRI initiatives to bring the world's business leaders together, the IIC was clearly the most prestigious. It was the brainchild of Hoot Gibson and of Henry Luce, publisher of Time-Life. Gibson recalled that he approached Luce in 1957 with a proposal for a senior executive event, worldwide in scope. He said that SRI would organize and operate it if Time would put up the money, to the tune of about a third of a million dollars. Luce agreed and sent SRI a check for $333,333.33.[E]

The IIC became the first worldwide summit of chief executives and gave SRI an enormously favorable reputation overseas. It was held quadrennially, and attendance was restricted to CEOs and was by invitation only. Because San Francisco was an attractive place to visit, the conference was always held there. At the outset, the IIC's purpose was a general one, "stimulating economic and industrial development in the free world."[F] It was to take a forward look at the world's economy. Each Conference centered on two critical topical, themes chosen to interest a large set of international executives. Attendees could also suggest themes, and a few non-industrial experts who had keen insights about the future of the industrial-based economies also attended. Often, SRI specialists in a given subject would moderate the smaller panels.

The first IIC met in San Francisco in October 1957 and it began with a flurry. Henry Luce, who chaired this first conference, said such a forum was needed so world business leaders could share ideas and learn from each other. Because of the enormous needs of developing and recovering countries, the two themes of the first Conference were investing in developing countries and trade liberalization. The meeting ran for 5 days and was attended by more than 600 business leaders from 63 countries—the largest such forum of its time.

The IIC succeeded in achieving not only consistent attendance from the world's industrial elite, but also proved to be a place where new and sometimes provocative ideas were aired. A series of examples:

SRI. (Weldon B. Gibson, *SRI – The Take-Off Days*, Publishing Services Center, Los Altos CA, 1986.)

1957 – David Sarnoff, CEO of the Radio Corporation of America, predicted the wide use of "self-operating machines" in the manufacturing process.

1961 – J.E. Wallace Sterling, president of Stanford University, warned that the business communities of the developed countries had a responsibility toward the developing world to counter communist inroads there.

1965 – H.I. Romnes, chairman of AT&T, spoke of the day when "virtually any one of the world's households might be connected—instantly on demand—with virtually any other."

1969 – Giovanni Agnelli, chairman of Fiat, stressed that the corporation "must maintain a permanent exchange of ideas and experiences with society."

1973 – Sheikh Ahmad Zaki Yamani, minister of Petroleum, Saudi Arabia, spoke of the serious world energy problems and foreshadowed OPEC's plans for an oil embargo.

1977 – William D. Ruckelshaus, Deputy U.S. Attorney General, warned of the need to share the world's dwindling mineral and energy reserves more equitably and noted that "above all else, we need a new set of values."

1981 – Gordon Richardson, Governor of the Bank of England, outlined the necessity of "restoring balance in our domestic economies and balance between our domestic aims and their external consequences in an economically interdependent world."

1985 – Karl Otto Pohl, President of Deutsche Bundesbank, mentioned two time bombs ticking on the world economy—the debt problem and the trade imbalance. He admonished Japan and the United States to help in achieving better trade equilibrium.

1989 – Akio Morita, Chairman of Sony, cited the U.S. emphasis on short-term profit instead of long-term investment in developing quality products as the reason for the U.S.-Japan trade gap. Peter Drucker then responded that, despite Japan's success, it was past its peak and on a decline (see Figure 13-3).

1993 – Paul Allaire, Chairman and CEO of Xerox, pointed toward the need for corporations of the future to gather "the advantages of a large global enterprise and still have the speed of a small local company."

1997 – Renato Ruggiero, former Director General of the World Trade Organization on the future world economy prophesied, "What is clear is that this new information-based economy, free of many of the limitations of distance, time and resources, has the potential to add a new dimension to economic integration—a "borderless" dimension that could dramatically accelerate the growth and development dynamic in much of the world."

Because the IIC was a confluence of so many important industrialists and other dignitaries, SRI kept the profile of the conference purposefully low. Doing so was particularly critical during the turbulent 1960s and 1970s. Executives saw that they could attend with few worries about attracting unwanted attention. Overall, the Conference was applauded by country leaders for its insight into future global economic, social, and political trends. Some endorsements of the impact of the IIC follow:

- "In this world of borderless economies, we must strive to preserve the openness of each economic area in order to ensure global economic well-being and also create a world community. In my view, the IIC, which draws together top business executives from every part of the globe, goes a long way toward achieving this goal."—Tadahiro Sekimoto, Chairman NEC, Japan.

- "I have attended nine straight IICs, beginning in 1961... Over the years I have made valuable contacts and forged lasting friendships by participating in this extraordinary event. A businessman could travel all his life to meet the high-caliber people he can see at the IIC in just a few days. And its challenging discussions have alerted our Group to key international trends."—Suliman S. Olayan, Chairman, The Olayan Group, Saudi Arabia.

- "The IIC strengthens ties among the world's business leaders. This is important as the world becomes ever more interdependent and more competitive at the same time. In a global economy where business entities are partners as well as competitors, personal connections are invaluable."—Brian T. Loton, Chairman, Broken Hill Properties, Australia.

- "In an increasingly high-tech, high-speed business world, new ideas and personal contact are essential for building understanding and trust. There's no substitute for getting to know people face to face – that's what the IIC is all about."—James C. Morgan, Chairman, Applied Materials, United States.

- "The conference was a fantastic assemblage of the Free World's business leaders, and I was pleased with the informality and free discussion which prevailed. I still marvel at the organizational expertise which goes into arranging such a conference; I doubt that anyone else has the capability of so smoothly administering such a gathering." —Allan J. Newmark, President of the Kensington Organization Ltd.

The IIC was held 11 times over a 40-year period. It provided rare opportunities for CEOs to participate with one another in both open and private sessions, on announced and unannounced topics. Because the meetings took place only every 4 years, each conference had an abundance of pent-up issues to discuss. For example, the 1985 gathering argued the impacts of free vs. restricted trade practices from opening gavel to the last forum. But the meeting venues also provided nooks and balconies, as well as off-site interludes, for attendees to develop individual relationships. Those attending seemed to find the meetings a unique and interesting setting.

However, in spite of IIC's success in assembling hundreds of the world's business elite, in the end it did not turn out to be profitable for SRI, either in terms of projects that resulted from contacts with members or in regard to the balance sheet of the conference itself.[7] In some cases, more than a 100 people from SRI were involved one way or another in the ICC, but with the cost of that participation born by their own laboratories.[G] To help improve access to the world's CEO population

---

[7] It was not entirely by accident that just before the first conference, called the International Industrial Development Conference, SRI formed a new operating unit called the International Industrial Development Center. But SRI did not acquire sufficient revenues to offset the underwriting costs of the conferences.

Figure 13-3. The 1989 IIC (like all others, it was held in San Francisco).

to the European Economic Community (EEC and now the European Union).[8]

Canada and New Zealand were asked to join in such a group, but Canada and the United States had traditionally looked eastward in trade matters. Therefore, to get commercial leaders in the U.S. and Canada to cooperate, the Japanese multilateral advocate, Shigeo Nagano, ask for assistance from SRI's Hoot Gibson, who was known around the Pacific region for promoting the multilateral concept. Together, the two toured North America looking to drum up interest. In April 1967, a group of business leaders met in Tokyo to set up PBEC. Only Japan, Australia, and New Zealand were officially represented. The United States had four observers, and Gibson was there as a working advocate. Because of his early creative energies and his continuing help in defining the organization as it met in Hawaii in February 1968 to plan its first conference, Gibson became a founding member. When he became PBEC's fourth Director General in 1974, SRI assumed the Council's administrative duties.[H]

and to help staff the conference, in 1961 the New York-based Conference Board was invited to be a co-sponsor. Over time, individual corporations were also asked to fund parts of each conference and they did. But after a long period of underwriting the cost of organizing each meeting, in spite of the heady atmosphere it had created, and perhaps because of the failing health of its originator, Hoot Gibson, SRI discontinued its ICC sponsorship in 1998. No conference took place in 2001.

The Pacific Basin Economic Council

Like the IIC, the PBEC became a prestigious assemblage of business leaders, and over the past 35 years has evolved into a stable organization that has resulted in many contributions to the region. SRI had an important hand in its birth and growth.

During the 1960s and 1970s, many countries of the Pacific region were blossoming economically. Japan, Taiwan, Singapore, along with Australia, Canada, and the United States, were becoming important exporting countries. About the same time, relationships were being entered into among corporate officials in the region to explore common interests in trade and economies. One alliance, between leading industrialists of Japan and Australia, saw the virtues of broadening their bilateral arrangement. They also thought that the Pacific region ought to explore forming a counterpart

The Council, with bylaws and mission in hand, then, had its first general meeting in May 1968 in Sydney with delegates from the five founding nations, Japan, Australia, New Zealand, Canada, and the U.S. By 1983, PBEC had grown to include members from 17 countries.[9] It still functions today, more than 35 years later, with senior representatives

---

[8] The chief advocates were R.W.C. Anderson of Australia and Shigeo Nagano of Fuji Iron & Steel.
[9] PBEC's web page is www.pbec.org. That same year, 1983, the PBEC Council conferred its Founder-Lifetime Member Award on Gibson.

from more than 1100 businesses in 20 countries around the Pacific Basin with combined sales totaling over $4 trillion.

The Council was founded as a forum "for the exchange of views on economic and business issues affecting the region, and making these views available to Pacific governments and international agencies."[1] As evidence of its stature, PBEC's 1996 meeting in Washington, D.C. was addressed by President Clinton, three U.S. senators, and the Secretary of Defense.

As mentioned, Gibson became its Director General from 1974-1983, followed by SRI's Mark Earle until 1987. SRI extended its administrative duties to providing research into the economic and social development of the region. Though SRI's President William Miller ended SRI's role in PBEC in 1987,[J] Gibson was repeatedly honored as one of its founding members and as a prime mover in its continuation. PBEC is the oldest and most preeminent organization pursuing the interests of the Pacific economic community.

The Japan-California Association

As Japan developed into a powerful exporting nation, issues, perhaps inevitable, arose surrounding trade with the United States. Balance, or rather imbalance of payments, trade barriers, both policy-driven and informal, U.S. investments in Japan, and other issues became important factors in the relationship between these two trade giants. In early 1964, a Japanese trade mission, led by the Chairman of Fuji Bank, Yoshizane Iwasa, visited the United States. As part of the trip, the group met with Rudolph Peterson, President of the Bank of America. There, Iwasa proposed that a group of business leaders from Japan and California meet periodically to discuss these economic and trade problems. Iwasa's invitation was accepted and thus began JCA. The group met first in 1965. SRI was asked to handle JCA's affairs, and by 1969 there had been five meetings at which views were freely and fruitfully exchanged.[K] At that time, nearly 40 companies from Japan and 40 from California participated, and the Association became, in effect, a forum for business diplomacy.

By 1967, The JCA had settled on five major objectives:[L]

- Develop business and trade relationships between Japan and the United States, particularly the Western United States

- Create a greater understanding and appreciation of bilateral political, economic, and security relationships

- Exchange views on these issues and their effect on the Pacific Basin countries

- Examine ways in which companies and other economic institutions of the two countries can aid in the economic development of the Pacific Basin, particularly Southeast Asia

- Facilitate the development of close personal relationships among the collective senior executives.

Surrounding these objectives were a host of additional issues. U.S. executives who wanted to make long-term investments in Japan were frustrated by protracted delays of the Japanese Government. The imbalance of trade, which had strongly and permanently reversed itself in Japan's favor in the mid-1960s, was on everyone's mind, as was on-going Japanese reluctance to permit open U.S. imports and investments. In that regard, the President of Mitsubishi seemed to understand and sympathize with the U.S. trade difficulties. At a JCA meeting, he predicted an order-of-magnitude reduction in the number of restricted imports (then at 120) within 3 years, but admitted it would take strong determination. As it turned, out Japan hasn't yielded much in this area over the years.[10]

Nonetheless, Japan's trade with the United States was still enormous. The sum of their direct import-export business with the United States, plus purchases of oil and other raw materials outside the United States, but from U.S.-owned foreign corporations, comprised fully half of all their international trade.[M]

In regard to another, less confrontational side, some Japanese business leaders in JCA wanted to mutually pursue regional economic development. For example, Fuji Bank's Iwasa said, "As Japan's economic strength expands, Japan should utilize more of its resources for economic assistance and stabilization of the Asian region. It should thus relieve the United States of some of the burden it has been carrying."[N]

---

[10] In a talk before the American Chamber of Commerce in Japan in Tokyo in February 2000, Alan Wolff of Dewey Ballantine LLP noted that of the 424 pages describing trade barriers published by the U.S. Trade Representative, 58 concerned Japan, the highest of any nation.

 Because the issues have been so monumental, improvements have been hard to identify and the Association's impact difficult to assess. Over time, attention given to trade difficulties between the two countries may grow or wane, but progress in reducing the trade imbalance, at least on behalf of the United States, seems minimal.

Nevertheless JCA continues. Today it is known as the Japan-Western Americas Association (JWA). Forty-six Japanese companies from Sony to Honda to Japan Airlines, representing a broad spectrum of exports, are members of JWA. SRI no longer serves as the secretariat for U.S. participants, but SRI Board Chairman Sam Armacost welcomed the most recent annual meeting in 2001 as the Association's co-chairman. That meeting demonstrated the fruits of such gatherings. For example, the heads of both Boeing and Mitsubishi related how the two organizations had become much closer working partners on the Boeing 777 because of the access offered by information technology. The conference also illustrated how modern technology empowers greater employee participation and initiative within the typical Japanese company. These brief indications indicate that, after 37 years and 86 joint meetings, the third SRI-aided consortium is alive and contributing to international relations.

Regional Economic Development Meetings

As a result of discussions in the IIC, PBEC, and other associations in which SRI had a hand, numerous individual regional gatherings were held for which SRI was the major catalyst. (These were carefully orchestrated sessions and, though sizable, were by personal invitation only.) These sessions loosely came under the aegis of what SRI called its International Associates Program. For the most part, that community was a subset of the participants in the IIC who saw value, either altruistic or of self-interest, in joining with SRI to address situations around the globe where some economic need was evident.

Between 1966 and into the mid-1980s, SRI hosted more than 50 economic development meetings around the world—across the Pacific Basin, including Southeast Asia, in South America, China, Europe, India, Mexico, and even in the Soviet Union in 1974 when the Iron Curtain was still tightly shut. SRI's economists, along with other SRI experts, led by Gibson, were instrumental in organizing these conferences and given them their agendas. Sometimes, as in Indonesia, they even drew participation from the highest levels of the government, in this case President Suharto. For each conference, SRI staff prepared background material that pinpointed the region's difficulties so that the attendees could concentrate on specific solutions. Such gatherings were aimed at benefiting the host country or region and often did.

The First "SRI International"

Given all the above relationships, SRI was clearly involved in the international industrial scene. Because sponsoring and administering these associations rarely paid their whole cost, SRI sought two other avenues to make participation profitable. One was to seek project work from the participants as new opportunities and relationships developed. The other was the SRI International Associates Program from which SRI collected a small annual fee. In return, SRI periodically give Program members advanced information from its broad, collective set of non-proprietary investigations.[11] The practice was patterned

after an earlier Associates Plan, which started in SRI's first years and which consisted of industrial concerns and some individuals that saw enough merit in such an institute that they were willing to contribute to its growth. That group lasted for over two decades and by 1965 had 168 associate companies from across the United States.

---

[11] Under the auspices of the SRI International Associates Program, SRI formed yet another collection of CEOs. In

September 1981, it started The Menlo Group, consisting of approximately 250 top executives whose attendance was again by personal invitation. The Group was to focus on a better future for the world business system and to develop closer relationships with governments to make that happen. Quite naturally, the members of the Menlo Group were also members of the IIC and its meetings were held just before the IIC took place.

Finally, in an ironic twist, that part of SRI that operated so successfully, and made the very name of SRI a door-opener across the world, called itself "SRI International." That was, of course, the same name Stanford Research Institute adopted after its separation from Stanford in 1970. In spite of the name, however, the present SRI International no longer has the ear of the international industrial world. To understand its present international role, it is necessary to return to the two distinctions in SRI economic endeavors noted earlier. The business consulting side is gone (see Appendix B), but a small number of dedicated and talented staff in the Washington, D.C. Office continues to assist in improving economic performance and standards of living in many countries. That side of SRI's economic work carries on the tradition.

Endnotes

[A] Weldon B. Gibson, "The Story of SRI at 20 Years", the *SRI Journal,* Feature Issue 4, page 17, December 1966.

[B] Karl Folkers, an excerpt from SRI's Annual Report to its Associates, *SRI Journal,* 13, p. 12, January 1967.

[C] The description of international work draws on material from a rather comprehensive but informal "International Project History," compiled and written by SRI's Gordon H. Parker in 1987.

[D] Curt Carlson at the Gibson memorial ceremony, July 18, 2001.

[E] *SRI Journal,* 5(4), 1-4, November 1985.

[F] SRI's *Research for Industry,* 9(7), 4-5, October 1957.

[G] *SRI Journal,* 5(4), 3, November 1985.

[H] Esme Marris and Malcolm Overland, *The History of the Pacific Basin Economic Council,* PBEC, Wellington and Honolulu, May 1997.

[I] *The SRI Journal,* 3(5), 2-3, August 1983.

[J] Esme Marris and Overland, op. cit.

[K] SRI, *The Japan-California Association (JCA) Report,* SRI-International Report No. 13, August 1969.

[L] JCA Report, 1969, op. cit.

[M] JCA Report, 1969, op. cit.

[N] JCA Report, 1969, op. cit.

Chapter 14
Business Consulting and Development

The SRI Approach

The range of business development work at SRI has been enormously broad. That breadth stemmed both from the early corporate planning methodologies SRI developed and from its broad-based science and technology organization. While its methodological innovations created some of the first comprehensive corporate planning tools, SRI's technological underpinnings also enabled it to make crucial marketplace distinctions. Few, if any, of the competing management consulting firms were able to make such distinctions. Here were some overall characteristics of the SRI approach:

- New corporate or institutional planning methods were introduced that were well grounded in organizational theory and ongoing practice.

- The work was often technology-centered; that is, it dwelt on the relationship between management and its use of technology. The up-to-date nature of science and technology in the rest of SRI, though not always explicitly invoked, formed a basis for understanding how technology could or could not be used.

- The work was objective and care was taken not to compromise that objectivity in whatever relationship ensued.

- Though there were a few exceptions in the telecommunications, chemical, and petroleum industries, projects were generally not oriented toward large-scale, detailed, and long-lasting overhaul of corporate infrastructures.

- The problems tackled were often "rifle shots" rather than broad examinations.

- The work was almost entirely client-private, making it difficult to describe openly.

The latter two characteristics are especially poignant in light of the unscrupulous practices of some large accounting/consulting firms that have recently come to light. As a result of their desires for lucrative, long-term relations with their clients, they strayed from giving objective and truthful advice. In my long experience at SRI, objectivity was never a negotiable or abrogated aspect of its work.

We will start by recounting the development of planning methodology at SRI and, as strategic planning became a vital part of operations, by indicating how such planning gained a respectable foothold in corporate America. Other innovations such as new marketing analysis tools and providing planning information also flourished. We then offer selected accounts of how SRI contributed to important changes in corporate goals and missions. Finally, Appendix B briefly covers the regrettable atrophy of nearly all of SRI's Business Group.

Contributions to Corporate Planning

In the early 1950s, the pace of change in the United States seemed to quicken. New technologies were beginning to pour out of laboratories at unprecedented rates. Businesses had to somehow gauge these changes as opportunities or threats and react accordingly. These challenges to corporate life became an important stimulus for the fledgling Institute, and in the late 1950s SRI took initiatives in the area of corporate consulting, particularly planning, that brought it to a place of

preeminence in that field.[A] Drawing on its technical depth in industrial sectors like electronics, chemicals, petroleum, forest products, and a few others, SRI launched a variety of research and consulting services for the business community. In that endeavor adherence to Stanford's stipulation that consulting was an inappropriate activity for SRI had began slowly to erode.

Principals from the Institute group called Economics Research began to help corporations assess their strengths and weaknesses in the context of their changing business environments and to assist them in aligning their businesses. SRI believed there were three motivations for Corporate America to focus more intently on the future: growing complexity in operations, including international operations; the increased pace of decisions needed to remain competitive; and the variety of outside influences occurring, including the march of technology. The work was, in effect, corporate planning—supplementing the skill of entrepreneurs, who in simpler times would have gone it alone.

Because most of this SRI work was carried out for individual companies, the results were proprietary, and the generic innovations with which SRI helped systematize long-range corporate planning were themselves only slightly more public. This was also the time when SRI's widely recognized Long-Range Planning Service (LRPS), a subscription service for the corporate sector, was launched. That service continues today, over 4 decades later, in an SRI-affiliated company called SRI Consulting Business Intelligence. A brief account of the genesis and the contributions of that planning work follows, including important planning methodologies and examples of individual corporate assistance and planning services.

The Origins of the Long-Range Planning Service

In essence, SRI embarked in the 1950s on a mission of enabling the industrial sector to better cope with change. LRPS, housed in a program of the same name, was intended as a natural adjunct to that mission. SRI's Robert W. Smith (see Figure 14-1) provided the vision for this subscription service; it was based on ideas he had developed while at the Stanford Graduate School of Business. It was also motivated by the fact that SRI had competencies in a number of technical fields and that the economics part of SRI needed a revenue stream that could help smooth out the income from its characteristically short-term projects. He discussed the idea with Hoot Gibson in the early 1950s, but when they brought it before the Institute's Business Advisory Council, there wasn't much interest. So they set it aside.

A few years later, in the mid-1950s, Smith, then assistant director of Economics Research, invested a bit of his overhead money in trying

Figure 14-1. Economist Robert W. Smith.

to find out why certain companies in the decade before 1949 had grown so rapidly. He also had the insight to consider how they were doing at that time, 1954. Surprisingly, over 40% had either stagnated or disappeared altogether.[B] Smith asked whether an analysis of such information would help form a basis for long-range corporate planning and explored these issues in a series of memos around the middle of 1956.[C]

Gaining internal support and a small investment grant from his boss, Joe Lovewell, Smith prepared a sample report on forecasting the need for synthetic fibers. It was finished in April 1958. By summer, with that report in hand and armed with innovative ideas, Smith and a few SRI staff hit the road to test Corporate America's interest in a research-based forecasting service.[1]

The response they got was heartening, and in January 1959 SRI officially launched the first research-based, broad-scale service in support of corporate planning.[D] Not unexpectedly, it was called the Long Range Planning Report Service (the name was later shortened), and it had 73 notable corporate clients right out of the

---

[1] The proselytizing group consisted of Smith, Lovewell, Pat Dowling, Jim MacIsaac, and Bill Royce.

gate.[2] The plethora of subject areas, the time perishability of the information, and the pragmatic aspects of revenue generation suggested that the Service be a continuing one, paid for annually on a multiclient basis. The initial fee was something like $2,500 per year. An important leader in the early phases of LRPRS was N. Robert Maines, who, after leaving to direct planning for J.C. Penney, was replaced by Robert D. Bruce.[3] The Service grew rapidly and soon preempted the field. By 1962, it had over 250 clients and by 1967 over 400, 100 of which were foreign.[E]

As the Service matured, its basis seemed sound: since SRI was a *research* organization, the Program could provide a useful service that monitored changes in the technical, economic, political, and social fields. Moreover, it complemented other SRI work in corporate strategy and the planning assistance provided to individual firms. LRPS reports were of two general types: ones that prescribed the nature and benefits of the planning process, including who should be the responsible parties; and ones that addressed content, defining the present and 10- to 15-year horizons of specific business and technology sectors. The first type was to encourage corporate planning, and the second was to offer information of strategic interest to long-range plans in selected business sectors.

Regarding the planning process itself, the corporate sector was moving to planning as a matter of course. From a 1961 survey of Fortune 500 companies, SRI learned that 60% were undertaking formal long-range or strategic planning, another 24% were planning to do so, and only 16% were not.[F] By 1964, the number doing so had risen to 72%, with only 10% not doing so. A ground swell was in progress, and to take advantage of it SRI established early on a specialized group in the theory and practice of corporate planning. The group performed comparative studies on the planning practices in use and then developed a framework for business planning that many of its LRPS clients used. SRI examined all aspects of the planning process, including the reasons for planning, the responsibility of corporate executives and the line structure, ways to assess the market and competitive environments, the financial aspects

of planning, the interdependence of plan formation by all segments of the organization, and means to assure the successful execution of a plan. Between 1961 and 1994, SRI staff wrote about 75 reports on the methods and practice of corporate management and planning.[G] At one point, the subscription list exceeded 500, suggesting that SRI had clearly filled a perceived need.

In the area of forecasting, by the mid-1960s LRPS had published about 300 reports, with a rate of about 40 reports issued a year. These reports dealt with specific but diverse fields of interest such as cryogenics, microencapsulation, antitrust policies, nuclear power, consumer values, the labor force, electroluminescence, and pleasure travel. Authors were drawn from knowledgeable people across SRI, Stanford or other universities, or individual consultants. Often both technical specialists and economists or sociologists were paired to provide a balanced view.

Because just providing written material didn't always meet the needs of the client base, SRI also included opportunities for extensive interaction, ranging from directed technical assistance for individual companies to weeklong seminars for executive planners to engender more effective planning methods in their companies. In the area of forecasting, SRI included an inquiry service that provided interchange with the report authors, visits from key company personnel, and traveling seminars and roundtables. Another important feature of LRPS was its annual client conference, which brought 300-500 clients to the San Francisco Bay Area. Beginning in 1966, a conference was also held in Europe. All these efforts sought to assure an effective transfer of ideas and practices.[4] These closer relationships with clients also served to increase the Institute's technical business. Since LRPS reports were also a showcase of SRI's capabilities, they attracted some clients by the expertise they evidenced. From these interactions came new products and marketing concepts.

---

[2] For a list of the original set and how their participation continued, see Appendix I.

[3] The Program leadership following Bruce was: William S. Royce, James C. Selover, Richard C. Funkhouser, Merle Evers, Joseph E. R. Carrier, Paul E. Shay, Gary Anderson, and William D. Guns.

[4] Besides those people mentioned, other contributors to LRPS were: Pat Dowling, Jim MacIsaac, Robert Dawson, E. S. Calhoun, Arnold Mitchell, Dan Shearer, Eleanor Connolly, Riggs Monfort, Ken Taylor, Edith Molton, Gloria Esdale, Alice Greene, Jean Ware Nelson, Doug Hurd, John Gayle, and Millicent Craig.

Origin of the Term "Stakeholder"

Several novel concepts arose from these innovative practices. One was the notion of "stakeholders." In common use today, the term loosely describes all those parties who have a critical interest in the operation and success of any enterprise. SRI first formulated the term in about 1963.[5] Since then, the concept has grown to such global acceptance that formal theories and international conferences are now held on the concept of stakeholders.[6] Many, including economist Milton Friedman,[H] have said that the only purpose of a company is to make a profit for its shareholders; that is, the shareholders are the only stakeholder group to which managers are accountable. SRI's viewpoint, expressed years earlier, was that a corporation is beholden to more that just its shareholders and defined stakeholders as:[I]

A stakeholder in an organization is any group or individual who can affect or is affected by the achievement of the organization's objectives.

That very broad definition originally included the groups shown in a 1965 briefing slide: the shareowners, employees, customers, suppliers, lenders, and society (see Figure 14-2). In some respects, this is a set of participants any one of which, through their withdrawal, could cause the enterprise to fail. Many academics have created their own version of the concept by adding such stakeholders as the environment and competitors. In any case, SRI's definition clearly reflects today's climate for business better than any narrow construct such as just shareholders. Though shareholders are still perhaps the most important

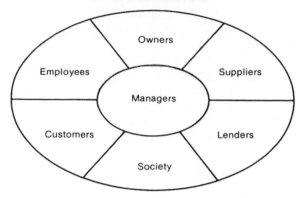

A BUSINESS REQUIRES THE WILLING INTERACTION OF ITS STAKEHOLDERS

Figure 14-2. The candidate stakeholders in an enterprise (from SRI's BIP Research Report 635, *Stakeholder Values and Corporate Success*, Sept 1980).

stakeholders, for managers to be successful today they must base their decisions on broader issues. SRI went on to develop methods for defining, analyzing, and showing the cross-impacts created by the expectations of the various stakeholders.

Another innovation from around 1965 was a computerized financial planning model that planners could use to determine the 5- and 10-year results of executing a strategic plan under various sets of assumptions. SRI's program, which was probably the first of its kind, used the dial-up feature of General Electric's (GE) Time-Sharing System in Cleveland and was thus available across the country.[7] As might have been expected, other consulting firms such as Battelle and A.D. Little soon began offering competing programs. New planning specialist houses also entered the field: the Boston Consulting Group (an SRI client that adopted SRI material), the Strategic Planning Institute, and GE-McKinsey. At the same time, the characteristically "faddy" business of corporate management methodology was cycling, and SRI efforts were being questioned. In addition, reductions in the LRPS client base caused SRI to re-examine its approach to planning. The result was the emergence in the early 1970s of new, more sophisticated planning and decision aids, in essence the sought-after next-generation tools. By the mid-1970s, the LRPS Program itself had

---

[5] According to Bill Royce (see Endnote D), the first printed use of "stakeholders" in a business sense appeared in LRPS Report 168 entitled *The Strategic Plan* published in April 1963. In the preparation of that report, Robert Stewart, Knight Allen, and Marion Doscher were discussing who should have influence on a corporate purpose. Doscher defined them as "stakeholders," to her an old Scottish term meaning those with a legitimate claim on something of value. Actually, its semantics go something like this: stakeholder is literally the holder of a wager but stake is also short for grubstake, an early U.S. Western term meaning an advance given to a prospector in expectation of a share in his finds. It thus conveys a natural interest in an enterprise. Regardless, it caught on and was used extensively thereafter. Because the term is now so common, a couple of external affirmations of its SRI origins may be helpful: see a paper on business ethics by Johanna Kujala at www.mcb.co.uk/ services/conteren/jun98/bale/kujala.html and Igor Ansoff's *Corporate Strategy*, McGraw-Hill, 1965, p. 34.

[6] An example is the Stakeholder Theory Conference, University of Toronto, May 1996.

[7] Manuel Stotomayor designed the program, called "Topline" to show how much a company could grow if it did its best. Walt Wiebensen of Engineering did the programming.

been revamped and given its present name, the Business Intelligence Program.

Methods in Corporate Planning

To see how this re-examination contributed to new corporate planning methods, it is necessary to return to the early 1960s when SRI's contributions to planning first began. According to Royce,[J] planning methodology began at SRI in response to LRPS clients who were pleased with SRI's information on *what* to plan for, but also wanted help in knowing *how* to plan. In 1962, SRI's first foray into this field came with the formation of a group under LRPS called TAPP, for the Theory and Practice of Planning. Robert F. Stewart, who had developed

and in early 1963 started an important series of LRPS reports on planning, the first of which was titled *A Framework for Corporate Planning*. This series was distilled into what came to be known as the "SRI System of Plans," which was widely copied and adapted in corporate circles. Figure 14-3 illustrates the system.

SRI also started other initiatives in the techniques of corporate growth and renewal in the early 1960s. A three-pronged, internal strategy unfolded consisting of: the planning process, which was embodied in TAPP; the creative thinking process, which grew into the Innovation Management Program under Joe McPherson (discussed later); and the Corporate Strategy Program under Knight Allen, which included techniques that promoted corporate

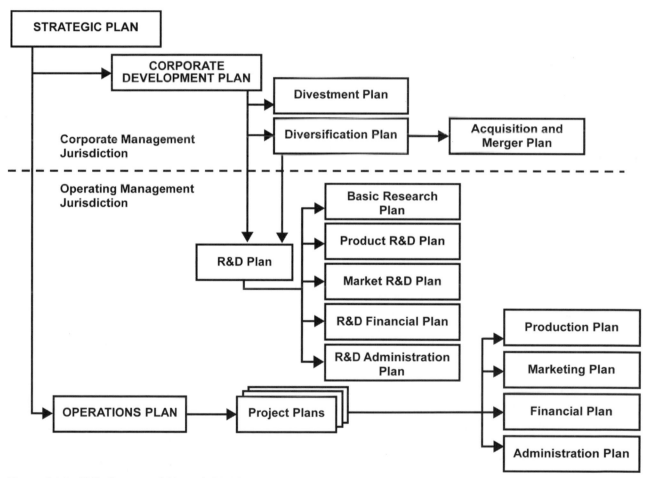

Figure 14-3. SRI's System of Plans (~1965).

some novel ideas in corporate planning at Lockheed, was put in charge of the new group[8]

adaptation and growth. From this milieu, with a number of linkages to the Stanford Business and Engineering Schools and close relationships with a few other pioneers in corporate

---

[8] Stewart also brought Otis Benepe and Marion Doscher with him from Lockheed. Birger Lie came, as a full-time "consultant," from the Norwegian Productivity Institute, and Albert Humphrey came from Boeing. Other SRI contributors

were Robert Smith, Knight Allen, Morse Cavender, Arnold Mitchell, Igor Ansoff, Robert Dawson, and William Royce.

planning, SRI gained prominence in both the methods and practices of corporate decision making and strategy definition.

These were fruitful times in this part of SRI. Out of the concepts mentioned above came a number of other innovations for looking at and conducting planning for any organization. One approach, a step-by-step logic method created by SRI's Otis Benepe, was intended to let a small team of planners build a strategic plan. This method was formulated as a *decision-making process* and drew on what has proven to be a long-lasting, repeatable rationale patterned on how humans normally approach such a challenge. They called it the Chain of Reasoning, and, as still practiced today, it looks something like this.

Values → Appraisal → Motivation → Search → Select → Program → Act → Monitor

Though the logic is simple and straightforward, the detailed method extensively defines each of the stages and their transitions, thus providing planners with comprehensive information and insights, and not letting them be hampered by *a priori* constraints.

These methods were taught to corporate executives in International Executive Seminars, which were held four times a year from 1965 through 1971 in the United States and abroad, and eventually involved 500 different companies. Importantly, the proposed methods often received early testing in real corporate settings, frequently tailored to fit the situation. SRI was careful to tell clients when a method had been proven in one or more companies, and never included the method in a LRPS or TAPP report until it had been successfully employed. Though successful, SRI management eventually decided this approach had become too applied, and handed the methods over to a set of employees who left SRI in 1970 to pursue the methods' use.[K] Those ex-employees called the methods Participatory Planning and then TAM, for Team Action Management, and they have been successfully using them for about 30 years, on both sides of the Atlantic.[9, L]

The value and intricacies of the logic chain above can also be seen in another feature that took on a life of its own. From the reasoning chain's first steps emerged the following question set about an enterprise and its environment:

- What is good about the present situation; that is, what is satisfactory?
- What is good about the future? What are important opportunities?
- What is bad about the present; that is, what are our critical faults?
- What is bad about the future or, in other words, what are the coming threats?

This method was called SOFT, an acronym keyed to the last word in each of the above questions. SRI presented seminars using this method in Europe for a time, and one of the attendees in Zürich, the consulting firm of Urick and Orr, embraced it and began using it. That firm changed the names slightly by letting S represent strengths and substituting W (for weakness) for F, rearranging terms to make it pronounceable, and creating a livelier acronym called SWOT. Such naming seems important only for recognition in the consulting marketplace but, in any case, the associated methodology has become almost generic to planning processes anywhere.

These planning methods and educational seminars that arose out of the TAPP effort also challenged the earlier Stanford stipulation that SRI should stick only with research. To allay Stanford's fears, SRI management invited the University's Graduate School of Business to provide such training in corporate planning, but it demurred. So, SRI proceeded, ultimately offering training to over 1,000 people between 1965 and 1971. But SRI's innovation in planning methods still wasn't complete. Two powerful methods for corporate decision making emerged that would also gain worldwide prominence: decision analysis and scenario-based planning. Much of the former came to SRI from the Stanford engineering area, whereas the latter was developed largely at SRI itself.

Not coincidentally, both of these new areas tried to help corporate planners cope with the inevitable uncertainties that influence future decisions or outcomes. One of the dominant uncertainties in any planning process is the type of future the company will face. Since no one can consistently forecast such things as the environment for competition, regulation, or market demand, SRI adopted early on the use of both statistics and alternative futures. The

---

[9] The basic dogma of planning created at SRI, including those mentioned, were put widely into practice in the United States, Mexico, Scandinavia, England, and other European countries. Today, these methods are in full use in the planning exercises of over 100 companies.

former is more aligned with decision analysis and the latter with scenario planning.

Alternative Futures and Scenario Planning

The notion of building a hypothetical future and then trying to project resources ahead to somehow profit in that future is probably an ancient one. Governments and futurists have used it to gauge policy, to budget, and sometimes even to deploy resources. The noted Cold War futurist Herman Kahn used similar techniques to imagine the future climate for conflict. The modern name for such an exercise is scenario planning, and SRI has been using that technique for a wide range of assignments since the late 1960s. SRI has some claim to being the first to formalize the technique and give it broad utility.

The need for a way to look more formally at the future arose at SRI in about 1969 in work SRI's Educational Policy Research Center was doing for the U.S. Office of Education, the Department of Transportation, and the Environmental Protection Agency (EPA). The Center's director was Willis Harman, a noted electrical engineering professor from Stanford who had redirected his professional life.[10] New tools were needed to help the U.S. government understand the implications of new or proposed policies. For example, SRI created 10-12 scenarios for the EPA, each with a central concept or theme. In these initial efforts, the themes were arrived at in brainstorming sessions. Thus, the planning sessions in these nonmilitary governmental agencies were devolving into a practice in vogue at the time, alternative futures. But it soon became apparent

to the SRI researchers that a tighter coupling was needed between alternative futures and decision-making, especially if the approach was to find good use in the corporate world.

In the 1970s, several people who would become noted in this field became associated with the Center: Peter Schwartz joined the Center in 1973–1974, and Pierre Wack of Royal Dutch Shell and Ian Wilson of GE became colleagues/clients. The Center, plus these people and SRI's Arnold Mitchell, made significant contributions toward making scenario-based planning appropriate for corporations. In essence, it became a more rigorous, repeatable, less personality-driven methodology that could guide corporate planning. Further, to engage senior executives, only a few different scenarios could be used. In 1978-1979, a new, six-step, circular or reentrant process emerged that schematically resembled that shown in Figure 14-4.[M] This process had three important innovations:

- A decision focus
- The concept of scenario logic
- A high-impact/high-uncertainty matrix to identify the scenario logics.

Scenario logics are essentially a way to organize the various scenarios or outcomes to assure each has a consistent and logical basis and is adequately differentiated from the other alternatives.

Typically, these are not just a mean and two extremes, but rather a set of futures, each of which has a core or basis that can be

---

[10] Harman spent about 16 years at SRI and during that time and afterward left a broad imprint on thought—ideas that were not just limited to gauging the future for corporate or government planning. Some of his ideas had important implications, such as the impacts and implied responsibilities of multinational industries when they, rather than governments, come to dominate the human condition. Others were more mystical, such as his early and extended experimentation with LSD. Noted author Art Kleiner reviews in his book, *The Age of Heretics* (Doubleday, New York, 1996), some of SRI's impacts on New Age thinking. In particular, he asserts that a book by Harman and his SRI colleague, Oliver Markley, *The Changing Images of Man* (Pergamon Press, Elmsford, NY, 1982), gave the best introduction yet as to how conventional organizations should address the more holistic concepts of a planet of limited capacity. That book, which contained contributions by other SRI staff and noted mythologist Joseph Campbell, was written during Harman's stay at SRI. *Heretics* also attributes to SRI the bringing of the term "paradigm" into wide (over)use.

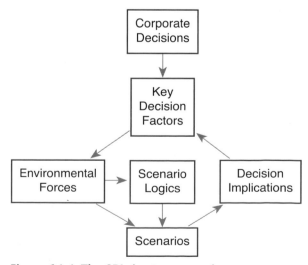

Figure 14-4. The SRI six-step scenario methodology (from Business Intelligence Program Report 822).

independently substantiated. Nor are the futures simply optimistic or pessimistic. Sometimes a "wild card" option is included when a specific event or decision could conceivably cripple the enterprise.[11] The scenarios can also account for social, economic, political, and technological change.

It is important to note that scenario planning, as it was developed at SRI, was mostly qualitative and intended less to predict outcomes than to understand the forces that would drive an outcome. Through gained insight or foresight, such planning helps order perceptions about different futures. It also helps prevent being misled by or even preoccupied with extrapolation of the present situation. More specifically, scenario planning has worked well in three corporate settings: forecasting the future of a business unit; treating a general, corporate-wide issue; and tackling a very specific corporate decision. As in all strategic decision practices, those who are responsible for executing a decision *must* be intimately involved in the planning—sometimes a difficult stipulation to carry out.

Though scenario planning typically doesn't hone in on specific predictions, some of SRI's positions may have seemed otherwise to a tunnel-visioned corporate executive. For instance, take SRI's interaction with Henry Ford II.[N] SRI was developing a notion emerging in the United States that it called "voluntary simplicity." Given the oil embargo of 1975 and the subsequent rise in oil prices, this notion meant, among other things, smaller, more economical cars as a component of the coming "frugality." In a project with The Ford Motor Company, Schwartz, Mitchell, and others concluded that this concept had two important implications: smaller, less profitable cars and an opportunity to provide better services to maintain existing ones. Henry Ford II had heard this future from his internal planners but didn't like it, and he was also at odds over this future with the company's charismatic President, Lee Iacocca. Ford had come to SRI because he hoped the Institute would provide a dissenting opinion. Schwartz made a presentation to Ford and his entourage at SRI. On hearing SRI's

confirming view of a future with more economical cars—and one that persisted for 5–6 years rather than 2—Ford turned to his assistant and revoiced his skepticism: "The Arabs are gonna go away…and Americans ain't gonna want Jap cars." He then offered to Schwartz, "If they wanted 'em, we would do 'em, but Americans don't want 'em."[O] Ford would go on to experience "devastating losses" without small cars, and the Japanese would make substantial market incursions.

Most of SRI's work in scenario planning has addressed fairly circumscribed problems, including scanning the external environment before internal corporate initiatives are put into practice. Clients have included oil companies such as Royal Dutch Shell, ARCO, Statoil of Norway, Amoco, and others interested in the often-volatile future price and availability of crude oil, not to mention demand and pump price. Energy providers such as Pacific Gas and Electric have also used scenario planning. Another role for SRI has been to enable a company to adopt such scenario planning methods for internal purposes. Du Pont is a good example of a large company that, with SRI's help and encouragement, adopted this methodology for use in its planning activities.

With this new methodology in hand, SRI formed a new Strategic Environment Center around the beginning of 1979, led by Schwartz. Ian Wilson soon joined. In 1982, Schwartz left SRI to take Pierre Wack's place at Royal Dutch Shell. Wilson and Tom Mandel became principals in the Center. All this movement didn't interfere with the collegial and ongoing relationships the developers had created. After about 30 years, scenario planning still is carried on by SRI's affiliate, SRI Consulting Business Intelligence. Bill Ralston leads the activity, and some of its more recent influences have been felt at companies such as Weyerhaeuser and Rohm & Haas.

So, in a world of considerable flux in corporate planning methodologies, scenario planning has been in existence for over 30 years. Its base of acceptance in both the academic and corporate communities remains strong. SRI was pivotal in both the development of the methodology and in its continuing practice.[12]

---

[11] As indicated by Bill Royce, SRI urged a company building and operating ships to carry liquefied natural gas from the Mediterranean to the United States to consider a situation in which the king of the source country decided to prohibit export of the gas. That scenario did happen, and the company had followed SRI's advice and had an alternative plan in place.

---

[12] In 1987, Schwartz, Jay Ogilvy, and three futurist colleagues founded Global Business Network, a planning company operating in Emeryville, CA. Both Schwartz and Ogilvy have

Decision Analysis at SRI

As the name suggests, decision analysis is a model or methodology for decision making. In essence, it is a structured way of thinking about how a particular decision or action taken may or may not lead to some desired result. Once a particular decision to be made is identified, statistical methods or logic are then used to represent different forms of uncertainty about important input parameters and about how they are processed to estimate a result. At best, the methodology reveals the relationships between actions and objectives in quantitative terms.

The technique, given a well-formulated pending decision and enough information, comprehensively applied, can provide decision-makers with options whose uncertainties fairly glisten with precision. In effect, the decision is expressed so that the risks and benefits are quantitatively known. Here is a brief example: a CEO had to decide whether to place a new product on the market. The company faced not only uncertainties about market size, timing, and competition, but also about possible government regulatory impacts. After a bevy of multidimensional analyses of costs, risks, and possible benefits, the decision eventually was reduced to the following: proceeding with the product would provide a 20% chance of an overall $88 million profit and an 80% chance of losing $4 million.[p] The decision analysis technique successfully distilled the problem, but the choice was still not easy; it was influenced by personal tolerance for risk or reward.

Decision analysis originated at Harvard and Stanford. Awareness of formalisms for organizational decision-making under stated conditions of risk and benefit came through interdepartmental discussions at SRI in about 1963.[13] Shortly thereafter, a number of joint internal seminars in applied decision theory were held between SRI and Stanford's group in Engineering Economic Systems. Professors Ron Howard of Stanford and Howard Raiffa of Harvard introduced the new field. That interplay led directly to the establishment of a

Decision Analysis Program at SRI in 1968, headed by James E. Matheson,[14] who, with Carl Spetzler, had come from Stanford.

Over the course of a little more than a dozen years at SRI (1969-1983), the successful application of decision analysis to SRI clients was wide and varied. In the commercial sector it was used to evaluate new products, define market strategies, analyze facilities expansion, devise a commodity buying strategy, derive the value of information in mineral exploration, and develop financial portfolio management models. In government the technique has also been applied to space exploration, nuclear reactor development, weather modification, forest fire suppression, and national energy policy (see section on oil shortage later in this Chapter).

One of SRI's legacies for decision analysis is the set of companies formed by those who left SRI to practice the field. They include:[15]

- Decision Focus Inc. (Executive Development Inc.)—Warner North
- Applied Decision Analysis (a subsidiary of PriceWaterhouseCoopers)—Adam Borison, Stan Friedman, Lee Merkhofer, Pete Morris, and Lynn Weber
- Strategic Decision Group—Carl Spetzler, Paul Skov, and James Matheson
- Litigation Risk Analysis—Marc Victor
- Strategic Economic Decisions—Horace "Woody" Brock
- The Beron Group and The Litigation Risk Management Institute—Bruce Beron.

As a final word in this area, SRI effectively had two groups employing this technology, but from different slants. Matheson's approach gave more emphasis to the single, profound, strategic decision on which the company's future hung. The second group, headed by Spetzler and Paul Skov, called its approach Strategic Management; it considered multiple, intricate, and coupled decisions. In 1978, Spetzler and Skov perfected their techniques in projects for GTE and Merrill Lynch, and within a year they had set up their own SRI program

---

written books and published other insights on preparing for the future. Coincidentally, one of their colleagues was Stewart Brand, who spent some time working with Doug Engelbart in the early days of SRI's Augmentation Research Center.

[13] According to Royce, Oliver Whitby of SRI's Engineering Group advised the corporate planning staff to engage some of the leaders in applied decision theory, including the decision analysis creator at Harvard, Howard Raiffa.

[14] Jim Matheson joined SRI in 1966 as a young Stanford Ph.D. working in systems analysis. He helped found a new company, Strategic Decision Group, in 1981 and is currently Chairman of SmartOrg.

[15] Another nonprofit company that concentrated on the future, but was not associated with the decision analysis or planning methods, was The Institute for the Future, founded by former SRI employee Dr. Roy Amara in 1968.

(see a later section about one of the Merrill Lynch projects). This group prospered until the two principals left SRI in 1983. As seems characteristic of SRI, change fosters both success and failure. Decision analysis work lasted for perhaps 13 years at SRI, with the heyday perhaps in 1978-1981. Matheson left SRI in the summer of 1980, and 2 years later Spetzler and Skov left to form the new company mentioned above.

Innovation Search

While much of SRI interests in planning thus found its way outside the Institute, some continued here in several forms. One of the most enduring and most influential was the Innovation Search mentioned above. This was a form of exploration built around the diverse nature of SRI's technical awareness and the personality of its able facilitator, Joe McPherson. The idea emerged after a number of executive planning seminars were held in which McPherson noted a shortage of ideas. SRI's Joe Grippo, a colleague of McPherson's, suggested a form of brainstorming that would draw on specialists from SRI's broad talent base.

The notion was straightforward: bring the principals of a company to SRI, let them explain their challenges as they saw them to a set of SRI experts in fields of potential interest, and then open up a usually wide-ranging exploration of what opportunities the company might want to consider. The Innovation Search was, quite simply, gently guided brainstorming that left the sponsor with a variety of good ideas for future products or sometimes whole new technologies. Its power consisted of the participation by key company people and informed SRI technical staff. The interaction was leavened by the depth of knowledge of the SRI technical participants and the fact that, as researchers, they were inherently used to breaking molds and venturing ideas. This operation continued successfully at SRI for over a decade, and a wide range of sponsor types took advantage of it.

The SRI Business Intelligence Program

What began 50 years ago as LRPS eventually became the SRI Business Intelligence Program in 1976 and continues today as SRI Consulting Business Intelligence (SRIC-BI).[16] Considering

all the vagaries and variability of the corporate economic sector and the fashion-like cycles of business consulting methods, that is remarkable staying power. Its present mission is similar to its initial one: to identify the defining forces of change, thereby helping clients expand their perspectives and then take needed actions. The activity continues to exploit its relationship with SRI's resident technical experts. SRIC-BI still publishes more than 70 documents a year on a wide variety of high-interest topics such as neural networks, mobile communications, e-cinema, consumer behavior, knowledge management, e-learning, genomics, e-commerce, fuel cells, broadband, and consumer finance. Some of these are drawn from a list of 40 current technical topics that SRIC-BI has selected as important and in which the Institute has resident expertise.

Supporting the published forecasts is ongoing advice tailored to specific companies and the use of scenario planning. SRIC-BI's contributions to clients' corporate strategies center on forecasting future technologies and potential products and services. A materials company looking to enter the structural ceramics market uses SRIC-BI to locate a potential joint venture partner, an R&D company with a new technique for making ceramics; a joint venture is formed, and the new company then enters the structural ceramics market with several products. A guidance system company identifies a new parallel computer architecture and licenses the new technology; this architecture will be at the heart of the firm's new products. A chemical company terminates an investment in a polymer matrix composite when it is advised of the likelihood of poor future returns. These topics are indicative of SRIC-BI's ongoing work.

---

[16] LRPS was renamed the Business Intelligence Program in 1976 under Paul Shay. It was later headed by Gary Anderson and then by Bill Guns. Following the demise of the Business Group at SRI in the late 1990s, SRIC-BI became an employee-owned affiliate of SRI in 2001, and Bill Guns heads the new company.

Market Segmentation

VALS™

Most of us are repelled by the notion of being categorized, and we may find such categorization particularly repugnant if someone believes our reactions to consumer offerings are predictable. All of us think of ourselves as independent and capable of rational judgment each and every time we make a purchase. The fact that a process leading to that predictability has an arcane name like psychographic segmentation only adds to our skepticism. Nonetheless, psychographics, along with demographics, has become a pillar supporting today's advertising strategies. SRI developed such a system almost 30 years ago, one that still has wide utility and acceptance. It is called VALS™.[17]

VALS™, which stands for Values and Lifestyles, is an SRI invention of the late 1970s. The brainchild of SRI's Arnold Mitchell (see Figure 14-5), VALS™ was intended to aid manufacturers and other marketing groups better define which segments of the population to direct their products to.[18] Given the billions of dollars being spent on advertising, deriving as much yield as possible from each such dollar spent would be aided by directed advertising.

Established in 1978 and with revised versions still in use today, VALS™ is one of the first major consumer segmentation systems based on lifestyle characteristics. It has been used throughout the United States

Figure 14-5. Arnold Mitchell, creator of VALS™.

and in Japan and Europe to aid in product design, development, and positioning, and to enhance advertising effectiveness and corporate image. A tool like VALS™ is particularly helpful early in the introduction of a new product, when defining a significant relationship between the new product and its principal market. A couple of examples:

- A U.S. watch manufacturer, Timex, used VALS™ to identify a target population for a new blood-pressure monitor for home use. The targeted groups were two: the "societally conscious" and the "achievers," and all aspects of an advertising campaign were directed at them. The company captured 34% of the market within a year, compared with 9% for its closest competitor.

- As a new service, a Minnesota medical center planned to offer cosmetic surgery, which turned out to be an area about which different groups of consumers had sharp differences of opinion. VALS™ segmented groups of potential users, and the Center placed advertising in publications read by the segment deemed to be the most receptive. The campaign was so successful that the advertising campaign had to be discontinued after a few weeks because of overwhelming response.

---

[17] Most of the material covered here comes from an interview with and the writings of Bill Guns, whose familiarity with the history of VALS™ and leadership of a new SRI company that uses it, give him a good perspective on its concept and history.

[18] Mitchell's first work in the consumer values arena was a 1963 report for SRI's Long Range Planning Service. In his work on VALS™, Mitchell tried to explain the fragmentation of values among Americans. Many clients found the social movements of the 1960s and 1970s difficult to understand. Mitchell's work offered a theory based on the notion that a new mind-set had emerged in the United States, a mind-set that was "inner-directed." Mitchell made the case that this new mind-set was motivated in ways different from the American archetype and that many of the apparent changes in social values emanated from people who had this internal, intrinsic-to-self point of view.

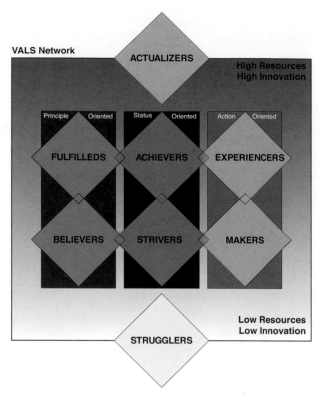

VALS Network

ACTUALIZERS

High Resources
High Innovation

Principle Oriented · Status Oriented · Action Oriented

FULFILLEDS · ACHIEVERS · EXPERIENCERS

BELIEVERS · STRIVERS · MAKERS

Low Resources
Low Innovation

STRUGGLERS

Figure 14-6. A consumer typology from VALS 2™ which was created to achieve better statistical performance and in the process went from 9 to 8 segments.

Uses such as product repositioning also work. A foreign car manufacturer introducing a sport utility vehicle saw an expensive and award-winning television advertising campaign fail to result in any increase in sales. Using VALS™ it targeted a new, rebellious consumer group using a "breaking the rules" theme, and sales increased 60% in 6 months.

VALS™ has many other uses such as designs for targeted mail programs and the selection of corporate media spokespersons. In one of its first applications, VALS™ also helped in the selection of a company logo. Two advertising companies were vying for a Merrill Lynch account, and one used VALS™ and Arnold Mitchell to propose a single bull as the firm's logo. That company won, and the next day their competitor became a VALS™ client (see later in this chapter for the story).

How is psychographic segmentation made? Figure 14-6 presents the VALS 2™ model, which starts, as a point of departure, with a matrix-like typology. The horizontal

axis represents an individual's *self-orientation* while the vertical axis has to do with the consumer's available *resources*. The elements of the matrix are then given one-word descriptors for adult consumers fitting that specific area. Regarding *self-orientation*, most people are motivated by one of three powerful forces: principle, status, and action. As an example, principle-driven consumers are guided in their choices by abstract, idealized criteria rather than feelings, events, or approval. *Resources*, on the other hand, include not just material means but physical and psychological dimensions as well.

To understand the depth to which each category goes, here is the explanation of an "experiencer:" "Experiencers are motivated by self-expression. As young, enthusiastic, and impulsive consumers, Experiencers quickly become enthusiastic about new possibilities but are equally quick to cool. They seek variety and excitement, savoring the new, the offbeat, and the risky. Their energy finds an outlet in exercise, sports, outdoor recreation, and social activities.

Experiencers are avid consumers and spend a comparatively high proportion of their income on fashion, entertainment, and socializing. Their purchases reflect the emphasis they place on looking good and having 'cool' stuff."[Q]

Armed with an understanding of the concept, let's briefly review how VALS™ and its SRI program activity unfolded. Mitchell started the VALS™ Program in 1978 to explore and then codify both existing and changing American values. In the summer of 1981, Marie Spengler joined him to lead a team of people that could help clients understand and exploit the VALS™ point of view. Key players in that group were Jay Ogilvy, who led the research effort, and Brooke Warrick, who led the marketing and consulting efforts. Although they found success in the advertising companies and those that depended on them, some marketing professionals were not impressed with VALS™. Either the segmentations were too broad and difficult to differentiate or the process was thought unworkable. "When SRI made a presentation to the Market Research Council, they were laughed out of the room."[R] Nevertheless, by the mid-1980s there were 130 VALS™ clients, including major TV networks, advertising agencies, publishers such as *Time*, and major consumer companies such as AT&T, Avon, Coca-Cola, General Motors, and Procter & Gamble.

The VALS™ program also had several types of services under its umbrella. The Leading Edge Program conducted annual surveys of consumers to explore Americans' changing values and opinions, and to provide reports to clients about important new ideas. For example, Donald Michael wrote the world's first report on organization learning for the VALS™ program in 1980. Ogilvy wrote a report, *The Experience Industry*, in the mid-1980s that was substantially ahead of its time. Mitchell's business bestseller, *Nine American Lifestyles*, made him a bit of a celebrity and created an image of the VALS™ brand that continues today. According to SRI's Fred Weil, VALS™ changed the way that advertising companies conducted their surveys and ran their focus groups.[5] Rather than just determining the respondent's sex or income or making demographic assumptions, surveys began including questions to assess the respondent's psychographic segment. Through such groundbreaking efforts, VALS™ gained national attention in the 1980s as an important new tool for building market strategies. One indication of its popularity was its appearance in a Gallo television ad. In the early 1980s, in a famous commercial from Bartles & Jaymes (a Gallo company), a folksy, understated Ed Jaymes had a flip chart on his front porch and was lecturing his colleagues about new-fangled marketing ideas. The diagram on the flip chart was the VALS™ system graphic!

After Mitchell died in 1986, the VALS™ team began to update the system. SRI assembled a team led by François Christen and leading researchers from Stanford and Berkeley to develop a system that would be based on more enduring traits of Americans. This effort led to VALS 2™, which was completed in 1989 and debuted in 1990. Based on psychological attributes and individual difference measures, the new system was far more robust as a statistical tool than original VALS™. VALS 2™ identified three "self-orientations" as the foundation of the system. But it dropped the concept of "inner-directedness" because of better statistical measures in the new system. Figure 14-6 shows the eight groups of consumers.

Old clients were uneasy with the new design at first. Many were heavily invested in the original VALS™ and loved the system and the intuitive insights that it offered. (Even today, some clients use the familiar concepts from the old system.) VALS 2™ suffered some significant birth pains. However, acceptance has grown as clients have seen the reliability and enduring quality of the new system.

The VALS™ team continued to develop other tools. In 1990, a team led by Bruce MacEvoy created Japan VALS™, the first general non U.S. system. From other efforts, led by MacEvoy and W. Lee Ruggels, came GeoVALS™ in 1994 and UK VALS™ in 1996. They then created iVALS™ as a tool to explore the emerging Internet surfer. Today, the VALS™ Program emphasizes several applications: product development, strategy, communications, and positioning. Many of the famous VALS™ cases are based on positioning and advertising campaigns that appeal to each individual mind-set. The Program continues to serve clients in a variety of categories. Projects in 2000 included work in telecommunications, yogurt, travel, automobiles, and real estate. Now under the ownership of SRI Consulting Business Intelligence, VALS™ is still evolving to meet specific needs around the world.

Business Consulting in Sweden

For the 25 years between the late 1950s and the early 1980s, it would be hard to overestimate the influence SRI had on the commercial sector of Sweden and, to a lesser extent, the other Scandinavian countries. During that time, SRI's management consulting side had hundreds of projects and came to be the most prominent consulting firm in that region of Europe. Although it is difficult to completely assess SRI's impact 20 years later, we will try to convey something of the value left by what may have been 100 different SRI staff members who contributed to the region from offices in California, London, and Stockholm itself.

In the mid 1950s, Weldon "Hoot" Gibson of SRI, through an introduction from Stanford's Ernie Arbuckle, became acquainted with two of the most important men in Swedish industry, Marcus Wallenberg and Axel Johnson.

Wallenberg's principal influence was in banking, which also placed him in high leadership positions in many industrial companies. Johnson was the third generation of leaders by that same name who had built perhaps a hundred companies in consumer goods, foodstuffs, trade, and shipping. Between the two, they controlled many of the major financial institutions and industrial companies in Sweden. Both of these men had attended SRI's International Industrial Development Conference in 1957 (the predecessor of the IICs mentioned in Chapter 13).

Sweden had not been ravaged by World War II, and the decade following the war found Sweden's industrial sector profiting enormously from its ability to participate in the reconstruction of those countries that were destroyed. This period of industrial prosperity and absence of competition from Germany and Japan engendered a growing complacency and arrogance that did not go unnoticed by people like Wallenberg and Johnson. As competing countries rebuilt with modern, efficient plants, the Swedish leadership saw an urgent need for industrial modernization and engaged SRI to help. By the late 1960s, SRI had about 15 professionals residing in Stockholm and total contract revenues there of about $2 million per year. Over the decade starting from the early 1960s, SRI project revenues from Sweden were probably higher than from any other foreign country.

After completing a few projects for the Johnson group in 1956–7 and one in 1958 for the large Wallenberg mining company, Atlas Copco, two important additions were made to the SRI-Sweden staff. Swedish clients recommended that SRI hire Raoul Gatien, an industrial engineer and management consultant who had spent some time in the American automobile industry in Detroit. Gatien turned out to be pivotal in SRI's entrance into the Swedish marketplace, and he soon launched three large and extended projects: one for the Wallenberg group's ASEA (a General Electric type of company) in 1959; one to revamp part of the operations of the Scandinavian Airline System (SAS) that began in 1962; and the third to rekindle work for the Johnson group in 1963. By the time Gatien died in 1971, SRI had worked for about 45 Swedish companies in industries that included banking, candy, dentifrices, pulp and paper, glassware (Orrefors), department stores (NK), cars (Volvo and SAAB), appliances (Electrolux), fertilizers,

railway equipment, steel, machinery, and power companies.[T] Accordingly, SRI had become the "consultant of choice" throughout Sweden and Scandinavia.[U] Later, the large Soderberg family of companies also became a client.

The SAS Work

A job for SAS brought the second important figure to SRI-Sweden: Dennis Finnigan, then head of SRI's consulting practice in electronic data processing. Finnigan became a favorite consultant to the Wallenberg group and an integral part of its entry into the world of computers and data processing. It was a time for streamlining both organizations and administrative procedures. This industrial operations research work became widely enough known that it was also adopted by large portions of both the Johnson and Soderberg combines.

The work for SAS illustrates SRI's crucial role in Sweden.[19] Finnigan and Al Lee (both of whom later became head of SRI's Management Systems Division) won 10 years of continuing projects with SAS, which became SRI's largest commercial client during that time. Work for SAS included:

- In 1962, Finnigan had the lead responsibility for SAS's first worldwide communications-based computer reservations system. This project brought people from SRI, SAS, IBM, and other organizations together during a 2-year effort to create a unique, real-time, on-line system for passenger reservations, check-in, and follow-up. The project resulted in new computer hardware and software that IBM took first to the rest of the airline world and later to banks, insurance companies, department stores, and other industries.

- SAS had bought an automated cargo-handling system for the Copenhagen airport that was over budget and late—and didn't work. Finnigan was asked to look into it, and although he was unfamiliar with the system's innards, he could clearly see what it wasn't doing. Back at SRI, he went to the Engineering Group and talked to Jack Bialik. Within a week, Bialik and a couple of his cohorts left to spend several months in

---

[19] The SAS consortium was created as a partnership of the three Scandinavian countries. Each country had an equal private and government stake. In Sweden, which held three-sevenths of the total, the three industrialists mentioned above were important participants in the private holdings.

Copenhagen. There they wrote one of SRI's few formal reports on its Swedish work.[20] They had determined that the system suffered both from hardware and software problems, and they opened their report by saying, "the system was doomed to failure"! They then proceeded to defend this conclusion. The report enabled SAS to terminate the project and even recover some of its costs. From this example, the stock of all SRI staff in Sweden soared. In reality, however, it was just SRI responding in its typical tailored and objective fashion.

Other Restructuring Work

Finnigan's other major restructuring projects were with Saab-Scania, Electrolux, ASEA-Brown-Boveri (ABB), Stockholm's Enskilda Bank (see box), and various companies of the Axel Johnson group.

The latter case is interesting. The 132 companies in the Axel Johnson group were trying to understand the new role of data processing and how they should enter into this increasingly critical arena. Johnson himself, like most leaders of the day, did not know exactly what "data processing" meant, or how to proceed in regard to it. He asked SRI to help interpret the role data processing should play in

his organization. But rather than trying to build a template for how each of the 132 companies might introduce data processing to its operations, Finnigan suggested that Johnson start a 133rd company! Because of their common, group interests, Finnigan proposed the establishment of a data processing service company to serve the other companies' data processing needs. The new company, DATEMA, not only became the model for other industrial groups in Sweden and in Germany, Britain, Holland, Italy, and Japan, but by also taking on business outside the Johnson group, it became one of the Johnson group's largest companies.

Administrative Rationalization

To return to the question posed at the outset about the poor state of the Swedish industrial base compared with the newly renovated firms and practices in Germany and the United States, Finnigan's approach came to be called "administrative rationalization," The approach had several major components:

- The project had to have the active support of top management. Usually the president or CEO became chairman of the project steering committee.

- The client had to assign high-quality, full-time personnel to the project who later often became the ones to implement the recommendations.

---

[20] The results of virtually all SRI's work in Scandinavia were reported orally or in letter reports.

- The project teams had to be drawn from a wide range of departments within the company. This exposure, then, became a cross-training opportunity.

The last stipulation was mirrored in the SRI team itself, which comprised both management and technical skills, drawn from throughout the Institute to assure a comprehensive perspective on the task at hand. As each rationalization project was completed, a small client/SRI team was left in place to help assure that enough expertise was available to carry out the recommendations.

In total, Finnigan's work in Sweden was both pervasive and noteworthy. His legacies there came from both his supervision of many of the SRI efforts as well as his individual contributions, some of which continued after he left SRI in 1981. The superior quality of his work was noted by the King of Sweden in 1982 in his award to Finnigan of The Royal Order of the North Star, the Swedish equivalent of knighthood (see Figure 14-7). To quote briefly from the press release:[v]

> "Mr. Finnigan is a veteran of the Swedish scene, having been engaged in various assignments almost continuously for more than 20 years. He first arrived in Sweden in 1959 to assist Scandinavian Airlines System with a reorganization plan.
>
> Over the years Mr. Finnigan has worked with most major Swedish business and industrial organizations, such as the two automobile manufacturers Volvo and Saab, electronic and electric companies such as L.M. Ericsson and ASEA, the Swedish Match Company, the Johnson Group of shipping and industrial companies, Atlas Copco, Alfa Laval, banks, etc. He has also helped public enterprises such as Vattenfall (hydroelectric energy) and the Telecommunications Administration."

The release further stated that the medal was for "the creation of good and useful establishments" and the training of hundreds of "Swedish women and men." Though not mentioned in the press release, some examples of the people SRI trained were:

Figure 14-7. Dennis Finnigan and his Order of the North Star award from the King of Sweden.

- Knut Hagrup and Jan Carlzon, who both became presidents of SAS
- Percy Barnevik of ASEA, later ABB, and now chairman of the Wallenberg holding company Investor AB
- Bjorn Stigson of Flakt, who now leads a World Business Council of over 120 companies trying to advance sound business development with conservative use of the earth's resources
- Goran Ennerfelt, president and CEO of Johnson AB
- Gosta Bysted of Electrolux, now vice chairman of Johnson AB.

During the latter part of his work in Sweden, Finnigan joined SRI's Office of Research Operations, where he remained supervisor of the work in Scandinavia.

The following box exemplifies the quality of character of both SRI and its people, and gives evidence of the kind of organization SRI aspired to be. For his work in Scandinavia, Finnigan won SRI's coveted Gibson award in 2002.

Recreation and Tourism

SRI was one of the first research organizations to perform multidisciplinary research in the areas of recreation, tourism, and the arts. Until then, most ventures in these fields were planned simply as the fulfillment of someone's dream—a philanthropist or entrepreneur, designing "by the seat of his pants." In several cases, SRI pioneered research methodologies that others later emulated and standardized. Here are a few examples.

"Project Mickey"

Walt Disney's first notions were of a modest but "magical little park" where kids and their parents could have fun together. He envisioned it on 8 acres adjacent to his Burbank studios, a place where his employees and their families could go and relax. But then World War II came along, and any realization of his dream had to be put on hold. During that hiatus, however, his vision continued to grow, and by the end of the war it was clear that to build his "little" park would need a lot more land and a lot more money.

While Walt Disney and the Disney studios had a remarkable vision of an amusement park and what it might contain, they had few skills related to designing, building, or managing it. It was through an SRI client in the Los Angeles area, famed architect Charles Luckman,[21] that they learned of SRI. Walt Disney himself phoned the Los Angeles SRI office and spoke with Harrison "Buzz" Price. "What do you guys do for a living?" was his opener. A good question, and the answer must have pleased him because by the end of the day SRI had secured two Disney projects.

Through this brief interaction, then, "Project Mickey," as it is termed on the Institute's project logs, came to be. Although these first projects lasted just about 6 months, the SRI project team would come to exercise considerable influence over the location and operational design of the park. Starting in June 1953 and funded at $27,960, Project Mickey became the first of many projects in tourism at SRI and certainly the one with the most lasting impact. The leadership for the first phase of the project, site selection, came from SRI's Los Angeles office in the person of C.V. Wood (who used initials only), a first-rate entrepreneur. As evidence, by 1954, during the project's second phase, Roy Disney hired Wood to become the Executive Vice President and General Manager of Disneyland and to oversee construction of the park. As a result, SRI's Price led the second phase, which concentrated on economic feasibility and planning.

As stated, the first phase of the SRI work was related to location and demographics. Initially, the SRI team compared 10 regions in the Los Angeles basin. The bases of comparison were population growth, weather, and other precise criteria to avoid sites already extensively developed, oil fields and reserves, bad topography, airports, and land under government control. About 100–200 acres were sought, somewhere in Los Angeles County or Orange County. Walt Disney's only stipulations about where to place the park were that he didn't want it near the beach and the land should be relatively flat. On the basis of climate and access to population, the region was narrowed to one encompassing 5 miles on either side of the Santa Ana Freeway and extending from the Los Angeles County line to Santa Ana. Within this area, SRI studied 10 potential sites, and these were ultimately reduced to a rank-ordered set of four. By August 1953, a formal report was submitted, indicating that SRI's first choice was the 139-acre "Ball Road Subdivision" along the Santa Ana Freeway

and East of the San Gabriel River (see Figure 14-8). The Disneys agreed.

These walnut, citrus, and bean farms, then, would yield to one of the world's most famous kingdoms. The land price, from some 17 owners, was expected to average about $6,200 per acre. It was bought for less—$4,600 an acre. This phase of the project went so well that, as mentioned, Roy Disney later offered Wood the job of constructing Disneyland. Wood in turn hired a retired Admiral and former SRI client, Joe Fowler, to manage day-to-day construction. He also asked his former colleague from SRI Menlo Park, Bill Platt, to undertake ongoing financial tasks and some construction supervision. Completing the construction of such a unique environment in just 18 months was clearly a remarkable accomplishment—one that, in retrospect, might have put its scheduled grand opening at risk.

The second or operational planning phase began in about October 1953. This aspect of the study started with initial assumptions about attendance that predicted a peak rate of perhaps 28,500 visitors per day, with a total of 2.5 million visitors per year. These first figures would produce annual revenues of $5 million, operating costs of not quite $4 million, and an 8-year payout.[W] By the end of the study, however, attendance estimates were pegged at 5 million per year, and capital requirements, first estimated at $5–6 million, were revised upward to over $9 million.[X]

To understand such operations better, SRI held discussions across the United States with more than 10 major amusement park operators, four ride manufacturers, and others.[22] SRI's financial planning was detailed and included revenues from parking, admission, rides, food, and souvenirs; the operating organization required; and even the type and number of turnstiles to be used. Consideration was also given to how much walkway space was required for peak loads and the kind of services needed to keep the public happy and free of fatigue. The report was capped off with some detailed schedules that showed an advance opening in mid-1955.

The construction of Disneyland was both a marvel and a nightmare. The 18-month schedule was tight under the best of

---

[21] He had designed both Cape Canaveral and Johnson space centers and Boston's Prudential Center.

[22] Much of this survey was done by Bill and Barbara Spaulding during the summer of 1953. Bill also was in charge of the removal of 10,000 orange and 4,000 walnut trees.

the project. The creative notion was to offer major vendors a promotional tie-in to the park; that is, allowing them to become an "official" airline, soft drink, hotel, etc. These associations helped cover the growing gap between the initial estimate of around $9 million to the $17 million it took to open the doors. Some financial people openly speculated whether any amusement park could ever repay such a huge investment.

Contrary to some recounts, SRI was not involved in the more thematic aspects of the design. It was Walt Disney's idea for not one, but four, linked sections of the park that would offer families a variety of novel experiences all on one site. Each section would present a combination of traditional rides, enriched by the Disney

Figure 14-8. The designing of Disneyland (clockwise: The Orange County property, Walt Disney with C.V. Wood and Harrison Price of SRI, a rodential consultant, an artist's sketch, and the Disneyland Castle under construction).

circumstances, all of which seemed to be absent. Trees tagged red and green for removal or not all fell to a color-blind bulldozer operator. The watercourses, so prominent in the design, wouldn't hold water in the loamy Orange County soil. Construction was also plagued by strikes and bad weather. Perhaps most importantly, all this effort was totally new, and in many cases the designers had to make important changes during the course of construction. These "unpredictables" all had their cost impacts. Given the present size of the Disney empire, it may seem odd that the escalation in construction costs was a major problem, but it was. Money for such an enterprise was difficult to find, and Walt Disney would come to put a lot of his personal money into the project. Thus, the rising costs were ominous.

But when Wood moved to Disneyland, he had an idea for helping meet the rising cost of

touch and an ample supply of the Disney characters. The "four-leaf clover," as the layout was called, would turn out to be excellent at dispersing crowds. Also, Disneyland, as it already was being called, would be spotlessly clean, staffed by freshly uniformed personnel, and serve wholesome food.

Almost exactly 2 years after SRI became involved, including an amazingly short 18 months of round-the-clock construction, Disneyland opened on July 17, 1955. The opening was not intended to be general, but one geared toward select people and their acquaintances—some 15,000 tickets at the most. However, tickets came to be issued freely, even duplicated, and the crowd swelled beyond any expectation. Wood reported that some enterprising people had placed ladders over the barbed wire near the stables at the back of the park and were charging $5 per entrant to use them.[Y] Clearly, Disney lost track of how many people entered that first day. And there were access problems as well. Because the Santa Ana Freeway was not yet completed, Wood had arranged with the state for the new Harbor Blvd. exit to be paved. Traffic was still horrendous, and the total inflow reached perhaps 33,000 people on what came to be called Black Sunday.

Promotion for Disneyland was greatly aided by the new ABC television series that featured Disney stories and characters.[23] But that first day the parts of the park that were unfinished were hidden from the television cameras. Also, beyond the cameras, other aspects of the first day did not go well. Rides failed, food ran short, a gas leak occurred, asphalt was not yet set, and the press was generally uncomplimentary.[24] In retrospect, the hurried schedule undoubtedly caught up with them. As a result, a committee took over running Disneyland, and Walt Disney himself moved on site into a few rooms over the park's fire station. The kinks were worked out in a few weeks, and Disneyland was an "immediate" success. Crowds continued to be substantially greater than those for which anyone, including SRI, had planned. But Wood's days at Disney were numbered. Though they had dealt with countless construction difficulties, including the trade unions' impact on a tight schedule, hiring and training people, and traffic and parking, the early operations were not at all smooth. Because of operational glitches and in part because his strong leadership skills were a bit in competition with his boss, Walt Disney, sometime in late 1955 Wood lost his job.

During the construction, Price continued SRI's preopening work for Disneyland in the area of merchandising, which eventually developed into 30 Disneyland shops. While most of the segments of Disneyland are now familiar to everyone, one, called Holiday Land, which was intended to change with the various holiday seasons, was never built. By the time Disneyland opened, the site had grown to 190 acres and included space for the Disneyland Hotel. Also during the construction

period, Disney and the adjacent town of Anaheim worked to annex Disneyland. Part of the background for that annexation was another Disney-sponsored SRI study by Platt that revealed the cost benefit of Disneyland for Anaheim.

For nearly all of the SRI people who worked on Disneyland, either directly, as did Wood, or indirectly as did Harrison, Platt, and others, this was their first venture into the tourism world. It is a tribute to the talent that SRI attracted that these people helped Disneyland off to a good start, showing where it should be located and that for its expected level of attendance it could be profitable. Given the uniqueness and complexity of construction, including mundane problems like getting the porous soil to hold a lake, the construction phase was amazingly short. The first year's attendance reached about the 5 million SRI had estimated but, needless to say, the popularity of the park thereafter far outstripped anyone's estimates. That first year, each person left behind $5 in expenditures, an amusement park record. Because of its uniqueness and in spite of the rushed opening, the project established SRI as a pioneer in research on recreation and tourism.

From Disneyland, Wood went on to supervise the building of other parks in Massachusetts and New York City, as well as recreation developments around the country, notably Six Flags in Texas. He became President of all of the Warner Bros. theme parks. Along the way, he partnered with chain-saw tycoon Robert McCullough to develop Lake Havasu City, Arizona. As part of that project, and with no doubt planned incongruity, Wood transplanted the 150-year old London Bridge to the Arizona desert in 1968.[Z] Price went on to establish Economic Research Associates (ERA)— interestingly enough, with the aid of Walt Disney. Walt had tried to hire Harrison for several years, but when Harrison told Disney that he doubted he, Walt, would take internal advice, Disney "insisted" that he start ERA and even guaranteed its first 3 years of operation.[AA]

The Kennedy Center for the Performing Arts[BB]

In 1955, a group of civic leaders in Washington, D.C. prevailed on Congress to help establish a center for the performing arts worthy of the nation's capital. At the time, Washington had only one legitimate theater, the timeworn National, and only Constitution Hall for the

---

[23] ABC became a part owner of Disneyland in the beginning, and only later would Roy Disney buy back ABC's interest. Ironically, Disney now owns ABC.

[24] Interestingly, attention was brought to the unset asphalt by a short couple alongside SRI's Price as they were all entering the Castle. Price recalls that the woman's spiked heels were sinking into the asphalt, and she and her husband, Frank Sinatra, were complaining. H. A. Price, personal communication, October 15, 1999.

presentation of major concerts. Constitution Hall was out of favor with many because its owners, the Daughters of the American Revolution, refused to allow black performers there.

Congress authorized a District of Columbia Auditorium Commission to explore the feasibility and prepare designs for such a center, provided that private money could be secured to build it. The Commission was composed of a dozen prominent local citizens—a blend of politicians and "patrons of the arts." None had professional experience either in designing or in managing such a facility.

The Commission hired two organizations to help. The prominent architectural firm of Periera & Luckman[25] out of Los Angeles was to do preliminary designs. SRI Washington was to conduct a preliminary economic study to provide design and feasibility parameters. The two teams would work jointly on identifying and evaluating sites.

Members of the Commission were free with their opinionated guidance for the studies. One member wanted the center to be "as much as possible like the Met" (New York's venerable opera house). Another thought Carnegie Hall should be the model. A third desired a "completely modern, different place, suited to the times." Several were concerned that the new "opera house" should never host such lowbrow events as rock or jazz concerts. One thought it important for the hall to be the largest in the country.

Bill Royce drew the assignment to tour existing facilities around the country to obtain data on dimensions and capacities, utilization, costs and revenues, and, especially, the recommendations of experienced auditorium managers. The first shock to conventional wisdom came from Raymond Allen, then General Manager of the Metropolitan Opera, who showed Royce all the faults of this aging facility and urged: "Whatever you do, don't build it like the Met!" Next, the manager of Carnegie Hall disclosed that its only real moneymakers were the Friday evening jazz or pop concerts; the symphony and other classical shows depended on contributions to break even. "Besides," he said, "Our Board members think we're closed on Friday evenings."

Both managers cautioned against making the hall too large, because of potential problems with acoustics and the difficulty of filling it often enough. All respondents agreed it would be a mistake to try accommodating dissimilar events in a "one size fits all" facility.

Armed with such input, SRI's recommended a multiple-unit facility, and the unit capacities were close to those finally adopted.

SRI studied seven proposed sites, each of which had advantages and disadvantages. The most available, accessible, and least expensive site was on Theodore Roosevelt Island in the Potomac River. But it was in a nature reserve and, even in 1955, environmental concerns won out. Other sites were in congested areas, very expensive, or claimed by other federal agencies. Ultimately, SRI recommended the present site in the Watergate area.

When time came to present recommendations to the Commission, Charles Luckman, the architect known as "the world's greatest soap salesman" (he had briefly headed the Lever Brothers soap company), eloquently reviewed a series of alternative designs, each more dramatic than the last. The Commission members were charmed. Then Royce had to get up and run through several charts of dry statistics to establish the economic parameters and financial feasibility of the project. What a contrast! But based on the Luckman designs and SRI's recommendations, the Commission set out to raise more than $7 million to build the center. Times were tough, money was tight, and the government held to its insistence on private financing. The project languished.

Then John F. Kennedy was elected president, his wife Jackie established a new level of culture in the Capital, and the *Camelot* aura attracted more big money. So, the project proceeded and the new D.C. auditorium complex was well under way when the President was assassinated. It seemed most fitting that the new center be named the Kennedy Center for the Performing Arts. (Maybe more for Jackie than for Jack?)

Seattle's Century 21—The First Financially Successful World Fair

For more than a century, communities that wanted to celebrate their accomplishments would sponsor "world fairs" or exhibitions. They always attracted much attention, often more from their own people than from

---

[25] This is the same Luckman noted earlier regarding SRI's introduction to Disney.

moneyed tourists. And they always lost money, costing more than their promoters' estimates. In addition, they usually left behind a group of unsightly "white elephant" facilities. Local leaders regularly hoped to recoup the losses through tourist receipts, new business investments, or less tangible prestige.

In the late 1950s, a group of Seattle business and civic leaders got the urge for a world fair. They could raise the initial investment money, but they needed help selecting a site, choosing a "theme" to attract visitors, and setting financial limits on their exposure. To stage the fair the State of Washington created a Commission that included representatives of the City of Seattle, King County, business, labor, and other civic groups. A representative of the State Attorney General's office was designated as its legal advisor.

Edward Carlson, then CEO of the Western Hotels chain and later of United Airlines, was the Commission chairman, a fortunate choice. He insisted on running the fair in a clean, businesslike manner. To hold costs down, he extracted a "no graft, no strike" pledge from the central labor council and Chamber of Commerce. He held weekly breakfast meetings at which every item of planning and implementation would be openly discussed. And he made all participants stick to their budgets. Sven Eckdahl became general manager of the Fair corporation. He was experienced in such activities, paid close attention to detail, and later went on to help stage similar events in other cities.

In 1957, SRI's Pacific Northwest Office (SRI-PNW), based in Portland, won the contract to perform preliminary studies of the economic feasibility, site location, and theme develop-ment for the fair. Royce, then director of SRI-PNW, worked with the site selection and economic factors team of the Commission. SRI's Richard Raymond performed the "theme" research.

The Commission had chosen "Century 21"—more than 40 years before its arrival—as the general theme. Raymond toured the country to gather opinions about what features would attract tourists and have a lasting impact. Many opinion leaders agreed with him that, in the age of Sputnik and concern over the United States' eroding position in science, the nation was ready for a "serious" theme, not merely a "fun" fair.

From Raymond's work came the emphasis on science, space, and the environment, to be presented in interesting and participative exhibits. The federal government agreed to sponsor the Pacific Science Center as a focal point; it continues today as a venue for both professional and public science activities. Countries that sponsored exhibits were encouraged to stress similar themes, with many "hands-on" displays.

The two main economic problems were: (1) choosing a site that would be convenient for visitors to reach, but not too expensive to develop, and (2) limiting the basic investment to what could be amortized within the 2-year limit imposed by the International Commission on World Fair Exhibitions, which sanctioned such events, to prevent undue competition. As it turned out, the chosen approach solved both problems. The leading initial candidate site was a large field near the Seattle-Tacoma airport, which its owner wished to develop and which would be convenient for air travelers but distant from the city. All other available sites were too small.

Then, at one of the breakfast meetings, someone mentioned that an area just northwest of downtown might be made available. The old National Guard armory needed to be replaced; the city auditorium, equally aged, needed modernizing; an athletic field owned by the Seattle School District might be used for outdoor events. These were separated from an open space and some dilapidated houses by a cluster of religious and civic buildings, including the Catholic chancery, a Masonic temple, a Protestant church, and a Jewish synagogue.

"Could we possibly incorporate all these facilities into our World Fair, if we assure each of their owners of having better facilities when all is over?" "No way," some members answered at first. "You'll never get all those folks to cooperate."

But Carlson and Eckdahl began to see the possibilities. Royce suggested they try a "McGoozle" on the various organizations involved. (McGoozle is known among lobbyists as the fine art of getting another person to do what you want him to do but to make him think it was his own idea.) Each member of the group was assigned one or more organizations to contact and sell them on the idea of becoming part of the World Fair. One by one, the organizations fell into line. Finally, none could be the one who blocked the plan, although the school district was the last holdout. Each became a proud sponsor of an exhibit in the fair, thereby reaping its own public relations rewards.

Thus, the Commission gained a most desirable site at the modest cost of helping to refurbish several existing facilities, plus a modern opera house to replace the old auditorium. Only one new building had to be built, in addition to the Pacific Science Center, which was federally sponsored. The armory became the international food court, with the replacement armory sited elsewhere.

Two more investments contributed to the success of the fair. A monorail line was built from downtown to the fair site, using transportation system bonds. It still carries commuters and tourists back and forth on schedule. A group of private investors' idea for a landmark tower with a revolving restaurant on top became the Space Needle, still a profitable landmark on the Seattle skyline.

The Century 21 Exhibition was the first world fair ever to be financially successful, at the same time leaving Seattle with an improved infrastructure—several buildings that enhanced the city, rather than deteriorating into eyesores as happened in so many other locales. And SRI helped show the way. The group at SRI would go on to assist in the planning of large fairs in New York (1964), Montreal (1967), Japan (1970), Melbourne (1973), and Philadelphia (1976).

Athletics[cc]

Over several decades, SRI's Recreation and Tourism Economics program worked on a number of projects involving athletic facilities. Until his untimely death in the mid-1980s, Eric Duckstad headed most of this work. One of the earliest was a new arena for basketball and hockey in Portland, Oregon, built in the late 1950s. Another was the Superdome in New Orleans. Unfortunately, the Superdome became a case where implementation departed grossly from plans. All observers agreed that SRI's work was well done and that the facility was fine when built. However, the endemic corruption in New Orleans resulted in large cost over-runs and political scandals. A more satisfactory result of SRI's work was a stadium for football and other outdoor events in Edmonton, Alberta, Canada

SRI's work on athletic facilities brought contacts with leaders of the National Football League (NFL), who had growing concerns over players' injuries. SRI was hired in the mid-1980s for a multidisciplinary study of measures to reduce the number and severity of injuries from professional football.

The study began with analysis of the numbers, types, and causes of injuries to players. SRI proposed, for the first time, a gradation in the severity of injuries. This system gave the NFL a way to quantitatively assess which injuries needed the most attention and the causes that led to the prevalence of each. From the analysis of such a spectrum of injuries came proposed changes that ranged over a wide field: better conditioning of players, improvements in the various types of playing surfaces, better equipment (especially the design of helmets), and rule changes. To gauge the effects of various artificial turfs, SRI proposed a "punishment index"—an approach that factored in the effect of cleat size and length on injuries on various surfaces. SRI also noted that some players' failure to wear the normally prescribed equipment contributed to injuries as well.

On the management and financial sides of the NFL, SRI was involved in League expansion and movement. In specific studies for Commissioner Pete Rozelle, SRI recommended expansions for Seattle and Tampa Bay in 1976 and for the transfer of the Baltimore Colts to Indianapolis in 1984.

Reno Gambling

Finally, a study that got SRI into a controversy: In the mid-1950s, William Harrah, owner of a major gambling casino in Reno, became interested in ways to make commuting from the Bay Area to Nevada easier for potential customers. He asked SRI to study the feasibility of chartered bus service at favorable prices, rather than having customers drive their own cars. Without addressing the economic or moral aspects of gambling, the SRI team looked at possible origin-destination routes, comparative transport costs, days and times that people might want to go, and other factors for a chartered bus system, and submitted the results to Harrah.

Somehow, the word got out to the public. Self-appointed critics complained to the powers at Stanford University that "SRI was doing research to help gamblers." The newspapers editorialized; radio commentators commented. Pastors in some churches fulminated. SRI's nonprofit tax-exempt status was questioned. Ultimately, SRI executives had to explain to Stanford and the public that we had not "done research on gambling" but only on a transportation economics question, that the client's business was legitimate in Nevada, and

that SRI did pay taxes on work for commercial clients. In the end, Harrah and other casino operators helped set up a charter bus service to Reno, but kept the operations at arm's length. SRI maintained its policy of being available to work for any legitimate client, but also strengthened its procedures for careful screening of potentially controversial projects.

The Birth of SWIFT—The Interbank Network

SWIFT, an acronym for the Society for Worldwide Interbank Financial Telecommunication, is the organization whose facilities communicate virtually all financial transactions among international banks. Its role has become essential to international banking, and in 2000 it accommodated some 7,000 users in 192 countries, transmitting more than 1.2 billion messages involving value in excess of US$5 trillion.[DD] SWIFT was founded in 1973 by nearly 240 banks, mostly in Europe. SRI's role in SWIFT began as its founding members, struggling with both concepts and national differences, recognized the need for help in converging on both functional and organizational design. SRI's principal entrée into SWIFT came from its work for Midland Bank in England, but also linked to SRI relationships in Scandinavia and even reached back to its creation of automatic check processing for the Bank of America (BofA) in the 1950s. [EE,FF]

The idea for an international interbank financial transaction network began in England in the deliberations of a domestic bank cooperative called the Interbank Research Organisation, located in London. The spearhead for the concept that became SWIFT was Charles Reed of that group. SWIFT was to be a neutral, somewhat autonomous organization with oversight by representatives of its member banks. But when the organizational and functional design effort broadened to involve banks from the European Community, the group encountered difficulties not unlike the United Nations. It was then that the members recognized the need for a separate party to guide the deliberations and help resolve their differences. Thus, Reed asked Don Fiske of SRI whether it could take on roles such as offering advice, facilitating discussions, helping resolve differences, and ultimately

gaining consensus among the participating member banks. Though the initiative was clearly European, the United States, in the party of the American Banking Association (ABA) and banks like City Bank, BofA, and Chase Manhattan, also participated, one of which led to another SRI linkage.

On BofA's side of the pioneering ERMA project was Al Zipf, whom the bank hired in the early 1950s to guide its movement into automatic check and data processing. Zipf ultimately became BofA's most knowledgeable person in that area and its Chief Technical Officer. Later in his career, as one of BofA's representatives to the technical committees of the ABA, he became aware of the growing volume of international checks and other financial instruments. It was the early 1970s and yet the conveyance system of the day, incredibly, consisted of couriers who filled the skies moving paper from one bank to another. So, while U.S. banks may have had some reluctance about European leadership in this area, to those like Zipf, it was eminently clear that a worldwide network was needed to handle the relentless increase in international financial transactions. In his ABA role, Zipf sought to identify a consultant to facilitate the emergence of SWIFT.

Recalling the good work that SRI had done on ERMA and perhaps because of our independent status, Zipf called SRI's Dennis Finnigan to see if SRI might be interested in helping create such a capability. Finnigan promised to look into it and immediately got in touch with Fiske who, coincidentally as mentioned above, was already in discussions with the SWIFT leadership. SRI reacted quickly to this opportunity, winning a project to help create SWIFT.

When SRI arrived on the scene, the basic functional and organizational concepts were being explored, albeit by a somewhat dysfunctional working group. As mentioned, the organization sponsoring the initiative was the Interbank Research Organisation, in London, and its internal name for the project was simply the Message Switching Project (MSP), governed by a steering committee. Under this rubric, several design subcommittees were created. One was The Organisation and Legal Sub-Committee of which Fiske became a member. Under the auspices of the MSP and with participation of its members, SRI prepared the major founding documents for SWIFT, its organizational structure, and its by-laws.[GG] These documents, in the form of SRI reports, established the basis for operation, financial arrangements including SWIFT's nonprofit status, and the roles of the member banks. Because of legal considerations, the organization was located in Belgium, which gave rise to calling the organization a "Society," a nontaxed class of organization under Belgian law. Interestingly, and relevant to the power of acronyms, the early name for the new organization was the Society for International Financial Telecommunication.[HH] Within a month, and presumably for its nice connotation, the acronym became SWIFT. Finnigan indicated that SRI originated the name as part of its authoring role.[II]

A good example of SRI's involvement in the genesis of SWIFT was its helping to find a founding president for the organization. Fiske was visiting Menlo Park and was having dinner at Finnigan's home in the spring of 1973. When Fiske noted that SWIFT was looking for a person who could aggressively launch the company, Finnigan immediately thought of someone he had mentored and knew well who had been in charge of data processing at Scandinavian Airline System (SAS) and had come to the United States to avoid Sweden's onerous tax situation. His name was Carl Reuterskiold, and he was living at that time in New York but was homesick for Europe. Finnigan called him that same evening and learned that Reuterskiold was interested, but lamented that he couldn't be available until October. As fate sometimes plays out, that's exactly when SWIFT was scheduled to get off the ground, so Fiske nominated him for the job and he got it. SRI also helped identify and recruit the chief financial officer, as well as individuals for several other key roles.

As the SWIFT system was beginning to take shape, member banks were still worried about how secure the system would be. SRI was asked to examine and review both this issue and other aspects of its technical design.

In October 1976, SRI conducted a study that was intended to be an operational audit; that is, until the initial system operation was delayed. That delay meant that SRI was forced to examine the security of the SWIFT system *design* rather than operation.[JJ] The report made extensive recommendations on procedures, access, physical, and network security for both SWIFT and its member banks. Examples and summaries of the SRI recommendations follow:

- In the absence of written security procedures, SWIFT should develop a written security policy governing external banks or public disclosures to be issued by the Director General and maintained by an information control officer for the entire SWIFT organization. Specific actions were cited.

- Given the size of the financial stakes involved, SWIFT should examine its need for insurance to cover the loss of information.

- Member banks should take a number of actions (spelled out) to give physical protection to its terminals and logical protection to its SWIFT access positions to protect against unauthorized entrance into the SWIFT system.

- The link between the member bank and each country's (or region's) terminal concentrator should be encrypted, and all uses of the public switched network for such linkage should be logged.

- Extensive recommendations, ranging from security to operational effectiveness, were made for the operation of the regional concentrators and the switching centers.

After the SWIFT system went online, SRI continued to examine its operations. A study for an information management system was completed in 1983, the usefulness of expert systems for SWIFT was examined in 1985, the qualifications of cryptographic algorithms for the User Security Enhancement Project were reviewed in 1991, and other more sensitive security work followed.

Thus, SRI was a party to the establishment and ongoing success of SWIFT. Reuterskiold would lead the organization through its first 17 years, and for over 25 years SWIFT has operated successfully, expanding to become the cornerstone of international banking transactions that involve trillions of dollars each year.

Changing America's Investment Habits—
The Merrill Lynch CMA

Background

In the opinion of many, a financial revolution occurred in the United States over the decade between 1965 and 1975.[26] It was a time when average citizens saw a significant increase in their discretionary income and when a new financial world opened to help them manage or invest it. At the beginning of the period, there were myriad but separate places one could go for investment, such as banks, savings and loans, brokers, and the government. These were the traditional institutions, and they seemed as permanent and unchanging to consumers as the earth beneath their feet. Each of these areas was isolated from the others and everybody, including the leaders in each sector, was ignorant of other options. More importantly, each sector worked to keep it that way. That ignorance was fortified by barriers placed around the various financial sectors, particularly the banks. Many of the restrictions arose from laws or conventions that were traceable to the Depression of the 1930s and were intended to protect investors by barring their banks from making speculative investments. These restrictions, then, were invoked on behalf of depositors...or so it seemed.[KK]

To this backdrop we also add the environment that SRI offered in the early 1970s. It was, to be sure, one of the most enabling of times for inquisitive financial analysts willing to invest in the promise of discovery; that is, looking beyond the obvious or the incremental. Such people enthusiastically embrace latitude in their research pursuits and in this case the right people and circumstance came together to make something important happen.

Getting Started in the Financial Industries Sector

The year was 1974, and an SRI Board member had casually inquired of President Charles Anderson whether the Institute was working in the area of financial services. His premise was that it might be a fruitful area of business for SRI. Well, SRI wasn't in that field and, more than likely because Anderson shared the Board member's opinion, he asked a senior member of the Decision Analysis Department, Carl Spetzler, to set up a group in financial services. By September of that year, Spetzler had established a group he called Financial Planning and Management in Al Lee's Management Systems Division. As mentioned earlier, Spetzler was a practitioner in the new, mathematical, and arcane field of decision analysis, and he professed to know nothing about financial services. The new organizational name probably reflected Spetzler's bias and the slant he wanted taken in the area he was asked to start.

Getting at the Fundamentals

As with many SRI staff, Spetzler was a brilliant analyst. His lack of familiarity with the business of financial services served as an invitation, perhaps incentive, for him to ask fundamental questions rather than to cower behind unfamiliarity or ignorance. So, from his own curiosity and a few projects he was able to wrangle, he began to get a picture of a very fragmented industry. As is frequently the case, basic questions from good analysts often lead to new insights. The strong compartmentalization he and his colleagues saw seemed both unwise and arbitrary—perhaps conditions that everyone had simply grown used to. Some of the fragmentation could be attributed to (mis)interpretations in what the law permitted[27] and some simply to choices by each fragment's leaders. By count there were 22 kinds of

---

[26] The discretionary per capita income as tabulated in the *U.S. Statistical Abstracts* shows a marked increase from 1965 to 1980. The inflation-fed increase of over three and a half times during that period probably at least made people *think* they had more money, and even with inflation subtracted, it was still a real increase of more than 40%.

[27] The Banking Act of 1933 laid the groundwork that tried to keep banks, in particular Federal Reserve Banks, from indirectly placing their depositors at risk through a bank's own speculative investments. Hence, there were limits on a bank's right to purchase stocks. Most people didn't bother to recognize, however, that banks were not prohibited from purchasing securities and stocks on behalf of their customers, especially through subsidiaries.

financial institutions, including banks, savings and loans (S&Ls), brokerages, insurance companies, and the like. This complicated array of investment options, they surmised, would naturally baffle most mainstream households, leaving them susceptible to high-powered investment salesmen who were by design usually myopic.

On the investment-provider front things were also undergoing change. New concepts in financial services were slowly emerging around what most thought were Gibraltar-like laws and stipulations left over from the Great Depression. S&Ls were offering Negotiable Order of Withdrawal Accounts that seemed for all the world like checking accounts but were offering greater interest. Discount brokerages appeared. And feeding these innovations was the dramatic, if inflation-driven, increase in Americans' financial assets.

Quite naturally then, SRI's preliminary assessment of the situation found it to be mainly one of opportunity. In the normal SRI mode, Spetzler and his cohorts plied the waters of the financial institutions looking for an opening for their new concepts about the emerging investor. They won a number of contracts, one with Merrill Lynch that will be returned to later, but they believed they needed a lot more information to confirm their suspicions and to provide a better basis for proposing any changes to potential clients.

But getting such authentic information for SRI usually meant finding a sponsor, and the job loomed large enough that they chose to fund it through a multiclient effort. Armed with some intuitions, the Financial Services Group launched what would eventually become a $1.5 million survey/study. As with many multiclient projects, sponsorship solicitation continued over the course of the work. They called the project "Consumer Financial Decisions" (CFD), and its objective was "to provide a unique, comprehensive overview of consumer financial requirements, behavior, attitudes, and decision processes in the total financial services marketplace." Barbara Casey was project leader with Spetzler as supervisor.[28]

The survey ultimately involved 6,000 households from all levels of the income ladder and produced revealing information about how Americans behaved financially, at least as of May-July of 1978. The survey instrument covered 5,000 items in 200 pages, but even so the response was exceptional.[29] It gave SRI a unique view of the marketplace in which all of the various financial institutions were working, one way or another. A few of the many important findings in 1978 were:

- Of their total expenditures for financial services, households spent a whopping 84% on insurance and liability (mostly mortgage) payments.

- Households were highly risk-averse, with the less affluent ones being 60% (male) to 72% (female) percent willing to assume only a minimum risk.

- Many households, particularly the nonaffluent,[30] used low-interest-bearing passbook savings accounts for a wide range of financial objectives and, remarkably, 26% mistakenly used them as a hedge against inflation.

- Households displayed a lot of inertia regarding financial decisions, ultimately moving mainly to external stimulation. Much of this was due to ignorance.

- 93% of households had a checking account, with median balances of $500 for household with incomes below $15,000 and of $2,500 for those with incomes above $50,000. Sixty percent of the affluent had multiple checking accounts.

- The revolving feature of credit cards was indicated as "very" or "extremely" important by 50% of nonaffluent and 30% of the affluent, and most people didn't see their credit card balance as a loan.

- The average number of financial vendors the nonaffluent dealt with was 12, with 20 the average for the affluent (see Figure 14-9).

- Savings account balances were relatively high as shown in Figure 14-10.

The newly acquired information revealed something very important to those who conducted the project and derived its findings. They saw a time coming soon when

---

[28] Major SRI contributors were: Barbara Casey, project leader, Carl Spetzler, supervisor, and Catherine Chavez, Tom Goodrich, Tom Horan, Dustin MacGregor, Mary Schuelke, Harry Solberg, Michelle Swenson, Ken Frantz, Louise Herndon, Andrew Kahr (consultant), Mike Pralle, Robert Shullman, Robert Stambaugh, and Gary Tuckman.

[29] The surveys were conducted by well-known pollsters like Gallup, who paid participants from $10 to $20 to complete the voluminous poll. Most of the retrospective survey was written by Andrew Kahr.
[30] The threshold for affluence was set at $30,000.

tremendous flexibility would be offered to the typical investor either by new or existing financial institutions that would break out of their narrow range of investment services. No small part of that perception were the insights of the consultant Andrew Kahr whom SRI had brought on board. Through his decision analysis connections at Harvard, Spetzler had heard of Kahr's brilliance in interpreting copious amounts of data. Kahr was good not only at spotting patterns and trends and deducing customer behavior, but at finding or manipulating legal ways around existing regulations.

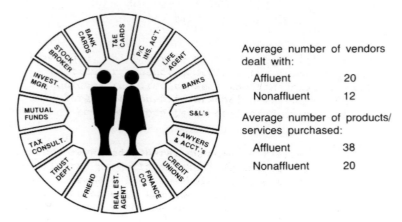

Households have multiple financial relationships

Average number of vendors dealt with:

Affluent 20

Nonaffluent 12

Average number of products/ services purchased:

Affluent 38

Nonaffluent 20

Figure 14-9. Financial connections in the average household (*Consumer Financial Decisions*, © SRI International, 1979).

The Effect of Insight on Marketing—the Power of New Information

Even at the outset, some implications of the public's investment habits were clear:

- The banks were enjoying large and easy profits on their reinvestment of passbook deposits, and these passbook accounts would become the vendors' battleground.

- The old adage in the brokerage houses that 10% of the customers provided 90% of the revenue was actually overstated.

- Since the average individual saw nearly all financial decisions as both important and complex, his governing financial characteristic was simply inertia, and it was the vendor who had to overcome that tendency.

- No vendor was moving toward revolutionary shifts in product delivery that would increase the convenience and value for the customer.

- An integrated delivery system would have major impacts on financial firms.

To SRI, these insights looked more like opportunities than threats. They knew that the inertia of a potential investor could yield to a more personal and individualized relationship with a vendor. An awakened investor might yield his fear of complexity to a professional who could simplify his

financial decision space without destroying the diversity of products available.

Merrill Lynch and the Cash Management Account

While these insights were being conveyed to the 50 or so sponsors of the multiclient study, SRI returned to the companies it had been pursuing, anticipating applications for many of the concepts and opportunities CFD revealed. One of these that had already made leanings toward new financial offerings was Merrill Lynch. Its President, Donald Regan, was among those who also saw the revolution in financial services coming. He was looking for growth and had a vision of a multiple-product company that was not only a brokerage house but also offered real estate and insurance services, as

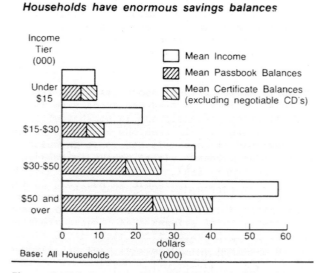

Households have enormous savings balances

Figure 14-10. Average American household savings balances (*Consumer Financial Decisions*, © SRI International, 1979).

well as a much leaner, much less regulated form of conventional banking.

To see the evolution of these ideas inside Merrill Lynch, let's return to SRI's early interactions with them. In December 1975, one of Regan's lieutenants, Chief Financial Officer Tom Chrystie, spent a day in Menlo Park brainstorming with a number of the SRI people who had participated in the earlier mentioned CFD survey. According to author Joseph Nocera, Chrystie had already received a bunch of SRI proposals, but had called Spetzler to tell him, "no thanks."[LL] But Spetzler persuaded him to come and spend a day at SRI, which he grudgingly did. It was a long day, and the SRI staff had plenty of ideas. It was toward the end of the day that the notion of a cash management account (CMA) began to unfold. This concept permitted a single investor to access a wide variety of investment options under not only one investment company, but one investment account! Among other things, this meant that there was no idle money. Even that portion upon which checks could be drawn, a money market account, would have higher returns than conventional checking accounts at a bank. Kahr was probably the person most responsible for the new concept.

The tangible result of that day at SRI was that Merrill Lynch entered into a contract with SRI to identify new financial service opportunities. A phased approach began with SRI's first making a comprehensive profile of Merrill Lynch's existing financial services compared to those of its competitors and then working with the firm's staff to rank-order new opportunities. The ranking was based on two criteria: Merrill Lynch's projected 1981 market size and its profit potential. Later phases went on to develop the specifications for diversification alternatives. Some of the issues SRI examined are indicated by this example from its proposal:

"In order to anticipate the future role of branch locations, it is necessary to understand what values are being served by visits to branches. Why, for example, are so many checks deposited at bank branches rather through the mail? And, on the other hand, why have experiments at bill payment by telephone been failures? It is also necessary to understand why residential mortgage debt has risen far more rapidly than the value of the housing stock, and why bankcard debt has expanded at an even faster pace. At the same time, the fact that many individuals have had immense quantities of collateral, which they could have used for secured borrowing at more favorable rates, but did not, remains unexplained. To what extent are consumers aware of and sensitive to the costs of their borrowings? On what bases do they decide how much to borrow, on what terms, and from whom?"

James Fuller was project leader, with Kahr as a principal consultant. The questions posed by this study no doubt led to the need for the more complete, multiclient survey, and it would feed new and relevant information into this work.

An Uphill Fight at Merrill Lynch

Since Chrystie was a lieutenant of Regan's, he was the natural person to whom to propose CMA. But he had two helpers, both consultants. One was a long-time high-level advisor to Merrill Lynch and the other was Kahr, who had, with others, broached the CMA notion to Chrystie at SRI. In April 1976, after substantial secret preparation time within Merrill Lynch, the proposal was presented to Regan and his management team. The postpresentation discussion was full of the most negative rancor: The scheme was too complicated. The money made on the free balance would disappear. The scheme was illegal. Regan listened quietly to these objections and, leader that he was, opted to do it.

The obstacles, both inside the company and out, were substantial. Inside, there was foot-dragging from the commission-compensated account managers who didn't understand the new system and saw it as an expensive diversion. Outside, Merrill Lynch's legal staff had to spend 3 years meeting challenges to the new services as they entered many states. State bank boards and commissions, congressmen, and state legislatures were trying their best to protect local banking institutions from this threat. State by state, however, the Merrill Lynch lawyers won.

Back inside Merrill Lynch, for the first time the true assets of those customers who chose to use a CMA were revealed. It showed just how small a role the skeptics inside Merrill Lynch had been playing. After some learning time by Merrill Lynch sales staff, they began to embrace CMA's flexibility. Chrystie had assumed that perhaps 100,000 customers might opt for the CMA, but by the mid-1980s that number was well over a million. As to the loss of income from the free balance, it was more than made up for by the annual fee itself. And, when inflation continued into the 1980s, the CMA's success became particularly evident. The banks with their regulated interest accounts started to look as out of date as their columnar entrances. SRI had been the seedbed for an offering that truly changed the financial landscape for both the vendors and the average investor.

There is an interesting footnote to this story, keyed by the single Merrill Lynch bull shown in the logo at the beginning of this section. Maybe as many as 25 years ago, Merrill Lynch had chosen bulls as its company logo to associate itself with a growing bull market. Its television commercials showed a herd of bulls wandering around Wall Street and in various other unnatural settings. The advertising campaign hadn't done much to increase business, so the firm put its advertising account up for competition. Merrill Lynch still wanted to be known as "bullish on America," however, and so this was the challenge it gave to the competing agencies: Keep the bull as our corporate symbol but give us something that works better. Two giant advertising firms emerged as leaders in the competition, Young & Rubicam and Ogilvy & Mather. Young & Rubicam was aware of SRI's new framework for market portrayal called Values and Life Styles (VALS™) (see earlier section in this Chapter) and visited SRI for help. To Arnold Mitchell, the leader of the SRI group they visited, the answer was obvious: Investors are, to be sure, herd animals, but that's not the image they have of themselves—they see themselves as solitary. So simply use one bull! The individual investor was, after all, what Merrill Lynch was trying to attract. Young & Rubicam won the competition, and Ogilvy & Mather signed up with VALS™ the next day. Merrill Lynch adopted the single, confident-looking bull as symbolic of the single, confident investor, and that icon presents the firm's public image to this day. Following introduction of the new logo, by Merrill Lynch measure, the ability of people to recall the Merrill Lynch icon shot up from 8 to 55%, and the firm's share of New York Stock Exchange business rose 2%. [MM]

This work for Merrill Lynch spawned similar groundbreaking SRI projects for American Express and Sears.

Facing the Oil Shortage of the 1970s—Whose Dipstick Do You Believe?

In October 1973, the Arab oil ministers met in Kuwait and agreed to an oil embargo against Western countries. Though this was clearly a political or ideological decision precipitated by the Yom Kippur War, it has been taken as a watershed moment in the availability of energy for the industrialized world. For over 20 years an increasing fraction of U.S. oil had been coming from foreign sources, so this action obviously raised the specter of dependency. Because the availability and price of oil are governed by economics, politics, and the notion of finite reserves, all abetted by emotions surrounding oil dependence, the subject is both complex and prone to exaggeration.[31] Both operationally and psychologically, the embargo had hit the United States in one of its most sensitive and vulnerable spots, the gas tank.

If you were driving in the mid-1970s, you were undoubtedly affected by or at the very least remember the gas lines. If you could find those stations that had gas available, you were faced with long lines and sometimes the wait for service was a half-hour or more. Probably the greatest realization this automobile-centric population faced was just how easy it was for someone on the other side of the planet to curtail, with impunity, what was at the same time one of our most coveted freedoms and one of our indulgences—going where we wanted, when we wanted. As a result of this inconvenience, the consuming public, driven by various combinations of fear and opportunism, concluded that we would face starkly higher gasoline prices, perhaps forever. The vast majority of industry analysts and even the federal government were proclaiming that higher oil prices were simply inevitable (see box). The situation was viewed as so dire that the government printed almost 5 billion

---

[31] The growing U.S. dependence on foreign oil was real. In 1972, about 25% of oil was imported, and that fraction would peak at over 46% in 1977. (Source: "Annual Energy Review-1997." Energy Information Administration, Department of Energy; found at www.eia.doe.gov/emeu/25opec/sld002.htm)

An April 25, 1977, article in the *San Jose Mercury News* quoted a Midwest Research Institute multiclient report that saw oil prices continuing to rise sharply. By 1985, the study said, foreign oil would be $26 a barrel and by 1990 it would exceed $37. More importantly, it stated that "world demand for oil will begin to outstrip supply by 1985." Perhaps not coincidentally, the CIA was also advising President Carter that the same crossover between supply and demand would occur in 1985.

In an article in the November 1973 issue of the *Annals of the American Academy of Political and Social Science*, S. David Freeman, director of the Ford Foundation's Energy Policy Project, stated on page 5: "If energy growth goes on at something near present rates, it will take a combination of all our current supply sources, going in high gear to feed demand. Imports alone cannot do it." According to SRI's Pat Henry, $100-per-barrel oil was a "point of recognized discussion in communities such as the World Energy Conference."

gasoline-rationing coupons, which it did not destroy until 1984.[NN]

But at SRI another viewpoint was emerging. SRI had been working on a variety of energy-related topics since about 1966.[32] The SRI perspective on the future price points of oil began to form in about 1967 when Marathon Oil came to SRI wanting to learn about the technology and costs of producing oil from coal.[OO] This brief study suggested to Pat Henry (see Figure 14-11) and Russ Phillips that much was to be learned about the role of synthetic fuels and their impact on the future price of oil. As though to verify that assumption, three

Figure 14-11. Sr. energy economist, Tom Boyce, (left) and Energy Center director, Pat Henry.

separate multiclient projects were soon started in this area. These enabled SRI not only to design a framework or model for gauging the price of oil in the context of all energy sources, but also to gain a unique and confident understanding of the world's oil, gas, and coal reserves themselves. Then came the 1973 embargo, and suddenly the quest for a better understanding of where the future price of oil was headed became intense. As a result, the client base and scope of the existing multiclient projects were enlarged.

Thus, through its own initiative and in response to client need, SRI's Energy Practice acquired an industry-government mission to evaluate the trends in not just oil but energy supply, demand, and cost in their broadest senses. How did the world's known oil reserves appear when examined and measured as a function of recovery cost rather than using the flat, per-barrel cost assumption common at the time? Using their individual recovery and production costs and the quantity of their reserves, what role did energy alternatives to crude oil play in energy forecasts? Alternatives ranging from natural gas to uranium were examined in detail. Intuitively, any comprehensive study of the demand-price elasticity of crude oil should contain all such energy sources but, surprisingly, such a perspective had not been developed.

So, from a newly compiled database on the world's oil and natural gas reserves, basin by basin, through a careful examination of crude oil alternatives and their competing costs, and through the experience and thoughtful reasoning of the staff, SRI arrived at a very different position.[33] It was one of continued oil

---

[32] An Energy Department was founded at SRI in 1966 under Sherman Clark. This unit concentrated more on subjects like energy rate bases and regulatory matters. According to Pat Henry, SRI Vice President Ken Beggs gave the subject of oil futures a push in the late 1960s that spawned departments in Energy Economics and Energy Technology. By September 1974, these departments had consolidated under Pat Henry as the SRI Center for Energy Studies. It was in this Center that SRI's position on future oil pricing developed and was then spread around the world.

[33] Former Exxon geologist Joseph Pelline, through countless informed inquiries to oil companies and oil-producing

availability and with only a modest increase in price over the long term! I clearly remember hearing at the time that SRI's appraisal was out of step with the conventional wisdom. That conventional position was clearly driven by the gas lines and the expected aggressive pricing policies of the oil-producing nations, all further exaggerated in the media by notions of the limited size of domestic and world reserves. Many saw the fuel "shortages" as portending a permanent reduction in our standard of living.

As a result of the Arab oil embargo, SRI began a range of multiclient studies to predict the parameters of the world's energy situation in the last quarter of the century.[34] To determine the future supply and demand of energy, and forecast the price of crude oil itself over the long term, SRI had to examine all competing sources of energy. Beyond this general, recovery-cost expression of supply, it was also necessary, of course, to estimate future demand on a worldwide basis. Because of a number of factors such as more gas-efficient automobiles, demand forecasts were actually decreasing over time.[35] One metric in an SRI article written for the *Harvard Business Review* showed that in 1970 a barrel of oil contributed $140 to U.S. GDP.[pp] To illustrate an increased efficiency in the use of oil, that contribution was predicted to increase to $191 by 2000. To show the validity of the SRI concern about how demand might change, the actual number for 1999, the last year available, shows an even greater contribution to the GDP of $223 per barrel of oil consumed. (All these figures are in 1978 dollars.)

Thus, the SRI assessment had a grounding that other analyses either didn't have or chose to ignore. Given that oil is a depletable resource, here were some other SRI perceptions:

- The position that would best serve the needs of most OPEC nations, especially those such as Saudi Arabia and Kuwait with large

reserves and relatively small populations, would be to maximize their oil revenues in the long-term sense. Driving oil prices inordinately high would unleash a host of what for them would be undesirable responses, including:

  - The development of new oil reserves in other countries, reserves that had not previously been economical to develop (e.g., reserves in remote and hostile environments such as deep offshore or the Arctic)

  - Expansion of the development and use of new technologies to enhance the recovery of oil from known reservoirs or to produce oil from solid fuels such as coal and oil shale and even solid wastes

  - Government policies (e.g., automobile and appliance efficiency standards, energy-efficient building codes, energy taxes) to reduce energy and oil consumption

  - The substitution of other fuels (e.g., coal, natural gas) for oil

  - The development of new energy technologies (e.g., nuclear, solar, wind, methane) to reduce the demand for oil

  - Slower global economic growth to reduce the demand for imported oil.

- Some U.S. politicians seized on the occasion to advocate oil or energy independence. They sought a wide range of initiatives that would bring the money to pursue new energy sources to their constituencies. Most of these proposals, however, looked promising only if the cost of oil were to increase dramatically.

These perceptions, then, suggested that the best strategy for oil-producing nations was not to escalate oil prices, but to pursue policies that would promote the long-term dependence of oil-consuming nations such as the United States on imported oil. This meant setting the price low enough to block the development of new oil reserves, energy conservation, and alternative energy sources. If prices were to rise to the then often-mentioned $100 per barrel, future revenue streams—on which many if not all OPEC members depended for their major source of national income—would be reduced.

One of the first revelations of this ongoing analysis and its clear consequences for a more

---

countries, meticulously compiled the SRI database on world oil and natural gas reserves as a function of recovery cost.

[34] The SRI studies from which this insight came served a broad community of oil users and producers: those who sold into either of those markets, or to government. Many SRI professionals participated in what turned out to be an important series of large multiclient and single-client projects. Among them were Pat Henry, Joseph Pelline (formerly of Exxon), Bill Schumacher, Jay Kopelman, Gene Harless (formerly of Texaco), Arvind Jain, Bert Louks, Tom Boyce, Stan Field, Ed Kinderman, Carl Trexel, and Jeff Witwer.

[35] Demand itself was, of course, increasing. The forecasts were showing a decline in the increase in demand.

moderate future price of oil came at a 1975 SRI Board/Council Meeting. With such oil notables in the audience as Fred Hartley, Chairman and President of Union Oil of California, and H. J. Haynes, Chairman of the Board of Standard Oil of California, Pat Henry related the growing SRI position and some of the reasoning behind it. The responses of oil industry leaders at the meeting and subsequent written statements showed that they disagreed, at the time, with the optimistic tone of the analyses. The demand for such information, however, remained intense and pervasive. SRI people like Henry and others were presenting, both in the United States and abroad, the message of the collective SRI team.[36] Henry was interviewed on the CBS Walter Cronkite program about SRI's position, which was running counter to the advice the CIA was giving President Carter. Many were skeptical about a future unburdened by skyrocketing oil costs. By early 1979, however, SRI President Charles Anderson was so comfortable and familiar with the SRI position that he gave the keynote address to the Sixth Annual Energy Technology Conference in Washington, D.C.[37]

In May 1979, SRI issued a seven-volume report to its private clients. Included was the prediction of the price of crude oil shown in Figure 14-12.[QQ] Given the then $10 a barrel price, the SRI team predicted the relatively modest growth shown. Only an expected average increase in recovery costs on some reserves pushed the price upward.

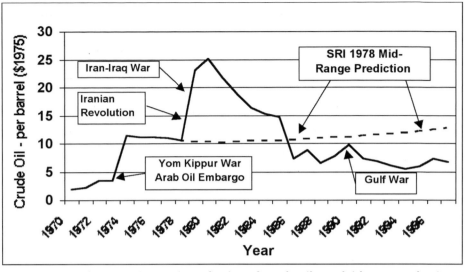

Figure 14-12. The 1978 SRI projected price of crude oil overlaid on actual price (all in 1975 dollars).

With some notable exceptions, the SRI predictions occurred. SRI's 1978 predicted price for crude oil, as it turns out, was too high over the long term. The actual price increases from 1978 to 1986 were the result of the unpredicted conditions of Middle East conflict. Production increases and falling demand caused prices to decline after 1981. Repeated attempts by OPEC to control its production after 1985 failed, non-OPEC production rose, and the real price of oil continued to fall. Since then, upward pressures have largely failed to materialize because the per-barrel cost to pump Middle East crude still sits at about $2–3.[38] In retrospect, then, SRI provided those who listened a long-term perspective that was based on solid data and sensible reasoning. The world's oil supply is inarguably finite, but care must be used in invoking that fact when the marketplace really isn't ready to acknowledge it. Because of the large reserves of low-cost oil from developing countries, the price of oil remains elastic. Such a market can respond to initiatives such as conservation and efficiency. SRI's message through the early 1980s was that the world would find a buyer's market in energy at least until the end of the century.[39] While the SRI estimate was lower than any of the day, as Figure 14-12 shows, it was still higher than the

---

[36] From an account by Henry's secretary, in the 6 years from 1973 to 1978 he had given over 40 presentations in settings that varied from U.S. organizations such as oil companies, schools and academe, industry, the Congress, and the CIA, and to foreign institutions as well. The SRI story became so prominent that by the mid-1980s nearly 100 government and commercial organizations were participating in the multiclient work.

[37] Given that all this work was sponsored under a proprietary multiclient study, how could the conclusions be broadcast so widely? The answer is that in such studies, SRI normally issues summary documents or papers on findings if they are deemed to be in the common good.

[38] So-called lifting costs can run as low as $1–2 in new oil fields such as Kazakhstan. (SRI's Tom Boyce, personal communication, April 2001.) Given such low costs, the price of oil on the world market is clearly defined by everything but cost.

[39] Tom Boyce, Energy Buyer's Market Throughout the '80s, *SRI Journal*, 2 (10), December 1982. At the time, Boyce was Director of the SRI Energy Center.

BRINGING THE SRI POSITION TO SAUDI ARABIA

As a part of SRI's support in creating a series of 5-year plans for the government of Saudi Arabia, one of that country's ministers came to SRI for talks. It was in May 1982, and SRI was still engaged in its ongoing multiclient projects to forecast the worldwide supply and cost of energy. Since Saudi Arabia was also among the sponsors of the project, SRI chose to give the minister a preview of its emerging conclusions, one of which proved to be of great interest to him: In your forecast use of available funds, they told him, it would be a mistake to plan on oil maintaining its then high price of around $50 per barrel (in present dollars). Instead, plan on no more than $20–25. Given Saudi Arabia's copious exports, this difference would greatly affect its ongoing planning. (The basis for the advice is that outlined in the main text.) The minister found the message so important that he invited the discussion leader, Tom Boyce, to come to Saudi Arabia to convey the advice first hand.

As a result, Boyce and Charles Greene flew to Riyadh and gave an expanded pitch in a 2-day workshop to government functionaries. Among other things, they reviewed the influx of alternative energy sources such as natural gas and nuclear plants that would find a ready market if oil costs were to remain high. That done, they were then invited to fly to the Saudi king's summer palace in Ta'if. It was Ramadan and the royal family and Council of Ministers were there, and they too needed to hear SRI's reasoning. Thus, Tom Boyce went to Ta'if for a midnight meeting. There, in the center of the Council, including the Oil Minister Sheikh Yamani, all seated in a circle on the floor, he repeated the SRI strategy. Rather than making any recommendations, in his 2-hour tutorial he explained SRI's reasons behind the projections, leaving them to their own conclusions. None of them uttered a word, and there were no questions at the end, but the 1985–1989 plan wisely reflected SRI's advice.

For better or worse, that same philosophy holds today. In many of the oil-rich countries like Saudi Arabia, the cost of getting oil out of the ground is very low, perhaps less than $2–3 a barrel. That low cost, together with setting the price at $25–30, gives them both an extraordinary return and plenty of margin that can be used to prevent higher cost alternatives from entering the energy market. To the bigger oil-consuming nations like the United States, that strategy is both good and bad news.

---

actual trend if we ignore the conflict-centered peaks.

As a footnote to this run of prescient insight, in 1975 SRI's Decision Analysis Department was helping Gulf Oil Corporation build a national energy model and gladly used the developing supply/demand data mentioned above. SRI ultimately developed the model on a global scale in one of its multiclient projects. The model built for Gulf was eventually passed to the U.S. government's Energy Research and Development Administration where, as a National Energy Model, it helped that agency develop its own energy data analysis system. The uniqueness of the SRI data compilation and insights began to erode when the U.S. Department of Energy established its own capabilities as the Energy Information Administration in 1977.

To close this account of SRI's assessment of oil availability and price in the last quarter of the 21st century, a cautionary note must be made. While SRI correctly showed how important it was to gauge our oil and gas reserves, and their energy alternatives, in terms of their cost of recovery, there is no avoiding the ultimate limits to our hydrocarbon reserves under any meaningful cost structure. Whether we look at our consumption versus discovery rates or ultimately at our consumption versus production capacity, such thresholds will ultimately be crossed, barring revolutionary alternatives to hydrocarbon-based energy. As this story goes to print in late 2004, because of worldwide demand and Middle East conflict, crude oil exceeds $50 per barrel. As a matter of some coincidence, in 1975 dollars this equates to about $14 per barrel, about equal to SRI's 1978 projections.

Thus, SRI was able to show that it is in the best interest of consumers, producers, and their governments to try to get the metrics and the equations as right as humanly possible. Otherwise, energy forecasts, inherently emotion-laden, will careen out of rational perspective with conflict and other unacceptable consequences.

Endnotes

[A] This history of planning development at SRI came from the individual writings of or discussions with Robert Smith, Bill Guns, Bill Ralston, Bill Royce, Al Humphrey, and Finn Birger Lie.

[B] From a memo in SRI Archives by Robert W. Smith and a 1956 SRI report by N. R. Maines, *Why Companies Grow,* of which over 500 copies were requested and distributed. An excerpt is given in *SRI Journal*, 2(1), 18-23, 1958.

[C] William S. Royce, "A History of Strategic Management and Planning at SRI," March 31, 1985 (an internal, informal paper but quite a comprehensive one).

[D] William S. Royce, "Origin and Evolution of the Stakeholder Concept," personal correspondence, January 31, 1998.

[E] Gibson, Chapter 13, op. cit.

[F] J. Knight Allen, The Rising Acceptance of Corporate Strategy, *SRI Journal*, Feature Issue 1, 9-13, 1965.

[G] William S. Royce, *Flexible Planning: SRI Approaches and Issues,* Business Intelligence Program Report D94-1803, January 1994.

[H] Milton Friedman, The Social Responsibility of Business Is to Increase Profits, *New York Times Magazine*, 122-126, September 13, 1970.

[I] R. Edward Freeman, *Strategic Management: A Stakeholder Approach*, Pitman, 1984.

[J] Royce, "A History of Strategic Management and Planning at SRI," op. cit.

[K] Albert Humphrey, personal communication, June 23, 2001.

[L] From communications with Albert Humphrey and Finn Birger Lie, son of SRI's Birger Lie (June-September 2001)

[M] Thomas F. Mandel and Ian Wilson, *How Companies Use Scenarios: Practices and Prescriptions,* Business Intelligence Program, Report 822, SRI International, Spring 1993.

[N] Taken from Art Kleiner, *The Age of Heretics*, Doubleday, New York, 1996.

[O] Kleiner, op. cit., page 290.

[P] Stanford Research Institute, *SRI's Investments in Tomorrow*, No. 8, Summer 1973.

[Q] From SRIC-BI's VALS web page, www.sric-bi.com/vals, August 20, 2004.

[R] Quote attributed to Dr. Herbert Krugman, a noted market researcher and former head of marketing at GE, on a University of Georgia web site, //parallel.park.uga.edu/~jpwilson/courses/fall98/VALS.html.

[S] Fred Weil, personal communication, July 26, 2001.

[T] Gordon H. Parker, SRI International Project History, (internal paper) March 1987.

[U] Dennis Finnigan, personal communication, February 2, 2000.

[V] SRI memo from Gordon Parker to SRI Management Council, January 8, 1982.

[W] C.V. Wood, Jr. and Harrison A. Price, "Disneyland—Cost and Planning Data," SRI Report to Disneyland, Inc. January 1954. Curiously, according to "Buzz" Price, this report was never formally submitted to the client, but the information must have been conveyed, at least in part through Wood's transition to Disneyland.

[X] SRI's, *Research for Industry*, VI (6), July 1954.

[Y] Randy Bright, *Disneyland—Inside Story*, Abrams Publishers, 1987.

[Z] "American Profile, West Edition," August 12, 2001. (a broadly syndicated newspaper supplement)

[AA] H.A. Price, personal communication, October 15, 1999.

[BB] SRI's Bill Royce provided much of the information and some of the writing for this and the following subsection.

[CC] Phone conversation with Joe Grippo (May 2003) who led much of the SRI work for the NFL.

[DD] Taken from www.swift.com on February 22, 2001.

[EE] This account of SWIFT draws on personal communications from Dennis Finnigan, January 19, 2001, and Don Fiske, February 9, 2001. In the period of the account, Finnigan was one of three vice presidents that headed SRI operations, and Fiske was head of the Management Systems Division for Europe.

[FF] See Chapter 2 about ERMA, the world's first automatic check processing machine.

GG *Organisation Recommendations for Proposed Society for Worldwide Interbank Financial Telecommunication (SWIFT)*, SRI Project 1570-2, March 20, 1972; and *Organisation Bylaws for SWIFT*, SRI Project 1570-2, July 14, 1972.

HH As found in the title of an SRI project report dated February 14, 1972.

II Dennis Finnigan, personal communication, January 19, 2001.

JJ J.M. FitzGerald, K. Drexage, and G.W. Boyce, *Society for Worldwide Interbank Financial Telecommunication,* Interim Report II, February 1977, SRI Project 5885, entitled "An EDP Security Audit," from October 25, 1976 to February 16, 1977.

KK Some of the information used here was learned from the following account of the dramatic change in investing habits of the U.S. middle class: Joseph Nocera's *A Piece of the Action—How the Middle Class Joined the Money Class*, Simon & Schuster, 1994.

LL Nocera, op. cit.

MM Thomas J. Murray, "SRI Charts An Ambitious Course," *Dun's Business Month*, February1985 reprinted with permission in *SRI Journal*, 5(2), 3, April 1985.

NN Franklin Tugwell, The Energy Crisis and the American Political Economy: Politics and Markets in the Management of Natural Resources, Stanford University Press, 1988, p. 1.

OO This account was prepared following a series of discussions with Bill Schumacher, Tom Boyce, and Pat Henry during the first half of 2001.

PP John P. Henry, V. Eugene Harless, and Jay B. Kopelman, World Energy: A Manageable Dilemma, *Harvard Business Review*, May-June, 1979, pp. 150–161.

QQ From Jay B. Kopelman and William J. Schumacher, *World Energy Stud, Vol. 1, Summary and Conclusions,* a Private Multiclient Study, SRI International, May 1979, p. 81.

Chapter 15
International and Domestic Economic Development

Selecting which of SRI's projects in economic development to describe is, like in all other areas of its diverse endeavor, very difficult. With so many efforts in so many countries, there is simply too much from which to choose. But in a few cases SRI's role was broad enough to affect an entire country with important and lasting changes, even though that contribution was not publicly known. In that regard SRI's projects in India and Saudi Arabia are described. More focused impacts such as governmental roles in telecommunications and intellectual property rights in England and the Philippines, respectively, are also covered. Outcomes of a number of other projects, both international and domestic, are included. Finally, there is the case of Zambia, one of the world's disadvantaged countries, where the repeated efforts of SRI and the World Bank show how enormously difficult it is to ease its pervasive and continuing economic struggle. As with other research areas reported in this book, the selections are often aided by simply finding those principals who are still reachable.

Helping Build India's Middle Class

It was the mid-1950s, less than a decade after India won its independence, when SRI entered into a working relationship with the Ford Foundation and its technical assistance programs in India and Pakistan. That third-party source of funding was the only means SRI had to work in the Asian subcontinent because of the low value of the currency there. India was struggling with tremendous economic problems brought about, in part, by its population growth and a general lack of small industries. India thus was effectively to serve as a crucible in which to test whether a very large and underdeveloped country could attain a more prosperous and stable economy through the motivations of individual citizens. Obstacles were abundant: strong regionalism buttressed by countless languages, opposing religions, and the intricate and pervasive caste system. Though outlawed in 1947, the caste system was still much a part of society in 1955 when SRI people arrived. Although the caste system was awkward for any hands-on American to deal with, more important by far, it was also inimical to generating the economic benefits of an entrepreneurial middle class (see box).

As is often the case in developing countries, both economic development itself and the ability to administer programs designed to create it were lacking in India. Furthermore, information about where a given sector of the economy stood and how to measure its progress was frequently unavailable. Accordingly, SRI's Dr. Eugene Staley (see Figure 15-1) began work in 1955 on the concept of a National Council for Applied Economic Research

Figure 15-1. Some of the SRI leaders in India during the last half of the 1950s (from left: Dr. Gene Staley, Dr. Ray Ewell, Ed Robison, and Bill Royce).

A MATTER OF SRI ACCULTURATION

A couple of episodes in Ed Robison's early experience in India illustrate the implications of the caste system for business. SRI needed to convey copies of a completed report across New Delhi one afternoon. When Robison asked an Indian associate assigned to work with him to deliver them, he was told that that was impossible because the "driver" wasn't there. When Robison asked him to do it using Robison's car, the associate replied that he couldn't do that kind of work. After some wrangling, Robison said that he would do it all himself, including driving his own car. But the impasse continued when Ed was told he shouldn't carry the reports to the car and that there was no one there "appropriate" to help him. Finally, after Robison voiced his consternation, "porters" were made available, one of whom he drove to the destination to ferry the reports up to the office there. Another incident was precipitated by a number of burned-out light bulbs in the office. When Robison asked that they be replaced, he was told that it would take days to process the requisitions. It was all right, however, for Robison to give his Indian associate the money to go the nearest store and buy some. Good! But when the gentleman returned with the bulbs, no one was available to screw them in.

These events were typical of the acculturation SRI staff would undergo as they learned to live in and come to respect the culture they were in.

(NCAER) that would gather needed data, then be able to speak authoritatively on prevailing economic conditions, and thereafter help evaluate new positions and directions. NCAER was also to examine industry-relevant factors, such as a tax structure, that were more favorable to foreign investments. Many SRI people helped train the Indian staff of the Center in investigative techniques and practices. This non-government, contract-research-based institution was established in 1956 and was unlike anything in India at the time. Now, almost 50 years later, it is perhaps the best, most unbiased, and most often quoted source in India in regard to a wide range of economic, consumer, and labor information.[1]

The need for more small industries was the focus of the second early SRI project. Here again, Staley, working with Dr. Raymond Ewell, designed a Small Industries Organisation (SIO) for the Commissioner of the Government's

Department of Industry. Their recommendation was submitted in 1954. By early 1955 Bombay, Calcutta, Madras, and New Delhi had Small Industries Service Institutes that, through sets of investigative teams, both determined the condition of small industries (those with fewer than 100 employees) and helped entrepreneurs attain needed skills in such areas as marketing, manufacturing processes, and management. This initiative helped focus government attention on those sectors of the economy that could improve noticeably with modest investment. And the program had rapid effects. In Madras, for example, the number of small industries rose from 1,524 in 1956 to 2,984 by 1961, almost doubling in 5 years.[A] These small-business programs, which are still part of India's economic development approach, are a means for promoting internal and external investment.[B] The SRI assistance continued for perhaps 10 years, and the insights and quality offered helped build SRI's reputation at the Ford Foundation and in the international assistance field in general.

---

[1] For example see: www.nira.go.jp/ice/tt-info/nwdtt93/183.html and related sites for the quality and breadth of this nonprofit research council. NCAER's annual revenues are about 21 million rupees or roughly $500,000.

Another early SRI idea was Harry Robinson's conviction that private investments from abroad were necessary to elevate India's economic condition. At his suggestion Indian Investment Centres were created in a number of economic sectors. Again, some of these centers are still operating.

Staley[2] and Ewell left India in 1957, and the SRI leader became Ed Robison, who assumed responsibility for the broad cross-section of work that had been started. In mid-1959, Robison returned to Palo Alto, and William Royce arrived to assume the program leadership of the work with NCAER; Everett Calhoun took over the work with the SIO. Royce was then joined by a highly respected Australian-born economist from the University of California at Berkeley, Dr. John B. Condliffe. By the fall of 1959, 9 SRI staff were living in India, and about 25 had lived or worked there for varying periods since 1955.

Other reflections on SRI's accomplishments in India can be found in the following nomination of Robison for the 2000 SRI Gibson Award for outstanding contributions to society:

- In 1957, Robison took leadership of both SRI development projects in India, the NCAER and the small industries assistance. His work resulted in a book he co-authored with Nanjundan and Staley, entitled *Economic Research for Small Industry Development*.[C] This book is a history of the Ministry of Industries program of work on economic research for small-scale industries.

- Robison's industrial survey reports on small industries resulted in the following economic improvements (paraphrased):
  – SRI assisted in forming several governmental policies at both the federal and state levels. It provided data never before available, including area development and marketing surveys, as well as training programs established in Madras for needed technical people.
  – Robison persuaded the Indian government to pay greater attention to the quality of products coming from small industries so that they could compete better

in domestic and world markets. • The program opened the way for liberalized credit to small enterprises by the State Bank of India and extended information services among the four development institutes that were created to aid small industries.

- One of NCAER's early achievements was a series of economic development studies for several states in India that provided them with a degree of planning independence from the central government.

As part of its promotion of small business, SRI also helped design and create in 1962 the Small Industry Extension Training Institute (SIET) in Hyderabad (see Figure 15-2). This school was founded to increase Indians' ability to develop small businesses by assisting and training the officers of small companies.[D] It continues today as the National Institute for Small Industry Extension Training and serves as another example of SRI's efforts to increase economic development through indigenous means. Over the more than a dozen years of SRI work in economic development on the Indian subcontinent, the staff of its International Development Center wrote 11 books.

Following the early years of concentrated on-site work, some SRI staff revisited India to help evaluate progress toward economic development. On the tenth anniversary of the Ford Foundation's involvement there, Robison and Staley returned to examine the progress of small industry development. Much more information was now available to make such an assessment. Given small businesses' growing share of India's industrial output (33% in 1960), they concluded that the prospect for small businesses and factories was "bright."[E] The Foundation's earlier contributions were bearing fruit.

Over the 10-20 years SRI was active in the Asian subcontinent, a large number of important Indian companies became members of its Institute Associates Program (IAP) and its quadrennial International Industrial Conference (IIC) (see Chapter 13 on Economic Development Meetings). In 1981, the Indian members of the IAP urged SRI to hold an investment and development meeting in New Delhi, which it did in December of that year. This gathering, which P.C. Nambiar, Chairman of the State Bank of India, chaired, was intended to make other countries aware of India's investment potential. It drew some 70 such representatives from outside India. As

---

[2] Staley had a remarkable career, serving on the secretariat of the San Francisco conference that drew up the UN Charter, helping establish the UN Relief and Rehabilitation Administration, and in 1961 leading an economic commission to Vietnam for President Kennedy (*SRI Journal*, 2(1), 9-15,1958). He also published several books on how to enable small businesses.

Figure 15-2. NISIET Center in Hyderabad, India.

background for that meeting, Robison wrote an appraisal of India's progress and the atmosphere for continued economic growth. India had become the world's tenth largest manufacturing country, was self-sufficient in many sectors, and had a substantial and growing middle class. Interestingly, India was perhaps unique among developing nations in consistently honoring its public and private sector debts. But in 1981, numerous impediments remained: India's uneasy relationships with its neighbors, a pronounced unevenness in economic progress across the country, cultural roots that fostered protracted decision-making, and some discouragement of initiative all continued to hamper progress.

With this conference, then, SRI's window on India was closing, but only after it had made a long and substantial contribution to India's economic development.[F]

Some of the initiatives taken in India and the quality of SRI work there led to smaller but parallel projects in East and West Pakistan. In the beginning, these projects also dealt with rural and small industry development. An example in West Pakistan was a 1958-59 Ford Foundation examination of the development of better business methods in agriculture. An SRI group consisting of Carlton Wood, William Bredo, and Laurance Bell also found that raising the standard of living there meant encouraging small businesses. As a result of their work, the Pakistani government established the Rural Industrial Service (RIS). Similar to government actions in India, two sites were recommended in Pakistan for RIS Centers. The centers first designed new farming methods for Pakistan and later developed ways to manufacture other equipment and supplies needed by local industries—items that had previously been imported. These Centers also served as training schools for the establishment of new companies. The conflict between West and East Pakistan (the latter is now Bangladesh) pre-empted further work by SRI in those countries.

Bringing Contract Research to Japan

SRI's large International Building in Menlo Park was dedicated in 1969. Leveraged into existence by the untiring efforts of Hoot Gibson, donations came from the Bechtel family for the basic building construction, with the furnishings given by a large number of international friends of SRI. Before its remodeling in 1997, the building's main wing for meetings had rooms known as Uemura, Ishizaka, and Keidanren. These names had roots in a Japanese organization with which SRI developed a long-term association that began in the mid-1950s—the Federation of Economic Organizations or, Keidanren in Japanese. The Chairman of Keidanren at that period was Taizo Ishizaka, later to be succeeded by Kogoro Uemura. When, at the I-Building dedication,

Ishizaka was shown the room that would bear his name, he was surprised and responded, "I will do something for you." The excellent calligraphy that came later to hang there was by his 80-year old hand.[3]

Other important industrial relationships developed early on with executives of important Japanese companies: Shibaura Electric Co. (Toshiba), Fuji Iron & Steel (Nippon Steel), Fuji Bank, and Nomura Securities. In the mid-1960s, Yoshizane Iwasa, the Chairman of Fuji Bank, and Shigeo Nagano, Chairman of Nippon Steel, were instrumental in creating, with important SRI assistance, the Japan-

---

[3] SRI has since leased a portion of that building, and the Japanese artwork is currently in storage.

California Association and the Pacific Basin Economic Council, respectively. These bodies came to be influential in the promotion of trade and investments across the Pacific Region (see Chapter 13).

Certainly, one of the biggest single impacts that SRI had in Japan was the creation of a research organization patterned on SRI itself, the Nomura Research Institute. In the late 1950s, Nomura Securities was looking for a way to contribute to the future of Japanese industrial and economic progress, while SRI was trying to further its position in Japan. Agreement between SRI and the president of Nomura resulted in the seconding of SRI's Dr. Carsten Steffens to Tokyo at the end of 1961. He worked with members of Nomura in the design of the nonprofit Nomura Research Institute of Technology and Economics (which had a familiar ring, NRI). The new Institute was established in April 1965 and within 18 months moved into a new $4 million headquarters in Kamakura, 40 miles outside Tokyo. One of the major vehicles in building NRI was SRI's international fellow program. Some 22 NRI staff spent from 6 to 12 months at SRI learning both research methods and the business processes of contract research. Early on, the new Institute was broadly based in science, economics, and business management. Today, NRI has grown to become one of the largest research organizations in Japan. It has 2,900 employees, $100 million capitalization, a number of subsidiaries, and offices in New York, Washington, D.C., the San Francisco area, and throughout the Pacific Basin.

Beyond contract revenues in Tokyo and Menlo Park, the founding of NRI helped SRI in several ways. First, Steffens moved to establish an SRI office in Tokyo in 1963, and where else but in the Nomura Securities Building in Tokyo. NRI became the first Japanese member of SRI's Long-Range Planning Service (LRPS) (see Chapter 14), with its membership paving the way for the entry of a number of other Japanese companies into LRPS.

Insofar as volume was concerned, most of SRI's other early work in Japan was of a multi-client nature. These studies were centered in the chemical industries as part of the Process Economics Program and the Chemical Economics Handbook (see Chapter 11). By the 1970s, however, more single-client contracts were being won, both in the Business Group and in Sciences and Engineering as well. In 1971, William Royce took Steffens' place as director of what was now the SRI-East Asia office. Before Royce left in 1976, the annual contract revenues had about doubled to $1.8 million per year. This larger volume enabled the establishment of resident research staff in Tokyo by 1974, which had grown to more than 30 members by the mid-1980s.

Although this ongoing work benefited many Japanese companies, Osaka Gas became particularly close to SRI. SRI's relationship with that company spanned a wide range of work involving all of SRI's major groups, beginning in 1982 with a $110,000 project to help the company define a "management vision for the 21st century." The idea was to help Osaka Gas break out of its traditional gas and energy roles by identifying new technologies and business opportunities. Among the first efforts was an innovation search, conducted in Menlo Park by SRI icon Joe McPherson, which defined some 1,000 possible new technologies or business areas. These opportunities were ultimately winnowed down to 3 or 4, and SRI began a series of projects to help explore these and other areas that unfolded. Two SRI people came to play important roles in this relationship: Shigeyoshi Takaoka helped develop the bond between the two organizations, was close to nearly all the senior executives of Osaka Gas, and eventually came to direct the SRI office in Tokyo; and Dr. Paul Jorgensen, vice president of the Sciences Group, became the highly respected advisor and the principal SRI contact. By the mid-1980s, Osaka gas was perhaps SRI's largest commercial client with more than 50 projects distributed across the Institute. This relationship helped swell the SRI project work in Japan to exceed $13 million in 1985.

During this time, several other notable Japanese clients joined SRI's ranks: Fujitsu, for which SRI worked for more than a decade in the field of information technology; Fuji Bank, computer modernization and investment banking strategies; Nissan Motors, marketing, interior car design, and, more recently, planetary vehicles; Sumitomo Bank, analysis of the transition of U.S. credit card practices to Japan; Nippon Telegraph and Telephone (NTT), a study on trade that indicated that the reason Japan was not importing U.S. information technology was not, as hoped, because of superior Japanese technology; and a host of other companies including Mitsubishi, Canon, Nippon Mining, Oki, Hitachi, Ricoh, and Asahi.

One final and interesting facet of our work in Japan was created by a fortuitous political happening. In 1986, amid the ongoing balance-of-trade difficulties that the United States was having with Japan, an agreement was reached between President Reagan and Prime Minister Nakasone that was intended to mollify U.S. concerns. Because of our large import/export imbalance and because Japan was perceived as taking advantage of the large sums the United States was spending on research, Nakasone agreed, mostly symbolically, to fund six research projects in the United States. The projects were competed for nationally and,

though the projects were funded through an individual company, in this case NTT, the choice of U.S. research contractors was more broadly based. Of the six projects, SRI won two for a total of $3 million over 3 years and received 60% of the allocated money. One project, performed in the Physical Sciences Division, examined coherent, time-domain optical memory (cryogenic) with extremely dense information storage and rapid access. The other, undertaken in Engineering's Artificial Intelligence Center, explored automatic natural language generation as part of human-computer dialog.

Bringing National Planning to Saudi Arabia

Saudi Arabia is a relatively young nation. The final integration of warring Arab tribes began just after the turn of the century, and by 1927 Ibn Saud (Abdul Aziz) was officially proclaimed King. In 1932, the country became the Kingdom of Saudi Arabia. The discovery of oil in commercial quantities in 1938 would come to give the country a significant role in the world economy. This rapid rise to international prominence, enabled by the infusion of foreign oil investment and technology, belied the general lack of internal development within the country, even in the late 1960s when SRI entered the scene.

Among the nations of the modern world, Saudi Arabia remains an anachronism. Not only is it an absolute monarchy as rigid as many of the middle ages, but in spite of its enormous wealth, its literacy rate is still low in comparison with countries of equivalent per capita GDP.[4] For example, although great strides have been made in the literacy of women, growing from about 50% in 1995 to 70% in 2002,[5] the percentage achieved is still lower than that in many poorer countries. Nonetheless, the past 30 years, beginning before King Faisal's assassination in 1975, have seen this nation, with more than 25% of the world's oil reserves and its largest oil exporter, broaden its economic base and create modern infrastructures in an almost unprecedented fashion. In the decade ending in 1976, the rural

population of farmers and Bedouins declined from 75% to 50% as people moved to the cities. That influx, plus the increased number of non-Saudi workers required to build the desired urban expansions, placed an enormous strain on cities, which had little or no existing infrastructures and clearly inadequate housing.

By the time SRI arrived to assist the Saudi government, the pressing need to deal with these changes was evident. The blueprints for change, amounting to $900 billion in government expenditures, took the form of a series of development plans. SRI made important contributions to these plans, with SRI teams providing the leaders of Saudi Arabia and its ministerial staffs, particularly that of the Ministry of Planning, a wider understanding of the public infrastructure and services needed by a state with huge oil resources.[6]

SRI's work with the Saudi Ministry of Planning amounts to perhaps the longest and closest relationship it has had with any foreign government.[G] The relationship was based on helping the Saudis develop a series of four 5-year plans. The first of these projects was won competitively in 1967-68 (see the following box), and they continued until about 1990.[7] According to SRI's Peter Duncan, the plans "provided these leaders and staff with a framework for defining the resources available and the objectives of the national leadership, and then helped to set priorities for the

---

[4] The huge revenues from oil products are not reflected in the per capita GDP (about $10,600 in 2001) because GDP does not reflect a transfer of one asset, depletable oil reserves, to another, financial assets.

[5] Estimates from the *CIA Factbooks* of 1999 and 2002. The decision to educate women was not made until the 1960s.

---

[6] As pointed out later below, SRI helped design the Ministry of Planning, which, before October 1975, existed as the Central Planning Organization.

[7] The last 5-year contract, valued at $8.7 million, was awarded in mid-1986.

SRI WINS THE SAUDI PLANNING ROLE

In late 1967, a letter arrived at SRI's Menlo Park offices from His Excellency Sheikh Hisham Nazer, then Minister of State and head of the Central Planning Organization. He invited SRI to bid on a contract to help the Saudi government build an effective program in economic and social planning. The World Bank, as a result of earlier SRI work, had suggested that SRI be a bidder. One of the bid requirements was a formal presentation in Riyadh. SRI was not used to spending that kind of travel money for proposals but did in this case. On arriving in Jeddah, Wilson Harwood (see Figure 15-3), head of SRI's International Development Center, was met unexpectedly by a U.S. Embassy staffer and taken to meet with the ambassador, who offered assistance and stressed that the U.S. government very much wanted a U.S. organization to win. That meeting was an immediate indication of the importance of the proposed work.

The proposal presentation and discussions over the next several days with the minister proved to be more difficult that anticipated. The minister was impressed with the hastily prepared flip-chart presentation and asked Harwood to prepare a formal proposal by the next day. That presentation immediately drew a request for pricing, and the minister would not accept Harwood's protestations that he was not authorized to price the work. Unable to phone Menlo Park, but with help from the Ford Foundation and ARAMCO on local costs, he gave the minister a bid of $1.3 million and went home to face the consequences.

The next interaction came after several months of silence when Nazer phoned from New York saying he wanted to visit SRI. After an afternoon of difficult negotiations in the International Building, the minister declared that it would be very difficult to fund anything over $1 million. When Harwood phoned him at his San Francisco hotel the following morning with a final bid of $1.025 million for the 2-year project, the minister laughed and accepted the bid. The contract date was August 5, 1968.

A measure of the esoteric aspects of the new relationship can be found in Harwood's diary as related in an internal SRI newsletter (SRI Intercom, No. 104, January 15, 1969). "The celebration which followed the signing [of the contract] was held [in the summer capital of Ta'if] on a dry sun-drenched hillside in two large tents, their long sides open to a fertile desert valley below. In one tent, some forty Saudis—Ministers, Deputy Ministers, government officials, the local Bedouin sheik, and I sat cross-legged or stood on several layers of colorful Oriental rugs. We drank aromatic Arabian coffee, highly spiced with cardamom and gingerroot, poured from long-beaked pots through palm fiber filters into tiny china cups. After several rounds of coffee, we moved to the other tent where we settled down to mounds of rice, lamb, dates, olives, goat cheese and butter, various fruits, and breads. Most of the eating was without the benefit of flatware but from yard-wide round trays placed on the rugs."

Later, in October, Harwood met with King Faisal. These formal affairs were indicative of the expectations the Saudis had for SRI work and the ability of individual SRI staff to interact at virtually any level of a client organization.

---

development within each 5-year period of economic and social development."[H]

The first 5-year plan finally got under way in October 1968, when three other staff SRI members, drawn from other overseas assignments, joined Wilson Harwood in Saudi Arabia. There were early staffing and acculturation problems, however, given the new environment for SRI—a foreign and culturally different kingdom halfway around the world with huge discretionary wealth.

Though the challenges the SRI project people faced were frequent and profound, the work performed was of good quality, and the relationship continued for almost 20 years. Critical to the success, of course, was getting talented, tolerant, and sensitive people to live in Saudi Arabia for extended periods. This meant that in many cases SRI had to go outside its staff to find experts willing to relocate. Tolerance was needed to cope with the crises inevitable with such close support work and in keeping a low profile. SRI's willingness to work in this fashion is just one of the many ways it reserved recognition for its clients rather than for itself.

Not until the first on-site SRI director, Peter Duncan, arrived in mid-1969 did the project gain the stability it needed.[8] He had been conducting other international projects for SRI and thus had some relevant background. The first insight that influenced the course and

---

[8] Peter Duncan was a specialist in economic development in developing countries, with experience in Nigeria, Brazil, Pakistan, Peru, and Cyprus. He was probably SRI's most accomplished leader for such efforts.

Figure 15-3. SRI's Wilson Harwood and His Excellency Hisham Nazer, Saudi Minister of State and President of Central Planning.

cations, power, water, and sewer systems. The work was to focus on national growth and on expenditures and investments that would reduce dependence on oil revenues.

Here it should be noted that the SRI work began amid relatively scarce national resources, not the seemingly unlimited Saudi wealth that was to follow. The outset of the planning process was thus one of reconciling the work needed with the limited oil revenues characteristic of 1969. Progress needed to be paced, and prioritization was critical. It was not until 1974 that the price of oil took a spectacular increase, and from that point onward the nature of the plans became more a question of just how accelerated the development could be. The second 5-year plan beginning in 1975 thus took a much different thrust, with a design for a boom in investment, industry, education, and other fields. But overarching all of these important adaptations among resources and their use was the need for modern information systems. These were an early priority.

continuity of the SRI work was Duncan's early development of a Plan Preparation Document. This set of guidelines, procedures, and forms helped both in collecting and presenting the information needed as the basis for the plans themselves. The areas the plans were to cover amounted to a cornucopia of varying governmental responsibilities. Education, health, agriculture, housing, water resources, social development, and certainly not the least, petrochemicals, were among the critical needs that this developing country needed to address. Infrastructure expansion included streets and highways, airports, seaports, telecommuni-

Thus, over the two decades of its involvement, SRI contributed to a wide variety of national needs. Here is a partial list:[1]

A SIMPLE MATTER OF TIME

Wilson Harwood encountered a totally unexpected example of cultural adaptation on his arrival in Saudi Arabia. His cab driver from the airport wore three wristwatches. On inquiry, he learned that there were three times in play: "airport time," on which planes arrived and departed; "Greenwich Time," which the British had left behind; and "national time," which was used by governmental offices and for calls to prayer. The last of these times was keyed to sunrise and thus varied each day with respect to the other two. On his second day, Harwood's brief meeting with the U.S. Ambassador at 10 a.m. somehow ran unexpectedly and uncomfortably close to one with a Saudi Minister at 6! Beyond his initial confusion over different clocks, Harwood would also learn that meetings in the Saudi culture were never precisely scheduled. Precise time just didn't have that much relevance.

- Development of the industrial sector
- Development of the agricultural sector
- Construction industry capacity and expansion
- Management plan for the Construction Development Office
- Assistance to the Ministry of Municipal and Rural Affairs
- Plans for organizing the new Ministry of Planning
- A simulator training system for plant operators in the process industries
- Curricula for medical and health services at the University of Jeddah
- Planning for vocational training
- Assistance to the Ministry of Health
- Plans for mobile hospital facilities for the Red Crescent Society
- Analysis of housing demand in Jeddah
- Demand for prefabricated housing in the eastern region of the country
- Need for hospitals falling under the Ministry of Defense and Aviation
- Market for computer-based educational systems.

Development Plan	Years Covered	SRI Leader
First	1970-1974	Peter Duncan
Second	1975-1979	Peter Duncan
Third	1980-1984	Ray Kelly
Fourth	1985-1989	Roland Wolfram
Fifth	1990-1994	(SRI not involved)
Sixth	1995-1999	(SRI not involved)

This list, together with the work mentioned below, gives a flavor of the comprehensive nature of the role that SRI filled.

Although the work was considerable, it is difficult to gauge the impact the SRI staff actually had. One way is to look at the degree of importance the Saudis today attach to the development plans in specific areas. First, it is helpful to note the above table showing the periods addressed by the separate plans and the SRI on-site leaders.

At the outset, the government itself was not set up to make or administer such plans. SRI's first job, then, was to help organize various governmental departments so that they could measure the ongoing progress and administer new policies and investments. That first year SRI helped establish an Industrial Studies and Development Centre whose goal it was to increase the contribution of the manufacturing sector to the overall GDP. More generally, an overall objective of the first and all subsequent plans was to diversify the Saudi economy away from one dominated by oil revenues. Any fluctuation in the price of crude oil would have

too pronounced an impact on available government-funded services. Here are the specific objectives defined for the First Plan:[J]

- Diversify the economy to reduce dependence on the oil sector and to balance economic development
- Maximize the use of available natural resources
- Reduce the high propensity to import and conserve foreign exchange earnings
- Balance growth in the industrial sector with priority help to industries with a comparative advantage
- Build competitive power in the industrial sector through higher productivity
- Increase the use of national manpower with less dependence on expatriates
- Balance industrial development across the various regions of the country.

Gauging such diversification and balance clearly required an assessment and forecast of the industrial sector over the 1970-74 time frame, which SRI provided. SRI's breadth helped it address the manufacturing sector—from food and beverages, through textiles and furniture, to metals and even light bulbs. The goal was a 12% annual increase in the contribution of that sector to the GDP. Critical to such an economic transformation were the continuing creation of infrastructure and the development of the needed human resources. Eight industrial cities were also built. Essentially all of these changes were financed by oil revenues rather than by private investment. Though private investments were an important part of the general development process, the official incorporation of private capital gained emphasis in the Fourth Plan. A measure of the success of this program was a three-fold increase in GDP from 1970 to 1992, and an accompanying increase in non-oil contributions from 46% to 67%.[K]

Several other sectors were addressed in the First Development Plan: agriculture and water use, specifically self-sufficiency in food production and the conservation of water; health and social services; transportation; road infrastructure; and minerals. Investments in agriculture and water resources increased cultivated land from 400,000 acres in 1973 to more than 8 million acres in 1993. By 1985, the country was satisfying most of its domestic needs in poultry, meat, eggs, milk, fish, and grain, even becoming a net exporter of wheat!

In 1970, the dominant means for movement within the kingdom was by vehicle. In a 1970 study, SRI examined the history of road construction projects and the means to pay for them.[L] At that time revenues from gasoline tax and license fees were posted directly to a general fund, and no notion existed about whether the road system was self-supporting or not. It wasn't, by a factor of at least 4. Recommendations were made for changes in the amount of tax and license fees, including the creation of a new tax on diesel oil.

Given the rapid increase in the price of oil, the financial commitment to the Second Plan was enormous. Whereas the first 5-year plan was allocated $7 billion, the second would require over $140 billion and that amount did not include a substantial private sector investment that had traditionally contributed more than half of all fixed capital formation within the kingdom. The following table provides a rough breakdown of the intended government outlay for the Second Plan, not counting recurring costs.

The plan continued to focus attention on manufacturing, but also addressed many other issues. A Real Estate Development Fund was established in 1975 to provide financing to individuals and private companies.[9] Since its inception, that fund has granted more than $27 billion to over 400,000 housing units. Also during the second 5-year period, Nazer asked SRI to completely redesign his organization as it became the Ministry of Planning. Jim Harsch, then head of Organization Management at SRI, went to Riyadh to prepare a detailed organizational design that was delivered in

MAJOR PROJECT DEVELOPMENT BUDGETS (Billions of U.S. Dollars)	
Sector	Project Costs
Defense	17.9
Manufacturing	13.0
Municipalities	13.0
Water and Desalination	9.6
Schools	9.4
Government Facilities	5.7
Housing	4.0
Airports	3.5
Health Facilities	3.5
Roads	3.1
Ports	1.9
Electricity	1.5
Holy Cities	1.4
Telecommunications	0.9
Agriculture	0.7

April 1976.[M] Regarding water use, the Fourth Plan indicated the need for a National Water Plan that would ensure the conservation of water, including water recycling in the major cities and the ongoing regulation of that scarce natural resource. To this day, however, no adequate national water policy has been enacted, and the government only recently formed a Ministry of Water Resources— something that SRI first recommended over 25 years ago.[10]

In preparation for the fourth and final 5-year plan in which SRI had a role, SRI conducted a worldwide economic assessment as it pertained to Saudi Arabia. This comprehensive review provided the important context for the 1985-1989 plan period. Two presentations of that external context were given, one at SRI in May 1982 and another shortly thereafter in Saudi Arabia. The presentation was received so well that the SRI presenters—Don Baron, Andy Kridl, Tom Boyce,

---

[9] According to Peter Duncan (personal communication of October 29, 2002), this housing money was extended to all Saudi citizens, but not expatriates. Their exclusion was due to the government's requirement that all companies contracting with foreign labor provide housing for them.

[10] Kelly had recently participated in a conference in Riyadh on water use, a need now taking on crisis proportions. Interestingly, the SRI influence still lingers in the Ministry of Planning as Ray Kelly is helping it prepare for the Eighth Plan. (Ray Kelly, personal communication, November 19, 2002)

SAUDI PLAN DEVELOPMENT TOTAL EXPENDITURE (U.S. DOLLARS) AND SECTOR ALLOCATION

Sector	Development Plan						
	1 (1970-74)	2 (1975-79)	3 (1980-84)	4 (1985-89)	5 (1990-94)	6 (1995-99)	7 (est.) (2000-04)
Total Expenditures (billions of U.S. dollars)	7.6	86.8	166.7	93.1	90.9	112.1	130.2
Percent Allocation							
Infrastructure	41	49	41	29	22	16	15
Economic Resources	28	28	31	20	10	12	9
Human Resources Development	21	15	18	33	48	51	56
Health and Social Services	10	8	10	18	20	21	20

Note: the Seventh Plan is in progress and therefore its values are estimates. Also, the total expenditures are approximate because of variation in exchange rates (Ray Kelly personal communication, November 25, 2002).

Charles Greene, George von Haunalter, Peter Hall, and others—were flown the next day to the summer capital in Ta'if to address the entire Council of Ministers. Also important to the project were its subsequent directors: Ray Kelly and Roland Wolfram. Other staff members included Phil Sorensen, Elye Pitts (perhaps the only speaker of Arabic among SRI personnel on the project), Bo Ericsson, Bud Soucie, Jack Van Zandt, Dianne Chaturvedi-Misr, William Grindley, Milan Radovic, Robert W. Smith, Tom MacHale, Ian Napier, Michael Gillibrand, Maclin Sommers, who passed away in Riyadh, and Ed Podesta, whose collection of recorded jazz found its way onto Saudi radio.

The Saudi government's system of 5-year plans continues. The above table, provided by Ray Kelly, who continues to have some role in Saudi planning, shows interesting alterations in priorities over the last 30 years. The biggest change is the shift from economic and infrastructure commitment to social needs. These trends were just beginning in the Third and Fourth Plans when SRI was still participating.

By all accounts, the design and implementation of the series of 5-year plans have brought considerable progress and self-sufficiency to Saudi Arabia. Though its efforts are difficult to quantify, SRI, by its presence at the early stages of the nation's economic and social development, clearly made a lasting contribution to its remarkable modernization. It is fair to say, however, that increases in the price of oil from 1970 to 1983 resulted in the budget surpluses that characterized that time and helped implement such ambitious plans. In 1983, however, oil prices fell and Saudi Arabia became a budget-deficit nation. But diversification had proceeded, and in 1994 only 35% of the country's $173 billion in GDP was from oil or its by-products. Oil, however, was still critical to the economy and to new investments since it still represented 90% of export income.

SRI conducted another important $8.5 million project in Saudi Arabia—this one for ARAMCO. The study concentrated on materials management throughout the company's vast, far-flung operations and concluded with recommendations for the data processing systems necessary to carry out the design.

Iran—Getting Caught in a Revolution

SRI was commissioned to assist Iran in its food production industry as early as 1959. In conjunction with the government agency, the Plan Organization of Iran, SRI helped in the transfer and use of a variety of food processing systems furnished through a U.S. government aid program. The work involved selecting the location of new food processing plants, overseeing their construction, training the supervisors and plant personnel, and even designing containers and their labels. For women workers, special attention had to be given to the design of working uniforms that were both sanitary and also conformed with the stipulations of their religion. The work of the SRI team, headed by John Perry and Hugh Landis, resulted in increases of 100% in the production of apricots, raisins, dates, and fish within 2 years. A problem encountered with fig production—early blackening from oxidation—led to SRI food specialists helping introduce sulfurization, as well as improving grading and packaging processes. With these changes, the value received for figs doubled.[N]

In the 1960s, many in the United States and at SRI viewed Iran as a country poised to make large strides in economic and industrial development, although social progress was an entirely different matter. Iran thus presented growing business opportunities for SRI. However, only in 1969 did a series of large consulting contracts begin there, and all dealt with energy and petrochemicals. Near-million dollar contracts were won to (1) develop a 7-year plan for national energy policy regarding fossil fuels and hydroelectricity, (2) conduct a petroleum distribution structure study and develop a computerized distribution scheduling system for the National Iranian Oil Co. (NIOC), and (3) develop a long-range energy plan for the Ministry of Energy. Principal staff members in these three projects were Carl Trexel, Tony D'Esopo, and Bill Schumacher, respectively. During this time, several Iranian business leaders became SRI associates, and many more attended the SRI-sponsored IICs of 1969, 1973, and 1977.

In the mid-1970s, the Shah asked U.S. military advisors providing liaison in that part of the world for advice about future telecommunications for Iran. When they responded by sending a couple of sergeants to Tehran, the Shah and his communications people were offended. The U.S. Department of Defense's research arm, DARPA, became involved and in turn asked higher level members of the research community to look into the request. As a result, several SRI staff members were dispatched to help. As it turned out, their efforts were directed to short-term fixes of what amounted to the antiquated equipment used by the Iranian police.[O] Following this episode, the Deputy Minister of State and the Head of the Informatics Department of Iran's budgeting organization contracted with SRI for a 2-month study to define the future directions for teleinformation for all of Iran. Given the existing state of

communications resources in Iran and the rapid growth the country was foreseeing, SRI advised a swift transition to the digital age with backbone transmission and switching systems, including packet switching. The system foreseen was to be an advanced, integrated one with wideband terrestrial, satellite, and cable components. When only analog systems were available, such as cable television, converters were necessary.[P] The system was well designed to stand the test of time, but the future simply did not unfold as anticipated.

In 1978, two projects began that would face insurmountable difficulties when the Shah was overthrown in 1979 and U.S. hostages were taken. One was with the National Petrochemical Co. to look into fiber materials. That project was halted with the fall of the Shah, but SRI eventually was paid for most of its work by the new government. Carrying out the other project, which exceeded $1 million and which continued for a time, was considerably more difficult.

In the mid-1970s, an SRI engineer from the Telecommunications Sciences Center (TSC), Ata Hamadani, had gone to Iran under Air Force sponsorship to conduct radar site surveys. While there, he took a leave of absence from SRI and began working for a consulting firm. Because SRI believed in the growth of business in the Middle East, Hamadani was subsequently asked to open an SRI office in Iran, which he did, reporting to Don Fiske, the SRI-Europe marketing manager in Croydon, England. After considerable legal hassle, that office opened in early 1976. One of the reasons for the high expectations for Iran was a $10 million project for NIOC, which SRI began to pursue in 1974. After a year or two of trying, SRI abandoned that pursuit, and by 1977 enthusiasm for work in Iran was swiftly abating. Nonetheless, Hamadani had become aware of an opportunity at the Ministry of Posts, Telegraph, and Telephone (PT&T). To modernize its telecommunications systems, the Ministry had hired AT&T to review its situation and make recommendations. AT&T did not characteristically contract outside the United States but did so under pressure from the U.S. government.

One of the recommendations of the AT&T study was to bring order to the radio spectrum and its use in Iran. That local knowledge of the systems being used and under whose authority they came was all contained in "little black books" (if they existed at all) with no unified knowledge or organization. To remedy that ignorance, their PT&T needed to buy equipment that would help determine use and begin to regulate the resource. SRI, having built such a spectrum examination and monitoring system for the U.S. Federal Communications Commission (FCC), was in a position to do the same for Iran's PT&T Ministry. SRI's Roy Stehle, who led the FCC work, bid on the project and won, or so it seemed at the time.

The first negotiations between SRI and Iran's PT&T on the purchase of mobile spectrum monitoring units (MSMUs) in the form of vans took place in the late summer of 1976. After SRI representatives traveled to Iran, an SRI proposal was accepted and a contract for $1.4 million was signed in early 1978. Getting started wasn't easy, however, because letters of credit on both Iranian and U.S. banks had to be written and battles waged to avoid paying the kickbacks expected by Iranian officials. Eventually, construction began but not without distractions. During the time the vans were being built, civil unrest in Iran was growing. Still, SRI applied for and received a U.S. export license. But in January 1979, the Iranian monarchy was overthrown, and SRI then had to deal with a new Iranian government. Through all of this, two MSMUs were designed and built in Menlo Park that were state-of-the-art facilities (see Figure 15-4). Their construction was enabled by ongoing progress payments from the PT&T Ministry. Then, and as part of the contract, it came time to train Iranian technicians in the operation and repair of the MSMUs. This led to the arrival in Menlo Park, 6 months late, of two Iranian PT&T engineers.[11] However, less than 1 month after their training sessions began at SRI, Iranians took hostages at the U.S. Embassy and the State Department canceled the export license.[12]

Figure 15-4. One of two radio spectrum monitoring vans built for the Iranian PT&T (November 1980).

Iran's holding of the hostages made for great awkwardness as SRI tried to finish the training phase. The Iranian trainees were as anxious to return home as the SRI staff were to have them do so. After the trainees left somewhat prematurely, the question of what to do with the equipment remained. The gravity of the situation, and specifically the U.S. State Department's embargo placed on the shipment of such equipment to Iran, left SRI in the middle of an international dispute. Nothing happened for months other than the repeated

---

[11] Actually, one was an engineer and one was an "engineer-watcher." Since the Shah had been replaced by a new, reactionary government, the PT&T Ministry thought it necessary to look out for its people while they were overseas. According to project leader Roy Stehle, one of the trainees was an astute engineer, and the other spent his time watching the other and reading the Koran.
[12] A brief recounting of the setting in Iran at the time follows: In the 1970s, Iran was trying to determine its future path. The Shah had instituted some new freedoms and participatory aspects of government, but at the same time

was searching for a non-Western, non-Eastern but Persian way. Coincidentally, SRI and the Iranian Institute for Political and Economic Studies sponsored a conference in Washington, D.C., in October 1977 to examine Iran's future. (The proceedings are in a book, *Iran in the 1980s*, published by that Institute in 1978.) Although they did not foresee the revolution, some of the Iranian contributors noted the reactionary forces at play and, in particular, the return to power of fundamentalists in neighboring states at a time when Iran was advocating careful liberalization. After a year of riots, martial law, and demands for his abdication, the Shah fled the country in January 1979. Khomeini returned from exile to set up an Islamic republic. In early November 1979, apparently in retaliation for the U.S. offering medical help to the Shah, 90 hostages were taken at the U.S. Embassy in Tehran. The United States proceeded to sever relations with Iran, embargo Iranian goods, and seize Iranian assets in the United States. The Shah died in July 1980, removing the principal Iranian demand on which hostage release was contingent. The hostages were released in January 1981 as President Reagan took office.

requests from the PT&T Ministry to ship the vans and the establishment of a U.S.-Iran Claims Tribunal in The Hague. The PT&T Ministry's claims and the SRI and U.S. counterclaims would continue to be heard there for years.

At this point of impasse, the PT&T Ministry had paid about $1.3 million of the original $1.4-million cost of the project and wanted its equipment. But for legal reasons, they would get neither the vans nor their money. The case was intricate and protracted, and it demonstrated another measure of the quality of the SRI project leaders and their ability to step into unfamiliar territory. Stehle was asked, with SRI contract and legal staff, to reconstruct all the history and find the relevant material that would constitute the U.S. position. That position proved sound, and the vans were never shipped. However, SRI, because of ongoing equipment maintenance and other legal costs, had to write off several hundred thousand dollars. Moreover, resolving the disposition of the vans took so long that the vans and their equipment eventually became obsolete and deteriorated before SRI could sell them.

Taiwan—A Few Economic Roots

In 1962, the Republic of China (Taiwan) asked SRI to study how the industrial economy of that island country could be expanded and its exports diversified rather than remaining dependent on two major commodities, rice and sugar. As was the norm in such undertakings, funding was provided by a third party, in this case the U.S. Agency for International Development (AID). SRI was not to consider industries already functioning, but to determine which new industries might have economic potential and how they might be established.[Q]

SRI's initial report on the assessment cited four new fields that appeared to justify further examination in the Taiwan setting: petrochemicals; electronics (particularly transistor radios); watches and clocks; and plastics and resins, including man-made fibers. Subsequently, separate SRI teams examined these areas individually, including how they might be implemented. These reports were then made to agencies of the Taiwan Government established to foster economic growth.

Within 3 years of the start of the program, an industrial complex of privately owned plants had been built or was in the final stage in three of the identified fields. A watch and clock plant was to be established soon. By the summer of 1966, 11 companies had started or were about to make a wide variety of chemical products such as nylon, polyvinylchloride, and detergents. These products were anticipated to add $50 million annually to Taiwan's foreign trade balance. Thirteen companies were making transistor radios for both domestic and foreign consumption. More than 1.5 million units were exported in 1965, adding $600,000 in foreign exchange. SRI can clearly claim some credit for this swift introduction of manufacturing capability that helped Taiwan rapidly move away from the need for foreign aid, eventually becoming second only to Japan as the leading industrial country in Asia.

Hong Kong's Transition to Chinese Rule

In the late 1980s, the British Crown Colony of Hong Kong's reversion to Mainland China was only a decade away. Though its economy was one of the miracles of the world, Hong Kong was experiencing some ups and downs. The double-digit GDP growth rates of the 1970s had given way to stagnation in the early 1980s. Part of the reason for this decline was increasing competition from countries like South Korea, Taiwan, and Singapore, complicated by worries over the upcoming return to China. In 1984, a Joint Declaration Agreement had been worked out between the British and Chinese governments to keep Hong Kong on a more or less even keel, but significant uncertainty surrounded how well the Agreement would be honored after transition. What would happen to the private ownership of businesses and property, and what about other individual holdings and wealth? Would Hong Kong's enormous role in the brokering of Mainland Chinese and other Southeast Asian trade continue? The document tried to assure that the transition would be smooth and that the robust economy of the region, with Hong Kong's role as a powerful Asian financial center,

Figure 15-5. Control tower of the new Hong Kong Airport.

would not be threatened. But the forces that drove Hong Kong and that were likely to determine its future were not limited to the two governments. The business leaders of Hong Kong, almost all of whom were Chinese, were the prime movers, and they were understandably worried about the long-term future, Agreement or no Agreement.[13] In retrospect, and fortunately for SRI, this was to be a point and time of great leverage.

The Agreement was naturally firm about matters such as territorial integrity and defense, areas in which the Chinese government required unambiguous sovereignty. However, virtually all other aspects (e.g., local government, taxation, private property ownership and transfer, trade, travel, foreign financial arrangements) were to remain essentially unchanged for the 50 years following July 1, 1997. This accommodation and its longevity were intended to protect the

economy of Hong Kong and to make the process of long-term planning predictable. With some assurance and stability, then, economic growth resumed in 1986. Nonetheless, because Hong Kong business and civic leaders felt the need for buttressing their future, a group of them formed the Hong Kong Economic Survey Ltd. and approached SRI. Their knowledge of SRI and its objectivity stemmed from their participation in the SRI-initiated business convocations such as the IIC and the Pacific Basin Association (see Chapter 13). SRI's Center for Economic Competitiveness responded and began work on a $285,000 contract in May 1988. The project leader was Douglas Henton.[14]

SRI looked into three major areas vital to Hong Kong: its role as a port and center of trade, its presence as one of Asia's biggest financial centers, and its future as a manufacturing sector. Of primary concern were both the 1997 transition and the growing competitive pressure Hong Kong was feeling from the other Asian economies. SRI first examined the historical role Hong Kong had played with respect not only to China but also to Southeast Asia and the rest of the world. In relation to these parameters, the influences of Hong Kong's physical infrastructure, labor, land costs, education, and many other critical foundations for an expanding future were assessed.

From these studies and with an eye to other relevant issues, such as the bordering Chinese territories and the political landscape in Beijing, SRI advanced a five-part strategy:[R]

- Maintain autonomy and preserve Hong Kong's uniqueness. Doing so would require the continuation of the existing law on which the economy was based and a set of international agreements on matters such as emigration and the 1997 transition.

- Improve the economic infrastructure. Doing so would entail three objectives:
  - Human resources. Identification of the local educational and training systems needed as well as the emigration/ immigration policies—both to increase the availability of key personnel.

---

[13] According to former SRI President Dr. William F. Miller, who was personally involved, other concerns also existed. One was the Chinese Government's concentration on growing the industrial strength of the area around Shanghai and the perhaps less important but nagging perception, typified by Deng Xiao Ping's daughter, that Hong Kong was only a place to shop; in other words, would the Government preferentially form or favor an industrial competitor to Hong Kong?

[14] SRI Project 6222 was a 1-year study commencing on May 11, 1988 and financed through Bodwin Ltd. Other project contributors were James Gollub, John Melville, Eric Hansen, Gary Anderson, John Cox, Richard Trampenau, and advisor William F. Miller.

- Technology initiatives. Increased capacity for R&D and industrial technology incentives.
- Physical infrastructure. Increased government support for airport, port, and other transport projects.
- Internationalize the Hong Kong economy by:
  - Forming a nonprofit, business-sponsored organization to attract overseas businesses.
  - Developing a world-class telecommunications infrastructure.
- Build Hong Kong-South China economic relationships and expand the economic links to the rest of China.
- Promote partnerships for Hong Kong's economic future. This strategy required a partnership between the Hong Kong government and its business community.

SRI issued the details of its findings and reasoning in a 300-page report, a summary of which it first submitted to selected members of the Hong Kong business community for feedback. The levels of access that SRI had in both Hong Kong and the Chinese government were impressive. Keep in mind that the principals sponsoring the SRI study were among the business elite of Hong Kong. For example, three of them were Mr. Vincent H.S. Lo, heir to a huge Hong Kong real estate, development, and construction operation; Mr. Victor Fung, chairman of the Hong Kong Trade and Development Council and a member of his family's $1.6 billion trading firm; and Mr. Tony Fung, the chairman of Yu Ming, one of the largest investment companies in Hong Kong and vice president of the Hong Kong Stock Exchange. These men and their business cohorts had much at risk, not just from the transition of Hong Kong to China, but also from myriad other concerns such as the rocketing price of property and the labor shortage; in short, the Territory's competitiveness. The historically laissez-faire economics of the British administration didn't seem to be helping much with any of these concerns.

To help convey the results of the study, SRI also met with Chinese leadership at the highest levels. In Mainland China, another transition was occurring that was effectively opening China's door to limited capitalism. In the uppermost Chinese leadership, perhaps the figures most aligned with that change were

Zhao Ziyang and Jiang Zemin.[15] Their pursuit of capitalism would be measured, of course, but the most recent decade has shown the remarkable impact of their initiatives.

Access to Chinese leadership would come principally through SRI's President in the late 1980s, Dr. William F. Miller. For a number of years Miller had developed such access, starting with student exchanges while provost at Stanford and continuing at SRI.[16] Also, an acquaintance of Miller's at Argonne Laboratories by the name of Chuan Chu had introduced him to the above two emerging figures in the Chinese leadership, Zhao Ziyang and Jiang Zemin. These varied connections gave SRI important opportunities to discuss the Hong Kong situation with Chinese leadership who were also thinking about it. These began with several meetings on industrial and research policy with the heads of the Development Research Center of the State Council, President Ma Hung and Vice President Wu Ming Yu, and with the Chairman of the Science and Technology Commission of the State Council, Song Jain. Both Song Jain and Wu Ming Yu would visit SRI several times in Menlo Park. With that preamble Miller then met with Jiang Zemin, then General Secretary of the Party, to discuss Hong Kong and the SRI report in the context of industrial development, industrial policies, trade, competition, and the consideration of Hong Kong and nearby territories as what is today a Special Economic Zone. Similar discussions also took place with Zhao Ziyang and Li Peng.[S]

Through these openings, SRI placed before the Chinese leadership the vital role Hong Kong was already playing in the commerce of South China and, moreover, how the brokerage of

---

[15] These two leaders were instrumental in beginning the economic reform of the late 1980s. As the project got under way, Zhao was general secretary of the Communist Party, but lost his position in June 1989 because of his sympathies with the Tiananmen Square protesters. Jiang followed him in the Party leadership and would become China's president in 1993. Perhaps also of importance was Jiang's career as an electrical engineer and his role as first vice-minister and then minister of China's electronics industry from 1981-93. He would then become mayor of Shanghai, where special economic districts were instituted that significantly changed the atmosphere for foreign electronics investment.

[16] William F. Miller, personal communication, December 12, 2002. SRI interactions with China started in 1979. In 1981 SRI helped China's Development Research Center sponsor the first international conference China had held since it reopened to foreign investment. It was held in Hangzho.

Mainland manufacturing could increase if Hong Kong were left to its own independent brand of commercialism. SRI's five-part strategy for Hong Kong also helped galvanize those who were still timid in the Territory, particularly following Tiananmen Square. But in spite of that event and others, significant capital investments have been made throughout China, and the manufacturing prowess of the adjacent South China provinces has grown extremely fast. Even Taiwan-owned manufacturing plants, along with their Taiwanese managers, are now operating on the Mainland north of Hong Kong.[T]

The Economic Plight in Equatorial Africa

SRI's work in Africa began in 1959 and continued until the 1990s. The Rockefeller Brothers Fund contracted for the first projects, in which SRI examined how impoverished countries might enter into new businesses, ranging from introducing a poultry industry in Ghana to a ceramics industry in Nigeria. Nigeria itself sponsored an important SRI study of its internal transportation services in 1960. A project for the UN made recommendations to Sudan on improving its food processing systems and establishing an industrial research institute. Nearly all of the work in Africa in the 1960s was sponsored by the U.S. Agency for International Development (AID); the work involved 12 regions or countries (e.g., Nyassaland, Morocco, Cameroon, Tanzania, Egypt). SRI's examinations often delved into the important sectors of national economy and well-being. Only two studies will be touched on here—a brief one in Cameroon and a much more detailed one in Zambia. These will not be SRI success stories, but they serve to illustrate the extreme difficulties in bringing economic vitalization to equatorial Africa.

Cameroon

In 1960, the southern or French colonial segment of Cameroon gained independence. Within a year or so the southern part of what had been two British Cameroon colonies voted not to join Nigeria but to join with the new government as West Cameroon. (Another, turbulent decade would pass before the remaining British colony would also join to make a united Federal Republic of Cameroon.) In the initial union, the new State of West Cameroon was virtually devoid of resources, having only a small agricultural and timber economy. Accordingly, in 1964, under the sponsorship of that new federal government and AID, SRI sent a team of economists and technologists to find ways to stimulate "all sectors" of the economy in West Cameroon. The SRI team, led by Frank Turner and composed of Philip Adams, Peter Duncan, Ed Podesta, and a few consultants, focused on West Cameroon's entire economy, its people, and its resources.

Under the contract, which was for about $175,000, the development team assessed the state's agriculture, transportation, telecommunications, business and small industry, healthcare, education and manpower, and the present and latent tourist industry. Input was made to the proposed 10-year development program (1965-1975), which sought to triple GDP and raise per capita GDP to about $150. The SRI team recommended that the banking institutions and sources of international credit and investment, then concentrated in the capital at Yaounde, be extended to West Cameroon. SRI also identified proposed investments whose revenue potential should attract investors. Firms then in East Cameroon and Nigeria could contribute significantly to initiate industrial products such as beverages, textiles, cement pipe, footwear, timber products, and plantations for tea, rubber, oil palm, and possibly pepper. Importantly, the new state also needed to be more adequately integrated into the development programs of the Federal ministries. Only then could the policies that governed the attractiveness of outside investment in West Cameroon be clarified.[U]

For a decade or so after independence, Cameroon was prosperous by African standards. But as with so many African countries the economy was at the ultimate mercy of what turned out to be unstable, often repressive governments. In spite of sometimes noble beginnings, these governments—and Cameroon's was no exception—often gravitated to despotism, with the economy at the mercy of the despot's whims or the turmoil that attended leadership transitions. In the late 1970s, those types of events indeed took place in Cameroon, and by 1984 the country's commodity-dependent economy, fiscal mismanagement, and civil unrest caused a decade-long recession and a large decrease in per capita GDP. While the 1990s brought some recovery to the region, the volatility of governance and other indigenous problems made helping African economies a gargantuan task. That truth was also brought home to SRI after it had expended great effort in Zambia, as detailed below.

Zambia and Copper—Struggles in a Developing Country[17]

This is a tale not of triumph but of frustration, a story about good intentions and a lot of work undertaken to surmount enormous difficulties but with few residual benefits. The work is thus important not for its outcome but for its illustration of the lengths to which SRI people and sometimes their clients have gone to help the developing world. It is also indicative of SRI's socially responsible work. The story here covers SRI work from the early 1980s to the 1990s to help revitalize the copper industry in Zambia.

Background

Located in south central Africa, Zambia was known as Northern Rhodesia during the British colonial reign. The area was colonized in the late 1800s by the British South Africa Company, and when that enterprise failed around 1924, the British assumed rule. The British South Africa Company had developed mining and commercial interests in the country that included the rich copper ore deposits discovered in its northern region in the early 1920s. Over the next 40 years or so Northern Rhodesia experienced the typical imperialism

and exploitation of the day. But with European knowledge and in spite of its interior location, it came to be one of the world's leading copper exporters, as well as a net exporter of food.

However, none of this relative success brought more than subsistence benefits to the native people, and little or nothing was done to prepare them to assume the technical and managerial roles so critical once the country became independent.

Zambia gained its independence peacefully in 1964, and its independence was accompanied by both good and bad news. The good news was that, unlike some of its poorer neighbors, it had a developed copper mining and smelting industry with a history of strong export value, and its per capita income was one of the highest in Africa. The bad news was that it was a single-industry country, and few, if any, indigenous people were qualified to run the pivotal copper industry. Some British expatriates stayed on to help run mine and smelter operations. But as the anticipated transition to independence and the possible nationalization of the copper industry appeared on the horizon, its foreign owners stopped making capital investments. As a result, the mines and smelters deteriorated badly.

Along with the deterioration of the copper industry, agricultural output decreased, changing Zambia from a net food exporter to a net importer. Zambia's first independent government was a socialist one that lasted for more than 25 years. Even though the country did not experience the degree of corruption that other emerging African nations suffered from, the government's economic practices, although well-intentioned, produced only economic failure. After a few years of private operation, the copper industry was nationalized, with the Anglo American Plc owners maintaining only a minority share.

However, the economy was worsening. Like all emerging African countries, Zambia's people were poor. At the time of independence, their $640 per year per capita income was higher than many of their neighbors'. By the early 1980s, however, when SRI first arrived, it had fallen to less than $500 per year, and by 1998 it was only $330. Zambia's problems were increasing dramatically.

While SRI's first work in Zambia began in 1966 with a brief examination of its transportation systems, it was 1983 when Dr. Eugene Thiers, director of SRI's Mineral and Metals Department of the Business Group, helped SRI win the first of two large rehabilitation projects for Zambia's copper industry (see Figure 15-6). That project, which

---

[17] Much of this account came from a series of interviews with Eugene Thiers, Bill Schumacher, Tom Boyce, and Gary Bridges (April 2001 to October 2002), all of whom had project leadership roles over the course of SRI work in Zambia. Boyce was also head of the SRI Energy Center at the time of the second large project.

Figure 15-6. SRI project leaders for the two major Zambian projects: Gene Thiers, Tom Boyce, and Bill Schumacher (left to right).

was funded by the newly nationalized copper company, the Zambian Consolidated Copper Mines (ZCCM), was a detailed diagnostic assessment as a preparatory step in modernizing the aging industry. This was clearly an opportunity to help a people in desperate need, and SRI's assessment would become the basis for a petition to the World Bank for funding the rehabilitation itself. That the rehabilitation of their copper industry might have been beyond even the powers of the World Bank to remedy wasn't considered. The need was simply too great. If the economy of Zambia was to improve, it had to start with its copper industry.

Both before and after independence, Zambia's almost total dependence on copper was dangerous economically. Since 1965, that industry has accounted for between 25% and 50% of the country's GDP—the amount depending mostly on the world price of copper. Significantly, in the early 1970s and in spite of a trend away from profitability and toward overemployment, a Zambian mine worker contributed 25 times as much to GDP as an agricultural worker and 3 times as much as a worker in manufacturing.[V] The lack of economic diversification meant that through the 1980s copper continued to account for 90% of foreign exchange for Zambia.[W]

The most important aspect of the Zambian dependence on copper and what brought SRI and the World Bank into action was that the Zambian government, in its 20 years of independence, had treated ZCCM simply as a cash cow.[18] Rather than reinvesting in the country's most critical industry, it siphoned the

money off into other domestic uses. Moreover, foreign exchange money, derived almost totally from the export of copper, was the only currency with which to buy foreign goods and services. The local currency, the kwacha, was highly unstable. Thus, the leaders of ZCCM, undoubtedly along with their government overseers, became preoccupied with the industry's gross foreign exchange currency and lost track of the profitability with which it was being generated. Importantly, it was at a time when competition in the world copper market was increasing. The government mistakenly believed that if it could continue to export the traditional 500,000 or so tons of copper each year and get foreign exchange money, that was all that was important.

As a consequence, as the 1980s approached, ZCCM's business had grown perilously inefficient and the necessary equipment and facilities had seriously deteriorated. Desperate for outside help, the new socialist government of President Kaunda sought funds from every quarter to upgrade mining operations and otherwise run the country. Both Western and Soviet Bloc loans arrived, but because of poor management and onerous stipulations placed on the aid packages, all new equipment, sent directly or purchased, included no spare or replacement parts. An unfortunate consequence was that, when new equipment broke down, it simply sat unused. Obviously, equipment from the West couldn't be used to help repair that from the Soviets and vice versa. In addition, a government tax on *incoming* mining and smelting equipment also served to reduce the flow of spare parts, further depleting the already insufficient stable foreign exchange money allocated to pay for them.

The falling world market prices for copper, combined with domestic borrowing in the late

---

[18] ZCCM was formed at the time of the government's purchase of the controlling interest in overall mine operations from a set of foreign investors with stakes in separate areas of Zambia's Copperbelt.

1970s that amounted to about 10% of Zambia's GDP, plus external borrowing, made indebtedness a huge factor in the faltering economy.[X] Nationalistic fervor didn't help either. A government policy to move expatriates out of important positions at ZCCM caused an outflow of skill, with expatriate employment falling from 16% in 1964 to 3.5% in 1983.[Y] Importantly, those who left had occupied the most critical jobs. This policy was reversed in 1982, but by then the damage had been done. To make matters even worse, mine output decreased, as did the quality of the copper ore. This affected productivity in two ways: the annual ore output per worker fell from 12.3 tons in 1973 to 9.7 tons in 1981, and yield fell from 43 tons of ore needed to produce 1 ton of copper in 1973, to 53 tons of ore needed in 1983. [Z, 19]

A failing economy, clearly exacerbated by inefficiencies; a volatile and shrinking world price for copper; and a siphoning off of reinvestment money to meet the country's employment and social needs, all contributed to a desperate situation in the late 1970s. Zambia was spiraling downward. Nonetheless, Zambia remained the world's third or fourth largest copper exporter in the mid-1970s, the Zambians within the ZCCM given responsibility for turning the company around were dedicated and hardworking, and the country had been spared the horrendous internal strife from which most of its neighbors suffered.

Externally, the World Bank and the International Monetary Fund were still willing to provide what surely must have seemed unrecoverable money to help rectify these enormous problems. As the 1980s arrived, as a condition for continuing World Bank loans, ZCCM was required to get outside help in formulating plans for more effective use of the international loans. Enter SRI.

SRI's First Large Project for ZCCM

SRI's specific role was to help ZCCM prepare for a low-cost $400 million loan from the World Bank. World Bank money had been pouring into Zambia throughout the 1970s. Production, after reaching a peak in 1976, was falling. The Bank was looking for a plan that would not only bring about higher production and profitability to ZCCM, but also help stabilize and enhance the Zambian economy.

This project eventually led to a series of five projects funded by the World Bank. But work started with ZCCM funding a comprehensive diagnostic survey of all of its operations. The table following shows the scope.

To address this array of tasks, the initial team, led by Eugene Thiers and consisting of five SRI staff and one consultant, left for Zambia in 1983. That first team included several former executives of international copper companies. As the projects progressed, they enlisted the help of perhaps 20 SRI staff members, as well as outside consultants. These included talent in metallurgy, mining, the economics of world trade, and organizational structure and training, as well as specialists from U.S. companies expert in mining and smelting processes and respected at the World Bank.

The team made its appraisal. They found that the mining operations were a serious bottleneck in reaching a production goal of 630,000 tons per year, and this finding suggested a 20% increase in development funds was needed for the two mines with falling production.[20] Metallurgical operations, while not pacing production at the time, had severely deteriorated and would limit production once mining operations were increased. Processing plants were observed to have excessive spillage and loss. Closer auditing and monitoring were needed to fix this problem. Purchasing and inventory practices were fragmented and required reworking to create common inventory and cataloging across all divisions to indicate overall critical equipment availability. Improved inventorying would also help avoid the accrual of unnecessary spare parts and promote the disposal of obsolete stock. SRI presented its final report to ZCCM in September 1983. The report was given orally, with written backup, and consisted of pointed and specific assessments and recommendations in all the areas of the following table.

---

[19] According to Thiers, the SRI on-site leader for the first several years, the reduction in copper per ton of ore was due to dilution—the result of poor mining practice that lets low-grade ore or waste earth from other shafts fall into adjacent areas yet to be mined. To the extent that this composite is re-mined, it is of a naturally lower copper content.

[20] In 1976, when Zambia was the world's fourth largest producer of copper, it reached peak production of over 700,000 tons per year; that amount compares to the 500,000-600,000 tons produced in the 1980s, and was comparatively huge in relation to the 256,000 produced in 2000. [MBendi's Email Mining News, www.mbendi.co.za]

ZCCM AREAS OF SRI INVESTIGATION	

Operations
  Mining
  Metallurgical Plants
  Productivity Measures
	Facilities
	  Underground Equipment Maintenance
	  Open-pit Equipment Maintenance
	  Metallurgical Equipment Maintenance

Budgeting
  Capital
  Operating
	Central Services
	  Computers
	  Purchasing Practices
	  Inventory Control
	  Accounting Practices

Personnel
  Zambianization
  Training
  Discipline
  Motivation
	Other
	  Corporate Planning
	  Duplication of Efforts
	  Communications
	  Transportation

To drive home existing problems and their implications for future budgets and budgeting, SRI presented comparisons with copper-producing facilities in other countries. The data showed ZCCM to be less efficient in cost per ton mined for surface and subsurface mines, somewhat more competitive in ore concentration, and quite efficient in refining and smelting processes. To be continuously alert to company competitiveness, a common accounting and budgeting practice across all divisions was needed. SRI thus recommended that operating and capital budgets and long-range planning be integrated across ZCCM.

Most telling, though, was that corporate objectives and the role of corporate planning were not clearly understood across the company. Disparities also existed between short- and long-term operational planning and between capital and operating budgets. Recommendations were also made in training and organizational structure.

Following SRI's input, ZCCM successfully presented the revitalization plan to the World Bank, and a $150 million loan was disbursed. Both ZCCM and the World Bank praised SRI for its thoroughness and objectivity.[21] Now it was time for the changes to be carried out—a hugely more difficult job—and SRI would continue to

be involved. Five more, somewhat smaller projects ensued, all concerned with implementing the recommended procedures in planning, budgeting, materials management, and the monitoring system and tools with which to carry them out. These projects lasted from the end of 1983 until mid-1986.[AA] Beginning in 1987, SRI undertook a further series of three projects on organizational training (see the box at the end of the section). With this training work, the total contract value for this initial work came to nearly $2 million. To what extent were SRI's recommendations implemented?

As operating procedures were changed and equipment upgraded, productivity started to increase and unit costs dropped. That was clearly rewarding. But frustration set in soon after the SRI team left Africa. Some of the promised actions can be found in the previously referenced World Bank report:[BB]

- In February 1984, the government and ZCCM admitted the need for reducing the work force, trimming the compensation for Zambian workers, and closing uneconomic mines. The president had rejected similar proposals as late as 1982.

- A 5-year production and investment plan was to be prepared for the World Bank by December 1985. (SRI's work would contribute here.)

- The government and ZCCM were to agree on taxation and dividend policies by the same date.

- The government agreed to allocate to ZCCM, for its use only, the foreign exchange equivalent of $350 million in 1984 with future allocations subject to World Bank approval.

All these actions appear positive and in keeping with SRI's recommendations. Some 4,000 workers were let go;[22] the structure of ZCCM was streamlined; and review, procurement, and planning practices were revamped. But Zambia's nearly total dependence on the Copperbelt remained.

---

[21] Gulhati (op. cit.) indicates that this intensive rehabilitation program, the first serious attempt to address ZCCM's problems in a long time, preceded loans of $148 million from the World Bank, the European Economic Community, and the African Development Bank in March 1984. Tom Boyce indicated that the experts on the SRI team had done their work well.

[22] Still, just under 6% of the 67,000 workforce.

Unfortunately, the copper industry supplied not only the only income for the people in the Copperbelt's vicinity, it was also the only source of electricity, drinking water, sewage treatment, and medical care.[CC] Needless to say, it was difficult for the government to shut down a depleted or low-producing mine. In more direct fiscal ways, government actions had predatory effects on the industry. In 1983, the government had initiated a 4% tax on the gross value of exports. That tax continued to increase, reaching 10% in 1985. Then, when a plan was introduced to devalue the local currency, the Government doubled the export tax to 20% to keep ZCCM from windfall local currency gain. Though a compromise reduced the export tax to 13%, that tax, together with the normal tax on net profits, severely damaged the fiscal engine that was to drive the rehabilitation of ZCCM. Furthermore, the government failed to create a long-term plan for taxes and dividends for the copper industry that would provide for the reinvestment needed. Thus, unwise government leadership managed to undermine the principal means for economic revitalization of the country, and SRI's work came to naught. The copper exports critical to Zambia's economy continued to decline.

SRI's Second Project

In 1991, the Zambian electorate ousted the long-standing and ineffective socialist government, installing a multiparty, democratic government called the MMD in its place. With the copper industry still bringing in virtually all foreign exchange money, yet still unprofitable, the question arose about returning it to private ownership. Given ZCCM's troubled history, that appeared to be the only reasonable course, but it was also clear that many would oppose any such action. In June 1992, the new Government established the Zambian Privatization Agency to promote the selling of government-owned industries, including ZCCM.

SRI's return to Zambia came from an invitation faxed in early 1992 by a trusted, knowledgeable, and respected ZCCM leader, Edwin Koloko,[23] who was involved in SRI's earlier work. He was now in charge of

privatization at ZCCM, and his request was straightforward. Could SRI help the government and ZCCM bring their copper business to a point of profitability so that it would bring a greater return when sold? This was rather like painting a house before selling it to bring a higher price, though the work entailed was infinitely more complex. Unlike the 1984 study, this study would not be an open-ended planning exercise. Given the government's near-term privatization interests, rapid results were imperative. However, seeing them through would turn out to be a much bigger challenge than the diagnoses and changes SRI had tried to make 10 years earlier. This endeavor would take somewhat less time, about 3 years, but would approach $18 million. The work was again funded by the World Bank, which was still trying its best to help Zambia turn the corner to self-sufficiency.

This time Bill Schumacher was the project leader with Tom Boyce as his deputy (see Figure 15-6); the two alternated in being on site in Zambia. They recruited many of the same people who participated in the first project, although many more would be added. This time, however, all were more aware of the difficulties in making changes in Zambia even when everyone's intentions were good. To create more rapid and lasting improvements, the project would have to have sufficient clout to invoke wholesale changes, which would have to be made while the SRI people were still involved.

Following a brief appraisal phase, SRI developed a work plan for the project that created 12 analysis and implementation modules (AIMs). Each module was assigned a team, led by SRI or its subcontractor specialists, and staffed jointly with key ZCCM people. These teams were not just study groups; they also had to worry about implementing the changes needed. The following table shows the aspects of ZCCM operations addressed.

Each AIM had a specific set of objectives, issues, plans, schedules, and, importantly, deliverables. Deliverables included both a summary of findings and an action plan; that is, something executable. The AIM work was to be carried out during the first 6 months of 1993 with consequent changes to ZCCM operations occurring soon thereafter. It was up to AIM 12 to assess the commercial value of ZCCM's operations, based on the implemented AIM

---

[23] A Ph.D. in international economics, Dr. Koloko had left a university teaching position in Pennsylvania to return to his native country to help out. SRI staff knew him to be both capable and of high integrity, and representative of many of the Zambian people with whom SRI worked.

AIMS FOR ZCCM OPERATIONS IMPROVEMENT	
1. Geology, Reserves, and Resources	7. Training
2. Mine Operations and Planning	8. Maintenance Management Systems
3. Smelting/Refining Operations and Planning	9. Material Management Systems
4. Finance and Accounting	10. Marketing
5. Human Resources	11. Environmental Review
6. Corporate Organizational Structure	12. Divestiture and Privatization

recommendations, and to define a strategy to maximize that value for Zambia.

The output of the teams was thorough and voluminous. Their first integrated output was an interim short-term corporate plan. To help project both corporate needs and the ongoing ZCCM financial situation, the plan recommended critical actions needed from each team and also addressed external factors such as the price of copper and cobalt (in this case a copper coproduct), the availability of essential goods and services, and the tax situation. Considering the size, history, and importance of ZCCM to Zambia, this undertaking was both difficult and important.

The AIM implementation activities were often extensive. New foremen were placed in those areas of the mines and smelters where most improvement was needed. This time the smelter was the biggest bottleneck. Overemployment remaining from the socialist government meant employees would have to be laid off. Because ZCCM had been conducting sales in dollars and paying for expenses in local inflationary currency, daily financial assessments were impossible to make. Substantial changes in an item's cost would occur between the time it was bought and when it was paid for. Consequently, SRI retained an accounting firm to bring in some of its people, working with an Australian mining company, to Zambia to install a whole new computer and bookkeeping system.

A notable achievement was getting ZCCM to pay more attention to its cobalt resources. Zambia has perhaps the world's largest reserve of cobalt. Cobalt is not only about 15 times more valuable per pound than copper, it also represented a product diversification. Moreover, the company's easily accessed copper tailings were rich in cobalt.

Originally, the AIMs were intended for short-term turnaround and SRI's/ZCCM's interim plan extended only to 1995/96. However, a pressing need developed to look out to 10- and 30-year horizons in support of buyers who had long-term interests in profitability. But between these two periods and before privatization had run its course, the price of copper took a dive that would frustrate the privatization process. In 1998-99 copper fell from around 90¢ per pound to 70¢, and apparently neither SRI nor the Zambians saw that price decline coming. Given the expectations of the Zambian government and the reality of the marketplace, this change effectively delayed privatization. What capital selling did occur was handled by Rothschild Bank, and SRI was never privy to that process.

Outcome

While the original intention of ZCCM and the government might have been to seek a single buyer that would make the investments needed to return production to where it was 20 years before, it didn't turn out that way. Either because the government saw ZCCM as its "crown jewel" and had an exaggerated view of its worth, or because it placed too many conditions on the sale (e.g., responsibility for cleaning up prior environmental pollution), it ultimately wanted more than any buyer was prepared to pay.[24] It had broken ZCCM up into 11 component packages, each of which was for sale. The first and perhaps most important consequence of this decision was to drastically delay the sale and thus the inflow of cash. This delay severely affected production and caused substantial reductions in GDP, particularly in 1998 when the price of copper fell to 70¢. The other, seemingly obvious downside was that the more valuable pieces would sell easily, but those with greater problems might find no buyer at all, leaving the Government with the

---

[24] According to *African Business*, December 1997, the government and ZCCM were asking $1 billion for two prominent ZCCM divisions that included six mines and their associated copper refining facilities. A consortium that included Phelps Dodge bid only a third of that amount, and negotiations broke off.

cost either of continuing operation or of cleaning up.

Privatization in Zambia began in 1993 and continues. The privatization process included not just ZCCM, but banks, insurance companies, utilities, and oil and telecommunications companies as well. The biggest parts of ZCCM were among the last to be sold, but not until early 2000. Curiously, the buyer of the final part, and of a number of other ZCCM assets, was the large South African company, Anglo American Plc, the prenationalization owner in the 1960s. ZCCM remains a minority stakeholder in a number of the new operating companies.

Did SRI make a positive contribution to the life and times of ZCCM? Certainly it did. But long-term benefits for the Zambian people as a whole are harder to pinpoint. The SRI project staff speak very highly of the Zambian people they came to know. Many were trained abroad and knew their field well. Many helped carry out SRI's recommendations better than the few expatriates who were still in leadership at ZCCM. SRI and its subcontractor colleagues worked with dedication and brought a great deal of expertise to the project. As with many consulting situations, the consultants brought a fresh perspective that those immersed in the problem either did not have or found too much difficulty in implementing. While each incremental task SRI and its associated experts completed seemed to make a temporary difference, in retrospect and in aggregate, they were effectively overwhelmed by governmental predilections and the international economic climate.

A final lesson for this kind of endeavor may be to recognize the enormous inertia of poor countries and their accompanying ability to absorb great amounts of aid without reflecting much change. Even though copper, because it brought in solid currency, was the best single leverage on the Zambian economy, it is but one aspect of a complex socioeconomic and cultural matrix. Lasting changes in such an environment must treat the entire country and must somehow involve the majority of citizens in working toward a solution. It is a measure of the good people of Zambia that, with but one brief coup attempt in 1997, they have spared themselves the tribal and anticolonial hostilities that have befallen many African nations. By 1999, Zambia's GDP growth was again positive; it was the world's largest producer of cobalt but still twelfth in copper production. Nearly all of the mining assets had been privatized, and the new owners committed $2.5 billion to improve efficiency and expand operations.[DD] Some 250 other companies had also been privatized. But the country's rise to self-sufficiency, particularly given the onslaught of HIV/AIDS, where one in five adults are infected,[EE] still seems illusive and distant.

One of the major difficulties in postcolonial Zambia was the lack of an education system for training people in the operation of the important copper mining and processing industries. Accordingly, part of the service SRI provided in the 1980 phase of the work was staff training. Because of the broad need for skilled indigenous staff and the dependence of the general population on success in the Copperbelt, this work, and the training part in particular, was as socially responsible as any SRI would ever undertake. In spite of the overwhelming problems and the physical and cultural distances, those who went to Zambia to gain the insights necessary to evaluate and correct the situations they found developed a fond attachment for the people and knew that what they were doing was truly beneficial work.

SRI's training work began with a failure. Its first proposal for this phase of the work was rejected in favor of a competitor, who, it turns out, performed poorly. This was learned when the manager of ZCCM's Supply Department came to SRI in December 1984 and among other things wanted to talk to the people who had written the SRI training proposal, Gary Bridges and Paul Jones. This manager invited Bridges to go to Zambia and make a needs-analysis of the human resources department, but he indicated he could cover Bridges' expenses only. So, salary-free, Bridges spent a week there and concluded that the 700-person department could benefit from sending groups to the United States for customized training—something that would prepare them for their current and future jobs.

Accordingly, four sets of 12 Zambians spent approximately 3 months at SRI and 12-13 other relevant locations such as the Magna Copper Mine in Arizona. These SRI sessions were supplemented by four 2-week sessions in Zambia. The outcome of this training was very satisfactory. Attendees acquired needed management and assessment skills, learned how to interact with the other nationalities with which they had to deal, and received some sense of career planning.

The conditions for the average person in Zambia were dramatically illustrated when the students arrived at SRI. Some came with their personal possessions in paper bags. Because their company had given them a comfortable living allowance for the trip, on Tuesday mornings the students were taken to a local thrift shop where they bought needed clothing. As their departure neared, some bought huge suitcases to fill with things for their families—including food. These were graphic lessons about a less privileged world.

For the half-dozen SRI staff members who participated, the training phase was a very satisfying time. The Zambian students who came to the United States participated in teamwork-building experiences at nearby personal and professional development sites, went on excursions, and were entertained at staff members' homes where they prepared their native food and everyone sang Zambian songs. One of the trainees named his daughter after one of the SRI team members, and some of the relationships continue to this day. This project thus serves to illustrate the caring and empathetic nature of the SRI staff.

Postwar Revitalization in Lebanon

SRI is engaged in ongoing work in modern Lebanon that continues the tradition of the work described above, but now conducted in the economics practice that is part of SRI's Policy Group. Though the Business Group's efforts were discontinued in 1998, this economics practice has functioned successfully for the past 20 years as part of the Center for Science, Technology and Economic Development based in Washington, D.C. Its mission has been the same throughout its tenure: to help struggling economies right themselves and bring about a higher standard of living. Whereas many staff members have obviously contributed, John Mathieson is the one who has led the economic policy group to a position of worldwide respect in its work in 115 countries and more than 60 states, regions,

and communities (see Figure 15-7). Here we consider one of its major ongoing projects—the economic revitalization of Lebanon. Now in its fourth year, the work is sponsored by AID.

In the 30 years following WWII, Lebanon, and Beirut in particular, had been one of the Middle East's most prominent financial and tourist centers. But in the mid-1970s, a protracted civil war, heavily influenced by outside interests, radically changed Lebanon. This story thus begins in the aftermath of that war, which ravaged Lebanon for more than 15 years. The struggle there has faded from world attention because of other Middle East strife and the tendency in Lebanon not to discuss the war or its ramifications for fear of threatening the reconstruction process.

Figure 15-7. John "Matty" Mathieson, director of SRI's Center for Science, Technology and Economic Development.

The fragile system in Lebanon had been unraveling due to the increasingly radical actions of the Palestinian Liberation Organization (PLO) and other groups of Palestinians, who had resettled in Lebanon and Jordan after being forced out of Israel. The conflict started in earnest in 1975 as politicoreligious battles were fought among competing religious factions—Christians and Shiite, Sunni, and Druze Muslims. Almost at once external forces joined the fray, with Israel supporting the status quo Christians, and with Syria and other Arab states backing the Muslims. By the late 1970s, Israel, worrying about its northern border, would also enter the conflict, invading Lebanon in 1982. Private armies were formed and major powers, including France, the United States, Russia, and a variety of UN peacekeeping forces, tried to intervene. As a result, the civil war became even more complex. Though a peace treaty was finally signed in 1989, turmoil continued until 1991, and the wartime factions remained as impediments to post-war recovery, hindering cooperation in rebuilding. That is one reason why Lebanon sought outside help.

AID, which had been offering humanitarian aid during the war, shifted its emphasis to rebuilding after the treaty. By 1996, it was providing money for community groups and universities to reconstruct infrastructure and train people in relevant fields. But the economy was in a shambles and getting worse. Consequently, in 1997 AID asked SRI to assist in the economic revitalization efforts as the first U.S. consultant to arrive after the post-war travel ban was lifted.

The first job SRI tackled was to determine the most effective means for stimulating sustainable economic growth. SRI concentrated on two areas: the creation of a macroeconomic model for use by Lebanese policy makers and industry cluster development. The model was used to help understand the chronic budget shortfalls that were contributing to a huge and continuously increasing national debt, a towering 120% of GDP at the time. The segments of industry selected for improvement were agriculture, light industry, tourism, and regional financial and business services. SRI's first year was devoted mostly to design and the establishment of relationships of trust with Lebanese stakeholders. Because both the government and the private sector had bought into SRI's public/private collaboration approach, even among competing factions, AID proceeded the next year with implementation. Through all of this, SRI created partnerships not only with government and industry participants, but also with working partners, including the Lebanese American University and the Beirut-based firm, Information International. The implementation of these selected economic reform packages continues today.

SRI's strategy for the 1999-2000 fiscal year was to involve Lebanese stakeholders in building action plans. The stakeholders (incidentally an SRI-coined term[FF]) included both private and public sector leaders. The action plans used specific, targeted initiatives to solidify the various industry clusters and indicated what should be done to create a collective competitive advantage. Take, for example, the tourism cluster. Before SRI's work, each of the depressed hotel businesses acted alone. To help spur tourism, SRI designed and facilitated a private-sector-led Council for Tourism consisting of major hotels and tourist associations. Other SRI initiatives included crafting a new hotel rating system, conducting tourism worker training activities, and developing a series of marketing and promotion strategies and activities. As discussed below, SRI's approach is working.

In 2002, the emphasis changed slightly to encouraging the industrial clusters identified to embrace various regions in the country, including rural areas. As an example, for

Southern Lebanon SRI identified the elements needed to build an economic zone: human and natural resources, infrastructure, and existing enterprises that could be expanded. SRI began working with rural olive oil producers and growers of herbs to take advantage of expanding overseas markets for these products. In the tourism area, SRI helped develop package tours for rural ecotourism and cultural tourism to take advantage of Lebanon's rich natural and historical assets. The SRI team also helped reduce the "digital divide" by assisting in the establishment of community-based Internet centers in rural areas.

Strengthening the various parts of the commercial sector is, of course, a necessary long-term step in economic revitalization. But it is clearly not a quick road to solvency at the central governmental level. That involves either reduced expenses or increased taxes, or both. In the meantime, Lebanon's burdensome deficit continued to grow as a result of the high costs of postwar reconstruction. One role SRI played in this equation was its advocacy of a value-added tax, or VAT. Starting in 1998, at the request of the Minister of Finance, SRI prepared a full analysis and a complete rationale for invoking a VAT. That tax was finally initiated in February 2002 and, along with some hoped-for expenditure reductions in 2003, should help reduce future deficits.

How have SRI's suggestions been working? Feedback from the Lebanese government and private sectors has been encouraging. But, like all high-inertia systems, including governments used to satisfying different constituencies by providing public employment, such economic reforms take time. As noted, the economic picture was dismal when SRI's work began. Public debt was, and remains, extremely high, further exacerbated by artificially high interest rates. However, there are encouraging signs that the Lebanese economy has turned around. In spite of the highest debt-to-GDP ratio in the region, in 2000, a zero-growth year, the UN economic agency for Western Asia forecast Lebanon economic growths of 1.4% and 2.5% in 2001 and 2002, respectively. And, in fact, according to the Lebanese Central Bank, Lebanon's GDP grew by 3.6% in 2002 at an inflation rate of 1.8%. Whereas the International Monetary Fund projected a negative $1 billion balance of payments for Lebanon in 2002, the country produced a surplus of $1.5 billion. That growth is attributed to an increase in both tourism (nearing a million visitors in 2002) and the number of new industrial firms (doubling over the 2 years ending in 2002). Lebanese banks are also regaining some of their prewar status as the strongest in the region. Holdings at the end of 2002 were almost $43 billion, or 2.5 times GDP. VAT is also expected to work, as indicated by a budgeted revenue growth for 2003 of about 18%, and budgeted expenditures are slated to decrease by about 7%. If both initiatives work as planned, the deficit should go down substantially.[25] Only time will tell, but the initiatives are in place.

If and when Lebanon returns to economic health, it will, of course, be hard to gauge just how much SRI's work has helped in that process. But SRI's ongoing participation in the joint government-industry initiatives has certainly made positive contributions.

---

[25] Fourth quarter 2002 numbers from the Ministry of Finance as quoted by the Economic Research Unit of the Bank of Beirut and the Arab Countries.

Intellectual Property at Risk in the Philippines

Intellectual property rights (IPR) are the legal means governments use to ensure that the producers of new arts, science, and technology reap the rewards of their investment, effort, and creativity. However, such rights face a variety of new challenges around the world. Theft of intellectual property (IP) in Southeast Asia in particular represents one of the world's biggest impediments to the integrity of IPR, with numerous IP-pirating factories found in countries in the region. The advent of software as a marketable commodity, with its underlying digital technology that enables all forms of software and entertainment media to be copied cheaply with complete fidelity, means that the lure of piracy has become too attractive for some to ignore. Illicit replication is a problem both for the countries where the counterfeiting takes place and for countries to which they export the illegal goods. Globally, the loss from IP infringement to the United States alone is estimated at nearly $10 billion annually, and one of the primary culprits is the Philippines. Although that country had been trying to deal with the problem for the past 20 years, when the digital decades arrived, its laws proved outdated and its enforcement, typical of the nations in the region, was weak or effectively nonexistent.

SRI, which had developed insights into IPR practices in developing countries under an AID project concluded in 1990,[GG]was invited by the Philippine Exporters Confederation in 1992 to map out a comprehensive strategy for the reform of that country's IPR policies and practices. SRI first examined the adequacy of the existing laws and then tackled the various investigative, prosecutorial, and judicial parts needed for an effective enforcement process.

Before detailing the SRI findings, we need to understand why the Philippine exporters were concerned in the first place. What factors motivated them to want to improve the treatment of IPR? Beyond the intrinsic goal of establishing and strengthening respect in Philippine society for the efforts of its inventive and artistic population, at least one important external reason motivated them to want to enforce IPR laws: trade with the United States. That trade is critical to the Philippines because the United States is by far the country's largest export market, exceeding $1 billion annually.

Because U.S. imports amount to perhaps a quarter of that amount, the United States is obviously interested in how its IP is treated in the Philippines. A U.S. evaluation of IPR efforts indicated that the Philippines should be on the U.S. Priority Watch List. Being added to that list had considerable implications for tariffs on Philippine exports to the United States—adding perhaps a half a billion dollars annually. The Philippines has been on and off the list. In 1993, under an agreement between the U.S. chief trade negotiator and Trade and Industry Secretary Rizalino Navarro, the Philippines was removed from the list. Part of the reasoning for doing so may have been the steps the country was taking to revamp its IPR activities.

Let's now look at what the SRI study found and the effects of its recommendations. According to an account in one of the Philippines' leading newspapers, SRI found the following shortcomings in its examination:[HH]

- Constraints on IPR adjudication
  - Low priority given to IPR protection
  - Inadequate resources and training for IPR enforcement
  - Possible judicial bias against foreign multinationals
  - Lack of knowledge of IPR laws among agents and courts
  - Lack of coordination among IPR enforcement agencies
  - Overall inefficiency in the judicial system
  - Corruption
- Legal problems
  - Overly technical and stringent evidentiary requirements
  - Inadequate fines and criminal penalties
  - Tenuous legal authority among enforcement agencies to expedite violations
- The adjudication system
  - Difficulties in getting receipts to prove sale of counterfeit items
  - Difficulties in establishing identity of IP violators
  - Problems in finding witnesses to sign affidavits
  - Limited availability of judges

- "Protection" offered to infringers by "influential friends"
- Lack of storage space for seized goods
- Prosecution difficulties
  - Respondent's inability to answer subpoena and notices
  - Liberal extensions by prosecutor for respondent to appear in hearings.

The review, in short, uncovered pervasive weaknesses in the Philippine IPR activities. The recommendations were in keeping with the increased emphasis on IPR in the Uruguay Round of the General Agreement on Tariffs and Trade (GATT) and included the increased prevention of IP violations and the streamlining of the IPR adjudication process.

What happened next is interesting. Within a couple of weeks of the public announcement about the study, President Ramos committed publicly to the strict enforcement of IPR, something he had informally done during the final presentation of the SRI report in February 1994. He instructed Secretary Navarro to work with other government officials to task the Supreme Court to establish special IPR courts. Initiatives already under way, such as an Interagency Committee on IPR, were strengthened by his reaffirmation of a 1971 international accord on IPR. His public statements also vowed that Filipino inventors,

artists, writers, performers, composers, and musicians would gain international recognition of their rights and that, "The role that the intellectual property system plays in the country's economic and industrial development cannot be overemphasized." This was the domestic spin on what also was a critically important export trade issue. But the underground industry's infringement on IPR ran deep.

The SRI study had both immediate and continuing effects as the Supreme Court formed special IPR courts in 1995 and as new IPR laws emerged in 1997. However, no legal change is any more effective than its enforcement, and anyone familiar with policy reform in a developing country like the Philippines can tell you that ongoing vigilance is required, particularly when powerful interests are at stake. The actions taken as a result of SRI's recommendations had enormous potential, but enforcement of the new changes was not sufficiently permanent. As a result and also in 1997, the Philippines was once again put on the Priority Watch List, in part because of the IPR courts' inability to seize pirated materials. As recently as 2002, the Philippines was spending only $500,000 on IPR enforcement, the country remained a major haven for illicit manufacture and sale of media like DVDs, and U.S. Trade Representative Zoellnick still included the Philippines on the Priority Watch List.

Assessing a Country's Science and Technology Practices

SRI, through its Center for Science and Technology Policy based in Washington, D.C., has found an important research niche in evaluating a nation's commitment to science and technology (S&T). For years the group has worked with the National Science Foundation (NSF) in the evaluation of NSF's own programs and of those the Foundation shares with other regions of the world. As a result of these efforts, SRI's reputation in this area has become truly global in scope. As evidence, it has performed S&T evaluations for Argentina, Australia, Brazil, Chile, France, Germany, India, Italy, Japan, Malaysia, Mexico, South Korea, Sweden, Taiwan, the United Kingdom, Venezuela, and others. We briefly look at three of these evaluations: one for Malaysia, one for the U.S. Congress regarding S&T cooperation with Latin America, and one evaluating our Department of State's Fulbright Scholar Program.

Malaysia

In the last two decades, SRI has undertaken more than 20 projects sponsored from within Malaysia. While these projects were mostly for private corporations, including those in petrochemicals, many were conducted for the Malaysian government. These latter projects concentrated on an extended assessment of Malaysia's ability to implement advanced manufacturing technologies. Malaysia was anxious to participate in burgeoning Southeast Asian production of the components for the information age. One government-sponsored SRI project in the mid-1990s assessed whether Malaysia had the human resource potential for a planned increase in its S&T industry.

Interest in this subject area began in 1992 as Malaysia's Ministry of Science, Technology, and the Environment began a biannual assessment of achievements and the state of its human resources in technology. In particular, the ministry wanted to know whether the Malaysians could use S&T to usher the country into the ranks of developed nations. In work jointly sponsored by the Ministry and the UN's Development Program, SRI also looked at the country's investments in R&D.

As part of that evaluation, in 1995 the ministry asked SRI to help gauge the present situation and predict what would be needed out to a 2020 horizon. This ambitious, 2-year undertaking involved large-scale, multidimensional surveys of Malaysian industry and the kinds of talent both currently employed and needed; the kinds and levels of investments required and who might offer them; and the educational system, including overseas training.[II] The setting at that time found that part of the world in an economic slump, and Malaysian ministers were wondering if that slowdown would erode their S&T base.

While many perceived a shortage of technical talent, there were no data to back that belief. As a result, SRI conducted surveys that probed more than 3,500 companies that might use scientists and engineers. More than 60% responded, giving a statistically significant basis for helping build the econometric models needed for the long-term forecast of labor demand. The industry response confirmed an estimated 20% shortfall in technical talent. Moreover, the most critical shortages were in the high-skill levels needed to drive the targeted areas of economic expansion. The good news was that the trends were positive and that the government had already put in place many of the policies, programs, and investments to address the problem.

The SRI project team, led by Catherine Ailes (see Figure 15-8) and Roberts Coward, made recommendations affecting the educational system, various kinds of R&D investments, and labor and R&D policies. The work was so well received that in May 1998 the large, well-supported report was made an official document of the Malaysian Cabinet and used in setting government S&T policies. Though the fraction of Malaysia's GDP devoted to R&D is low, it has been growing; from 0.22% in 1996 to 0.5% in 2000, with about 60% of that percentage coming from the private sector.

Figure 15-8. Catherine Ailes, director of SRI's Program in Science and Technology Policy.

U.S.-Latin America S&T Cooperation

In the 1988 Authorization Acts for the NSF and NASA, Congress directed that the NSF work with other federal R&D agencies, including the Department of Energy (DOE), carry out an independent study to first assess and then promote U.S. collaboration with Latin America in science, technology, and space. This requirement became the impetus for an SRI project with NSF. As one can imagine, the subject was amorphous, given the breadth of the tasks and the unevenness with which our neighbors to the south engage in S&T. To limit the scope of the investigation, the topics to be considered were confined to biology, astronomy, geosciences, physics/materials science, and engineering. Moreover, the work concentrated on five countries: Argentina, Brazil, Chile, Mexico, and Venezuela. Though the report to Congress resulted in a bill that never became law, it was and remains one of the only descriptions of such hemispheric collaboration. Selected outcomes of the study follow.

Beginning in the late 1970s at a time of political unrest in Latin America, the S&T relationships the United States had with the region lost visibility and perhaps the interest of most Americans, including lawmakers. A decade later, the flow of U.S. S&T funds to our Latin neighbors continued to diminish. Similarly, the number of Latin students coming to the United States peaked in the 1982-83 school year, whereas the numbers of those from Asia and the Middle East continued to rise. Even specific initiatives, such as one with Brazil in 1986, didn't affect this trend. On the other hand, intrahemispheric concerns about economic development and trade have become more visible concerns in recent years. Does a relationship exist between S&T and the ability of Latin American countries to gain greater economic stability and independence? Another dimension in the relationship has been the practice in Europe and Japan of picking up the S&T slack in Latin American left by the United States.

First, the SRI team looked for the extent of ongoing cooperation in the chosen disciplines. With the exception of specific areas such as astronomy and remote sensing, where the Southern Hemisphere offered unique access to space, the various S&T fields evidenced more potential than practice. A common theme, however, was a sophisticated research community that was underused because of lack of funding, instrumentation, and access to information. And there seemed to be a desire to increase hemispheric scientific interaction through graduate fellowships, personnel exchanges, and enhancements in communications, especially computer networks.

Perhaps the major conclusion of the study was that S&T could play an important role in solving Latin America's international debt problem and, through growth, in having the region secure an improved place in the global economy. Panels, led by U.S. researchers and comprising U.S. and Latin American members, were assembled to identify a variety of ways that these changes could take place and the organizational means needed to carry them out. Recommendations were made for each of the chosen technologies, for each of the five countries, and for specific methods to improve human resource development, research exchange programs, instrumentation upgrades, library quality, and communications.

As a result of SRI's defining the problems, the NSF has undertaken initiatives to increase its involvement. One recent example is a joint enterprise with DOE to fund the Pan-American Advanced Studies Institute, which offers short courses that are intended to stimulate collaboration among early career scientists and engineers. Intrahemisphere networks that include most Latin American countries have

grown up among the various scientific centers. Though the outlay for R&D as a fraction of GDP is still low in Latin America (0.5% or one-fifth that of the United States), the 1990s saw a 36% increase in technical publications, second only to that of China. Finally, high-technology manufacturing, including pharmaceuticals, grew steadily in the 1990s in Brazil and Mexico, and Mexico and Costa Rica are now net exporters of high-technology products. Thus, progress is being made.

Assessing the U.S. Fulbright Scholarship Program

The Fulbright Program for international educational exchange has become an integral part of U.S. public diplomacy. Since its instigation just after WWII, the program has benefited more than 250,000 men and women, U.S. and foreign, in a wide variety of academic disciplines and has involved over 140 countries around the world. The Program is funded by the State Department's Bureau of Educational and Cultural Affairs, and that organization asked SRI about 3 years ago to review its practices and the value of its outcome to the United States. Of the Fulbright Program's seven components, SRI was asked to examine the Scholar Program—both for U.S. scholars sent abroad and visiting scholars—and the U.S. and foreign components of the Student Program.

In September 2002, SRI issued a report on the U.S. Scholar Program, those U.S. scholars sent overseas. SRI found strong evidence that the program is meeting its goal of promoting mutual understanding and cooperation with other nations. The executive director of the Fulbright administrative arm said, "The study demonstrates and quantifies the impact of the...Program for the first time. It underlines the value of the program to America's international relationships and also to Americans' understanding of other nations. At a time when the world is so endangered by lack of understanding, the...Program is a beacon of hope." The SRI researchers found an unprecedented level of agreement among all Fulbright alumni, foreign and domestic, that their experiences were valuable, and that they had acquired a deeper understanding of their host countries and a heightened awareness of social and cultural diversity.

The U.S. survey consisted of a random sample of slightly more than 1,000 Fulbright alumni whose grants ran from 1976 to 1999. Specific results included:

- The grant activities were diverse, not just classroom teaching.
- Virtually all grantees became active in their local communities.
- The overwhelming majority of the scholars were able to impart new knowledge, form ongoing collaborations, and later welcome host country colleagues on their visits to the United States.
- Three-quarters of scholars used the experience to bring a greater international flavor to their home campuses.

- A large majority reported that participation gave them expertise they would not otherwise have had.

The SRI staff is now condensing information from interviews with foreign scholars about their experiences in the United States (e.g., a Ukrainian web site mentioned that the SRI team met with nine local Fulbright alumni in May 2002). SRI analysis of its interviews with Visiting Scholars will be forthcoming. In the aftermath of 9/11, many Americans are wondering how nations and cultures can gain better understanding of one another. If the ongoing work supports the early results, SRI may be able to provide the first evidence of the value of the Fulbright Program in achieving that end.

Telecommunications Privatization in Britain and the Birth of Vodafone

In 1979 the conservative government of Prime Minister Margaret Thatcher adopted a policy that would create a 10-year program to privatize large sections of the economy, including industries such as coal, steel, and water, which had been nationalized under a previous socialist government. In Britain, as in many European countries, telecommunications was still part of the public sector of the economy. Privatization of telecommunications in Britain was therefore of great interest to governments across Europe and elsewhere because it would bring about two financial windfalls. One was simply the government income inherent in the transfer process itself. The second derived from the need to move this industry into the digital age, wherein those costs could be transferred from the public to the private sector. In Britain, telecommunications was almost entirely held by the public company, British Telecommunications (BT).[26] But a desired step, preliminary to its privatization, was the government's policy decision to open up the new cellular communications world in Britain to competition.

Though private ownership and operation of telecommunications services already existed in other countries, most notably in the United States, such arrangements were not common in Europe. This action of the Thatcher

government can be seen as a vanguard for a trend that still continues more than two decades later in many corners of the world. But our story about SRI's hand in this (r)evolution opens and, to a great extent, closes in Great Britain.[JJ]

In the summer of 1982 the British government initiated the privatization process by opening up a part of the telecommunications market by means of inviting bids for a license to run a privately operated national cellular phone service. BT would also be given a license automatically. The government saw the need to get a first-class cellular phone service up and running quickly to provide BT with serious competition. BT was considered lethargic, overstaffed, and in need of a wakeup call. In addition, this exercise would provide some guidance on the implications of subsequently privatizing the whole of BT.

The government agency tasked with managing this privatization was the Department of Trade and Industry (DTI). The person to lead the effort within DTI was Jonathan Soloman, who had recently worked in Downing Street for former Prime Minister James Callaghan. Soloman was charged with the stimulation of the electronics industry and the revitalization of the telecommunications industry in the United Kingdom. However, DTI did not have the internal expertise to evaluate the cellular bids that would follow and hence

---

[26] BT was formed in 1981 by its extraction from the British Post Office to be come a state-owned corporation with a near monopoly on telecommunication.

requested the outside help of Robert Perrin of SRI's London office.

Robert Perrin had developed a strong personal track record with DTI and had a close working relationship with Soloman. Perrin had led an SRI project that provided a series of very high-level seminars on the technical, industrial, economic and social implications of developments in the microelectronics industry. This series, which used a range of speakers from SRI-Menlo Park, bolstered SRI's credibility by providing wide exposure to SRI among top-level decision makers in both the private and government sectors. It was in these circumstances, then, that Soloman invited SRI to bid for the needed assistance. The familiarity with DTI and the important link to Soloman energized Perrin and the SRI-London office and eventually helped SRI-Menlo Park overcome its initial reluctance to bid.

This diversity of view reveals an important aspect about SRI. SRI management had notable reservations over the years about the role of overseas offices, which were opened and staffed largely by the Business Group. Were those offices to be independent research entities with a degree of self-determination, or were they required to support operations in Menlo Park, leaving most of their activities devoted to marketing? This ambivalence surfaced from time to time, and the indecision no doubt hindered the growth of the Institute. In spite of this issue, however, SRI conducted numerous successful projects in which Menlo Park people were temporarily assigned overseas. This cellular telephone project happened to be one of those.

Another bit of fortunate timing followed the microelectronics seminars. SRI-Menlo Park had decided to form an electronic industry section in London and chose Charles Mason to head it up. This move proved to be ideal for the DTI opportunity because Mason had previously been an attorney of the U.S. Federal Communications Commission. Mason's background in the US, where telecommunications services were offered privately, albeit regulated, was valuable in England, where such knowledge was in short supply.[27] He was also to be a vital link with Menlo Park resources. Hence, in the summer of

1982 Robert Perrin and Charles Mason passed an oral examination before a set of DTI staff and won the contract.[28]

The aim of the project was to help set up the process and specific criteria for evaluating bidders for the new, privately offered, part of the cellular service. Once the criteria were in hand, SRI was to evaluate each bidder. This work was to be carried out with attention to the Thatcher government's objective: creating real competition and achieving visible "success" with this private licensing effort. Because that outcome was so important, SRI at times met personally with Kenneth Baker, the DTI minister. Because such comprehensive cellular service was in its earliest stages, the decision-making process had to be invented "on-the-fly." Of critical importance was that everyone involved view it as fair.

SRI selected four dimensions for bid evaluation: technical, marketing, financial, and management. In each category several criteria served as "gates" that could shut out unqualified bidders, whereas others were less stringent but still helped rank the applicants. Of the seven initial bids, one was rejected early for obvious flaws and one was voluntarily withdrawn. Evaluations continued for the remaining five. Then, to allow those bidders to adapt to what was sought, the evaluation was carried out in a flexible and interactive manner. That ongoing evaluation made SRI's job both more difficult and more important.

The technical evaluation began with the SRI-Menlo Park team of John Lomax, Dan Allan, and Aki Shohara creating a technical performance model. This mathematical model, embracing a variety of technical factors such as channel reuse and spectrum efficiency, enabled direct engineering comparisons of the proposed systems and their ability to provide an acceptable nationwide quality of service. Keep in mind that the government had not yet specified a cellular standard, and that bidders drew on emerging standards from the continent or the United States.

Having a common basis for comparison was critical. Another important technical factor was that the new private cellular switching system would almost certainly be all digital, whereas

---

[27] However, the U.S. long-distance telecommunications market was itself in the process of being deregulated, along with the breakup of AT&T; the latter occurred on January 1, 1984.

[28] Project 4845, Radio Telephone License Application Appraisal, was initiated September 9, 1982 and was scaled in cost according to the number of bidders. The contracted price was $165,620.

BT's primary land line telephone network was still analog. Because 1982 was a time of transition from analog to digital switching, given the latter's innate ability to offer more services, the new company would have the advantage over existing BT equipment. That equipment's continued use was locked in by depreciation schedules that were many times the life cycle of the new digital systems.

After conducting a technical evaluation of all the bids, the Menlo Park team came to the view that although some of the bids were thorough, none of them came up to the required standard. Consequently, all the remaining bids were rejected. Curiously, all five bidders had links to large private telecommunications companies with considerable technical backup and were indignant that SRI was criticizing their bids on technical grounds. Philips in the Netherlands was particularly scathing, brushing SRI-London aside and flying a large team direct to SRI in California. Insisting their bid was technically sound, a lively scene ensued as numerous faults in their technical plan were exposed by SRI staff. The Philips team quickly returned home to redo their submission.

But as it turned out, after numerous discussions between SRI and the individual bidders about critical problems in their technical approaches, one bidder withdrew and the remaining four were coached to a level of technical acceptance that passed the "gating" muster. This normalization was viewed as desirable, if somewhat surprising in a competitive bidding process, because of the required consistency and interconnectivity of the combined cellular-wireline system.

The overall conclusion of this first phase, then, was that all bids had strengths and weaknesses. One could not say one was technically stronger than the other. The British government was therefore told that the bids could not be selected purely on technical grounds; the wider issues of finance, market appraisal, marketing, and general staffing needs also had to be compared. In this way the other dimensions became the deciding factors.

On the basis of its in-depth marketing expertise, some acquired in a recent study of the Swedish Telecommunications market, SRI found that the first round of proposals was vastly inadequate in this area. Only one bidder even addressed the nationwide market. Others devoted too little attention and resources to marketing and educating the public on the potential benefits of cellular services, which were largely a curiosity to the man in the street. Some also drastically underestimated the market, providing, in SRI's eyes, too little competition for BT services. In the financial area, one bidder had the clearest understanding of the tariff structure and the highest estimate of system users. Two others either had inadequate financial resources to launch a successful system or were too conservative in their growth projections. One bidder (Racal-Millicom) had a bold plan that committed it to installing seven regional control switches in the first year of operation. SRI later learned how appreciative the remaining bidders were for the initial criticisms.

To deal with this more comprehensive phase of the evaluation, the SRI project members included Jacques Popper, Frank G. Pyne, and Alan Thurgood.[29] Pyne was a chartered accountant and led the financial study. Thurgood led the management evaluation, believing the management plan was now a very important part of the decision. This was particularly critical in the light of the uncertainties a new private company would face in providing telecommunication services across Britain. The focus of SRI's evaluation in this regard was telling:

- Business and service record of the lead/sponsoring company.
- Similar records of the other active members of the consortium
- Caliber of the proposed management team
- Ability of the active members of the consortium to handle a venture of this nature
- Flexibility and ability to manage change
- Commitment of the lead company and the consortium members
- Perception by management of the opportunities and risks presented by the venture.

The discussions held with Kenneth Baker, the minister involved, were to consider these wider issues. It was a high-visibility project. The telecommunications industry was very excited, yet in SRI's opinion, none of the bids were good enough. SRI therefore proposed to give each bidder a critique of their proposal. Each critique

---

[29] Alan Thurgood was the former managing director of ITT companies in England.

would obviously be different, and each company would be guided in the right direction to make their bid acceptable.

This novel approach generated a range of reactions. Some were too proud and confident to listen, and challenged SRI's ability to criticize their bid fairly and knowledgeably. However, one bidder's response was quite different. Racal was the leader of the Racal-Millicom bid. Millicom, a U.S.-based, Swedish-owned R&D firm, had a sound base in U.S. cellular technology. Racal was a relatively small manufacturer of military (mostly Army) radio equipment and sold nothing to the public. Gerry Whent ran the most profitable side of Racal and saw his market was declining. He persuaded his chairman, Ernest Harrison, to go in for the cellular bid. Many on Racal's board were initially against this move, but Whent was eventually given the go-ahead, provided he first resign his current job.

Gerry Whent was a tough, astute executive and was very quick to learn. Faced with SRI's critique, he readily agreed that Racal's marketing plan was ineffectual and their financial plan seriously incomplete. Although Racal's own estimate of market size was far in excess of all the other bidders, Whent readily accepted the SRI reasoning that even they had grossly underestimated the market potential for cellular communications.

Whent gratefully grasped SRI's comments. Then, with great enthusiasm and a greatly increased budget, he took over the entire top floor of a large Heathrow hotel and rapidly flew in extra staff from Sweden and the U.S. They all worked round the clock and weekends. Armies of advertisers, accountants, and lawyers were summoned while secretaries toiled endlessly. The outcome was an immensely improved and impressive bid that far outshone those of the other bidders. They decided to call the new venture Vodafone.

Given this turn of events and the resulting offering, SRI decided that Racal-Millicom was the best bidder, and that they could indeed give BT serious competition. SRI therefore recommended that the government select the Racal-Millicom bid. The SRI team had been convinced that cellular telephones had an enormous potential for growth, far beyond what a complacent BT or even the other bidders had estimated. The scale of Racal's planned investment surprisingly eclipsed by a wide margin the plans of their competitors, who were already in the telecommunications market and would have been expected to know latent customer demands. Subsequently, some complained that Racal's investment plans were unreal, and that they would never be implemented as promised in their bid. But it could be asserted that this Racal plan, created at high speed and under very great pressure, nevertheless became the foundation of Vodafone's subsequent success.[30]

But the evaluation battle was not over. Because of its overall importance, controversy surrounded the decision and the DTI decided to appoint three very senior impartial and well-respected executives to provide a second opinion.[31] The panel agreed to review the process as long as they were allowed 8 weeks to do so. So, the SRI team was requested to justify, under detailed scrutiny, how it had conducted its evaluation, made its analysis, and reached its conclusions.

Quite naturally, this critique was initially viewed with misgivings by the SRI team. However, to the team's great relief, these three wise men quickly declared they were unanimous in their agreement with SRI's methodology and conclusions. One of them, Sir Brian Carlsberg, subsequently was appointed the chief executive of the Office of Telecommunications, the cellular industry's adjudicator and watchdog. He had said that much of the methodology used by SRI was subsequently used as their standard practice, and Frank Pyne's financial modeling was especially appreciated. With the review panel's affirmation, then, the government accepted SRI's recommendations and announced Racal-Millicom the winner.

Time would show that Vodafone not only out-competed the BT cellular system in Britain, but would go on to become the world's largest supplier of cellular services.[32] Chris Gent had

---

[30] Regarding its ability to compete effectively with BT, Vodafone quickly jumped to holding a 55% UK market share and has always remained ahead of BT. This was yet another example of a worldwide trend; the ensconced wireline carriers often failed to lead changes in personal wireless communications, digital or not.

[31] Such a top-level audit of a project was unusual. However, the political, financial, and competitive implications of the initiative were monumental, and DTI was being careful.

[32] Sometime after the DTI work, Mason, Perrin (both then at another firm), and Dan Allan of SRI conducted another project for a gentleman who was hired into Vodafone from ICL. The project suggested that Vodafone introduce value-added cellular services such as stock quotes, which proved

been brought in after the bid was won, and in due course took over from Gerry Whent while Ernest Harrison (by now "Sir") had resigned. An article in the 25 January 1999 issue of Business Week provided a depiction of Vodafone's ascension to the top of the industry and gave a striking example of the assimilation of cellular service. Chris Gent was watching a cricket match in Australia when he heard Bell Atlantic was offering $45 billion for the largest U.S. cellular provider, Air Touch. Using his cell phone, and without returning to England, he quickly put together his own $55 billion stock and cash offer. The deal was eventually approved, making Vodafone, then Europe's largest mobile telephone company, a worldwide giant with $10 billion in annual sales and a capitalization of $105 billion.[KK] As of April 2003, Vodafone's subscriber list is the world's largest at 112 million users. The SRI team was proud of its prediction of the explosive growth of cellular services in 1982 and of its insight in how that market should be addressed. What better confirmation could one expect?

Returning now to the specific area of privatization, SRI was asked by DTI's Jonathan Solomon to undertake a second much smaller, but still significant, project. This was to help with one of the issues associated with the actual privatization of British Telecommunications. The Treasury wanted the privatization to raise £4 billion from the sale of BT shares. The questions were: What was the approximate value of a BT share, how many shares would therefore need to be sold, and consequently, what proportion of the company would then be left in government hands? To address these issues SRI needed to know, at least in general terms, the scope for cost cutting at BT (e.g., staff redundancies), price increases in relation to other European countries, and the expected revenue increase from market growth. An attendant question was: How does one balance the desire to increase prices with the political and economic desire to keep down inflation?

To get a handle on these questions, SRI conducted a short comparative analysis between BT and other European PT&T's yet to be privatized, as well as telecommunications offerings in Japan and the U.S. After removing effects like inflation and currency exchange, it became apparent that BT was much less efficient than corresponding providers

elsewhere. Though BT customers had only seen a slight increase in costs in the last decade or so, measured in hours worked to pay their phone bills, their costs remained far above those of Germany and France where corresponding costs had dropped substantially in the same period.

SRI also determined that the quality of telephone service and availability of lines in Britain had diminished. BT's gross had been decreasing steadily since 1977, whereas the profits of similar services in other European countries had been flat or positive. On top of this bad news, SRI learned that because BT had begun the transition to digital switches, its capital costs had risen 30 % over the previous 2 years. DTI leaders were concerned at the reported state of their flagship enterprise where, on a comparative basis, BT was losing value.

The privatization of BT continued, and by the end of 1984 just over half its ownership was sold to the public. The remaining part was sold in two halves, one in December 1991 and virtually all the remainder in 1993. The total cash returned to the British government from the BT transition was of the order of £15B.[LL] BT plc is now a worldwide telecommunications company with over 2 million shareholders.

As a final word on the effort in Britain, it should be noted that the template SRI and DTI employed for cellular evaluation became a pattern for other such transitions around the world.[33] The rapid and immense success of Vodafone also showed how much profit there was in cellular communications. Furthermore, the privatization of BT showed other countries that, not only was privatization possible, but doing so would generate a large windfall for the departments and governments involved. The investment bankers also became interested, given the large sums of money involved and the attractive underwriting fees. Between 1984 and 1999 about $244B of state-owned telecommunications systems, worldwide, were privatized, involving 90 of the 189 members of the International Telecommunications Union.[MM]

---

[33] Many countries closely followed the British template including Australia, Belgium, Brazil, Canada, Colombia, Commonwealth of Independent States, Denmark, France, Germany, Hong Kong, Hungary, India, Ireland, Italy, Jordan, Mexico, New Zealand, Norway, Poland, South Korea, Spain, Sweden, Thailand, and Venezuela.

---

profitable. The gentleman's name was Chris Gent, the current chairman of Vodafone.

Domestic U.S. Economic Development Assistance

City of Austin, TX—Creating an Opportunity Economy

The choice of the catchy phrase, "Creating an Opportunity Economy" was deliberate on the part of analysts in SRI's Public Policy Center. In the spring of 1985, they had completed a landmark project that was to help transform Austin, Texas, into one of the country's leaders in the new information economy. While communities around the world have tried to mimic Silicon Valley's success, Austin is one of the relatively few that seriously embarked on such a transition, and one of the very few that succeeded in doing so.

The SRI study began in the summer of 1984 as an examination, sponsored by the city's Chamber of Commerce, of the economic outlook for Austin. But as stated by the sponsors in the foreword to SRI's final report:[NN]

> "What began as a largely traditional look at economic development for Austin ends not with a simple prescription for jobs. Rather, SRI International has taken us right to the heart of this community, Austin's people, all of its people."

The study was to look 15 to 20 years into the future and, as it turned out, the SRI group came to share in the excitement of the changes foreseen for Austin and helped provide the necessary stimulus to amplify that momentum.

The SRI team, led by Ted Lyman,[34] entered the project with the comprehensive objective of developing "a long-range strategy that builds on community strengths and aims at broad-based economic and community development." Loosely, what they found was a stable employment base stemming from Austin's being the Texas state capital, a source of educated talent as the site of the University of Texas, and an influx of technology companies that began in the 1960s with IBM and Texas Instruments and continued into the 1970s with Motorola and Advanced Micro Devices. This technology presence received a significant vote of confidence in 1983 when the nation's first private-sector R&D consortium,

Microelectronics and Computer Technology Corporation (MCC) chose Austin as its headquarters in a competition with 57 other cities.[35] Austin's success in winning this competition and the critical collaboration between the Governor of Texas, the University of Texas, and local business leaders, also persuaded 3M Corporation to move five of its divisions, including its R&D operations,[OO] from Minnesota to Austin in 1984.

Another important factor was the increase in population in Austin and the surrounding area. Building permit issuance for residences grew nearly 11% in 1982 and was even higher from 1983 to 1984. These dramatic changes were prompting local planning offices to forecast population increases of more than 50% between 1985 and 2000. As can be seen in Figure 15-9,[PP] such estimates proved to be conservative. Along with population growth were positive changes in household income; 1982 data indicated that Austin had fewer low-income households and a vastly higher percent of upper income households than national averages. For households making more than $35,000, Austin had more than twice the national average—31% versus 13%. These remarkable changes were certainly cause for an examination of what lay ahead, as were less favorable economic trends in Texas that lay behind the positive statistics.

Oil prices were falling and with them the general Texas economy. The rising non-farm employment of the Austin area would flatten out, as is also evident in Figure 15-9. But it was the arrival of MCC that prompted local leaders to ponder the future of Austin's economy and to approach SRI to help develop the city's first long-range economic plan since 1957.[36]

---

[34] Other members of the team were Tom Chmura, Jim Gollub, Doug Henton, John Melville, Paul Shay, and the Center Director, Steve Waldhorn.

[35] Austin's winning of MCC was good evidence of the benefits of working collaboratively. A $25 million laboratory facility, financed by University of Texas and private funds, was built at the University research center and leased to MCC at a nominal cost. Thirty-two endowed chairs of $1 million each were established, and MCC employees received fellowships, teaching positions, subsidized home loans, and other benefits. (Susan E. Engelking, *Austin's Opportunity Economy: A Model for Collaborative Technology Development*, Annals of the New York Academy of Sciences, April 1996.)

[36] SRI won the project competitively, assisted by its reputation for insightful economic analysis and strategic planning, and by a visit to SRI by a group of Austin business

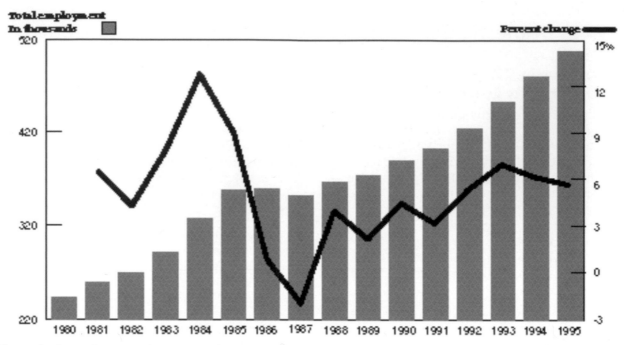

Figure 15-9. Nonfarm employment in the Austin, TX, metropolitan area (Texas Employment Commission and John Sharp, comptroller of Public Accounts).

The SRI investigators found an Austin area industrial transition under way but within the context of a continuing statewide economic malaise already in its fourth year. This combination would, in retrospect, provide a propitious time for a look at the future.

SRI's first step was to create a socioeconomic profile of the greater Austin area, including demographics and the major sectors of its economy. For demographics, SRI determined where new housing was being sought and how the reactions of the various zoning agencies would modulate that demand. Five economic sectors were chosen for analysis:

- R&D (creating new knowledge)
- Technology manufacturing (translating new knowledge into products)
- Technology-based information (software, telecommunications, etc.)
- Government services
- Support services.

SRI examined each sector to learn where recent employment growth had occurred and where it was projected to grow. These assessments were critical to developing a future strategy, and these five sectors would become the framework for recommendations to follow.

To give the Austin leadership a perspective about what lay ahead, the SRI team posited two possible futures: The first, called "Muddling Through," found the community, instead of pursuing a diversified economy, a new infrastructure, and the technical education of its future employees, slipping into complacency that allowed local industry to purchase goods and services outside the community rather than locally. The other scenario was essentially the antithesis:

- A diversified economy to weather business cycles
- Locally trained workers, as opposed to imported talent
- Planned investment in infrastructure
- A sufficient and rich diversity of local suppliers
- Maintenance of the public-private partnership that had been working.

Some of the first conclusions that SRI drew were that Austin was no longer dominated by the stable and predictable employment flowing from the University and the state government. The city was, in fact, now more subject to external changes, and those changes were of concern to the average citizen in regard to whether the current quality of life would continue or become vulnerable. That same quality of life, SRI suggested, was an important

---

leaders who happened to be in Silicon Valley luring firms to Austin.

ingredient in continuing to attract high-technology companies. Another finding was that increasing employment in just the service or support sector did not produce monetary growth and would therefore not be effective over the long term. Only the export of goods could do that. More specifically, SRI suggested that Austin could distinguish itself over the next 15-20 years by creating an advanced information and knowledge economy, and indicated what should happen in each of the economic sectors listed above.

SRI also included an action plan as part of the final report. This plan concerned two major and complementary areas: economic development and quality of life, with specific recommendations concerning:

• Economic growth and diversification
• Education and training
• Physical infrastructure
• Amenities and quality of life.

In addition, recommended roles for each of the major leadership constituencies in Austin—business leadership, local government, educational institutions, and community groups—were also indicated.

One of SRI's most important insights was that, because of the type of economy Austin was building, an inherent linkage existed between its continued economic progress and its quality of life. First-rate education and training, improved social, cultural, and recreational amenities, and a up-to-date physical infrastructure would be critical to attracting the kind of industry and people that would help avoid a "two-tiered" economy of well-paid "knowledge workers" and the rest of the workforce. Emphasis remained, however, on continuing the collaborative actions of the community's major leadership constituents and the state. Let's see what unfolded.

Through the collaborative efforts of all players, SEMATECH settled in Austin in 1988. Created from a federal government/U.S. industry partnership to battle the Japanese dominance of the semiconductor industry, SEMATECH was, like MCC, another one-of-a-kind collaboration and highly sought after. Its choice of Austin over several competing cities was another plum for the community, and allowed the city to profit from exposure to the many companies that made up both the SEMATECH and MCC consortia.

Also by the late 1980s, a critical mass of commercial R&D organizations was at work in Austin. In addition to the University, SEMATECH, and MCC, applied research was going on at Motorola, IBM, 3M, Radian, and other firms.

As an aid to entrepreneurship, Austin Ventures was formed in 1983, and the University formed the Austin Technology Incubator (ATI) in 1988, to which the Chamber of Commerce donated $25,000 a year. Michael Dell started his computer company in 1982 while a freshman at the University, and it has grown into a $35 billion corporation. In 1988, *Inc.* magazine named Austin the number one entrepreneurial city in the United States, based on the number of new companies being created. By 1996, the number of technology-based companies in the Austin area exceeded 900, and by 1999 the Austin area was second only to San Jose in the level of venture capital funding.[QQ]

Behind all the high-technology growth lie the SRI recommendations for a program of metropolitan consensus-building. Evidence of the importance of that philosophy is cited in a paper written at the University of Texas:

"…several studies of the Austin area have confirmed the importance of public/private networking to the region and its specific incarnation of the new economy.

An important study of this time emerged in 1985. Conducted by Stanford Research Institute International (SRI) [sic], the report provided a road map for the Greater Austin Chamber of Commerce. The report recommended that Austin create new networking organizations to 'bring about community consensus on key issues.'… Building on the momentum of the SRI report of 1985, the Austin Chamber commissioned a similar goal-setting study entitled *Next Century Economy* in 1998."[RR]

Indeed, SRI came upon an environment that had both a growing technology sector as well as an emerging process of collaboration between the government, the university, and private enterprise. SRI recognized the value of what had begun and helped formalize the collaborating, consensus-building process that it found. The Austin leaders did this so well that

Austin became perhaps the fastest growing high-technology center in the U.S. But SRI also prominently positioned the area's concern for quality of life, including not only cultural and social needs but a desire for growth without the burden of the high cost of living so evident in Silicon Valley.[37] In the years since SRI's 1985 study, "quality of life" indicators have become a significant measure used by communities across the country to attract technology-intensive industry.

New Seeds for Nebraska and Iowa

A second SRI economic development study—this time at the state level—was for Nebraska. In contrast to the existing, focused technology momentum of Austin, the population of this agricultural state had a much wider span of interests, and the need for economic restructuring was also much greater. In spite of the dominance of agriculture, the consensus was to find ways to insulate Nebraska's economy from the diminishing demand for agricultural products and declining government subsidies. Not only was the State's economy tied too tightly to basic agricultural commodities, the State's population growth rate was declining as its young people left for more promising opportunities in other states.[38] Thus, SRI faced a conceptually more difficult problem, when it was retained in 1987 by a group of prominent business leaders from across the state with money provided by Omaha's Peter Kiewit Foundation.[39]

Given the state's population diversity and distributed rural component, SRI's first task was to gain a sense of what was important across the state. It was easy to see that as farming became more efficient, the number of farmers needed would decline, as would the economies of the small farm-supported towns that dotted the countryside. And that small-town economy was important, for at the time Nebraska had about 600 cities of less than 5,000 people each. The only population or economic growth was occurring in the two major cities, Omaha and Lincoln, but much of that growth was in

services, a narrowly based economic sector insofar as overall state growth was concerned. By conducting more than 100 interviews across Nebraska, SRI compiled an interim report that assessed the situation, conveyed the spectrum of opinion, drew preliminary conclusions, and posed a range of economic development strategies.

Even in this interim point of the project, however, SRI was forced to arrive at a rather stark conclusion:

"Nebraska can elect to work hard but defensively at maintaining the narrow focus of its economy, slowly diversifying but remaining largely at the mercy of outside forces. Or it can choose to build a broader, more diversified economy for itself…. SRI believes that Nebraska has only one feasible choice: make the most out of agriculture but also develop its services and manufacturing sectors in a concerted way."[SS]

This broadly based information gathering process was a necessary preamble to focus the state's business, government, and community leaders' attention on the same information. The next step, then, was to share this conclusion with the state's people to obtain their opinions about what directions were most promising and acceptable.

To get the word out, more than a half million copies of the summary report were distributed as a Sunday newspaper supplement in every paper across the state in the spring of 1989.[TT] This information then became the basis for countless town meetings and community discussions. SRI team members participated in a large share of these meetings in discussions about the generalized costs and benefits associated with new accessible technology, the statewide infrastructure required, greater entrepreneurship and innovation, and the increased need for skilled and adaptable people.

With SRI's report, the forceful leadership of the governor, and the general consensus developed through the town hall meetings, leaders began to implement an array of public policy reforms at the state and local levels designed to begin Nebraska's economic shift from commodity agriculture to a more diversified economy. Examples included new institutional economic development mechanisms, a Food Processing Institute at the

---

[37] Austin's cost of living is considerably cheaper than that of other major American cities—about even with second-tier cities such as Portland, Salt Lake City, and Denver. (*Cost of Living Index – comparison of major U.S. cities*, taken from www.ACCRA.org, June 2001.)

[38] The State's growth rate in the 1980s was 40% lower than it had been in the 1960s.

[39] The Nebraska Press Association was the administrative "home" for the project.

University of Nebraska, Lincoln, and an insurance industry technology center in Omaha. Leaders of "second-tier" centers in central and western Nebraska began focusing economic development efforts not on attracting new retailers but on building up the supply base for an emerging manufacturing sector.

While Nebraska remains one of the country's leading agricultural centers, manufacturing and information-intensive services (e.g., telecommunications, insurance) have grown to give the state's economy better balance than was the case before SRI's suggested strategies for economic diversification.

In the same vein, but considerably later, SRI addressed the state of the State of Iowa. In 1999, SRI conducted a similar economic analysis and made suggestions about what might constitute a more favorable economic future of Iowa. Like Nebraska, the average age of agricultural workers in the State was increasing as younger people left for more lucrative jobs elsewhere. The study looked at existing enterprises and the talent pool coming from the universities. SRI concluded that Iowa offered opportunities for attracting companies or home-basing of new ones in three areas: life sciences, advanced manufacturing, and information technology. Like the Nebraska work, the study motivated interest; however, in this case, the depressed fiscal situation left even those who wished to make such investments wondering if they could be afforded. In January 2003, Iowa's governor proposed to the legislature the creation of a $500 million state development fund.[UU] Biopharmaceutical companies are among those the state is trying to woo, but it's too early to know what is likely to transpire.

Endnotes

[A] The Ford Foundation, *Development of Small Scale Industries of India—Prospects, Problems, and Policies*, Report of the International Perspective Planning Team to the Indian Minister of Industry, July 1963.

[B] As a case in point, see www.thanjavurcity.com/sisi.htm for a government small business organization, but also an associated academy for software and information technology development.

[C] S. Nanjundan, H.E. Robison, and Eugene Staley, *Economic Research for Small Industry Development*. Asia Publishing House, Bombay, 1962. (Also a part of a large set of SRI reports on small industry.) Two other related books resulting from this work are: Eugene Staley and Richard Morse, *Modern Small Industry for Developing Countries*, McGraw-Hill, New York, 1965; and Robert W. Davenport, *Financing the Small Manufacturer in Developing Countries*, McGraw-Hill, New York, 1967.

[D] "The Story of SRI—20 Years," *SRI Journal*, Feature Issue 4, December 1966, p. 21.

[E] The Ford Foundation, "Development of Small Scale Industries of India—Prospects, Problems, and Policies," Report of the International Perspective Planning Team to the Indian Minister of Industry, July 1963.

[F] A good summary of SRI's contributions in India is put forward in the *SRI Journal*, Vol. 4, Second Quarter, 39-76, 1960; and *SRI International Journal*, No. 47, 1981.

[G] Some of this account of the SRI planning and advisory work for Saudi Arabia was taken from a 1986 internal International Project History by Gordon Parker.

[H] Peter Duncan, personal communication, October 29, 2002.

[I] Gordon Parker, op. cit.

[J] *A Report on Projections for the Manufacturing Sector for the First Five Year Plan*, SRI Project 8464, January 26, 1970-July 31, 1971.

[K] Data taken from www.saudiembassy.net.

[L] Willard D. Weise, *Short-Term Assignment for Road Planning*, Project 8464 for the Central Planning Office, March 26, 1970.

[M] James A. Harsch, *Management Assistance for Reorganization of the Ministry of Planning of the Kingdom of Saudi Arabia*, SRI Project 4600-20, Central Planning Office, April 28, 1976.

[N] *SRI Research for Industry*, 11(6), November-December 1959.

[O] George Hagn, one of the participants, personal communication, December 11, 2002.

[P] Robert F. Daly, Lloyd I. Krause, Dieter Lohr, and Lawrence R. Rojahn, *Future Directions for*

Tele-Information in Iran, SRI Final Report, Project 4410, Iran–Minister of State, August 1975.

[Q] Weldon B. Gibson, "The Story of SRI," *SRI Journal*, Feature Issue No. 4, 22, December 1966.

[R] *Executive Summary , Building Prosperity: Five-Part Economic Strategy for Hong Kong's Future*, SRI Project 6222, September 1989.

[S] William F. Miller, personal communication, May 10, 2004.

[T] *Business Week*, December 9, 2002, pp. 50-58.

[U] *SRI Journal*, No. 7, pp. 8-11, November 1965.

[V] Philip Daniel, *Africanization, Nationalization and Inequality: Mining Labor and the Copperbelt in Zambian Development*, Cambridge University Press, London, 1979. Quoted at www.american.edu/projects/mandala/TED/zamicopp.htm.

[W] *Wall Street Journal*, July 13, 1982 and interviews with Tom Boyce, April 25, 2001 and Bill Schumacher on May 4, 2001. Both these gentlemen were project leaders in the two large SRI projects in Zambia.

[X] Ravi Gulhati, *Impasse in Zambia—The Economics and Politics of Reform, Economic Development Institute of the World Bank*, Report No. 8078, July 1989.

[Y] Gulhati, op. cit.

[Z] Gulhati, op. cit.

[AA] The early SRI Zambian project numbers for assessment and revamping were 5500, 6066, 6611, 6900, 7800, and 8779. The training projects were 4047, 5900, and 7357. The later privatization projects in the early 1990s were 1376, 2317, 4300, 4308, and 9701.

[BB] Gulhati, op. cit.

[CC] Roy Price, personal communication, May 9, 2002. Price contributed to some of ZCCM's materials management reforms.

[DD] *African Business*, December 1997.

[EE] CIA, *World Fact Book 2002* (www.cia.gov./cia/publications/factbook/geos/za.html)

[FF] See Chapter 14 on business consulting and development.

[GG] Peter Boone and John Mathieson, *Intellectual Property Rights: Assessment of Current Policies, Practices, and Options for AID Initiatives*, Final Report on Project P0 8331, USAID Contract PDC-0091-C-00 9092-00, December 1990. Report deals with the general question of intellectual property protection in developing countries.

[HH] Estefania S. Ermita, "Adjudication still Problematic," *Manila Bulletin*, Monday, February 28, 1994. The SRI study was led by international economists Peter Boone and Ophelia Yeung, with the participation of Philippine consultants Rico Domingo and Carlo Carag.

[II] Catherine P Ailes, H. Roberts Coward, Robert C. Dauffenbach, and Joel L. Barries, *Forecasting Malaysia's Science and Technology Human Resources and Research and Development Investment Needs Leading to the Year 2020*, Final Report, Project P1819, February 1997.

[JJ] This section, compiled with the assistance of Charles Mason (January 2001), Robert Perrin (March 2001), and Dan Allan (March 2001), is a corrected version from the first printing, thanks to the efforts of Robert Perrin (June 2006).

[KK] *Businessweek,* January 25, 1999.

[LL] Calson Analytics note on telecomm privatization: www.calson.com.au/privatisationnote1.htm, 7 July 2006.

[MM] Endnote LL, op. cit.

[NN] SRI International, *Creating an Opportunity EconomyEnhancing Quality of Life in a Changing Community*, SRI Final Report for the Austin Chamber of Commerce, April 1985.

[OO] The Greater Austin Chamber of Commerce, *Austin's Evolution—University Town to High Tech Center*, May 2001.

[PP] Carole Keeton Ryland (Texas Comptroller of Public Accounts), "Austin-San Marcos Metropolitan Area Profile," in *The Texas Economy* and at www.window.state.tx.us/ecodata/regional/capital/capasmsa.html, May 2001.

[QQ] Engelking, (Footnote 36) op. cit.

[RR] Samuel Paul Jacobs, *Networks of Public/Private Cooperation for Economic Development: The Case of Austin, Texas 1983-1999*, TC 660H,

Plan II Honors Program, University of Texas, May 3, 2000. (The next assessment for Austin was performed by ICF Consulting, which is made up of former SRI employees. In a project also led by Ted Lyman, the award was an indication of Austin's confidence in SRI's earlier work.)

[SS] SRI International, *New Seeds for Nebraska–Strategies for Building the Next Economy*, SRI Summary Report, 1987.

[TT] *New Seeds for* Nebraska, op. cit.

[UU] "A new Iowa vision," *Omaha World-Herald*, January 31, 2003. The article cites the SRI impetus.

fulfillment. These adventures in the ongoing process of innovation are enormously strengthened by the objectivity and integrity inherent in the Institute's research ethics.

Most of those in the trenches at SRI will tell you that working here is not easy. Exhilarating perhaps, but not easy. Researchers at SRI epitomize self-determination as they discover or help discover their own futures. Whether acting alone or as part of a project team, they train themselves to be responsible for both the genesis and completion of sponsored work, and above all to satisfy their clients and, in the process, themselves as well. Were it for commercial purposes alone, such research would, quite simply, be called entrepreneurial. Though it is difficult for me to know just how typical my long SRI experience has been, I think I know of SRI at its best. For me, it was indeed an exhilarating life shared with truly exciting and splendid people.

SRI's Visibility Problem

For several reasons SRI has had a bit of a visibility problem over the years. First, and most importantly, contract research by its very nature lets those you are working for determine whether results are disseminated publicly and, if so, the extent of that dissemination. Sponsors may give full and open credit to SRI for the work done, including the opportunity to publish, they may simply keep the results secret, or they may attribute whatever advancement to themselves…all of which may be legitimate. Second, perhaps with the exception of professional journals, the Institute often chooses not to publicize even where it was free to do so. Clearly, an increased attention to the commercialization of its intellectual properties feeds the tendency to not publish at all. Finally, there is the lack of distinction between SRI and its parent University that sometime gets blurred. As a result, few—even within SRI—were or are fully aware of the scope of its achievements. Some examples of SRI's visibility problem follow.

Automated Banking

The December 1999 issue of the *Proceedings of the IEEE*, the main publication of the world's largest professional electronics group, takes a retrospective look at a "classic" 1972 paper, the "Social Role of Computer Communications" by IEEE Fellow, R. M. Fano:[A]

> A major force that has led to the use of computers in the operation of society is the growing volume of transactions of various types that must be handled. For instance, the Bank of America was led, in the middle of the 1950's, to pioneer in the use of computers by the realization that manual handling of checks would have required, in the foreseeable future, the entire adult population… (p. 2130)

On the televised ACM Computer Bowl in 1994, the Toss Up Question 7 was:

> We are all familiar with the term ATM standing for Automatic Teller Machine.

But way back in the 1950s, the Bank of America installed one of the first computerized banking systems, built by GE. It was called ERMA. What did the letters ERMA stand for?

The answer, which was correct, was: Electronic Recording Machine, Accounting.

Both instances illustrate SRI's long-standing visibility problem. For it was SRI that formulated all the design concepts for ERMA, gave it its name, and first built and demonstrated the system. For the banking industry, the results of SRI's work were momentous: not only did ERMA become one of the world's first large dedicated computers, but it changed forever, procedurally as well as mechanically, fundamental banking processes. SRI's role in the work was not revealed, primarily because the computer-based process was so groundbreaking that the Bank of America wanted it to be kept private. SRI's dedicated work over 4 years to demonstrate the concept before handing over its manufacture to GE was acknowledged only fleetingly. Were it not for a Harvard business case study and a resulting article in the *IEEE Annals of Computing* in 1993, SRI's role might have been ignored forever. [B] Even this limited exposure didn't alter the above lack of awareness.

Personal Computing

Of the hundreds of accounts of the beginning of personal computing, most place its origins at Xerox's Palo Alto Research Center, at Apple Computer, or at one of several small companies that were the first to try to develop hardware profitably. However, SRI defined and demonstrated many of the original concepts defining and enabling personal computing in the mid- to late 1960s, before either Apple or the Xerox Center existed. Only within recent years have its foremost visionaries, Doug Engelbart and a few members in his SRI laboratory, begun to receive recognition. Even then the confusion with Stanford University often arises just as it normally does with the first computer network transmission in 1969 between UCLA and SRI, which is often attributed to the university.

Drug Discovery

The Web page of the Walter Reed Army Institute of Research (WRAIR) makes the following statement about the malarial drug halofantrine:

> "discovered by WRAIR, halofantrine underwent preclinical and clinical development in our department.... Halofantrine was approved in 1996, and since then, the drug has been used by millions of people for the treatment of falciparum malaria."[C]

While it may be within a sponsor's prerogative to make such claims, halofantrine was discovered and developed in SRI's Life Sciences Division between 1965 and 1975 in work for WRAIR funded through the U.S. Army Medical Research and Development Command.[D] The Army needed a new drug for use in Southeast Asia because of developing resistance by the falciparum form of malaria to the existing drug, chloroquine. SRI also invented a modified form of halofantrine, called desbutylhalofantrine, which was SRI's original first choice for WRAIR. That drug has fewer side effects, but is still in clinical trials. The Army claims to have discovered that drug as well.

Economic Development

India's National Council of Applied Economic Research (NCAER) is that country's most authoritative source of economic and social information. Working in partnership with both the Indian government and its private sector, and in cooperation with national and international institutions, it has been compiling the information needed to understand India's economy for 35 years. An account of its genesis on its Web page mentions that this nongovernment research center was "founded in 1956 by the Ministries of Industry and Finance, Government of India in cooperation with the Ford Foundation." Had the whole story been told it would have indicated that NCAER was the idea of SRI's Dr. Eugene Staley who went to India under Ford Foundation sponsorship to help revitalize the Indian economy. Finding that the country had no information to use in assessing its economic condition or to gauge progress, he proposed the SRI-like research center, calling it NCAER. Similarly, SRI designed the National Institute of Small Industry Extension Training to train small business owners to help build India's middle class. Both institutions are vital and influential today, but SRI's essential role in development has disappeared from the official history.

The Ubiquitous Digital Fax Machine

While electronic mail was struggling to emerge into the mainstream information flows of the 1980s, many were surprised by the rapid growth in sales of the facsimile machine. Its digital version was fast, cheap, and increasingly omnipresent. One company that helped lead that surge was the Japanese office equipment and imaging company Ricoh. With some justification, it assigns the first digital fax transmission to its RIFAX 600S machine in 1973, and claims to have invented the unit.[E] But, once again, the first machine was built at SRI under a 1970 contract with Savin and CBS; Ricoh subsequently acquired the rights to the machine. SRI had worked with other providers of optical scanners, compression algorithms, and modems to design and build that first digital facsimile machine.

Endnotes

[A] The retrospective view appeared in the *Proceedings of the IEEE*, 87(12), 2130-2135, December 1999, and the original paper was in the same journal, 60(11), 1249-1243, November 1972. Neither mentions SRI.

[B] A. Fisher and J.L. McKenney, "The Development of the ERMA Banking System: Lessons from History," *IEEE Annals of Computing*, 15(1), 1993.

[C] Retrieved February 16, 2000, from http://wrair-www.army.mil/depts/ pharmacology/Drugs.htm

[D] W. T. Colwell et al., *Journal of Medical Chemistry*, Vol. 15, 1972, p. 77.

[E] From an interview of Jim Ivy, President of Ricoh (USA) Products Group, by the *Digital Times,* September 5, 2000. "Ricoh...created the first digital fax machine, which was a Ricoh invention."

A Brief History of SRI

Though much of this history is based on material referenced in the ongoing endnotes and footnotes, some, beginning with SRI's separation from Stanford University, comes from the author's own research and impressions. It does not represent an official position by either SRI or the University.

Stanford Creates a Research Institute

Stanford Research Institute, or SRI, was founded as a subsidiary of Stanford University to pursue goals the University had in common with industry in the western United States. SRI's Articles of Incorporation, or its Charter, which were drafted in autumn 1946, indicated that the Institute's mission fell within the broad purposes of the University. Two of the provisions in the University's Founding Grant were relevant to the new Institute:

to assist, by experimentation and research, in the advancement of useful knowledge and in the dissemination and practical application of same

and

the public at large, not alone the comparatively few students who can attend the University, are the chief and ultimate beneficiaries of Stanford University.

Thus, in the abstract, the Institute was to operate very much in accord with Stanford's original aims. The University's direct influence was stipulated in SRI's Charter; namely, that the University Trustees would be the general members of the SRI corporation and elect the Institute's directors; that SRI would promote the educational aims of Stanford; and that, should the Institute ever be dissolved, SRI's net assets would be transferred to the University.

The beginning of SRI was the consequence of the creative dynamics of perhaps a dozen people. However, arriving at an alignment of purpose was anything but simple. At least three, and perhaps four, independent groups or

players played a part in SRI's genesis. These separate entities first looked not to Stanford's Charter but at the need for a research enterprise in the Far Western United States, one that would operate under the aegis of a university. Most of this unfolding is well documented in the first of two volumes on the early days of SRI by Weldon B. Gibson, who was known locally as well as internationally as Hoot.[A]

The earliest of these groups consisted of two Stanford chemistry professors with administrative roles, Robert Swain and Philip Leighton, and a prominent alumnus, Dudley Swim. Swain, who would serve briefly as acting president of Stanford during the tenure of Ray Lyman Wilbur, began discussions about a University research institute as early as the 1920s. The three issued a concrete proposition in late 1942, but it was not until after World War II that interest in the idea intensified. In the late summer of 1945, after informal discussions with Stanford President Donald B. Tresidder, they formally submitted to him their concept for an institute at Stanford.[1] Tresidder reacted with interest, and within 2 weeks he had dispatched Leighton and Swim on a tour of Eastern U.S. research institutes. Around that time two separate groups of industrialists were working on a similar idea.

One of those initiatives was by a group of three Southern California industrialists, who in July-August 1945 conceived of a Western applied research organization they called the "Pacific Research Foundation." The group consisted of Maurice Nelles, Morlan A. Visel, and Ernest L. Black, all executives of Lockheed in Burbank, California. Having heard of a similar interest in the Bay Area, Black presented

---

[1] Interestingly, Swim and the others thought the Institute ought to have two major thrusts: "consulting and research and patent development for its own account." The former, at least in the form of management consulting, was discouraged by the University in the early days of SRI, and royalty or patent-based income, with a very few exceptions, did not become a principal focus for SRI until the early 1990s. In a chronology of Stanford/SRI history compiled in January 1995 by lawyer Kirke Hasson (Pillsbury, Madison, and Sutro), the Swain committee also recommended that half of SRI's "annual earnings" go to Stanford.

their proposition to the third—and the most effective group—which was led by San Francisco industrialist Atholl McBean. In spite of two, perhaps more, developed concepts for a research institute, it was McBean who gained the ear of Stanford's Vice President for Development, Alvin Eurich and, in turn, that of Tresidder. Before the end of 1945, McBean, with encouragement and financial support from other Northern California executives, won the support of Tresidder and Eurich that eventually brought SRI into existence.

Another person whose ideas had an important impact on the type of organization SRI became was Henry T. Heald, president of the Illinois Institute of Technology and later president of the Ford Foundation. The San Francisco industrial group had asked Heald to visit a variety of university and industry research facilities on the West Coast and to make recommendations about a possible new research institute in the West. Following an 8-day tour of the region, he met with the group in San Francisco on January 24, 1946, and they concluded that an industrial research institute on the West Coast was needed.

In a short, 900-word report, Heald fairly well described what SRI would come to be: He indicated the need for an institute that would engage in high-quality industrial research for individual companies, associations of companies, and government agencies at all levels. He stated that the institute must have a first-class staff and adequate space and facilities. The final recommendations were clear and to the point:

> "it is strongly recommended that a research foundation.... be developed on the Pacific Coast...located at and operated in close affiliation with Stanford University."

> "...industrialists interested in the establishment of a research organization [should] ask Stanford University to organize it, provide the University moral support...and...an initial gift of $500,000."

> "...the Foundation [should] be organized as a separate corporation with trustees including several members of the Stanford Board.... The President of Stanford, or some other chief administrative officer, should be president of the Foundation."

Heald also advised the business leaders to move quickly to begin the organization, leaving its future nature to be determined by subsequent events.[B]

Within a month of Heald's report the Stanford trustees agreed in principle to create Stanford Research Institute. Tresidder then asked the University's counsel Morris M. Doyle to draft a charter and the search began for an Institute Director. The degree to which the efforts of the other, earlier parties influenced the ultimate definition of SRI is hard to gauge, but the propositions clearly converged in the Office of the President where the final structure of SRI was defined. The faculty committee's recommendations that the Institute be nonprofit, that a contractual arrangement allow the University to control the Institute, and that it have a range of activities from basic to applied industrial research that would help strengthen University-industry relationships were enacted. Thus, out of this somewhat chaotic genesis, SRI emerged as a separate organization, a nonprofit subsidiary of Stanford University.

Stanford's Dean of Engineering, Fred Terman, was also sympathetic to an applied research organization tied closely to science and technology. His notion, however, centered more on providing a place where faculty and students could pursue their own interests as opposed to those of Western industry. Terman was seeking to bring more science into the engineering part of Stanford and hoped that a new institute could support that goal. Though Tresidder did not implement Terman's desire for such close University ties, Terman did help attract some of the early Institute's talent and urged them to enter the emerging field of electronics.[2]

Papers for the incorporation of SRI were filed with the State of California in November 1946 and the University trustees accepted the charter the following month. Stanford thus formed SRI and the president of the University became the chairman of SRI's Board of

---

[2] Stewart Gillmor, Terman's biographer, indicates that Terman was also interested in a research institute that would work closely as an applied technology arm of his part of the University. According to a conversation with Gillmor in June 2000, Terman urged Jesse Hobson and Ralph Krause, both early and pivotal SRI leaders, to come to SRI. Terman also permitted some sharing of Engineering faculty ideas with SRI and also made some joint faculty/SRI appointments. Gillmor's book, *Fred Terman at Stanford* was published by Stanford University Press in October 2004.

Directors, first Donald B. Tresidder, then Acting President Alvin C. Eurich, followed by J. E. Wallace Sterling. Eurich, who was also the University's director of development, became vice chairman of SRI's Board, indicating that, at least at that moment, the University viewed SRI as integrally tied to its own growth.[3]

The new SRI Board consisted of 32 prestigious Western executives.[4] In less than 2 years, SRI also formed a council of SRI Associates, additional business leaders with some interest in SRI, to help underwrite the Institute and build connections between it and the industrial community. A 1950 report to the Board indicated that of its industrial (commercial) work, 68% came from California, 13% from other western states, and the remainder from other parts of the country. Furthermore, some 75% was industrial and 25% governmental.[C] Thus, the early linkages forged were indeed with industry. But these, as it turned out, were never enough to sustain SRI's growth, and government work was needed from the outset.

In spite of the University's preference for industrial work, SRI's dependence on government sponsorship began essentially at once. A passage from the Institute's first annual report, covering October of 1946 to the end of 1947, reads:

> "The acceptance of research, with a minimum of planned and directed sales effort, has resulted in unbalance between governmental and industrial research; 69 per cent of the work during 1946 and 1947 was for governmental agencies and only 31 per cent for

industrial sponsors. This unbalance arose because of the relative ease with which governmental research could be obtained.

No more governmental research will, in general, be accepted unless the contracts provide for enough overhead to cover expenses, and then only when surplus space can be used and when industrial research is expected to stem from the governmental research. A governmental project may occasionally enable us to add to our staff people who are needed for other reasons, or may help pay for research that is planned for other purposes."[D]

Thus, the predilections were clear, but industry contracts, Western or otherwise, proved unable to meet the financial demands of the growing Institute. The same report noted that four of the most important Western industries—nonferrous metals, paper, food, and forest products—spent, respectively, 62¢, 39¢, 19¢, and 7¢ of every $100 of value-added from manufacturing on research. These staid industries obviously wouldn't offer much potential support, no matter how competent SRI became in those areas. Given that many companies also had their own small research groups and that information technology was yet to emerge, it is not surprising that the Institute had to seek government funding. SRI's growth needs came from attracting good people, and doing that meant acquiring up-to-date capital facilities and the buildings to house them. New, essentially free quarters were found in Menlo Park and were adequate, but good capital equipment would require appreciable discretionary income.

During these early years the University continued to formulate and enforce policies that influenced the kind of work that SRI conducted and, at least indirectly, the kind of people it hired. In early 1947, SRI's first director, William Talbot, hired Maurice Garbell as the Director of Aerophysics Research. Part of Talbot's instructions were that "no research activities should be undertaken between the Institute and any agency which will conflict with the interests and well being of the various university departments and that every effort will be made to cooperate with these departments." Talbot wanted closer and collaborative ties with University faculty and access to graduate students, but the University

---

[3] From SRI's second director, Jesse E. Hobson, comes this reflection: "You may remember that Dr. Tresidder (Stanford President) died suddenly in early 1948 after I agreed to go to Stanford but before I arrived. As I think now about the next two or three years it becomes more and more apparent that one man really made possible the development of Stanford Research Institute and that was Dr. Alvin C. Eurich, Acting President of Stanford University. He gave me and the Institute outstanding support and confidence in the face of rather strong skepticism, doubt and—in some cases—out right antagonism. We would never have survived through the fall of 1948 without his very strong support with the Board of Trustees of Stanford Research Institute. There were two months that Fall when I did not know until the last day of the month whether or not we could meet our payroll and I knew there were those who wanted to close the Institute, take the loss of four or five hundred thousand dollars and forget the whole affair." (Charles J. Maisel and Treva W. Jones, *A History of Stanford Research Institute*, SRI internal publication, October 1962.)

[4] Appendix C lists the 1949 SRI Board.

proved unwilling.[5] In fact, within 6 months he and Garbell had violated Talbot's own stipulation by submitting a proposal to the Office of Naval Research (ONR).[E] Furthermore, in December of that same year SRI's Carsten Steffens told Tresidder that Talbot had said SRI would become a completely separate organization.[F] This and other such developments probably did not sit well with Stanford's president, for by early 1948 Talbot was gone, replaced by Jesse Hobson of the Armour Research Foundation in Chicago.[6]

Terman would assist in bringing Hobson, a fellow electrical engineer from Purdue, to SRI. Within a month, Hobson was followed by another Terman colleague who would also become very important to SRI: Tom Poulter, after whom SRI's Poulter Laboratory is named. Terman's links with the wartime Radio Research Laboratory (RRL), which he had led at Harvard, and with ONR would also bring strong talent to SRI. First, Ralph Krause and Tom Morrin, both from ONR, came as Director of Research and Director of Engineering, respectively. Shortly thereafter, a dozen or so former RRL engineers also came west to help create SRI's Engineering Division.[7] Like Terman, Hobson himself initially advocated a close interaction with the departments of the University. While some of that early interaction occurred in both the sciences and engineering, it neither amounted to much nor did it grow to a point of advocacy on either side.

Given this situation, operational autonomy from the University was inevitable. The University's oversight began to diminish as it and the Board gained confidence in Hobson. As the Institute gradually achieved profitability, it embarked on a growth path that soon gave the University pause in considering what it had created. Stanford conducted an organizational and financial audit in 1950 to gain a snapshot of SRI, including its reputation and its needs. That audit, initiated by the SRI Board, revealed that the Institute was indeed growing rapidly. It had achieved research revenue of nearly $2 million in 3 years, whereas comparable research organizations had taken from 2 to 10 times that long to do so. The audit also praised the quality of the SRI staff and its national prominence in three of its five major areas of work. The report also revealed the early existence of what would become a chronic problem at SRI, the quest for adequate capital equipment. The outlay in 1950 was about one-third the $5,000 per researcher that was then considered a minimum.[G]

Staffed with competent and creative research talent, SRI soon grew to be a vibrant and self-realizing organization. The Western industry-laden SRI Board came mainly to appoint the SRI president. With but few exceptions their benign but distant interests brought little work to the Institute. SRI's research practices became, and remained, the responsibility of its senior staff and first-and second-level managers.

In retrospect, these were heady days. SRI's uniqueness, at least in a Western setting, brought many important people to its doors and to the convocations it would hold. People like David Sarnoff [8] and Vannevar Bush would stop by or lend association. These episodes are well chronicled in Gibson's two books.[H]

SRI developed a culture defined by competent work and an uncommon freedom to pursue a broad diversity of problems important to both industry and government. For 20 years it grew in staff and revenues, but over much of its life it has had trouble creating enough discretionary money. SRI was, of course, an institute and not a company. Semantically, an institute normally exists in support of a cause

---

[5] Ernest Barbour O'Byrne's Ph.D. thesis, *The Research Institutes of Stanford University* (June 1951), quoted an interview with Talbot revealing that the reason was essentially a salary imbalance. Salaries were higher at SRI, which caused consternation among faculty members and their students. Many years later, I also became aware of Stanford faculty members' concerns about losing their good graduate students to SRI before they finished their Ph.D.s. Over the years students have been able to continue their thesis work once becoming SRI employees, as I did, but that was not a common practice.

[6] In the early days, SRI tried to steer a path between universities, with their basic research bent, and consulting or the very focused laboratories of commercial companies. In the *San Francisco Chronicle* of December 15, 1952, SRI director Dr. Jesse Hobson reiterated that position. He went on to say that a recent increase in projects stemming from the Korean War was "more government work than we'd like to do."

[7] Gillmor, op. cit., and the RRL *Phone Directory* of 1945. Interestingly, on SRI's first project for ONR, exploration of the natural rubber-producing potential of the guayule plant, ONR's contracting officer was Charles Hilly, who for years would head SRI's contracts group, and Wilson Harwood, who held budget approval authority at the Naval Research Laboratory, and who later joined SRI's Business Group, and opened SRI's work in Saudi Arabia (see Chapter 14).

[8] David Sarnoff, whose fabled RCA research laboratory would become part of SRI in 1987, in the feature address at an SRI Associates Program on November 14, 1951, extolled SRI as "an outstanding example of the natural partnership between research and industry."

whereas companies exist to earn a profit. In any case, SRI was, by both design and practice, a nonprofit organization.

Initially, SRI was housed on the Stanford campus. But within 8 months of its founding SRI moved into a part of the surplus Dibble Army Hospital in nearby Menlo Park. That facility had been built to handle some of the increased patient load on the Letterman military hospital in San Francisco that was anticipated as a result of the expected invasion of Japan. Opened in 1943, the hospital was used for a few years mainly as a place for dentistry, for difficult reconstructive surgeries, and for rehabilitating soldiers who had eye damage or had been blinded. More than 16,000 patients were treated there. But, with the war over, it was closed in early 1946 and declared surplus.[1] Today, more than a half-century later, many of its original, "temporary" buildings are still in use at SRI and by the City of Menlo Park. Once off campus and out of sight, so to speak, the Institute got its legs and grew, and the University exercised less and less influence over its offspring.

Thus, time and circumstances changed the relationship between SRI and Stanford. The distancing had grown so great that by the late 1950s the two had few joint facilities, projects, or clients. A relatively few staff members had joint appointments at the two institutions, but the University trustees were still SRI's ultimate governing body.

In the mid-1960s with the coming of the Viet Nam War, student unrest grew across the nation. That unrest was manifested at Stanford by demonstrations against the classified work that went on in some of the University's engineering laboratories and at SRI. Student demonstrations were held at SRI's Hanover Street location in Palo Alto adjacent to the University and at SRI's main offices in Menlo Park. Because the demonstrations precipitated a fundamental change in SRI's status, a bit more detail is warranted.

The Separation from Stanford

It is safe to say that the tenor of student unrest surrounding the Vietnam War derived from dissatisfaction with the policies and actions of both the U.S. government and the country's largest corporations. Some student factions at Stanford harbored the same opinions and

targeted Department of Defense (DoD) work on campus, the industrial alignments of the University's trustees, and SRI for demonstrations. Student concerns began to be voiced as early as 1965 when it became known on campus that SRI had two government contracts concerning chemical warfare. Those concerns intensified in 1967 when they learned that SRI had also taken on contracts relevant to the war in Southeast Asia. In April of that year some students began picketing in front of SRI's Menlo Park campus, as well as at some of Stanford's engineering laboratories. Their protests soon crystallized into demands to end all war-related or classified work, specifically that involving the war in Southeast Asia. SRI's economic development work for developing countries also came under fire as being conducted only to further the self-interests of large corporate sponsors. Almost all of that work was, in fact, sponsored by foundations and international assistance groups.

The students' lack of specific knowledge about the balance of work under way in the engineering laboratories of both institutions and SRI's economic development work did little to temper their outlook. Any association with the DoD or big business seemed enough to levy harsh, sometimes accurate, but usually unfounded demands concerning both the work being conducted and the relationships that led to it. SRI's chemical warfare work, for instance, had been almost exclusively defensive in nature—seeking ways to cope with such a threat. SRI was also investigating counterinsurgency techniques needed for the Vietnam War. As a practical matter, the details or legitimacy of the work made no difference, and the campus and local press followed the students' activities in copious detail. By the end of 1968, the protesting students, along with not a few faculty members, sought SRI's separation from the University.

By early 1969, the demands of the students had become legitimized in University-sanctioned meetings, and Acting President Robert Glaser formed an ad hoc committee to review the association with SRI and to make recommendations. After 6 months of study, including substantial information that SRI provided the committee, the majority of the committee recommended terminating the association with SRI, asking for SRI to compensate the University for its loss of the

Institute.[9] During the committee's deliberations, however, the students, realizing that a separate SRI could proceed freely, had reversed their earlier position. A new facet of the protest, called the April 3rd Movement, was born. That orientation was also reflected in the committee's minority report, which was written by two faculty members who were sympathetic to the students' demands. Their position asked for closer University ties with SRI; a stipulation against military-related work, including counter-insurgency and other contracts related to the war in Southeast Asia; and the requirement for an SRI oversight committee.

Meanwhile, at SRI discussions were being held about the relationship with the University, research freedom, and self-determination.[10] Surveys reflected that the vast majority of the SRI staff had no stomach for others defining what constituted "moral" work and wanted independence. SRI President Charles Anderson and several of the SRI leaders expressed their clear indignation at the notion of a moral oversight by the University community in any form.[11] From the outset, SRI leadership had taken the position that work for a duly constituted U.S. government was, by definition, in the public interest and a legitimate and worthy endeavor. Many SRI leaders, particularly those on the management consulting side, agreed with the original student demand for separation, if not with their reasoning. Another crucial factor was that government contracting agents so disliked the growing uncertainty that

they held up contracts SRI had already won. Given these conditions at SRI, the urgency the trustees felt about resolving the crisis soon, and the ad hoc committee's recommendations, separation became unavoidable. In effect, the thinness of the institutional relationship between Stanford and its research institute could not survive the clamor of the time as amplified on campus, the streets, and in the press. The trustees issued a statement on May 13, 1969, laying the groundwork for SRI's separation from the University.[12] Importantly, they put no restrictions on the kind of research SRI could undertake. But other terms of the agreement that would seriously affect SRI were still to come.

As with many divorces, freedom had its price for SRI. Most onerous was an agreement to pay the University from 0.5% to 1% of its *gross revenues in perpetuity*.[13] As a nonprofit

---

[9] Apparently, President Glaser conveyed to Hoot Gibson at the time that the relationship between the University and SRI had to change (Weldon Gibson, personal communication, June 1, 2000).

[10] As early as November 1968, Stanford Trustee and SRI Board Chairman Arbuckle appointed a subcommittee to study the SRI-Stanford relationship. Among the eight board members on that committee were Trustees Morris Doyle and Ed Littlefield. On the University side Arbuckle was also chairman of the trustees, and a bit later he set up a trustee subcommittee on the SRI question that consisted of Littlefield, Fred Merrill, Thomas Pike, and its chairman, Morris Doyle! Whether the deliberations of this overlapping assemblage retained much independence is doubtful but at least they should have been efficient. As it turned out, essentially all of these men came to a position of wanting to protect SRI as separation occurred; that is, up until the question of a financial settlement arose.

[11] According to a Stanford University press release dated April 30, 1969, President Anderson, in a presentation to a Trustee committee on SU-SRI relations, eloquently defended a widely held SRI opinion. He attacked the "arrogant suggestion that a small group that does not represent a majority viewpoint should rule on the moral acceptability of research" and he was "indignant, then incredulous" that such a review committee could be taken seriously by University people.

[12] According to Anderson, the trustees' quick action was prompted by contacts from SRI's Board. In an address to SRI associates in December 1969, Anderson also recalled how this decision by the trustees provoked consternation among those students who were seeking to control SRI as part of the Stanford family, and they rioted. SRI suffered some damage, and more than 100 students were arrested.

[13] The formula stipulated that SRI's payment would go from approximately 1% of *gross* to 0.5% after $25 million had been paid to the University. According to Dr. Gibson (personal communication, June 1, 2000) SRI Board member Edgar Kaiser suggested this draconian obligation as an acceptable middle ground that might avoid two potential lawsuits surrounding the high valuation of $21–45 million that the Scott Committee had placed on divestiture. One suit might have come from the University or its faculty if the valuation was lower than the Committee suggested, and one might have come from SRI or its staff who might have found the expected fee so high that it jeopardized SRI's ability to exist. In August 1969, at least one member of the SRI Board, Paul Davies, thought that if Stanford was paid anything, it ought to be small. But in December 1969 a memo from the SRI Board to the trustees was drafted and approved. It suggested granting Stanford $25 million provided SRI's name and charter purposes remain unchanged. That memo was passed unanimously by the SRI Board with members Doyle, Fuller, Pike, and Guggenheim, all trustees, abstaining. In an expression of the closeness of these negotiating parties, the memo was then submitted by President Anderson to Morris Doyle as chairman of the trustee subcommittee on separation! Clearly, the University trustees, as general members of SRI, could effectively control the SRI Board. Thus, one could view this situation as a built-in conflict of interest or an opportunity for the quick resolution of a family dispute. The settlement, while onerous for SRI, took on the aura of the latter. (Curiously, contradicting the above Board Minutes and stated dates of tenure, Trustee Ed Littlefield asserts in a letter to Paul Cook on December 5, 1994 that the two boards had no common members at the time.) A memo from the SRI Board to SRI chemist Felix Smith in January 1970 concerning his complaint about conflicts of interest,

corporation with a large portion of revenues from U.S. government grants and contracts with strongly regulated fees, this seemingly small alimony became a substantial and continuous drain on SRI's discretionary resources. By 1989, SRI had given more than $25 million to the University in accordance with the separation agreement. In spite of provisions in the agreement for no payment when SRI's financial health was at stake, some of these annual payments amounted to more than SRI's net profit for the year.[j, 14] Other stipulations had to do with abandoning the use of the Stanford name after 1974 in the Institute's title and continuing to honor those purposes in the SRI charter relating to the University, including reversion of SRI assets to Stanford if SRI were dissolved. These financial terms meant that the modest loan from Stanford at SRI's creation has returned an enormous value to the University.[15] Thus, through this separation, Stanford Research

Institute became independent on March 31, 1970.

One of the terms of the agreement was that SRI could continue to use the Stanford name for 7 years.[16] During that time, the transition had little effect in SRI's marketplace, but eventually SRI had to establish a new identity with many clients. Of all the stipulations, however, the "alimony" payment to Stanford was the most burdensome. Otherwise, SRI continued its tradition of independent research and development and was no longer subject to University stipulations about the practice of management consulting.

Thus SRI became and remains a nonprofit, independent contract research institute. It has no endowment and therefore exists through the initiative and creativity of its staff. Its contracts are with many levels of government and industry, worldwide. It has had offices at one time or another in about a dozen countries. It is a place of uncommon intellectual freedom and it relishes its objectivity and competence.

The 1970s at SRI

While the separation from Stanford raised some turmoil for a time, it had no measurable impact on the ensuing 1970s. Over that decade, SRI's rate of revenue growth averaged around 10%. Each year a new revenue record would be set, but, as indicated by a relatively stable staff size of around 3,000, much of those gains were inflation-driven. Just as important as this consistency, however, was the realignment of some of the sectors from which the revenue flowed. Under Anderson, two trends were evident: one was a steady increase in the fraction of revenue from the U.S. civil, or non-DoD, sector. The other was an increase in international business. Both were important diversification factors. In 1970, SRI opened its first overseas research division in London and called it SRI-Europe. Over the next 15 years or so SRI would continue to build on its worldwide

states that because trustees didn't participate in the drafting of the settlement proposals, there was no conflict!

One case could have been made for SRI not paying Stanford anything since its original investment had been repaid with interest. Because Stanford had created a *nonprofit* corporation, its value, in the opinion of some, lay in public trust, at least until dissolution. Although Paul Jorgensen, former SRI Senior Vice President, said he raised this issue as a SRI Board member, it was never pursued. Perhaps because SRI's charter stipulates that upon dissolution, the assets of SRI pass to the University (another nonprofit entity), Stanford's counsel at the time, Warren Christopher, believed that the removal of trustees as SRI general members was grounds for substantial payment to the University. Though one option at the time was to dissolve SRI, it had no favor among the trustees.

[14] A February 1979 memo from Stanford's William Massey to SRI's Harvey Dixon indicates that while Stanford was willing to grant SRI a loan, it would not change the agreement. So this requirement continued until 1990 when SRI President Miller negotiated some exceptions to the 1970 payment agreement when SRI's financial stability might be threatened. The agreement was revisited in 1997 with further stipulations. These negotiated changes invoked promissory notes in lieu of payments during some years and outright relief in others. As of this writing in 2004, SRI is again paying the approximately one-half percent obligation defined in the 1970 agreement.

[15] According to the *San Francisco Chronicle* December 15, 1952, the Stanford trustees had advanced SRI $625,000, with six San Francisco banks providing another $600,000. Both were being repaid at the time of the article. A letter between SRI Board members, from Paul Davies to Stephen Bechtel on August 25, 1969, indicated SRI had paid off the Stanford "loan." Moreover, in a presentation to University Trustees on April 30, 1969, SRI President Anderson stated that SRI had not only repaid the $625,000 loan, with interest, but had also *voluntarily* given the University an accumulation in excess of $800,000, some of which came from times when SRI was but marginally profitable.

[16] The original separation agreement stipulated that SRI would refrain from using "Stanford" in its name following the agreement's fifth anniversary, March 31, 1975. The stipulation was amended in January 1975 to add another 2 years. The SRI internal phone book of March 1977 for the first time contains only "SRI" with "SRI International" appearing there the following September. SRI changed its Articles of Incorporation to reflect the name change in April 1980.

reputation in the areas of business consulting and economic development.

Overall, SRI staff continued winning new contracts. In 1972, it submitted more than 2,000 proposals of all kinds. By 1974, SRI had over 2,000 clients in more than 40 countries and, over the course of 1977, saw some 2,200 projects under way. The decade's business vitality continued well into the 1980s. But as exciting as the endeavor was to its research participants, SRI's long-term financial picture continued to be uncertain due to uneven and difficult-to-predict profitability.

The 1980s and a New Emphasis

For most of its existence SRI has struggled to be adequately profitable, and as the 1980s opened this trend continued.[17] Inflation-adjusted revenues were flat, and government-limited fee structure constrained gross income. Within the business of contract research perhaps the largest influence on income is the fraction of the research staff that is billing time to project. Specifically, the financial swing between billing research labor to overhead and charging it to a client project is huge. Though other overhead costs must also be controlled, managing that one parameter is critical if not easy. Though the sheer number of research staff vying for projects at any one time would seem to even out the revenue stream, the vagaries of the varied markets they visit imposed an unpredictability to financial operations including income. This difficulty has haunted most top-level managers at SRI. Was there a way to help reduce the financial impact of that uncertainty?

Arriving in 1979, SRI's new president, William Miller, decided to look into another form of income, one that would be tied to SRI's ongoing creation of intellectual property. Over its history, SRI had done a small amount of licensing but it had mainly used its intellectual property to win new projects. Serious attention to commercialization meant not only altering that earlier tendency but also taking a more aggressive stance toward retaining those properties in the first place, rather than always assuming they belonged to the client.

Miller had been Stanford's provost but perhaps more significant for this discussion, he was a co-founder of the highly regarded Mayfield Fund, one of Silicon Valley's important venture capital firms.[K] In July 1980, about a year after his arrival at SRI, Miller convened a small task force under Don Fiske, vice president of the Management and Economics Group, to look into establishing a for-profit SRI subsidiary to engage in commercialization. Their work culminated in a recommendation to form the wholly owned SRI Development Company (DEVCO), which would serve to separate SRI's contract research from its new ventures into the commercialization of its intellectual properties. Miller's next action led to an important decade-long relationship in how SRI would handle its intellectual properties.

In April 1982, SRI entered into a three-way agreement with DEVCO and a new venture capital firm, CommTech International. CommTech was to be managed by a general partner, but SRI as a limited partner was to receive one-third of CommTech profits. CommTech was also to pay SRI a percentage of the license fees and royalties it received from directly licensed SRI technologies and 50% of the up-front licensing fees of any limited R&D partnerships. The intention, of course, was to realize value by facilitating the flow of SRI technology to the commercial marketplace. CommTech was to court institutional investors for partnership funding and use that money to form limited partnerships, start new companies, or fund SRI to develop a technology further. In return the arrangement was exclusive, with CommTech having first right of refusal for all SRI-owned technologies for 7 years.

To promote this new type of business internally, in 1981 Miller dusted off SRI's staff royalty-sharing policy and tuned it to give 25% of initial royalties to the inventor(s), with a decreasing scale according to the total royalties received. This was a generous arrangement, and I remember my pet reaction was that it would help retain some staff members by "scratching their entrepreneurial itch" (an itch that was becoming one of Silicon Valley's worst allergies). Though the practice had the potential to create internal schisms between those whose work naturally led to commercialization and those whose work didn't, it was necessary to the new income strategy. In late 1982, Miller also established a Technology Commercialization Office to work with CommTech in seeking SRI

---

[17] Note that research institutions are not necessarily created to make money. Like all organizations, however, they must have enough discretionary resources to adapt and secure their future position (see Appendix D for a plot of revenue).

innovations and realizing their commercial potential. SRI was then poised, it seemed, to gain income from its commercially relevant work. Though with this process Miller raised some commercialization awareness around SRI, he didn't see it as displacing SRI's core business of research. Importantly, he saw its contribution as being not more than about 5% of revenues.[L]

One example of the new awareness was a review of the artificial intelligence (AI) field. About this time AI was becoming highly touted, with forecasted annual markets of $5 to $10 billion. SRI was a premier player in AI research and so everything fit.[M] But in part because AI was a difficult to implement technology and still emerging, nothing came of the initiative. On the other hand and about that time, some SRI AI specialists left to seek their own fortunes with no participation by SRI.[18] SRI made no attempts at AI commercialization and though a lot of other companies did, the market for AI did not materialize.

As this change was taking place at SRI, forces were at work in the U.S. Congress that would support SRI's commercialization initiative. In 1984 it passed the Bayh-Dole Act. This legislation granted to nonprofits the rights to commercialize intellectual property they had developed under government grants or contracts. This act served to remove the ambiguity of ownership of the results of SRI's government projects with that potential. Now SRI could get paid to explore a technology of interest to the U.S. government and then capitalize on its commercialization as long as doing it involved domestic rather than foreign partnerships. This seemed tailor-made for SRI and its work for agencies like NIH, NSF, and the research arms of the DoD. This entitlement has been exploited many times since and is still an important component of SRI commercialization strategy.

GE's Gift of the RCA Laboratories and a Continuing Focus on Commercialization

In late 1985, Jack Welch, the chairman of GE, purchased RCA. As in all acquisitions, consolidation became an issue: both GE and RCA had large, reputable corporate research laboratories, and the technical overlap between them was considerable. The RCA laboratory in Princeton was some 200 miles from the GE laboratory in Schenectady; that distance was too far, in GE's opinion, to consolidate even non-overlapping parts. Wondering how to proceed, GE hired SRI to help assess the overlap and indicate possible directions to take. At Princeton, the leadership and staff took an active interest in the proceedings, and one of the alternatives discussed was becoming a stand-alone contract research entity. The director, James Tietjen, mentioned various options, including that of independence, to GE management. Roland Schmitt, then head of the GE Laboratory, didn't think that option would work, but explored it anyway with a National Science Foundation Board acquaintance, SRI president William Miller. It undoubtedly didn't take long for the business-savvy Miller to see the opportunity.

During the course of SRI's review, one option that had already arisen was for GE to give the laboratory to a nonprofit corporation and enjoy the resulting tax benefit. Of course, SRI itself was such a corporation, and Miller was anxious to open another SRI-associated facility on the East Coast. As it turned out, Welch became interested in the idea, as long as he could believe the laboratory could make a successful transition. Both Tietjen and Miller got to make their cases in person to Welch, although separately.[19] Welch believed the odds were good enough, and Miller happily agreed to receive the laboratory. Thus, in April 1987, the RCA laboratory became the David Sarnoff Research Center, a wholly owned subsidiary of SRI. As part of the transfer and to help make it possible for the new Center to make its transition to self-sufficiency, GE guaranteed $250 million in research funding over the new Center's first 5 years.[N]

---

[18] Peter Hart and Richard Duda left to form Syntelligence in 1980, Earl Sacerdoti became a vice president of Teknowledge in the same year, and Gary Hendrix helped form Symantec in 1983. To the extent that any of these companies ultimately succeeded, it was not with products dependent on AI technology.

[19] Welch, on the occasion of Sarnoff's tenth anniversary, spoke of Miller as the "true hero" of the transformation "turning a tranquil enclave of technology into a P&L center."

But, moving from a somewhat protected position in a large corporation to self-sufficiency in an open contract research marketplace took a toll. To control overhead costs, Sarnoff had to release about one-fourth of its staff. Because of an attractive early-retirement package that GE offered, this reduction was made in a very humane way. But to help Sarnoff get its legs, Tietjen and Miller agreed to let the Center maintain some distance from its new owner in Menlo Park, at least as far as revenue generation was concerned. The skills of the two organizations were dissimilar enough that competition at the outset did not seem to be a problem. With GE's pledged assistance, a pledge transferred to Thomson CSF of France when it bought GE's television business at the end of 1987, Sarnoff successfully made the transition to contract research. Its people had acquired the skills to market its research to both the U.S. government and to industry, worldwide.

Sarnoff's tradition of innovation thus continued. But in addition to contract research, it also sought to create new companies, to bring new technologies to the marketplace, and to benefit from equity creation—and did so with much greater emphasis than its parent, SRI. But that increase in emphasis would eventually arrive in Menlo Park. Through its selection of subsequent SRI presidents, SRI's Board made it clear that this direction, and equity generation in particular, was to frame the future Institute and help solve the ongoing problem of marginal profits.

At SRI proper the commercialization of its retained innovations continued to receive noticeable attention but with mixed results. The exclusive CommTech arrangement was not creating either the licensing or equity values that were hoped for. Yet in the later part of the 1980s the entrepreneurial atmosphere continued to grow in Silicon Valley, and it found its way inside SRI. To follow up on an example cited earlier, the sanctioned AI exploration had yielded no licensing or equity initiatives but there was still an interesting footnote. In about 1988 two members of the AI center left to form a software company. While producing none of the exciting AI advancements that had been explored, the new company nevertheless became successful and by the early 1990s returned, through gifting,

several million dollars to SRI.[20] This exploration into AI says something about the difficulty in searching for and selecting commercial winners. The attractive options may lie in the shadows formed by the glare of those that are more technically advanced. But to stay the course, one of Miller's final actions before leaving SRI in 1989 was to extend the unpopular CommTech agreement for another three years!

The Decline of SRI's Business Group

Another thread in SRI's evolution that was facing important challenges about this time was economic and business development—performed in what we have called here the Business Group[21]—which had been a significant part of SRI from its very beginning. For perhaps three decades, from the mid-1950s to the mid-1980s, this part of SRI had grown to attain worldwide stature. SRI became known for assisting both developing countries and corporations around the world manage the changes and challenges they faced. But across the 1980s the Business Group began to suffer financially; that is, it was requiring subsidy from the rest of SRI. The reasons for this decline are unquestionably many and subject to individual interpretation, but I briefly examine a few here.

The work done in the Business Group was quite different, actually complementary to that in the rest of SRI. Over the years the Business Group hosted the overwhelming share of the Institute's work from the commercial sector. While the remainder of SRI had some commercial leavening in its dominantly government work, a portion of that came from labor loaned to Business Group projects. Thus, though the Institute as a whole appeared to be diversified across a set of uncorrelated research markets, internally the separate groups were considerably much less diverse. The diversity within the Business Group was exemplified by economic development work for governmental

---

[20] More detail on this company and aspects of the CommTech arrangement can be found in Appendix D.
[21] To be clear, this refers to the practice of economic and business development and consulting centered in Menlo Park and does not include a vital and continuing practice of these areas centered in Washington, D.C. That latter activity has always been part of what is referred to in this book as the Education and Policy Group.

jurisdictions and business development for corporations.

From SRI's beginnings to the early 1990s, the Business Group had a continuing stream of large noncommercial projects, mostly international economic development work for foreign governments, foundations, and international aid agencies. Given the longer duration of these projects, they provided a flywheel effect for contract revenues and income. The smaller, problem-solving projects that the Group was getting from the commercial sector tended to be expensive to win and to execute. In the early 1980s, the Group's leadership separated the economic development and business consulting organizationally. While not intended to decrease Business Group diversification, the reorganization did serve to illuminate each of the components more clearly.

But both sectors of the Business Group's work began to decline into the 1990s. Competition in business and management consulting was growing rapidly. In addition to direct competitors like Arthur D. Little, the large accounting firms were entering management consulting. With their insights into company problems, they had greater access to CEOs in areas such as long-term planning and strategic guidance. While SRI had earlier provided the foundation in areas like strategic planning and innovative business practices, these same CEOs were now prone to thinking of SRI as a technology-oriented problem solver. Even the leaders of Japan's Osaka Gas, with which SRI had had a long-term close relationship, did not turn to SRI when the company wanted to reorganize in the 1990s.[o] Being relegated to technoeconomic work was a continued frustration for many of the Business Group leaders who sought the more profitable long-term support relationships that the major accounting firms were securing. I remember Management Council meetings where Business Group leaders indicated that they were discouraged by client surveys that pigeon-holed the Group as only technology consultants.

There was another view on that topic, however. According to one set of Business Group executives, the decline in SRI's business-consulting sector dated from when principals inside the Group began a voluntary withdrawal from collaboration with the technical side of the house.[p] That reservoir of technical talent was believed by many to be a valuable differentiator in the marketplace of business consulting. In any case and for whatever reasons, the Group's financial health continued to suffer.

One of the ongoing successful parts of the Business Group stemmed from its early innovations in strategic planning *methods* and the services that ensued. SRI had made rich contributions to both the information needed for planning and to the planning methods and tools that could help corporations and other organizations confront their futures. By the 1990s this was called the Business Intelligence Program (BIP) and it continued using these tools in particular scenario planning and market segmentation techniques.

Another notable facet of the Business Group was the corporate gatherings it would organize. Worldwide conferences such as the quadrennial International Industrial Conference that continued for 40 years and new associations across the Pacific Basin were evidence of SRI's stature. But as purse strings tightened, these activities, somehow affordable in the Group's heyday, were now looked at with a more frugal eye. Because such convocations had not been profitable in and of themselves, SRI decided to discontinue them. As a result of these factors and more, the Business Group had become marginalized by the early 1990s, and rather than try to reinvigorate it, a different operating model would be imposed.

The Arrival of a New and Active Chairman

In 1993 Paul Cook was named the new chairman of the SRI Board. He would become its most active chairman since the Institute's earliest days. In January 1994, Cook brought in a new president, William Sommers, whose major experience was in management consulting at Booz Allen Hamilton. Because of that background he soon saw that SRI's business development or consulting side was operating under what he viewed as an inappropriate cost-plus-fixed-fee contract system. This system, driven by government auditing regulations applicable to the technical and educational parts of SRI, made profit sharing, a conventional management compensation approach in the consulting world, impossible. Though some thought had been given to demand-based pricing under

President Miller, most contracts remained fixed-fee.

Sommers was correct in viewing these SRI practices as seriously inconsistent with *his* particular perspective on management consulting. If the Business Group were to conform to *his* notions, something had to be done. Whether his was the operational model the Business Group should follow, whether the world of the large business consulting firms was the right marketplace for SRI, and whether the existing staff, who were vital to the transition, believed in that approach, did not appear to carry much weight. What was clear, however, was that his compensation system could not happen inside of SRI proper.

Thus, adopting the compensation and market template of more conventional management-consulting firms, Sommers moved in 1995 to convert the business side of the Institute into a for-profit subsidiary. SRI's business-oriented Board approved. The new entity was called SRI Consulting (SRIC) and its managers were to be given a more lucrative, incentive-based compensation with additional guarantees and perquisites totally alien to SRI. SRIC was formed around so-called "rain-makers," who were to create the high-valued relationships with those corporate clients that could afford to pay the higher prices that such compensation systems required. This orientation ran counter to SRI's traditional culture, which from the beginning had been more academic and much more egalitarian. While escaping from that past was a specific objective, the majority of existing staff, who were not so oriented, found themselves in an uncomfortable world. Regrettably, while the new company was free of SRI, SRI was not free of it, and the SRIC conversion would turn out to be very costly to SRI.

To implement the changeover, Sommers brought in leadership unfamiliar with the abilities and market orientation of the former SRI staff. Within about 4 years SRIC had eaten up its inherited backlog, failed to win any new long-term clients, and required financial bailouts that were huge for SRI.[22] Nor did any of the "rain-makers" pan out. In spite of hiring about 30 allegedly worthy of that moniker, they proved unable to land substantive new projects. In the meantime, many of those more

traditional project developers that had transferred were leaving.

In the end, with but two exceptions, the Menlo Park part of the Institute was out of the economic development and business consulting fields. These were the venerable multi-client programs known as the Business Intelligence Program, begun at SRI in 1959, and the Chemical Economics Handbook that began in 1950. For a few years they remained the only meaningful operational part of SRIC and today both have left.[23] As noted earlier, important economic development work successfully continues in SRI's Washington, D.C. office.

Continuing Refinement of a Strategy for Intellectual Property

For most of SRI's history, its Board members had chosen to have a rather benign influence: reviewing compensation policy, watching the income and capital investment numbers, and choosing the SRI president. But with the arrival of Cook came his resolve to make the Institute a stable and profitable place. Besides the need to deal with the slipping Business Group his other, more passionate orientation was equity generation or start-ups. While temporarily acting as SRI's president, he brought his ideas in this regard to the Institute leadership groups.

As some of us in the Engineering leadership first listened to Cook's message of reform, there arose doubt about the permanency of some areas of traditional research; namely, those that had no commercial relevance. We wondered whether the unwritten but long-held tenet that any well-funded research area had implicit protection would hold up. Cook's emphasis was clear. First, he would remove any ambiguity about how much the Institute would be engaged in intellectual property commercialization. Second, he would closely watch the research areas or labs that had chronic profitability problems. He was a very successful veteran of the company-building world and seemed intent on playing that out at SRI. He cast the impression that research

---

[22] A good estimate is about $42 million.

[23] In 2001, BIP became an affiliated company, SRI Consulting-Business Intelligence, through a management buyout by its staff. In January 2004, the Chemical Economics Handbook and its related issues were sold to Access Intelligence, an information services company in Potomac, MD.

should, where possible, be tailored so as to ultimately create the value inherent in licensing and equity building.

It did not hurt that in the late 1990s the Silicon Valley model of equity generation was approaching manic proportions. As copious amounts of money flowed into start-ups, the surrounding area was becoming even more expensive to live in, and competition for staff was becoming critical. Simply put, Cook wanted SRI to *use* the Silicon Valley model rather than be victimized by it. To help cure SRI's financial woes, he wanted to incubate new, high-value companies, with their lucrative initial-issue equities accruing both to the Institute and to select people within it. It appeared as though he believed this course could build an endowment that would not only stabilize the Institute financially but eventually give SRI the freedom to pursue research of its own choosing.[24]

On Sommers' departure in December of 1998, Curt Carlson, who was in charge of commercial licensing and company formation at Sarnoff, became president. Given his previous job, his incoming strategy also centered on using SRI's intellectual property output to build not just a large research endowment but even to create a more attractive campus, free of the WWII buildings still in use. Those noble goals seemed possible. After all, the IPO wealth-generating machine was well-oiled and still purring all around the region. Rather than letting commercialization be a shared effort by existing staff, SRI hired mostly new people to intensify the process. Doing so, of course, required investments that would come from either the Institute's overhead for from the already marginal bottom line money. The impetus for commercialization was thus invigorated, but, for reasons elaborated on in Appendix D, there would come constraints on that kind of enterprise that are inherent to a contract research organization.

As important as anything internal, however, came something from the outside. Any inherent difficulty in commercialization, including an inordinate commitment of funds toward it, would find a sobering confirmation in the burst of the dot-com bubble in 2001. The almost immediate decrease in the availability of venture funds made the SRI initiative much more difficult to carry out.

Though still an important part of the SRI operational strategy, commercialization has been scaled back a bit and the core contract research business is again front and center. Unlike the early days at SRI, however, the commercially promising output of the research process will be carefully and continuously examined for value. Seeing how those two facets of operations fit sensibly together in a creative research environment and in the entrepreneurial environment of Silicon Valley will also continue to be examined. For the moment the SRI ship is upright and under sail. Under President Carlson's leadership SRI is again profitable, growing, and projecting vitality in its ongoing research.

---

[24] A bit more detail of the movement toward commercialization and its ramifications inside SRI can be found in Appendix D covering the SRI business model.

Endnotes

[A] Weldon B. Gibson, *SRI–The Founding Years* and *SRI–The Take-Off Years*, William Kaufman, 1980 and 1986, respectively. Hoot passed away in the late spring of 2001.

[B] This account of Heald's influence has been taken from an issue of the *SRI Journal* (Feature Issue 4, December 1966) on the occasion of SRI's twentieth anniversary.

[C] Maurice Holland, *Survey of the Stanford Research Institute*, report to SRI's Board, August 17, 1950.

[D] *First Annual Report of the Stanford Research Institute to the Board of Directors*, October 1946 to December 31, 1947.

[E] Stewart Gillmor, *Fred Terman at Stanford: Building a Discipline, a University, and Silicon Valley*, Stanford University Press, October 2004.

[F] Gillmor, op. cit.

[G] Maurice Holland, op. cit.

[H] Gibson, op. cit.

[I] *The Dibble General Hospital – A History*, published by Sunset Press, San Francisco, for the Hospital, May 8, 1946 (courtesy of SRI's Bruce Clark), and Michael Sranevik and Shirley Burgett, *Menlo Park California – Beyond the Gate*, Menlo Park Historical Association, Custom and Limited Editions, 2000.

[J] Letter of March 23, 1993, from SRI Treasurer, Don Andrews, to Stanford's CFO, Peter Van Etten.

[K] *SRI Journal*, Vol. 5, No. 2, April 1985.

[L] Ibid.

[M] SRI AI Task Force, *An Assessment of AI Technology Commercialization – Market Overview and Opportunities for SRI*, December 1984.

[N] A good encapsulation of the transition can be found in Miller's testimony to Congress (House Committee on Science, Space, and Technology) on July 13, 1989. A more complete story of the episode can be found in a local newspaper, the *Business for Central New Jersey*, April 2, 1990.

[O] Paul Jorgensen, personal communication, July 9, 2001. For many years Jorgensen was the SRI executive who worked most closely with Osaka Gas.

[P] William Bloom, Ken Colmen, and Doug McConnell, personal communication (in a joint conversation), June 28, 2001.

Appendix C
SRI's First Boards of Directors

SRI Board of Directors–1947
Chairman–Donald B. Tressider, President, Stanford University
Vice Chairman–Alvin C. Eurich, Vice President, Stanford University

Stanford Trustees
Charles R. Blyth	President	Blyth and Company, San Francisco
John E. Cushing	President	Matson Navigation, San Francisco
W.P. Fuller Jr.	Chairman	W.P. Fuller, San Francisco

Others
Atholl McBean	Chairman	Gladding, McBean, San Francisco
Paul B. McKee	President	Pacific Power & Light, Portland
D.J. Russell	Vice President	Southern Pacific, San Francisco
William L. Stewart Jr.	Executive Vice President	Union Oil of California, Los Angeles
James D. Zellerbach	President	Crown-Zellerbach, San Francisco

SRI Board of Directors–1949
Chairman–J.E. Wallace Sterling, President, Stanford University
Vice Chairman–Louis B. Lundborg, Director of Development, Stanford University

T.H. Banfield	President	Iron Fireman Manufacturing, Portland
S.D. Bechtel	President	Bechtel Corporation, San Francisco
Charles R. Blyth	President	Blyth and Company, San Francisco
A.G. Budge	President	Castle & Cooke, Honolulu
James F. Crafts	President	Fireman's Fund Insurance, San Francisco
John E. Cushing	President	Matson Navigation, San Francisco
Paul L. Davies	President	Food Machinery and Chemical, San Jose
Donald W. Douglas	Vice President	Douglas Aircraft, Santa Monica
J.H. Drum	Vice President	National City Bank of New York, New York
Paul C. Edwards	Associate Editor	San Francisco News, San Francisco
Alvin C. Eurich	President	State University of New York, Albany
R.G. Follis	Vice Chairman	Standard Oil of California, San Francisco
W.P. Fuller Jr.	Chairman	W.P. Fuller, San Francisco
F.C. Lindvall	Chairman of Engineering	California Institute of Technology, Pasadena
Edward D. Lyman	Partner	Overton, Lyman, Plumb, Prince & Vermille, Los Angeles
Atholl McBean	Chairman	Gladding, McBean, San Francisco
Garret McEnerney II		McEnerney & Jacobs, San Francisco
Paul B. McKee	President	Pacific Power & Light, Portland
Paul Pigott	President	Pacific Car and Foundry, Seattle
Alden G. Roach	President	Columbia Steel, San Francisco
S.W. Royce	President	Huntington Hotel, Pasadena
D.J. Russell	Vice-President	Southern Pacific, San Francisco
Tom Slick		Milam Building, San Antonio
William L. Stewart Jr.	Executive Vice-President	Union Oil of California, Los Angeles
Mark R. Sullivan	President	Pacific Telephone, San Francisco
Roland Tognazinni	President	Union Sugar, San Francisco
W.W. Valentine	President	Fullerton Oil, Los Angeles
Lingan A. Warren	President	Safeway Stores, Oakland
Brayton Wilbur	President	Wilbur-Ellis, San Francisco
James D. Zellerbach	President	Crown Zellerbach, San Francisco

SRI's Business Model and the Question of Adaptation

Again this appendix is formed from the author's experiences and impressions over 40 years at SRI. They do not represent any official view of SRI.

Contract Research— SRI's Core Business

Research carries the connotation of trying to introduce something new. If you enter into a formal arrangement to explore a new area, under specified terms and conditions, describing that work as "contract research" makes sense. But, if the contract is for developing something specific or predictable, a more appropriate term would be "contract development." Though that second term is never used at SRI, the Institute undertakes both kinds of work. And, clearly, losing track of such a distinction invites trouble. True exploration with only vague notions of outcome is clearly different from performing a specified task, in a limited time, with an expected outcome. Failure in true research should be forgiven, even though it is sometimes not, whereas failure to complete predictable development is often unforgivable—a sign of poor work or a badly written contract. Happily, much of SRI's work lies between these two limits, and outcomes are generally acceptable; however, the path followed to attain them may not have always been predictable.

Fortunately, a wide variety of organizations elect to fund contract research. In the United States research money that allows considerable exploration is mostly the province of the federal government. On the other hand, industry, whose needs are much more directed, may be blind to longer-term opportunities—a situation SRI has repeatedly experienced. Nonetheless, SRI has won its share of contracts across a varied spectrum of clients. Doing so is an important element in the diversification that characterizes its business model.

Because it was organized to conduct research much like its parent Stanford, SRI's revenue stems from thousands of projects, conceived and won by research principals. At its largest, SRI had more than 2,000 projects active in a given year, with individual researchers essentially working directly for their clients. In all, SRI has conducted over 50,000 individual projects, ranging in size from a few hundred to tens of millions of dollars.[1]

Because SRI's core business is contract research, its work primarily has consisted of *applied* research. But at an eclectic place like SRI, even that quite general term has not pleased everyone. The non-technical groups at SRI, those outside Science and Engineering, have occasionally found "research" too vague and uncertain a description for the work their clients want done. In the beginning years, however, applied research was, as a result of Stanford-issued policy, all that SRI was allowed to carry out; there was no room for what is today mostly referred to as management or business consulting. Not until the mid- to late-1960s, when the link to Stanford had grown vanishingly thin, did the open use of those terms emerge at SRI.

Regardless of their orientation, all externally funded projects lead to revenue, SRI's term for the money it bills its clients. As seen in Figure D-1, contract revenue grew over the years, reflecting first the increase in staff and then, after about 1965, mainly the effects of inflation. Not that a research institute's main goal should be growth, but current-year revenue clearly hides a relatively stable staff size. The constant dollars curve corresponds to a staff of around 3,000 people between 1965 and 1990.

The U.S. government's post-World War II emphasis on research offered a propitious time for SRI to grow. Moreover, industry was also

---

[1] SRI's project numbering system flows between 1,000 and 9,000 and is, therefore, on its fifth cycle of these numbers. To be exact, the first round of numbering started at 102. The next five rounds went between 1,000 and 8,999, and now SRI has a more endurable five-digit numbering system.

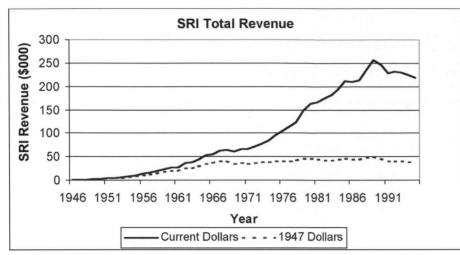

Figure D-1. SRI's annual contract revenue from its founding until the SRI Consulting separation.

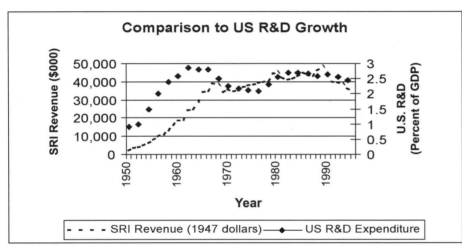

Figure D-2. A comparison of SRI's revenue growth with that of the U.S. commitment to R&D.

decade of its founding, SRI was doing international work.

Describing the business of contract research would not be complete without considering it as a working process. While contract research at SRI had its freedoms, in the absence of endowments researchers can never be free of their clients' preferences. However, those preferences have ranged widely—from extremely narrow, even utilitarian, to wide-open exploration of general goals. For the most part SRI researchers have sought the freedom to practice as their vision dictates, even to advance a new science or technology. Viewed in terms of a time horizon for realization, the best available compromise between complete freedom and specified detail is perhaps those projects whose impacts lay 5-10 years out. As

trying to profit from the new technology that had been developed during and after the war, and R&D as a percent of GDP really accelerated. A comparison of SRI's revenue, in 1947 dollars, with the percentage increase in U.S. R&D expenditures shows a similar pattern (see Figure D-2).

SRI's mix of projects is also worth mentioning. SRI was founded to serve business interests in the western United States and over the course of the first half-dozen years it did just that. But government-sponsored research has always been a large part of the SRI story and it was not industry, but the Office of Naval Research that sponsored the very first SRI project. Figure D-3 shows the fraction of SRI revenue over the years that came from the U.S. government versus that from commercial or international sources and though the size of the sector was not available for the figure, within a

mentioned, government research agencies and foundations often allow the greatest leeway, and commercial companies allow the least. The great goal of work in the sciences and technologies has been to have the freedom to invent or contribute to a totally new conceptual area like, for example, computer networking in the 1960s and 1970s. With such freedom, researchers know their work will be original, it is just a question of its eventual impact.

While a nonprofit institution, SRI still requires a source of net income that it can use to provide capital resources, hire new people, and make other investments in its future. At SRI that income is called the "contract fee," which is a line item on all contracts.[2] The fee is a small percentage of all other contract costs, including

[2] Exceptions are government or foundation grants, which have no fee and often require a reduced overhead rate.

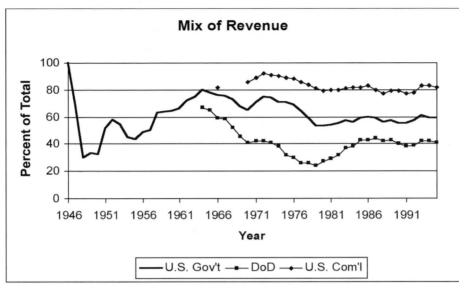

Figure D-3. SRI's revenue mix history. (Until about 1964, SRI distinguished only between government and commercial work. Since that time, each sector has been further divided and the above divisions from bottom to top are, respectively, U.S. government DoD, U.S. government non-DoD, commercial domestic, and commercial international.)

direct charges such as those for labor and materials and allowed overhead or indirect charges. In a full cost recovery scenario, where all direct and indirect charges are expended exactly as allocated, fee is the same as profit.

Before leaving this snapshot of SRI's initial business model, a word about its early culture and research staff is necessary. Much of early SRI was patterned after a university research environment; that is, it grew to be roughly discipline-centered. That it wound up this way was perhaps inevitable since the popularity of applications tends to come and go. Though new disciplines also arise, they do so more slowly. Real world projects, on the other hand, are often client-centered and multidisciplinary; yet they require individual disciplines to provide competent insights and innovative solutions. For most of its existence, SRI has attracted the kind of staff that wanted to expand an area of knowledge and, clearly, innovation becomes more limited when its roots are yesterday's knowledge.

Accordingly, SRI has always "enjoyed" a natural tension: extending knowledge about the most important scientific and technological concepts of the day, and applying that knowledge to solve specific problems. SRI's technical side has always wrestled with this dual need, and discipline-centered research has often proved the path of least resistance. Even

in new fields (e.g., artificial intelligence), disciplinary barriers can be quickly erected.

The U.S. Research Marketplace

In the United States research is funded in just three ways, one commercial and two by the government. Commercially sponsored industrial research accounts for by far the largest piece of the research pie, but industry conducts that type of research almost entirely in-house.[3] Moreover, the research is mostly of a short-term nature, directed at products a couple of years out or less. A few exceptions to this rule exist, such as Bell Labs, IBM, and Du Pont, but increasingly even they must respond to Wall Street's dictate that their parent companies show quarter-by-quarter profits. If a contract research place like SRI is already engaged in a particular technology, it can almost certainly conduct research in that area cheaper than a company's in-house laboratory's cost to enter it. But the business world's perception seems to be to the contrary. Underestimating the cost of internal research and the belief that an outside research firm cannot protect intellectual property are two frequent industry misconceptions.

Almost all long-term U.S. research has its origins in the federal government, as typified by NSF and the National Institutes of Health (NIH). With the disappearance of basic research in commercial laboratories, the funding these agencies, and others like them, provide is perhaps the most unfettered research money available. Unfortunately for places like SRI, such

---

[3] According to the National Science Foundation (NSF), in 1998 industry supplied about $150 billion or 66% of all U.S. R&D. A staggering 98% of that was used by industry itself, and 70% of that was used for the development of products and services rather than research. Industry performed 74.4% of all R&D, universities 11.6%, government 7.6%, and nonprofits like SRI 2.6% (from an NSF report at www.nsf.gov/sbe/srs/seind00/access/toc.htm)

funding is often reserved for universities whose overhead structure is lower as a result of being shared with the universities' nonresearch activities. SRI thus finds it difficult to compete in basic research, and over the years the fraction of its total revenue received from such agencies has almost certainly been less than 10%.

The third major source of research money is the Department of Defense (DoD) and, to a lesser extent, a few other Cabinet departments and NASA.[4] DoD offices, in particular the Defense Advanced Research Projects Agency (DARPA), offer some of the few sources of funding with enough continuity for research to proceed until a logical conclusion is reached. The programs they fund may determine several things: that a particular goal is unattainable or has no further application, that it can be transitioned to a military service for implementation, or that it can be transitioned to a commercial setting. For example, DARPA, with modest supplementary research funding from each of the Armed Services, has been important in advancing information technology in the United States. Even for DARPA, however, adaptation is necessary as the importance of certain technologies fluctuates vis-à-vis DoD missions.

Marketplace Adaptation

SRI, like any other public or private contract research organization, must adapt to the marketplace it finds. Adaptation at SRI usually follows two lines: tracking the steady advance of science or technology and sensing those problems that can be solved through the application of new technology or technology-enabled concepts. SRI's early days were characterized by a relatively noncompetitive contract research environment. While SRI was maturing, university-related, in-government, and even commercial-based research entities were also growing and presenting new competition. But it was literally an act of Congress that posed a new kind of competitive challenge for SRI. Prior to the 1980s, almost 80% of SRI's contracts had been secured

noncompetitively; that is, based on sole-source proposals. In 1984 Congress passed the U.S. Competition in Contracting Act (CICA) and in the space of about 3 years 80% of SRI contracts, at least in the Engineering Group, had to be won competitively—a complete reversal. That adaptation, which was forced by both law and competition, drove the cost of doing business significantly higher.[5]

Because winning contracts and thus revenue generation at SRI traditionally took place in the first two levels of the organization, it is there that virtually all meaningful adaptation occurred. Having 1,000 flexible, adaptable project leaders plying the waters of perhaps a 1,000 clients to explore mutual needs, proved an effective way to monitor and match market need. The only additional factor required was making sure that SRI's ideas and techniques were both relevant to clients and directed toward the future. If they were not, natural selection took place, and SRI management was obliged to prune the structure so that better opportunities ahead could be pursued. The present SRI management's marketing mantra seeks to assure prospective clients that whatever SRI undertakes, the result will create definable value for them in the future.

Fiscal Realities and Adaptation of Another Kind

The awarding of research contracts is fundamental to SRI's existence but that's not the only factor required for successful operation. Like any business, expenses must be controlled and there must be enough contract revenue to cover those expenses deemed essential.[6] Meeting this need has not always been easy and as a consequence the profitability, that is, the money needed for reinvestment, has often been problematic.

While some areas of research have remained "profitable" for many years in this nonprofit setting, many have not. The reasons for this unevenness range from the specific type of

---

[4] As a recent indication of the composition of government R&D, the 2003 allocation had the following breakdown: NIH $26.2 billion, NSF $5.3 billion, Department of Energy $8.2 billion, DoD $58.6 billion, and NASA $11.0 billion, out of a $117 billion total. The proposed 2004 R&D budget is about $123 billion with 51% to DoD and 22% to the NIH.

[5] The CICA as written by Congress was intended to avoid both research funding and nonprofits. However, both of those stipulations were effectively ignored in its application by funding agencies. (*Inside SRI*, Vol. 1, No. 2, June 1986.)
[6] Note that research institutions are not necessarily created to make money. Like all organizations, however, they must have enough discretionary resources to secure and expand their future position.

research, funding for which may go in or out of fashion; the type and quality of staff and their ability to convince clients that their ideas are worth supporting; and the clients themselves. More than half of SRI's funding comes from the U.S. government, and the government's regulation of the overhead and fees of its research contracts and grants govern SRI's profitability in that sector. Add to that limitation the cost of increased competition in the government sector forced by CICA and the result is that SRI's original business model has incurred a certain stress.

In addition to increased competition nationally, strictly local difficulties have affected SRI. The Institute's location on the San Francisco peninsula—one of the most competitive places for workers in certain fields and one of the most expensive areas to live anywhere—can significantly impede SRI's ability to attract staff to its main offices in Menlo Park. A second local factor has been the vast amount of venture capital available in the immediate region of Silicon Valley. That funding availability has lured many out of research and into the area's abundant start-ups, reaching its peak in the late 1990s. With those local stress factors in mind, SRI has, of necessity, taken on some of the traits that characterize the local business environment. Two very important factors will now be discussed that go a long way in defining a long-term SRI model for an activity we will call commercialization.

By the early 1980s, SRI began to reorient itself so that a greater portion of its income came from the licensing of intellectual property, including the creation of equity. Indeed, seeking a highly leveraged financial position by providing or participating in the seed round funding of a new company is tempting. But even seed round funding of numerous potential start-ups is expensive for a marginally profitable Institute. To the extent that such investments significantly erode the funding of new research opportunities or contribute to the overall overhead structure, they hamper SRI's ability to compete in its core business from which commercialization opportunities arise. Venture capital organizations, on the other hand, have few such distractions and can reduce their overhead nearly to zero if need be. This difference suggests a natural partnership: one with substantial money and a tolerance for risk and the other with little discretionary money and

an opportunity engine. The research institution produces the technology or other opportunity, and the investor community commercializes it—each capitalizing on its own strength.[7]

While easily forgotten, SRI's nonprofit status and charter require its work to remain in the public interest. It is this status, however, that enables SRI to enjoy an excellent position from which to create and use government-sponsored intellectual property. The 1984 federal Bayh-Dole Act, mentioned in Appendix B, stipulates that nonprofit organizations, typically universities, can take intellectual properties generated under government research contracts and commercialize them. This legislation came about as part of a government desire to stimulate the economy and has resulted in two important advantages for SRI. Research sponsored by the U.S. government gives individual researchers great latitude in seeking innovations and, once SRI has created a set of marketable intellectual property, it is free to commercialize it as it chooses (even overseas partnerships are allowed if, wherever economically feasible, manufacture is done domestically). Simply put, the model consists of conducting a lot of research and technology development under government contract and then gleaning from that work innovations that have an attractive commercial market.

While this type of commercialization is obviously desirable, not all research can lead to intellectual property positions that are of commercial interest. When President Miller first proposed this kind of initiatives around 1980, there were some who thought rewards to inventors might become a divisive problem. The increased emphasis on research for commercialization in the mid- to late-1990s again raised the question of fairness. Two things transpired to allay those concerns. One specified that substantial income from intellectual property would be directed toward needed capital investments in *any* research area and to the staff in general. Second was the fact

---

[7] The early dispositions in the history of SRI were not aligned with holding patents. From a Stanford Ph.D. thesis that examined the Institute in 1951 comes the following: "Stanford Research Institute does not desire to develop and hold its own patents. It prefers to have patentable discoveries made under sponsored contracts. One of the Assistant Directors explained this policy with the observation, 'A patent is just a license for a court fight.'" (Ernest Barbour O'Byrne, *The Research Institutes of Stanford University*, Ph.D. dissertation in the School of Education, Stanford University, SRI partial reprint dated June 1951.)

that not many such opportunities came to fruition anyway. But the commercialization process still carries important potential for the Institute and it is continuing to be explored. We will now back up and add a bit of detail to a number of important events that had a downstream effect on that subject.

SRI's Move Toward Commercialization of Its Intellectual Properties

Particularly in the context of today's IPO-frenzied world, it is odd that for most of its 50-plus years SRI did not use its patent positions wisely. For most of that period, SRI's Patent Office was lightly staffed, and its chief function was to secure patent positions that could be offered to potential clients as an incentive for new research contracts. Licensing was minimal and had few impacts, and though SRI was in the midst of the world's premier venture capital marketplace, those people stayed away in droves.

There were several reasons for this: one was the perceived fuzziness about the ownership of rights for work done for the government before passage of the Bayh-Dole Act; a second was that good, innovative research was too far in advance of the commercial marketplace. A notable example of the latter was that licenses to the mouse issued in the late 1970s and early 1980s yielded SRI less than $150,000. The mouse's value became apparent only in the declining years of its patent protection, which ran from 1970 to 1987.[8]

This somewhat intermittent approach to dealing with intellectual property commercialization started to change with the arrival of President Miller in summer 1979. Having venture capital experience, Miller was attuned to the potential of this kind of investment. So, Miller took several steps to place SRI in a better position to profit from its accrued intellectual properties. He set up an SRI holding company, revisited the Institute's plan for sharing royalty with its staff, set up a commercialization office reporting to him, and signed an agreement with a new venture capital firm that gave them first right of refusal on all

SRI-owned innovation.[9] He completed these important steps by 1982, but having done so did not see commercialization as being a huge preoccupation for SRI, estimating its revenue at something like 5% of the total.[A]

To give a flavor of the kind of action that followed Miller's initiative, consider the 1984 review given a popular field at the time, artificial intelligence (AI). The exploration began with an examination of SRI's inventory of AI innovations. Targets were identified and a report issued but in spite of that prominent and directed examination, no commercialization action was taken. Curiously, in the same laboratory at the same time, two software engineers were building software packages as part of their computer support activities. These were not AI implementations at all but either because these programs lay outside the AI-centered products they were seeking or because one of the programs was already under license, they were not considered by the task force.

One program was called EUNICE, which SRI had licensed in 1982. EUNICE enabled programs written for the increasingly widely used UNIX operating system to run on the also popular VAX computer from DEC that came with an incompatible operating system, VMS. The second SRI program, MultiNet, mated UNIX with the variety of local and wide-area networking protocols that were emerging at the time. These proved to be lucrative arrangements for SRI, netting several million dollars in the late 1980s and early 1990s. Some of that return came to SRI as gifts after their inventor, Dave Kashtan, and his AIC cohort left SRI to form a new and successful company called TGV.[10]

Note the contrast between the top-down exploration of a selected, seemingly attractive technology that didn't materialize versus a natural, unprompted flow of a needed, royalty-producing product that did—all from the same laboratory at about the same time.

Another SRI staff member, Phil Green, an inventor in ultrasonic imaging, was more adamant than anyone about the advantages of commercialization, both for the Institute and for himself. In the 1980s, he began investigating companies that were infringing on his SRI-owned ultrasound patents. Perhaps

---

[8] A critical factor of timing for the mouse was the Macintosh, which was introduced in 1984.

[9] For more details on these actions, see Appendix B.
[10] TGV stood for "two guys and a Vax" and became a small successful start-up; successful enough to present royalties and substantial financial gifts to SRI. TGV was eventually bought by Cisco Systems.

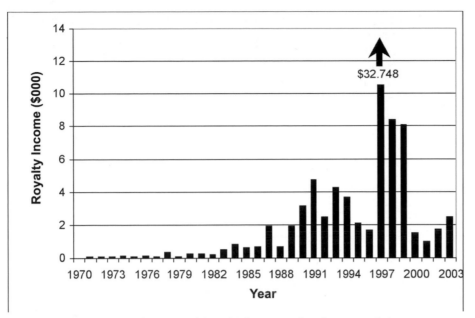

Figure D-4. SRI income from royalties. (Values are after inventors' shares are subtracted. Also not included are the sales of shares SRI accrued from the transfer of intellectual property.)

it was not welcome news to those at SRI whose technology was under prolonged scrutiny. Under the exclusive agreement, SRI lost all flexibility in exploiting technologies, as well as much of the incentive to do so internally. Whether SRI would have faired better by having retained control and having focused more interest on this issue is not clear, but under the existing arrangement, delays and failed promotions were the norm. I remember, in one case, meetings and arguments went on for years with one failed opportunity after another while other places were exploiting exactly the same technology. To most SRI inventors and managers, the agreement was simply a source of frustration.

surprisingly, many "infringers," as he called them, having received a straightforward notification and request for royalty payments, simply responded with periodic checks over the remaining life of the patents. Two firms that didn't cooperate were sued by SRI and ultimately saw a conviction with willful avoidance. All together these ultrasound infringement pursuits returned well over $50 million to SRI. Figure D-4, which shows SRI's royalty income history, net of inventor's share, clearly reflects the change in emphasis in this area and the ultrasound settlement forms the large promontory.

In the meantime, Miller's exclusive commercialization arrangement with the venture capital firm, CommTech International, was not succeeding as hoped. While it had placed some technologies in the market, far more failed or were left hanging.[11] If it was simply a measure of just how difficult and problematic such equity-building initiatives are,

A couple of other important risks will round out this discussion of commercialization at SRI and they have to do with its proper balance with research. First, research tailored to commercial products or services entails, by nature, a much shorter lead-time than does more fundamental work, including work that defines the state of an art. If SRI devoted all of its discretionary resources to research with time horizons in the 1- to 2-year time frame, it would almost certainly forego research that resulted in the fundamental advances that sometimes change the world (as did SRI's visionary efforts on personal computing in the mid-1960s and on digital networking in the 1970s). SRI should reserve some resources for visionaries who can see beyond the incremental changes on which the commercial marketplace thrives. Enabling such long-term vision is, after all, part of the original motivation for commercialization building an endowment big enough to grant that kind of freedom.

Another risk is the impact on laboratories that discover an important technology that is subsequently commercialized. Exclusive licensing agreements concerning such intellectual property can curtail or even deny future research contracts in that area for such a laboratory, as well as result in the loss of key

---

[11] A couple of examples that have had some success are the licensing of SRI printing technology to Accuprint and a very long-chain polymer to Dow Chemical. In the latter case, after some delay, CommTech made the original licensing agreement with Dow and when Dow didn't want to complete the investment needed to produce it, CommTech found a sublicensee who would. That firm is Toyobo who is manufacturing and selling it and trying to expand its use into the large bullet-protective vest market. SRI receives some royalty income from Toyobo. (Source: conversation with Bonnar Cox on May 20, 2004. Cox headed the SRI commercialization effort in the early 1990s.)

people. Some staff members will inevitably leave SRI to join the licensee, but those who remain should not be so encumbered in using the intellectual property that has been sold, that the parent laboratory becomes effectively dysfunctional. That did happen and through the efforts of SRI's current president, Curt Carlson, guidelines are now in place to prevent this win-lose situation, wherein once the golden egg has been sold, the goose that laid it is shot.

Finally, there is the question of balance following this excursion towards commercialization. SRI's core business is unequivocally contract research. That work will be closely examined for commercialization opportunities and perhaps even shaded at times to enhance such opportunities. But research not related to commercialization will also enjoy all the respect it deserves. That balance seems to be now present at SRI.

The Changing Nature of Research in the United States

For perhaps a decade or two, the U.S. government has taken initiatives to spur the national economy. The government has invested in precommercialization technologies, carried out by places like SRI and, in the case of the Department of Commerce, by small start-up companies. But research conducted by U.S. industry appears to be headed in a different direction.

Corporate America is in a quandary regarding the role of research in its future. Because of today's relentless pressure for high market value and profitability, corporate research facilities are being given stringent tests for relevance. Are their expenses justified by their contributions to the product innovations the company needs in order to increase its valuation or to capture or maintain market share? Corporate officers are questioning such utility, even to the point of divesting some of the best-known U.S. research laboratories. The trend seems to be away from long-term research with its vague goals, toward short-term research that directly serves product development. Some companies want to end internal basic research and argue that industrial research is at the end of an era.[B] Targeted are such venerated research operations as Bell Labs, Xerox PARC (now an independent research center), GE's Schenectady Lab, and others.[12]

The reasons for this change vary, to be sure, but a major one is that the ever-shortening pace of product introduction has undercut the more leisurely pace that has typified the traditional research laboratory. Open-ended research projects with outcomes that are difficult to determine are now seen as an unaffordable luxury, no longer worth the low probability of a market-altering breakthrough. Another important reason can be the financial health of the parent company. In the case of Xerox, the biggest reason for scrutiny was that the parent company is threatened by bankruptcy.

But we should also recall that industrial-sector R&D funding in the U.S. continues to increase both in absolute dollars and as a fraction of GDP, possibly as a result of greater acceleration of the product development cycle. Regardless, to the extent that long-term research continues, carefully selected outsourcing will be good for universities or places like SRI that provide steeper and thus more efficient learning curves.

In the meantime federal government actions continue the tendency started during the early 1990s. In the DoD, the narrowing of research horizons is perhaps best evidenced by one of its largest research sponsors, the Defense Advanced Research Projects Agency. There, emphasis has shifted to Advanced Technology Demonstrations, which are geared toward bringing technology to bear on important military problems rather than inventing new technologies, an area in which DARPA had excelled. By the same token, the Department of Commerce makes R&D allocations under the Advanced Technology Program to foster partnerships among government, industry, and academia for pursuing high-risk research intended to have significant commercial payoff. This program allows industry to extend its technological reach to promote new commercial products and conceivably even new companies.

---

[12] At Sarnoff's tenth anniversary, GE Chairman Jack Welch stated that, "GE R&D is...in the critical path of every major technology intensive program in each of our businesses. And every technical contributor in our laboratory is working on a project that is vital to a current business plan.... The undiverted focus must be on winning in the marketplace." (April 3, 1997)

How Will these Changes Affect SRI and Its Brand of Research?

The industrial world's shortening of its research horizons and greater emphasis on internally funded, rapid-paced product development, has several messages for SRI. If industry still wants to fund some level of long-term industrial research, the resulting outsourcing will provide potential benefit to SRI, particularly if SRI is already engaged in the appropriate field. Using SRI would often be cheaper for the industrial client than internally developing the skills needed. Moreover, SRI can bring to such projects its own intellectual property for exploitation. But if companies continue to cloister their short-term R&D projects internally, SRI will obviously be denied that particular market. And to the extent that corporations also abandon their longer-horizon research, SRI must look to the government.

On the face of it, contracting with an outside research institute ought to be an obvious choice for a company when it has little or no background or capacity concerning what it wishes to explore. Unlike university grants in such cases, which do not yield rapid results and for which preserving confidentiality is difficult, contract research houses such as SRI are skilled in meeting both requirements. Costs are also much more easily controlled with outside contractors as long as the sponsoring company is closely involved. Finally, a broadly based contract research organization has greater ability to employ a new technology, or especially technologies in combination, than does a typical, more narrowly focused company.

Endnotes

[A] *SRI Journal*, Vol. 5, No. 2, April 1985.

[B] Gordon Moore, "Some Perspectives on Research in the Semiconductor Industry," in Richard Rosenbloom and William Spencer (Eds.), *Engines of Innovation: Industrial Research at the End of an Era*, Harvard Business School Press, 1996.

Appendix E
The SRI Atmosphere—
The Roles of Research Staff and Managers

In spite of the many varied experiences people find in their work environments, such places have a definable culture or atmosphere. SRI has such an atmosphere and virtually every researcher I have known here, as well as many who support them, is aware of it. On balance, that feeling is invariably a positive one and I believe it stems from some combination of the independence they feel and the general level of proficiency they find. I also believe that the SRI atmosphere is immensely important to its staff, perhaps the Institute's most telling attribute, transcending the inevitable difficulties with people and situations that visit us all. Beyond the feelings of freedom and competence, SRI's atmosphere is also one of innovation and an enticing but illusive potential for interdisciplinary collaboration. The SRI atmosphere is carried dominantly by its people and the roles they have filled over its history. It is with some trepidation that I engage these subjects and it must be, almost by definition, a personal perspective.

Nurturing Innovation

Two extremely important attributes of an applied research organization are competency and innovation.[1] These say everything about the type of person who would be hired or would feel comfortable at SRI. In contract research both orientations must almost be taken for granted since no research client wants to pay for old solutions expensively rediscovered. But how are the right people found? With some risk, competency can be discovered or even measured at the time of employment. After employment, new areas of research can be learned, formally or informally. But the more difficult question concerns innovation.

Because evidence of innovation may be revealed by their prior work, SRI staff often come from research universities or other laboratories. The ponderous question, though, is whether innovation can be taught, enhanced, encouraged, or forced, or is simply an innate characteristic of some people. Good researchers are motivated to exploit their natural creativity simply by being among the first to originate a new concept, abetted, perhaps through competition with their peers. If a researcher is surrounded by peers who are each breaking new ground or setting the state of their art, it is very difficult not to do likewise. To make such an atmosphere possible at SRI, two provisions are necessary: finding the funds to support the innovative activity and making sure that the working environment does not become too administratively distracting. If reasonable encouragement within such an environment doesn't work, my 40 years of experience tells me that not much else will. In starting a new group, building that kind of atmosphere early is critical.

To illustrate how much innovation is intrinsic to the researcher, here are a couple of instances of how innovation sprang from nothing more conducive than a coffee break. Pure serendipity or the right people in the right atmosphere? The setting for one instance began with a rather protracted project with a West-coast paint company that was developing a new latex-based paint. A problem the company was having was the formation of bubbles in the paint that wouldn't dissipate before the paint began to dry. This caused a roughness in the surface that made it unusable. In spite of trying a large number of mixtures, nothing was working well enough. Meanwhile, another SRI laboratory had an ongoing project with a large Western firm that involved the processing of coconut meat it was importing from Africa. The company was extracting oil from the meat to sell to the soap industry, but the company also wanted to know what other uses there were for coconut oil and, just as important, what could be done with the coconut residue? From the

---

[1] Innovation, as used here, simply means introducing something new and different based on a creative insight or act. It could be an invention or just a new way of portraying a problem or its solution.

former, SRI chemists proceeded to develop a useful substance they called a "plasticizer" that helped plastics shape and hold their form. But, though they racked their brains, they couldn't find uses for the residual meat. Now the coffee break.

The paint researchers were complaining that while they had found a chemical that would smooth the bubbles out, they needed an oil base to go with it. A chemist on the coconut project bolted to his feet and pulled a notebook from his pocket. One of these three coconut oil fats, he said, has some peculiar molecular properties that you might what to look at. Out of a hunch came a double-barreled solution. Tests revealed that one of the coconut residues also fit the paint defoaming need, and it came into use in the other client's paint as well as that of several other paint companies.

A second instance came from a coffee break in the Engineering part of SRI and another cross-discipline question. Could a laser be built to replace the radio frequency sources used in weather radar? The result was the building at SRI of the first weather lidar, or laser-based radar, for probing the atmosphere. That story is unfolded in Chapter 9. While the common denominator here was a coffee break, needless to say it was the caliber and orientation of the people who attended them that made the difference.

One of the best evidences of a prolonged history of innovation at SRI was the creation in the 1960s and 1970s of the rudiments of personal computing. The rough vision existed, but the means to deliver the desired functionality had to be invented and then refined as it came into use. The development lasted almost two decades. But though retrospectively it was revolutionary, the magnitude and value of the innovation were not at the time evident to everyone. With no similar developments to look at, this work was almost totally SRI innovation. Unfortunately, innovation doesn't always take hold and this work ultimately ended at SRI in the failure of outside sponsorship.

Within the bounds of propriety, the SRI researcher is given wide latitude in areas of exploration. That latitude is part of the SRI atmosphere. While a few SRI research managers have constrained their people to pursue subjects in the mainstream of R&D, most are more adventurous. Thus, topics like psychographic segmentation of the consumer population for

marketing, or the use of computers to augment human intellect, or even questionable topics such as remote viewing and cold fusion have been given a good airing at SRI. On the other hand, SRI has always had an ethical atmosphere, and many opportunities that would not reflect well on the Institute, independent of outcome or remuneration, have not been approved. As one example, though perfectly legal, projects directly related to Nevada gambling to my knowledge have never been approved. As a practical matter, however, most discretion about whether to undertake a project comes from skepticism about whether enough support can be found to do a subject justice.

A Successful Contract Researcher

In my opinion, the people who make successful contract researchers at SRI have five necessary characteristics. They are *creative*, they understand at least one *discipline* well, like all good leaders they are *motivational*, and they have an ethic for *integrity* and *hard work*. A *creative* orientation naturally takes one beyond the expected or predictable to a broader range of solutions to a given problem or opportunity. It questions not just the invited answer but also the premise itself. On the other hand, creative thought must also be accompanied by enough knowledge to become a good point of departure for not only what changes should occur, but also whether they can be realized. In a contract research organization it is important that imagination exist at all levels of abstraction concerning a problem; that is, from the high-level statement of the problem or overarching goal, down to the details about how the solution might be implemented. This is a lot to ask of one person, so often a team of people is needed to span the levels of perception that many solutions require.

Regarding *disciplines*, it is difficult to make an innovative contribution unless one is steeped in at least one relevant discipline. *Applying* a particular discipline requires enough of an understanding to be efficient and productive in its use. Similarly, advancing the state of that discipline or art demands an even greater appreciation of it. SRI has always had people with such grasps across a set of important disciplines; not to have such a background obviously forecloses research in the areas to which such disciplines apply. SRI's strength has always been in the rich number of disciplines among its staff.

Having said all that, there are a very few, exceptional researchers who have the innate power to look at an opportunity, and quickly position themselves at the very frontier of the relevant field. Though it may take a year or two, they emerge with a totally new approach that makes a world of difference in the utility or accuracy of the selected field or even in the field's underlying science. Such people are wonderfully appropriate in a contract research environment.

Motivation is necessary in two critical dimensions: one, is the ability to lead a group of project people toward a responsive goal; and second, and perhaps more important, is the ability to sell a potential sponsor that SRI has the understanding, the insight, and the approach to bring new and competent solutions to bear on the sponsor's problem.

Because SRI is a contract research institute, it is obviously successful only when it has an adequate backlog of research contracts.[2] Those individual researchers who can consistently deliver such backlog effectively wear chain mail; that is, they enjoy an enormous protection against whatever internal buffeting occurs. Those who gain long-term sponsorship and do quality work are probably the most revered people at SRI.

The last researcher attribute is best evidenced by how truthfully and consistently one represents him or herself. For most of SRI's existence, that quality has given SRI a reputation for *integrity* and *objectivity* with clients. Some of this stems from the scientific ethic and some from the very direct relationship that exists between the project leader and the client. Personal integrity, of course, builds organizational integrity. SRI's Tom Boyce puts it this way: "When I came to SRI in 1983 and had to call on potential clients to market or explore new work, I was amazed at how accessible people were when you told them you were from SRI. One of the first places I went was the Philippines. I would pick up the phone and call someone cold and, assuming they were in, I could get an appointment that same day or at the latest, the next. That was very gratifying and, you know what? It made me want to leave that contact in as good or better shape for the next SRI person who might call. It was a bond of responsibility I felt in continuing our excellent reputation."

As with any organization, SRI has its leaders, both formally and informally designated. Over most of its existence, technical leaders have been perhaps the most venerated by the staff, either because they are innovative or because they repeatedly bring in significant research contracts by offering prospective clients innovative and timely ideas and solutions. The Institute has several ways in which it honors such people. Each year awards are given for lifetime accomplishments: two Institute Fellows for technical achievement, one person who has contributed substantially to mentoring others to greater achievement, and one for life contributions to society in general. Added to these regular awards is a post-retirement SRI Hall of Fame whose members are elected by the SRI Alumni Association. Appendix J lists all these awardees to date.

Interdisciplinary Research

It stands to reason that in an applied research world, so often driven by the problems at hand, work bridging distinctly different disciplines would be commonplace. But when an institution is defined by the presence of traditionally separated disciplines, interdisciplinary talents are not easily developed. Over my 40 years at SRI, there have been numerous times, both formal and informal, when the subject of building this kind of interdisciplinary capability has been brought up by management in general terms, as it tried to educate the staff on its virtues and how it could be achieved. If any of those top-down efforts resulted in any concrete interdisciplinary achievements, I am not aware of them. In spite of the legitimate view that there are often rich rewards for exploring the boundaries of two or more disciplines, our educational, research, and even reward systems, not all of which are internal, discourage leaving one's chosen field. Furthermore, because by nature interdisciplinary wedges are not easily foreseen, speaking in general terms about them accomplishes almost nothing.

Yet in a heterogeneous place like SRI, there should be countless opportunities for

---

[2] Success has more than a financial dimension at SRI. The quality of work, the stature of its staff in their field, and the degree to which its clients benefit are other valid measures of success.

interdisciplinary work. Even if not induced by management, these could come from the informal interaction of different researchers or from the awareness of a need that does not yield well to a unidisciplinary approach. The question is how to encourage its happening?

The best and perhaps only way such endeavors have been successful at SRI is when they arise within some individual who has both the capacity and interest to bridge multiple fields. It is not enough just to identify an interdisciplinary bridge; someone must actually build it locally. That takes a person who is proficient in at least one field and willing to develop a working knowledge of the other. These "bridge people" are a necessary but not sufficient condition for interdisciplinary work.

Beyond having the bridge person, a team is usually needed, and perhaps the most difficult aspect of interdisciplinary work is getting other experts who are steeped in or advancing the art in one field to divert their attention to another. There is clearly some security in remaining within one's own field and, since most research laboratories are organized by discipline, researchers may be reluctant to leaving their organizational home for something that by nature has more risk. If the new effort is difficult enough to require several years of dedicated investigation, that looms as almost a career change to the discipline-centered specialist.

But bridge people do exist at SRI and, if one's notion of interdisciplinary work is more modest (i.e., it can be spanned with a small bridge, so to speak, either in the art or time), a substantial amount of that work occurs. Examples such as the marriages developing between chemistry and material sciences or biology or the blending of chemistry and biology to define toxicology are now commonplace. Business and economics are also easily overlaid on virtually any engineering or scientific pursuit. Lacking at least one bridge person, however, even small bridges can sometimes be difficult to erect.

As a division director, I sponsored for over a year weekly lunches between computer scientists, linguists, automatic speech recognition people, and electrical engineers to discuss the advancement of human-computer interaction. Though the advantage of that goal was fairly clear, it was still difficult to draw people out of their familiar haunts to tackle what most people would think of as inevitable.

SRI had invented the world's choice for hand-screen coupling, the mouse, had as good an automatic speech recognition capability as anyone, had invented a handwriting recognition system in 1970s, and was steeped in natural language understanding and other artificial intelligence-based fields; thus, the initiative seemed very natural. Some success came in the formation of a Computer Dialogue Laboratory, a physical but not organizational facility where interaction research could go on and, eventually, it did inspire a very few people into melding automatic speech recognition with natural language understanding to improve on the accuracy of machine-recognized speech. But while that set the state of the art in terms of recognition accuracy, the most recent advancements in automatic speech recognition drew on other approaches and sheer machine power for their success. In the end, gaining a new plateau in human-computer interaction lacked the bridge person and, given no clearly identifiable sponsor with that interest, little came of it. There were no new technologies developed and no commercial successes. Agents, semi-autonomous acting pieces of network-mobile software, were advanced in these deliberations, but they didn't materialize at SRI until a bright young Artificial Intelligence Center (AIC) computer scientist later developed them. That approach did, coincidentally, return to enhance the functionality of human-computer interaction (see Chapter 4, a description of AIC work).

The Roles of Research Management

The position of management in a research institution is somewhat precarious, but not unimportant. Though a research organization's figure of merit is defined dominantly by the creative talents of its research staff, managers do have important roles. Just how important is quite honestly a function of your perspective, but there usually exists within a research management hierarchy a transition from close identification with the research staff and their culture to more remote but necessary preoccupations such as policy and profitability. While the manager rising in this hierarchy probably doesn't feel a creeping estrangement, nonetheless it occurs. Profitability, allocation of resources, and resolving interorganizational conflicts are some of management's duties, and they are all viewed as distractions by the myopic and impassioned researcher. It is probably the case that good managers in any setting maintain some interaction with the working level but in contract research, where the first two levels are responsible for most of the organization's success, it is crucial. These are the levels that provide virtually all revenue and client satisfaction.

An involved, walk-around manager is a benefit to any organization including those involved in contract research. Here, where the working levels are so critical to income production, it is important that managers identify with those levels and how they can be motivated and helped. You can easily see attempts by some research managers as they try to avoid any cultural transition as they move into management. One example is "dressing down." The "wearing of a tie" is often subordinated to the need for implied acceptance by the stereotyped, open-collared, sometimes disheveled researcher. Many hardcore male researchers I have known will go to almost any length to avoid neckties, wearing them only for the outside world, such as clients. Even then the strange combinations of shirt, tie, and jacket seem chosen to convey their discomfort. Male managers that don't wear ties consistently are likely to be paying some deference to the research culture and giving a little tip-off about their own self-perceptions.

Managing in a contract research organization is certainly more difficult if not more important than in one whose money flows in from the top and is allocated according to someone's preferences. In a contract research setting like SRI, the researcher is expected to decide on the area of work, win the sponsorship to carry it out, and convey to the client the relevancy, adequacy, and competency of the results. That is a great training ground, and in the eyes of a typical researcher, it doesn't leave a huge role for a manager above the laboratory level. There is a prepositional invective used at SRI that goes a long way in typifying its culture. A researcher may sometimes claim, "I don't work *for* SRI, I work *at* SRI!" Strangely, as distancing as it may sound, that statement is often spoken with fondness about how it feels to work at SRI. Accordingly, as a manager at

SRI, it was very difficult for me to assert that someone worked *for* me as opposed to *with* me![3]

So, what should a manager's role be at a place like SRI? As you might expect, the answer varies depending on the level of management, and there is probably room for a few different styles. For much of SRI's history, there were five levels of management. Now, there are, preferably, but four, albeit SRI is now much smaller. The first two management levels, those that direct a collection of projects called a program and the laboratory or center director, are still permeated by the research culture...what projects should be sought, what is the expected quality of the work, and who should be doing it. Except for financial aspects, management above that level is often discretionary, but just which discretions get exercised becomes critical. The starting or stopping of research areas, or programs, is an important middle-management activity perhaps not exercised frequently enough at SRI. At the highest management levels, that tendency to become disconnected from the producing levels must also be avoided or become simply an overhead load in the eyes of the research staff.

There are several important things that contract research managers at any level must do:

- Support a culture where creativity and innovation can flourish. Managers and not just researchers must be "keepers of the flame" at SRI; that is, they must be oriented toward preserving an atmosphere of innovation.

- Assure that the quality of work doesn't suffer under client or internal pressures.

- Administer the budget process and its allocations of required levels of performance. It is this process that should be used to reinforce positive outcomes and limit or terminate poor ones. Nonprofit institutes still require fiscal discipline.

- Resolve and correct interorganizational conflicts. Like everyone else, researchers can covet the same roles, clients, and projects as their fellow researchers. While internal

---

[3] Here I might usefully quote from a memo to my Division staff when I retired in the spring of 1998. It relates my true feelings about being a manager at SRI: "....Finally, I would like you to remember that whatever unfolds, you are the Institute. You don't just work *for* SRI, you don't just work *at* SRI, *you are SRI* and everything you do here has some impact on others, so let it be your best. SRI will succeed only if you do and it will fail only if you fail to meet your potential...."

competition can sometimes be beneficial, SRI is one place it must be controlled. A former head of Bell Labs mentioned to me that even Nobel Laureates engage in jealous wrangles.

- Help clear the roadblocks to interdisciplinary work, especially where the required working level participants have already embraced the venture.

- Set the parameters that enable attracting the necessary talent.

- See oneself as both motivating new and good research, but also as serving and enabling project winners and leaders. Micromanaging is even more deadly here than elsewhere and, in deference to overhead burden that is so important to initiative and success at the project leader level, managers should be lean in their supporting staff.

As with any organization, there are also some things that any manager must _not_ do, particularly from higher levels of management:

- Become so detached that you appear to be arbitrary and believe you are free to act without clear regard for the staff that is producing the revenue.

- Assume you can or should direct research content from the top down.

- Be assigned inordinate privileges in convenience, comfort, or financial reward. The exorbitantly paid and pampered CEOs of industry are a terrible model for a research institute.

- Fail to support and defend a researcher who has done good and relevant work objectively, even when the preferences of the client or others would have chosen some other outcome.

I will cite one of two incidents I had in the vein of this last point. We had a project with the FCC to quiet a car electrically so that forthcoming transistor circuits would perform reliably. In an unusual arrangement, our final contract payment depended on our success on an actual car. We knew the spark plugs and the distributor would be the culprits and devised inexpensive ways to modify them. But the automobile manufacturers, who didn't want to raise the cost of a car even one dollar, repeatedly rebuffed our efforts. We mentioned that reluctance in the final report to the FCC and suffered the wrath of the automobile industry association. Because the head of that organization knew the SRI president, we

researchers were called on the carpet and asked to delete that observation in the report. Our resolve to report what happened held, the report wasn't changed and, interestingly, we later received two contracts from that same association in the ongoing assessment of automobile ignition noise![4]

Next there is the question of upper management selecting, or more precisely preselecting, future research areas in which the Institute is to engage. Though several SRI presidents, sometimes in the framework of strategic planning, have tried this, it never has worked well. If such a new field is apparent to someone not intimately engaged, it is probably already too late in the competitive research marketplace. Those best equipped to make the determination are those who have both current knowledge of an art _and_ are pounding the street looking for opportunities day in and day out; that is, the research professionals or at best their first- and second-level managers. Managers at the second or third levels can sometime help when they form and maintain higher level contacts in client organizations where they can spot early the emergence of new research initiatives. Aided by such awareness, prompted by their own discovered opportunities, and faced with carrying out whatever they propose, it is the fertile minds of those engaged in the research where new research ideas best originate.

Finally, there is the matter of incentive systems. Over the past 20 years or so, SRI has experimented with different plans and one is in place at the moment that rewards good financial performance with limited bonuses. Its tailoring over the years has brought it to a general point of acceptance by the staff. In such an egalitarian research atmosphere, the danger arises when a bonus system becomes too large and concentrated in too few people. Lucrative bonuses, of course, can also play on the unfortunate temptation to distort actual performance in order to collect them. As mentioned above, highly differentiated privilege of any form for upper management is very unpopular in a contract research organization. To present a stark example of the damage a strong incentive system can bring to SRI, consider what happened in the late 1990s to SRI's Business Group. From its founding the Business Group had, like the rest of SRI, been an

---

[4] The SRI project leader, James Gaddie, personal communication, January 8, 2004.

organization of researchers, analysts, and principal investigators, each making their own way. In 1995 SRI's president changed that model to one typified by large management-consulting firms with very well paid, profit-sharing-oriented managers aided by replaceable minions who would do most of the work. I remember being asked to interview a number of these "rain-makers" and I did not find one that I thought belonged at SRI. The cultural clash was horrific and it was an important factor in the demise of the Group. Even if it would have worked financially, it could no longer, perhaps by design, be a place with any research content.

Certainly, research ideas cannot flow down from detached managers as tasks to workers not steeped in the required disciplines. The conversion was fatal to that Group and financially painful for the residual part of SRI.

Finally, there is the general question of management-employee relationships, one evidence of which is the presence of or efforts toward forming a union. To my knowledge this subject surfaced at SRI only once among the non-exempt (from overtime) staff in the latter part of 1976. The initiative lasted a few months and was then abandoned for lack of interest.

Companies Formed by SRI Alumni—
with or without SRI Involvement

The listing below is intended simply to illustrate the propensity of SRI alumni to start companies, in some cases multiple times. The assertion is that SRI often becomes a good training ground for entrepreneurs. Since SRI has kept no account of such initiatives at SRI, the list is compiled from casual knowledge. The compilation, therefore, woefully underestimates the true number of companies created. To appear on the list an SRI person or alumnus has to be a principal in the founding of the company. In the preponderance of the more than 80 cases listed, SRI was not directly involved.

Often a person leaving SRI will form a one-person consulting arrangement. Because of the sheer volume and difficulty in verifying such adventures, those cases are not included below. A number of companies have been started by SRI without SRI staff specifically joining the new company in the process. Among these are companies like Polyfuel, Artificial Muscle, Discern, and Cyance. That type of company formation is also not covered here.

As much as the sometimes-approximate dates will allow, the list is in chronological order. The format of each listing is:

Company Name (SRI staff member(s) involved) (founding date) (company purpose or product) (other information or ownership transfer if known)

Electro-Optical Systems (Abe Zarem, Emo Parro, James McCarthy) (~1955) (electrooptical shutter, aerial cameras, ion propulsion) (became **Xerox** Electro-Optical before 1967 and then sold to **Loral**)

Granger Associates (John Granger et al.) (1956) (communications, antennas, electrostatic dischargers for aircraft) (acquired by **Digital Switch Corporation**)

Fair, Isaac, and Co. (William Fair and Earl Isaac) (1956) (helps companies win new customers and new markets) (today, a worldwide company whose adaptive control software manages 85% of the world's credit cards and three-fourths of all U.S. mortgages; perhaps 1,000 employees)

Raychem (Paul Cook) (1957) (electrical insulation products, including ultimately shrink-wrap wire insulation) (purchased by **TYCO** in 1999 for $2.9 billion)

Economic Research Associates or ERA (Harrison Price) (1958) (tourism and recreational market analysis, including Disney World and many other theme parks) (sold in 1969 to **Planning Research Corp.**)

Ridge Vineyards (Dave Bennion, Charlie Rosen, Hewitt Crane, Howie Zeidler) (1959) (World-class cabernets and zinfandels by 1970s) (Sold to Japanese pharmaceutical owner A. Otsuka in 1986)

Explosives Technology Co. (Frank Burkdall, Ben Huber, Norm Zabel, Don Moore) (explosive products, including the guillotine cutters that separated the ascent from the descent vehicle in the first lunar departure) (sold to **Ducommun, Inc.** in 1971)

Telecommunications International or TCI (Bob Tanner and E.M.T. (Ted) Jones) (1961) (antennas)

Develco (Bud Rorden, Len Orsak) (~early 1960s) (general electronics systems)

Scientific Products, Inc. (Reid Anderson) (about1964) (electronic products including a metronome)

Applied Communications Inc. (Bob Weitbrecht) (~1965) (early modems for the deaf community) (Bob received honorary doctorate of science from Gallaudet University in 1974; company now known as **Weitbrecht Communications**)

American Microsystems Inc. (Warren Wheeler, who left for Philco in 1959) (1966) (integrated circuit and semiconductor design and manufacture) (bought by **Gould** in 1982 and exists today as AMI Semiconductor in Pocatello, ID)

Anderson-Jacobson (Reid Anderson, and John Van Geen as a consultant) (1967) (first major producer of acoustically coupled modems) (acquired by **CXR Telecom** in 1988, which is now called **Microtel International**)

Failure Analysis Associates (Bernard Ross, research physicist in NWRC) (1967) (scientific and technical analysis of failure modes and causes) (changed name to **Exponent** 1998 with broader consulting charter and now has 20 offices and 675 experts)

Finnigan Instruments (Robert Finnigan and William Fries) (1967) (smaller, cheaper gas chromatograph mass spectrometers) (now worldwide billion dollar company as **Thermo Finnigan** and **Thermo Electronics** building analytical equipment for drug testing, food production, and telecommunications)

Horner Associates (J. Kenneth Horner) (~1967) (computer-aided chemical design)

Systems Control Inc. or SCI (Phil Merritt, Jean Peschon, Robert Larson) (1968) (engineering systems)

Institute for the Future (Roy Amara and Andy Lipinsky) (1968) (futuring)

Computer Synectics, Inc. (David Jorgensen) (1969) (product unknown) (sold in 1973)

Verbatim (Reid Anderson) (1969) (data recording media, diskettes) (now subsidiary of **Mitsubishi Chemical**) .

Center for Continuing Study of the California Economy (Robert Arnold and Stephen Levy) (1969) (long-term studies and forecasts of the California economy for the public and private sector) (a vital concern for over 30 years)

Telesensory Systems (Jim Bliss) (1970) (aids for the handicapped)

DataQuest (David Norman and Bill Coggshall) (1971) (market surveys/intelligence in technical field) (bought by **ACNielsen** in 1978 and later by **Gartner Group** in 1995)

Electroprint Corp. (Gerry Pressman) (~1971) (electronically controlled stencil screening system for placing images on cloth) (financed by Sun Chemical)

Tragon Corp. (Herb Stone and Joel Sidel) (1974) (started as sensory evaluation, including taste testing; now expanded into broad business consulting for the food industry)

Decision Focus Inc. (Edward Cazalet and Warner North) (1976) (decision analysis-based planning and market analysis) (in 1997 merged with **Aeronomics**)

Systar (David Retz) (1977) (software applications for computer networking that served thousands of IBM mini- and mid-range computers)

Evergreen Engineering (Steve Johnson and George Eilers) (~1977) (product development, including medical instrumentation)

Katun Corporation (David Jorgensen) (1978) (office products, copier aftermarket) world's largest supplier of after-market copier parts with revenue of $360 million in 2001; sold to **Banc of America Investors** and **Svoboda Collins Inc.** in 2002)

Harrison Price Co. (Harrison Price) (1978) ("dean of recreation economic consultants")

Machine Intelligence Corp. or **MIC** (Charlie Rosen, Earl Sacerdoti, and others) (~1978) (AI application to assembly-line work)

Symantec (Gary Hendrix) (1979) (started as an AI-based database query language/system called QandA. Now a large producer and distributor of utility software)

August Systems (Bob Wing, John Wensley, Maury Mills) (~1979) (fault-tolerant software)

Strategic Decisions Group (Carl Spetzler, Paul Skov, and James Matheson) (~1980) (decision analysis-based planning) (bought by **Navigent** then in 2000 returned to **SDG** via a management buyout)

Litigation Risk Analysis (Marc Victor) (~1980) (decision analysis application to risk estimation)

Communications Intelligence Corp. (Hew Crane, Earle Jones, John Ostrem, and Peter Edberg) (1981) (handwritten input to computers including Japanese and Chinese; led to Jot and e-signature verification)

Strategic Economic Decisions (Horace "Woody" Brock) (1981) (decision analysis and innovation strategies)

Kestrel Institute (Cordell Green) (1981) (logic programming and AI software)

BusinessLand (David Norman) (1982) (PC sales/service to enterprises) (one of the first companies in PC sales and in 6 years rose to the world's largest supplier of computers with over $1 billion sales/year)

E*TRADE (William Porter) (1982) (online, discount equity trading)

Mirage Systems (Phil Fialer, Larry Sweeney, and others) (~1982) (military stealth technology)

Microbot (John Hill) (~1982) (miniature robots for teaching) (sold to **UMI** about 1991)

Etak (Stan Honey, Walt Zavoli, Larry Sweeney, and others) (1983) (digital maps for car and other navigation systems) (now worldwide offices and called **Tele Atlas**)

Syntelligence (Peter Hart and Richard Duda) (~1983) (AI software applications)

Vista Research (Harold Guthart and others) (1984) (remote sensing and signal processing including leak detection and location)

Metapath (Bruce Hunt, Tom Lunzer, Harry Chesley, and Marilyn Pullen) (1984) (local area networking equipment)

Digideck (Connie T. Chittenden and Charles S. Weaver) (1986) (digital data compression for high fidelity recording and transmission) (dissolved in 1994)

CCS Associates (Caroline Sigman) (1985) (started in analysis and risk assessment of chemicals to the environment and now in drug development and toxicology)

The Beron Group (Bruce Beron) (1985) (decision analysis methodology and tools)

Kimball Resources (Dennis Rohan) (1985) (energy management and trading services)

ANSA Software (Rob Shostak and Richard Schwartz) (1985) (built **Paradox** ("2 SRI PhDs") commercial relational database software) (bought by **Borland Software Corp.** in 1989 who licensed it to **Corel** in 1996 where it is still part of their office suite)

Comware Int'l (David Retz) (1986) (Built gateways for IBM systems into the Internet. Now in sensing storage, and display systems)

Interop (Dan Lynch) (1986) (conference on Internet communications and enterprise equipment) (formed after Lynch had been at USC for nine years)

Australian Artificial Intelligence Institute or AAII (Mike Georgeff and Graham Smith) (1987) (contract AI research in Australia)

Global Business Network (Peter Schwartz, Pierre Wack, and Jay Ogilvy) (1987) (futuring)

Global Internet Access Services (Dennis Rohan) (1987) (Internet service provider) (sold to **Verio** who sold it to **Nippon Telephone and Telegraph** in about 1996)

Litigation Risk Management Institute (Bruce Beron) (1988) (risk management and analysis)

TGV (Dave Kashstan and Ken Adelman) (~1988) (communications software and UNIX simulation software for VAX computers) (TGV stood for Two Guys and a Vax; Kashtan hired Craig Conway (former CEO of PeopleSoft) to head TGV and who sold it to **Cisco Systems** in 1996)

Teleos Research (Stan Rosenschein, Leslie Kaebling, Marietta Elliott, and others) (~1989) (robotic systems and devices)

FX Development Group (Dennis Rohan) (1989) (terminals for foreign-exchange, bond, and energy trading; used in ~800 trading companies worldwide) (acquired by **Dow Jones and Company** in about 1991)

Innovation Research of California (Josh C. Abend and later Richard T. Knock) (1991) (software that helps organize and facilitate the creative and innovation process in organizations) (became **Innovation Engines** in 2000)

Health Industries Research Company (Tom Mader and Terry Maccarone) (1991) (market research for healthcare, pharmaceutical, and managed care industries with offices in CA, PA, NJ, and AZ)

Menlo Biomedical (John George, Frank von Richter, George von Haunalter, and later Horst Wolf) (1991) (global pharmaceutical and healthcare research and consulting with profiles on 450,000 public and private companies) (parts purchased by London-based **Isis Research** in 2000 and then by **Synovate Healthcare** in 2003)

Health Strategies Group (Tom Mader, Dee Miller Prince, and Jeff Larson) (1992) (research and consulting to the healthcare products industry with offices in CA and NJ)

Nuance Communications (Ron Croen, Hy Murveit, Peter Monaco, Mike Cohen, and others) (1994) (automatic speech recognition)

Cybercash (Dan Lynch) (1994) (online financial transactions) (acquired by **Verisign**)

Genetrace Systems (Chris Becker, others) (1994) (drug leads via genetic profiling)

Neural Systems Corp. (Connie T. Chittenden and Charles S. Weaver) (1994) ("trainable" digital logic slated to increase digital recording density and communications rates)

enVia (Mark Cummings) (1994) (a "meta-company" or venture capital-like firm that launches companies in the wireless world)

GWcom (Frank Kuo and Jeng-Sheng Huang) (1994) (two-way pagers, and cell-phone data services in China) (now two companies, **GWtech** and **Byair**, with 3 million customers and growing at 25% per year)

Global Internet Software (Dennis Rohan) (1995) (Windows NT network security software) (purchased in 1997 by **Cisco Systems** for $40 million; product became basis for Cisco's PIX firewall system)

Intuitive Surgical Devices (Gary Guthart, now vice president) (1995) (surgical telepresence)

Rooftop Communications (Dave Beyer, John Hight, Bic Nguyen, Thane Frivold, Darren Lancaster, and Jose Garcia-Luna Aceves, with Ed Kozel on the Board of directors) (1995) (fixed site wireless internet access a la packet radio) (sold to **Nokia** in 1999 for $57 million)

Netiva Software (Rob Shostak) (1996) (scalable intranet database systems)

Cohesive Network Services (Dennis Rohan) (1996) (professional network engineering services) (bought by **Exodus Communications** in 1999 for $100 million)

Ordinate (Jared Bernstein) (1996) (product for automatic measurement of quality of spoken language)

4C Technology (Yigal Blum, Sylvia Johnson, and Paul Hart) (1996) (silicon-based preceramic polymers) (failed in 1999)

SynVax (Armit Judd) (1996) (synthesis and testing of biologically active peptides and their analogs; based on patents obtained while at SRI; targets are antivirals for flu)

SecureSoft (Mark Moriconi, Olga Korobkov, others) (1997) (secure database access) (became **Crosslogix** in 1997, secured $22 million in venture funding in 2000, purchased by **BEA Systems** in February 2003)

Pangene (David Zarling) (1997) (anticancer and antiviral enzyme inhibitors, radio sensitizers)

AgIndustries (Sally Landels) (1998) (market, competitive, and strategic analyses for the crop protection, agricultural biotechnology, and specialty fertilizer industries)

SportVision (Stan Honey) (1998) (television sport enhancements, including the glowing hockey puck and the virtual yellow first-down line in NFL games)

MobileSoft Technology (John Ostrem) (~1998) (China-based production of Linux-embedded operating systems in small and mobile devices)

DenseNet Corp. (Ravinder Kachru) (1998) (optical signal processing and switching)

SmartOrg (James Matheson and Don Creswell) (~1999 after a time at SDG above) (business development, R&D, and futuring)

DaVinci Heatlthcare Partners (Peter W. Davis, Roger Halualani, Pam Gutman, and Martha McDaniels) (1999) (healthcare markets, with focus on cancer care and related therapeutic areas)

Reactive Network Solutions (Livio Ricculi and Jagan Jagannathan) (2000) (security against network denial-of-service attacks)

Vocera Communications (Rob Shostak) (2000) (wireless communications systems)

Skypilot Network (Mark Rich, Bernie Yetso, and others) (2000) (wireless network Internet access)

China Mobilesoft (John Ostrem) (2000) (software for the mobile telephone and wireless device manufacturers for use in China) (successful products in telephones and wireless devices from 20 different vendors)

CONSULT it (members of SRI's Zürich office) (2001) (consulting in biotechnology, healthcare, pharmaceuticals, and chemicals, as well as venture capital)

Wireless Security Corp. (Dennis Rohan) (2001) (WiFi security systems)

Alterego (Saurav Chatterjee) (2001) (software engine tailoring Web page content to mall network terminals and devices) (acquired by Macromedia in 2002)

Packethop (Ambatipudi Sastri and Michael Brown) (2003) (packet routing systems for wireless networks)

Firetide, Inc. (Keith Klemba) (2003) (Network gear for low cost, rapidly deployable Wi-Fi service, used rights purchased from SRI)

Appendix G
Laboratory Directorship at SRI—Engelbart's Experience

The following account is based on SRI project files and interviews with a number of SRI staff members directly involved, including Dave Brown, Roy Amara, Bonnar Cox, Jerre Noe, Don Scheuch, Jack Goldberg, John Wensley, Earle Jones, and Bert Raphael.

Although Doug Engelbart's two decades at SRI saw monumental innovation and accomplishment, the environment was not always to his liking. In interviews and some articles about him, he relates his struggles with his administrative responsibilities and, at times, his SRI management.[1] Simplistically put, Doug believed that in some cases his SRI supervisors either didn't subscribe to his vision or perhaps didn't trust his ability to pursue it within the SRI framework. On the other hand, the sizable (at least for SRI) early funding that he received from SRI could not possibly have come from a set of uniformly disgruntled or skeptical managers. By way of partial explanation, he freely admits never having had a good grasp of the responsibilities lab directors face at SRI. So, partly to explore how such duties constitute a diversion for such visionaries and partly to provide a record of his dealings with his SRI peers and managers, we will explore this aspect of his stay at SRI. Beyond the personality differences one might find in any organizational experience, Engelbart's discomfort may come down to this: enjoying an environment that can offer a long-term opportunity to pursue one's goals, contrasted with the need to find and manage the resources necessary to carry them out. This process became critical as his group gained laboratory status. He called his lab the Augmentation Research Center or ARC.

Understanding Engelbart's position, first as a project leader and then as a lab director, requires understanding SRI's culture, which gives staff members who seek research contracts great freedom, but also heavy responsibilities, primarily for attracting sufficient outside funding to support their work. While SRI tries hard to tide its people across their natural funding gaps, its narrow profit margins mean that only limited funds are available to provide that protection. Also, research project leaders are responsible for defining projects, both technically and financially, and administering or managing them to the client's satisfaction. If a project leader does all of that well, a supportive, almost collegial role with his managers usually results. On the other hand, clear evidence of technical or financial trouble invites management participation at any stage of a project.

To understand the management issues surrounding Engelbart, it is helpful to divide his time at SRI into three parts: a gestation or investment period (1959–1964), a laboratory or operational period (1965–1975), and the termination period (1976–1977). This staging could apply to any growth area at SRI and a typical manager's role varies across such stages. According to Engelbart's account, the initial phase was characterized by a couple of disconcerting situations. As Engelbart embarked on pursuing his vision, his first manager suggested to him that he needed to become more practical or down to earth. It is hard to know just how appropriate this guidance was, but clearly Doug's future progress would depend on defining how his augmentation concepts could be realized and in this formulation stage, they were often hard to voice. In any case Engelbart did not appreciate such advice and solved this first problem by transferring to another laboratory. His second manager, again according to Doug, created a more serious problem, the unsolicited imposition onto Engelbart's newly won ARPA project of a colleague with a more traditional view of software and computing. Given Engelbart's singular view of how things were to be done, plus his strong desire to lead his own effort, an immediate and substantive conflict arose. Imposing a project team member with or

[1] Stanford and the Silicon Valley–Oral Histories, Engelbart interviews, Nos. 2 and 3. Found at http://www-sul.stanford.edu/depts/hasrg/histsci/ssvoral/engelbart/engfmst3-ntb.html.

above a project leader was contrary to the culture at SRI, where a new project is almost always led by the person who won it. Engelbart thought this second manager's action was important enough to recount over 20 years later.[2]

A review of SRI records and conversations with those directly involved suggests that Doug may not have been able to express his vision in a way that captured the imagination of his supervisors, or at times even his clients. The title of his first 1963 ARPA project was "Computer Facilitation of Computer Programming," not exactly the rubric under which Doug's dream could find full expression and one that might lead a supervisor to decide the client wanted a narrow interpretation. For example, when project leader Engelbart wanted a computer of his own, his supervisor thought ARPA's offer of connection with a remote timeshare host was possibly good enough. Moreover, by early 1964 the ARPA program manager insisted on demonstrable progress,[3] almost certainly before Doug's larger notions of "computer-aided work" had relevant functionality.

As external sponsorship increased in the early to mid-1960s, Doug himself would be promoted to first program and then laboratory leadership. Through the first two phases of Engelbart's career mentioned above, three themes consistently appeared in the comments on his performance by all five of his managers. One was Engelbart's outstanding creativity— "perhaps the most original thinker at SRI." Another was recognition of the value of what he was doing to realize the potential of the "man-computer research area." The third was the nearly unanimous opinion that Engelbart had difficulty with a variety of administrative and managerial roles. In spite of written assessments of such deficiencies, in August 1963 his second boss promoted Engelbart to SRI's first level of management, a program manager, albeit with a stipulation that he be responsible mainly for technical direction. Though carrying out that stipulation was not just Doug's responsibility, it was roundly ignored.[4]

Engelbart's relationships with his supervisors were certainly not all negative. One of the most telling aspects about how he was helped by his managers during the formative phase of the ARC was the consistent SRI investment funding that Engelbart received to help him hone his ideas and display them to potential sources of outside funding. Managers at least two levels above Engelbart must agree to commit discretionary funds. Engelbart would never have received $120,000 in internal funds, as well as some capital equipment, if there were any major concern about the recipient or what he was trying to promote.[5]

In the meantime Engelbart's ideas gained acceptance and outside support sufficient for forming a laboratory began to arrive in about 1964. Doug was promoted to lab director, and over the next decade NASA, ARPA, and others funded Engelbart's work and gave him the computers he needed to literally bootstrap his operation. For directors of successful labs, an SRI manager tends to offer only limited oversight. Management gives the program or laboratory director as much independence as possible, but holds him or her responsible for meeting technical and financial goals. Oversight emphasizes financial matters unless technical failure or undue risk seems likely. Good managers also make sure that all clients' needs are being met. In 1965 Doug's supervisor praised him for his growing involvement in the ARPA and NASA communities and by late 1967 that same manager proclaimed his insight, understanding, and expression of man-computer systems architecture, warning only that, because of Doug's inflexibility in his technical preferences, he may find it difficult to hold on to good people. But at this point, and for the following 4-5 years, Engelbart had empathetic division managers.

But Engelbart's role as laboratory director didn't ameliorate his dislike for his own administrative or managerial work. His staff turnover rate was also high. He was clearly aware of this limitation and admitted in interviews at Stanford that he might not have had the capability or inclination to be both a visionary and a manager. In those interviews he

---

[2] Stanford Interview No. 2, op. cit.
[3] See the account of the 1963-1964 time frame in Chapter 2.
[4] While their exact date is uncertain, some of Doug's internal problems involved inadequate computer access. According to his account given in the Stanford oral history interviews, even when he did convince SRI management to buy a machine for

his use, he soon found himself having to substantially share it with others. Since it wasn't a timeshare machine, his people's allocated time that got down to just 13 hours per week. This constraint was relieved only when the government gave him his own timeshare machine.
[5] At the time, this probably amounted to about 7 person-years of labor.

also mentioned requesting administrative help but it was denied, he said, since lab directors were expected to fill both technical and managerial roles.[6] But records indicate that his SRI managers also wanted him to get administrative support. Importantly, given the size of the ARC, Engelbart was free to acquire additional administrators on his own initiative and didn't. By 1972, to help lighten his load and to deal with criticisms of his staff about his inability to set short-term objectives, he approached his manager for help in delegating. That manager affirmed Doug's critical value to SRI and set up a small management committee to help. Toward the end of that year, when the ARC had over 40 people, Engelbart delegated some control to two assistant managers. While the move no doubt helped administratively, it didn't materially reduce the turnover that had characterized the lab since the early 1970s. And within a couple of years, other dragons appeared at the door to provoke the third and final SRI phase of Engelbart and his laboratory.

In a late 1975 discussion regarding his division's budget for the coming year, Engelbart requested that his Center be given an easier income budget to meet because of some new capabilities they wanted to develop. If agreed to, such decisions normally result in the other laboratories of the division picking up the slack, and they agreed to do so here. But 1976 didn't turn out to be a very a good year for a couple of the labs that had agreed to try to meet a higher than normal budget. As a result all the labs faced pressure to perform better or to cut costs. Engelbart's lab, despite its lower budget, became vulnerable, along with the other weakened labs, to the overall need for cost reduction. Such points of vulnerability are not uncommon at SRI since there is only a limited amount of money available to carry an unprofitable unit very long.

In part because of this uncertain funding situation and the associated internal pressure and in part because of the wanderlust of creative people, ARC staff members continued to leave. As mentioned, PARC was the biggest beneficiary. Richard Watson, who had been one of Doug's first assistant directors and who had helped develop the early roles for the Network Information Center (NIC), left for a government lab in Livermore, CA. Jon Postel,

who had taken his place, soon left himself.[7] By 1976 there were perhaps 15 or so professionals left in the Center, with a somewhat smaller number of research analysts providing the NIC services.

Another threat was a decline in external funding. By the beginning of 1975 the ARC had maintained its total size of over 40 people and had revenues of about $2 million annually. But that support would soon begin to wane. For some time the ARPA program managers who were funding Engelbart had often been critical of his rate of progress. Because of this problem, combined with the informal limits on the duration of ARPA programs, support started to decline. Although the critical role of the NIC continued to be supported, the decrease in research funding made it difficult to keep momentum.

There is no more important danger at SRI than an extended loss of external support and consequently no more important responsibility for a laboratory director than to somehow deal with it. SRI has only a limited capacity to underwrite any operation, particularly one as large as the ARC, so that meant either finding more work or reducing staff. Barring either of those, management has to act; either by helping restore funding or seeing that expenses are controlled. To the myopic visionary, this requirement may seem harsh, unsympathetic, and even arbitrary.

To find the needed income and still maintain his research directions, Engelbart started to sell NLS *services* on his timeshare host to government agencies. In the SRI accounting system, this income was hard to reconcile, especially as its volume became unpredictable, primarily as a result of the uneven acceptance of NLS. Accordingly, Doug's division director sought to have him divide the ARC into two parts, research and applications, and then seek normal research funding for what would become a smaller group. When this strategy didn't bear fruit, for whatever reason, he chose to replace Engelbart as director toward the end of 1976. That obviously didn't sit well with Doug and did little to alter the situation.

To understand the specific act by the division director and his new lab manager, it is

[6] Stanford interview No.3, op. cit.

[7] Postel, who had worked on communications protocols in the ARC, including TCP (see Chapter 3), went to USC's Information Sciences Institute, where he became one of the founding figures of the Internet.

important to understand their assessment of where the ARC and its NLS functionality stood. Although they saw the value of what Doug and the ARC had created in the 1960s, they also saw the world catching up in certain aspects of those innovations that had high market appeal, such as text editing. Though such new, competing functionality was but a small part of the total NLS package, they still thought Doug's directions were not adapting to the changing technology and his inflexibility was hampering his retention of creative staff. From this viewpoint, then, and with a technical leader they thought was unwilling to work with them to improve the lab's chances of succeeding, they decided to put the ARC up for sale.

Several firms were approached and even Engelbart, together with his NLS development staff, decided to bid. According to the new lab manager, that bid was a symbolic $1. But sometime in 1977, SRI's overall director of research operations learned of the interest of Tymshare Corporation of Cupertino, California, in providing new functionality for its users. At that time it was one of the largest providers of time-sharing services in the world. Since such services were the company's core business, and it used machines similar to those in the ARC, Tymshare believed that providing some of the unique features of NLS would give it a competitive advantage over other companies beginning to offer time-sharing service. Overall, the negotiations went on for over 6 months and, in an unprecedented move, SRI sold the ARC and its intellectual property to Tymshare

on January 20, 1978. SRI and Tymshare signed an agreement transferring the rights to NLS for $200,000 plus royalty stipulations. In order to stay with his created world of NLS and its nascent offerings, Engelbart and many of his researchers left for Tymshare. About a half-dozen decided to remain at SRI and transferred into existing labs such as the Telecommunications Sciences Center (TSC). The NIC and its perennial leader, Elizabeth "Jake" Feinler, also relocated to the TSC.

In short, Engelbart had to weather some tough storms at SRI, but the most important were the ones that face almost all innovators there. Engelbart's ability to develop his vision, at least to the extent that it laid the foundations of personal computing, clearly benefited from the freedom that SRI provides. But that freedom also carries the responsibility to gather the necessary resources, whether you are a project leader, a lab director, or higher. If that is impossible, for whatever reasons, the technical content, no matter how innovative, is of far secondary importance. While turnover of valuable staff members had been a problem in the ARC through the 1970s, the group's termination at SRI was thus governed more by external causes, by a funding world with its own limited capacity to persevere. Engelbart, with his vision firmly intact, now found himself immersed in the constraints of a profit-making organization, while the continuing development of personal computing took on a life of its own elsewhere.

Appendix H
First Radar Echoes from an Artificial Satellite

In the flurry of curiosity and interest following the orbiting of Sputnik, SRI radio researchers became probably the first people outside the Soviet Union to make radar contact with an artificial satellite. The initial part of this account is taken directly from SRI Staff Notes, October 1957. The article (shown in italics) gives a flavor of SRI's reaction to the event, but because of several inaccuracies, a number of edits are interspersed in brackets. The main purpose for including this story is its reflection on the natural and competent curiosity of SRI staff and how that curiosity leads them into purely voluntary and collaborative explorations.[1]

Special Techniques Group Tracks Sputnik with Radar

Staff members from the Radio Systems Laboratory are picking up and recording the radio signals from the Russian, man-made satellite at regular intervals. This, of course, is no longer news. However, the enthusiasm with which staff members attacked the problem of tracking down the satellite is worthy of comment.

The satellite's first pass was observed and recorded at the SRI field site on Friday, October 4, at 7 p.m. Engineers working under Dr. Allen Peterson, head of the Communication and Special Techniques Groups, set up radio-receiving and direction-finding equipment and went to work plotting the orbit and recording the transmitted "beep" signal.

The reaction of the press was immediate, and, soon, staff members were besieged with calls. Working voluntarily on an around-the-clock basis, sleeping in between passes, the engineers from the Radio Systems Laboratory have been maintaining a constant vigil on "Sputnik."

Lambert Dolphin, Ray Leadabrand, Ray Vincent, Bud Rorden, Rolf Dyce, Bob Rach, Roy Long, Ed Post, and other volunteers from the Engineering Division took turns at various operations.[2] *Hurriedly assembled, functional equipment (including an "analogue computer" made from a globe, scotch tape, string, and a wire coat hanger) was put into play and, as Ray Vincent said, "A crude but very effective 'analog computer' resulted which was instrumental in establishing the orbit."* [With only a rough idea of the satellite's velocity and altitude (it was in an elliptical orbit), the early Doppler and directional data from the satellite's transmission gave imprecise satellite locations. But using orbital mechanics and slide rules the orbit was iteratively refined. The globe mentioned was merely a convenient but coarse three-dimensional plotting surface on which the satellite's inclination and orbital tracks could easily be visualized.]

The activity up on the hill behind Stanford is now a fairly well coordinated operation. A few minutes before a "pass" staff members take their places. The radio direction finder is put into play and the operator reads observed bearings to a recording secretary at 10- to 15-second intervals. The recording equipment, tuned to the transmitting frequencies of the satellite, goes into action. Instruments scan, compute and record. Prior to this activity, the orbit has been accurately plotted on a giant plastic globe. Changes are made, new orbits are computed and, all the while, different voices are passing and periodically shouting instructions and observations which are plotted and fed to the computing center in the SRI bus, where Professor Leland E. Cunningham of the University of California works at orbit computation. [Prof. Cunningham was actually in U.C.

---

[1] The refinement of the story came from email correspondence from three of the SRI participants, Ray Leadabrand (May 31, 2004), Bud Rorden (May 31, 2004), and Roy Long (June 2, 2004) and from a phone conversation with Walter Jaye on June 25, 2004.

[2] Among the other SRI staff members not mentioned in the article but who were part of the vigilant group included Walter Jaye, Frank Firth, Loren Dye, Ron Presnell, Myles Berg, Ron Panton, Ralph Evans, and Howard Zeidler.

Berkeley trying to get the software of his new IBM 704 to work and didn't apparently contribute to the early calculations, which were all done by hand.] *Many persons outside the Institute have provided valuable assistance in their activity. Members from the Propagation Lab at Stanford University have coordinated their efforts with those of the SRI staff.* [Don Weaver, a colleague at Montana State in Bozeman was measuring the same things, thus helping to pinpoint the orbit. Another site with whom SRI was in contact was MIT's Millstone Hill radar. SRI was one of perhaps only four sites outside the USSR that would have been able to get a radar return from Sputnik.]

A few hundred feet away, SRI's radar van, loaded with transmitting, receiving, and recording equipment, is also a beehive of activity as the radarscopes are scanned for echoes from the satellite. "She's coming in loud and clear," someone shouts. A few minutes of concentrated activity ensue, then quietness settles over the group as "Sputnik" fades into space.

Data taken to the SRI bus, which has been pressed into service as a temporary computing center and dormitory, are analyzed. Computations are made by other volunteers who predict the time and location of the next "pass." The crew then relaxes, provided equipment adjustments or changes are not required. They sit around and sip coffee and discuss the next "pass." A few may try to catnap, but, within the hour, the satellite will be zooming in from somewhere over the Pacific. So, peaceful sleep is out of the question.

Comments

The caption on an illustration from the above-referenced Staff Notes indicates that the dish antenna had but a 12° beamwidth and thus, with the satellite traveling about 18,000 mph at an altitude of 300 miles, it would be in the beam for only about 12 seconds. While the radar apparently had the degrees of freedom to track planetary objects, it could not be programmed to do so. This meant that the dish had to be prepositioned from estimated orbital data and then the satellite's distance and rough direction would be verified when it passed

through the dish's beam. A short note in the November 1957 *Proceedings of the IRE* (Institute of Radio Engineers) by Allen Peterson describes the equipment set-up and data types in detail. The SRI radar dish was a 61-ft parabolic reflector. The procedure was to first learn Sputnik's orbit from Doppler and direction finding equipment, then predict when it would over-fly the Stanford field site, and finally position the dish so that the satellite would intersect its beam. Radar echoes were obtained when the 2-ft diameter satellite came within 700 miles of the site.

The SRI group was taking the above data on the satellite's signal approximately four hours after the Russians, at about 6 pm EST on October 4, announced it was in orbit. Promotional material on SRI's radar facilities indicated that the first radar returns were obtained 2 days after the launch. But the IRE paper states that the two radar returns detected on the morning of October 9 were from what was likely co-orbiting rocket staging equipment. Then, on the morning of October 10, 1957, a radar return from the satellite itself was obtained. According to Walter Jaye, the MIT Millstone Hill radar was down for maintenance at the time and therefore, in all likelihood, these self-initiated efforts resulted in the first such radar contacts with an artificial satellite, at least outside the USSR.[3,4]

The sheer existence of Sputnik brought a rapid change in the military posture and preparedness of the U.S., particularly the importance of space-directed radar systems. Radar programs that were on the verge of cancellation were hastily renewed, including some at SRI, and SRI was immediately given a contract from the Air Force to develop ways to more accurately track these new heavenly bodies.

---

[3] Walter Jaye, personal communication, June 24, 2004.
[4] There is indication that the Millstone Hill radar was manually directed to also get skin reflections from Sputnik "within a few days" of Sputnik's injection. (*MIT Lincoln Laboratory–Technology in the National Interest*, edited by Eva G. Freeman, published by Lincoln Lab, 1995, pp. 111–112)

Appendix I
First Client List for SRI's
Long Range Planning Service

The 74 charter participants of LRPS as of January 1, 1959.
(Companies after 74 joined later the first year.)

1. International Business Machines
2. Wellington and Company
3. Investors Diversified Services
4. Minneapolis Honeywell Regulator
5. Fireman's Fund Insurance
6. Shell Chemical Company
7. Southern Pacific Company
8. Time Incorporated
9. Dewey & Almy Chemical
10. Title Insurance & Trust Co.
11. Olin Mathieson Chemical
12. General Telephone & Electronics
13. Burroughs Corporation
14. Rexall Drug & Chemical
15. Allied Chemical Corporation
16. The Bendix Corporation
17. Lockheed Aircraft Corporation
18. North American Aviation, Inc.
19. Ford Motor Company
20. Prudential Insurance Company
21. Douglas Aircraft Company
22. Packard Bell Electronics Corporation
23. Rockwell Manufacturing Company
24. Consolidation Coal company
25. Philco Corporation
26. United States Steel Corporation
27. The Boeing Company
28. Rheem Manufacturing Company
29. Denver & Rio Grande Western Railroad
30. Stockholms Enskilda Bank
31. Goodyear Tire & Rubber Company
32. American Motors Corporation
33. Massachusetts Mutual Life Insurance
34. Dow Chemical Company
35. Hooker Chemical Corporation
36. General Dynamics Corporation
37. Ciments Lafarge
38. United Shoe Machinery
39. Union Carbide Corporaton
40. Owens-Illinois
41. Brunswick Corporation
42. Amsted Industries
43. Merck and Company
44. F.S. Moseley & Co.
45. Japan Chemical Fibres Association
46. Koppers Company, Inc.
47. Chrysler Motors Corporation
48. Bechtel Corporation
49. Underwood Corporation
50. Monsanto Chemical Company
51. B.F. Goodrich Company
52. Hughes Aircraft Company
53. Courtaulds North America, Inc.
54. Consolidated Mining & Smelting
55. Smith-Corona-Marchant, Inc.
56. Weyerhaeuser Company
57. The Lummus Company
58. Parke Davis & Company
59. Imperial Oil, Ltd.
60. The Pure Oil Company
61. Standard Oil Company of Indiana
62. General Electric Company
63. Northwestern Mutual Life Inc.
64. Puget Sound Power & Light Company
65. Baldwin-Lima-Hamilton Corporation
66. Technicolor Corporation
67. Aetna Life Insurance Company
68. Borg Warner Corporation
69. Royal Typewriter Company
70. Schwabacher and Company
71. Hercules Powder Company
72. Dean Witter & Company
73. Benton & Bowles, Inc.
74. Canada Air Lines

(later in first year)
75. American Cyanamid Company
76. Canadian Pacific Railroad Company
77. Del Monte Corporation
78. Empresa Geral de Fomento (Portugal)
79. Standard Oil Company of New Jersey
80. Food Machinery & Chemical Corporation
81. Merrill Lynch, Pierce, Fenner and Smith
82. Minnesota Mining & Manufacturing Company
83. Texas Instruments, Inc.

Appendix J
SRI Staff Awards

SRI Fellowship Award–for outstanding lifetime scientific and technical achievement

Year	Name	Contribution
1980	Edward M. Acton	Anticancer drug development
	Walter G. Chesnut	Atmospheric effects of nuclear explosions
1981	David M. Golden	Combustion products and atmospheric chemistry
	Arnold Mitchell	Consumerism and psychographic segmentation
1982	Gordon T. Pryor	Brain biochemistry and substance abuse
	Joseph H. McPherson	Facilitating human processes in innovation
1983	Ivor Brodie	Electron dynamics in vacuum, gas, and condensed matter
	Henry Wise	Surface physics of heterogeneous catalysis
1984	Margaret A. Chesney	Impact of stress on chronic health problems
	Masato Tanabe	Pharmacology of steroid hormone drugs
1985	Hewitt D. Crane	Multi-aperture magnetics, eye-trackers, signature pen
	Donald C. Lorents	Molecular energy transfer mechanisms in excimer lasers
1986	Jorge Heller	Controlled drug delivery mechanisms
	Barbara S. Vold	Monoclonal antibodies in cancer diagnosis
1987	Joseph I. DeGraw	Synthesis of antifolate cancer drugs
	Arden Sher	Properties of semiconductor alloys
1988	Philip S. Green	Medical instrumentation in ultrasound
	Ronald Swidler	Dyes, fabric modifiers, and color printing
	Oswald G. Villard, Jr.	Ionospheric-based systems and active radar stealth
1989	Gerry B. Andeen	Electromechanical devices and hydrodynamics
	Richard J. Waldinger	Theorem-proving and automatic program synthesis
1990	Thomas Piantanida	Visual perception and virtual reality
	Donald A. Shockey	Analysis of material deformation and fracture
1991	Hanspeter Helm	Ion spectroscopy, imaging in intense laser fields
	Richard C. Honey	Lidar and laser photocoagulators
1992	Charles A. Spindt	Vacuum, field-emission microelectronics
	Enrique H. Ruspini	Modeling and control of systems under uncertain conditions
1995	Mohsen Sanai	Shock propagation and impact dynamics
1996	Theodore Mill	Oxidation chemistry and its role in environmental impacts
	Eric M. Pearson	Advanced technology of military importance
1997	Gary E. Swan	Psychoneurogenetic links in alcohol and tobacco dependence
	Tom G. Slanger	Upper atmospheric chemistry and night airglow
1998	David Crosley	Spectroscopy of laser-induced fluorescence
1999	Charles Tyson	Predicting *in vivo* response to drugs and chemicals
	Earl Blackwell	Adding precision to GPS guidance and navigation
2000	Kristien Mortelmans	Screening the mutagenic potential of new drugs
	Marcy Berding	Understanding the defects in semiconductor material
2001	Keith Laderoute	Gene expression in tumor and normal cells
	Peter Neumann	Computer system integrity and security
2002	Lawrence Toll	Pharmacology of drug abuse
	David Cooper	Optical physics and laser spectroscopy
2003	Barbara Means	Introduction, use, and evaluation of educational technology
	Gregory Smith	Kinetics and chemistry of flames and other gases
2004	Jeffrey Bottaro	High energy oxidation processes
	John Rushby	Innovation, leadership in formal methods of software design
2005	Patrick Lincoln	Research in formal methods, security, computational biology
	Ripudaman Malhotra	Research in new and more efficient energy sources

SRI Mimi Award–for outstanding lifetime achievement in the mentoring and professional development of others

Year	Name	Contribution
1995	Dave Crosley	Coaching and support of young scientists
1996	Don Nielson	Proper balancing of managing and mentoring
1997	Werner Graf	Personal, professional development of co-workers
1998	Terry Middleton	Team building and negotiation
1999	Bob Brown	Sense of community and teaching of leadership
2000	Mary Wagner	Engendering confidence and competence
2001	Matty Mathieson	Team building, empowerment of professional growth
2003	Cynthia Ford	Growth, development of co-workers in info. systems
2004	Jose Blackorby	Developing skills and responsibility in new staff
2005	Christine Peterson	Fostering the prof. development, market awareness of staff

Weldon B. Gibson Award–lifetime achievement toward improvement in the general standard of living and the peace and prosperity of society and added special luster to the reputation of SRI

Year	Name	Contribution
1999	Douglas Engelbart	The origins of personal computing
2000	Edwin Robison	Leveraging the economies of developing countries
2001	The ERMA Team	The first banking computer
2002	Dennis Finnigan	Modernizing business practices, especially in Sweden
2003	Philip Green	Medical systems in ultrasound and surgery

SRI Alumni Association Hall of Fame (as of 2005)

Name	Contribution
George Abrahamson	Leadership in Sciences and overall SRI contribution
Catherine Ailes	Innovation and leadership in science and technology policy
Bernard Baker	Initiation of long-term cancer research capability
Emery Bator	Established first SRI accounting system
Frances Bohley	Administered SRI worldwide industrial conferences
Charles Cook	Growth in physical chemistry, overall SRI leadership
Dale Coulson	Analytical methods for pesticide residues
Bonnar Cox	Division leadership in information sciences
Hewitt Crane	Innovation: magnetic logic, eye-trackers, signature pen
George Duvall	Bringing Poulter Lab to international prominence
Kenneth Eldredge	Inventor of magnetic character system for bank checks
Douglas Engelbart	Value of computing to personal and group capability
William Estler	Early director of public relations; put SRI on world map
William Evans	Advancements of printing and television systems
Elizabeth Feinler	Leadership: first computer network registration service
Dennis Finnigan	Leadership in business modernization
Richard Foster	Analysis of U.S. defense systems and strategies
Michael Frankel	Military communication technology; division leadership
Gustave Freeman	Pathogenesis of human cancer and respiratory diseases
Weldon Gibson	Growth of SRI business consulting to worldwide stature
Jane Goelet	Early and long-term personnel administrator
Jack Goldberg	Leadership in establishing field of computer science at SRI
Bruce Graham	Creation of SRI's first entry into life sciences
John Granger	Leadership in building early SRI reputation in radio systems

Philip Green	Contributions to medical instrumentation
Melba Harrison	Long-time, personable SRI receptionist and supervisor
Marion Hill	Leadership in high energy compounds and their SRI programs
Charles Hilly	Long-time director of contract administration
Jesse Hobson	Second SRI director, spawned largest SRI growth
Richard Honey	Laser radar and laser photocoagulation
Earle Jones	Innovation in printing systems and lab/divisional leadership
Paul Jorgensen	Director of Sciences Group and overall SRI leadership
Fred Kamphoefner	Magnetics, optics, long-term laboratory leadership
Douglas Keough	Seismic sensor design and measurement
Ralph Krause	First Director of Research, set professional tone for SRI
Ray Leadabrand	Ionospheric radar, leadership of Engineering Group
Peter Lim	Contributions, leadership in development of anti-cancer drugs
Kenneth Lunde	Founder of Process Economics Program
Albert Macovski	Television technology and imaging
Frank Mayo	Early leadership in oxidation chemistry
John McHenry	Innovation, leadership in military systems; SRI management
Joseph McPherson	Leadership in client innovation searches
Arnold Mitchell	Creator of Values and Lifestyles program (VALS)
Chozo Mitoma	Pioneered methods for biochemical pharmacology
Tetsu Morita	Innovative lab director in electromagnetic systems
Thomas Morrin	Growth-oriented first Director of Engineering
Jean Ware Nelson	Long-term contribution to Long Range Planning Service
Gordon Newell	Leadership in toxicology
Donald Nielson	Computer networking, leadership in information science
Nils Nilsson	World-renowned pioneer in artificial intelligence
Jerre Noe	First leader of division in information sciences
Allen Peterson	Nationally known innovator in communication systems
William Platt	Operations research applied to economic development
Thomas Poulter	Early SRI leader and founder of Poulter Laboratory
Lorraine Pratt	Built library to SRI-wide importance
Kitta Reeds	Long-time editor; expert in design, writing of proposals
Edwin Robison	Improvement in the economies of developing nations
Charles Rosen	Founder and long-term leader in artificial intelligence
William Royce	Contributions, leadership in planning and economic systems
Donald Scheuch	Long-term leadership in Engineering and SRI overall
Robert Shreve	Long-term leadership in economics and management
William Skinner	Second director of Life Sciences; opened up Japan market
Felix Smith	Leadership: molecular physics and staff advisory group
Robert Smith	Founding of LRPS and opening of first European Office
Charles "Capp" Spindt	Development of field emission cathodes and applications
Marian Stearns	Education of disadvantaged children; staff mentoring
Robert Stewart	Frameworks for organizational and corporate planning
Ronald Swidler	Innovations in dyes, fabric modifiers, color printing
Larry Swift	Geophysics and blast effects measurements
Shigeyoshi Takaoka	Leading and expanding business development in Japan
Masato Tanabe	Anticancer drug development in the field of steroids
Carl Titus	SRI fund raising and builder of SRI Associates Program
Charles Tyson	Advancement in toxicology and drugs using in vitro testing
Robert Vaile	Growth and prominence of SRI role in physics
"Mike" Villard	Ionosphere-based radio systems and stealth technology
John Wagner	First director of human resources and staff advocate

Index

I n this index the names of individuals are those embodied in the text or figures. With few exceptions those names appearing only in footnotes or endnotes do not appear below. This is particularly true of project teams. To locate them, please look for the type of work in which the team was engaged. Staff members listed in Appendix F as starting new companies are also not listed below. To reduce confusion, all DARPA entries are listed below as ARPA.